BBC

Bitesize



Bitesize

# AQA GCSE (9-1)

# COMBINED SCIENCE TRILOGY

## REVISION GUIDE

## HIGHER

**Series Consultant:**
Harry Smith

**Authors:**
Byron Dawson
Karen Bailey
Kieron Nixon

# Contents

Tick off each topic as you go.

# How to use this book

Use the features in this book to focus your revision, track your progress through the topics and practise your exam skills.

## 2 Features to help you revise

Each bite-sized chunk has a **timer** to indicate how long it will take. Use them to plan your revision sessions.

Test yourself with **exam-style practice** at the end of each page and check your answers at the back of the book.

**Tick boxes** allow you to track the sections you've revised. Revisit each page to embed your knowledge.

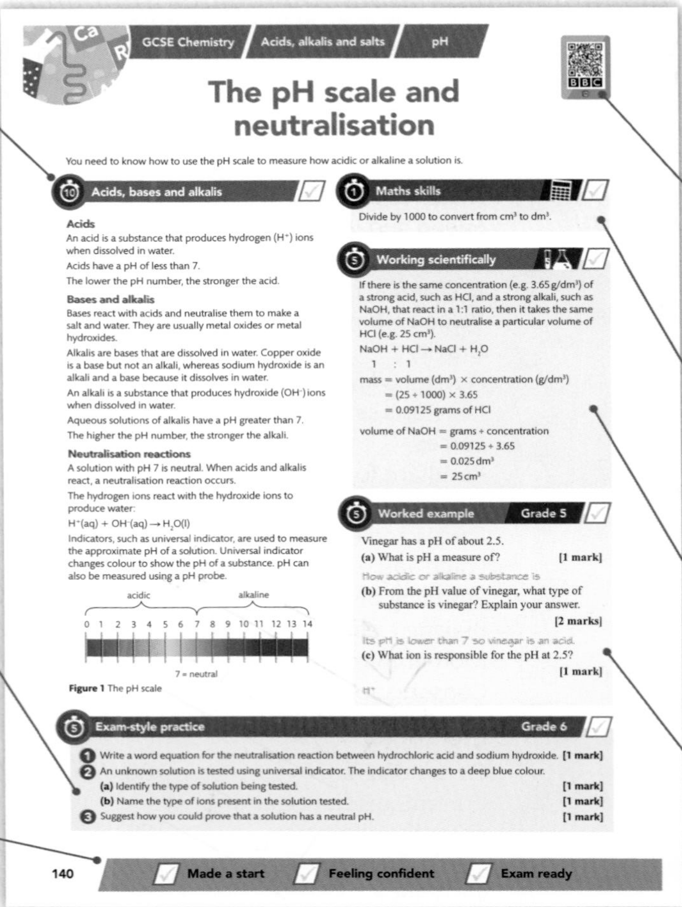

GCSE Chemistry / Acids, alkalis and salts / pH

### The pH scale and neutralisation

You need to know how to use the pH scale to measure how acidic or alkaline a solution is.

**10 Acids, bases and alkalis**

**Acids**
An acid is a substance that produces hydrogen ($H^+$) ions when dissolved in water.
Acids have a pH of less than 7.
The lower the pH number, the stronger the acid.

**Bases and alkalis**
Bases react with acids and neutralise them to make a salt and water. They are usually metal oxides or metal hydroxides.
Alkalis are bases that are dissolved in water. Copper oxide is a base but not an alkali, whereas sodium hydroxide is an alkali and a base because it dissolves in water.
An alkali is a substance that produces hydroxide ($OH^-$) ions when dissolved in water.
Aqueous solutions of alkalis have a pH greater than 7.
The higher the pH number, the stronger the alkali.

**Neutralisation reactions**
A solution with pH 7 is neutral. When acids and alkalis react, a neutralisation reaction occurs.
The hydrogen ions react with the hydroxide ions to produce water:
$H^+(aq) + OH^-(aq) \rightarrow H_2O(l)$
Indicators, such as universal indicator, are used to measure the approximate pH of a solution. Universal indicator changes colour to show the pH of a substance. pH can also be measured using a pH probe.


**Figure 1** The pH scale

**1 Maths skills**
Divide by 1000 to convert from $cm^3$ to $dm^3$.

**5 Working scientifically**
If there is the same concentration (e.g. 3.65 $g/dm^3$) of a strong acid, such as HCl, and a strong alkali, such as NaOH, that react in a 1:1 ratio, then it takes the same volume of NaOH to neutralise a particular volume of HCl (e.g. 25 $cm^3$).
$NaOH + HCl \rightarrow NaCl + H_2O$
1 : 1
mass = volume ($dm^3$) × concentration ($g/dm^3$)
= (25 ÷ 1000) × 3.65
= 0.09125 grams of HCl
volume of NaOH = grams ÷ concentration
= 0.09125 ÷ 3.65
= 0.025 $dm^3$
= 25 $cm^3$

**5 Worked example — Grade 5**
Vinegar has a pH of about 2.5.
(a) What is pH a measure of? [1 mark]
How acidic or alkaline a substance is
(b) From the pH value of vinegar, what type of substance is vinegar? Explain your answer. [2 marks]
Its pH is lower than 7 so vinegar is an acid.
(c) What ion is responsible for the pH at 2.5? [1 mark]
$H^+$

**5 Exam-style practice — Grade 6**
1. Write a word equation for the neutralisation reaction between hydrochloric acid and sodium hydroxide. [1 mark]
2. An unknown solution is tested using universal indicator. The indicator changes to a deep blue colour.
   (a) Identify the type of solution being tested. [1 mark]
   (b) Name the type of ions present in the solution tested. [1 mark]
3. Suggest how you could prove that a solution has a neutral pH. [1 mark]

140 Made a start Feeling confident Exam ready

Scan the **QR codes** to visit the BBC Bitesize website. It will link straight through to more revision resources on that subject.

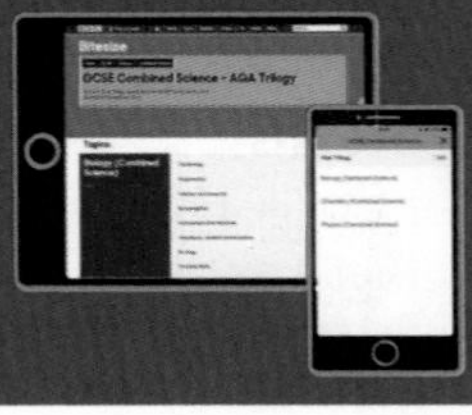

Questions that test **maths skills** are explained in callouts and in the *Exam skills* section at the back of the book.

Topics that are related to **working scientifically** are explained in callouts throughout the book.

Complete **worked examples** demonstrate how to approach exam-style questions.

## 2 Exam focus features

The *About your exam* section at the start of the book gives you all the key information about your exams, as well as showing you how to identify the different questions.

You will also find green *Exam skills* pages and purple *Practical* pages. These work through an extended exam-style question and provide further opportunities to practise your skills.

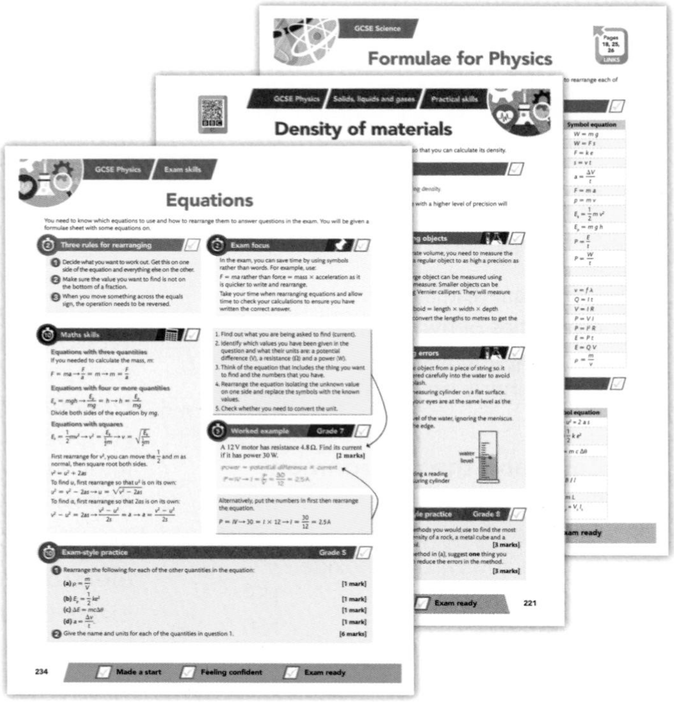


## 2 ActiveBook and app

This Revision Guide comes with a **free online edition**. Follow the instructions from inside the front cover to access your ActiveBook.

You can also download the **free BBC Bitesize app** to access revision flash cards and quizzes.

If you do not have a QR code scanner, you can access all the links in this book from your ActiveBook or visit **www.pearsonschools.co.uk/BBCBitesizeLinks**.

# Your Science GCSE

This page will tell you everything you need to know about the structure of your upcoming AQA GCSE Combined Science: Trilogy (Higher Tier) exams.

## About the exam papers

You will have to take **six** papers as part of your AQA GCSE Combined Science: Trilogy (Higher Tier) qualification: **two biology, two chemistry** and **two physics**. The papers will test your knowledge and understanding of different topic areas and your ability to work scientifically.

**Paper 1**
**Biology 1**
**1 hour 15 minutes**
**70 marks in total**

**Paper 2**
**Biology 2**
**1 hour 15 minutes**
**70 marks in total**

**Paper 3**
**Chemistry 1**
**1 hour 15 minutes**
**70 marks in total**

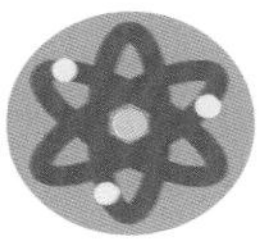

**Paper 4**
**Chemistry 2**
**1 hour 15 minutes**
**70 marks in total**

**Paper 5**
**Physics 1**
**1 hour 15 minutes**
**70 marks in total**

**Paper 6**
**Physics 2**
**1 hour 15 minutes**
**70 marks in total**

## Exam topics

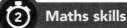

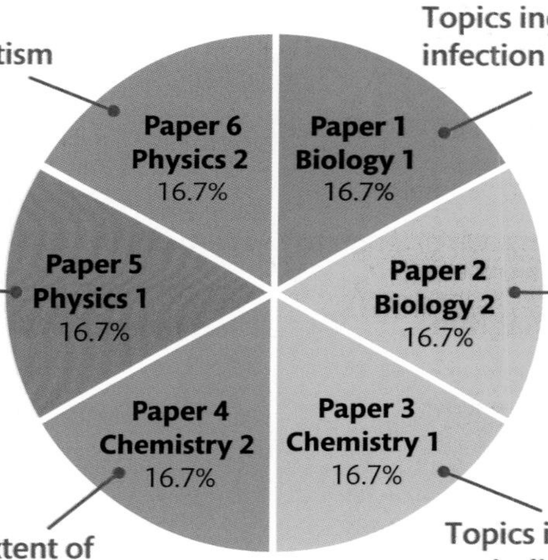


Paper 1: Topics include: cell biology; organisation; infection and response; bioenergetics

Paper 2: Topics include: homeostasis and response; inheritance; variation and evolution; ecology

Paper 3: Topics include: atomic structure and the periodic table; bonding, structure and the properties of matter; quantitative chemistry; chemical changes; energy changes

Paper 4: Topics include: the rate and extent of chemical change; organic chemistry; chemical analysis; using resources; chemistry of the atmosphere

Paper 5: Topics include: energy; electricity; particle model of matter; atomic structure

Paper 6: Topics include: forces; waves; magnetism and electromagnetism

## Maths skills

You will be required to demonstrate the following mathematical skills in your GCSE Science exams:

- rearranging equations
- interpreting data from graphs and tables, including finding a gradient
- converting units
- using standard form
- using ratios, fractions and percentages
- calculating mean, mode and median
- using geometry (volumes, areas, angles, working out sides of triangles).

## Working scientifically

There are 21 required practical activities you will carry out throughout your GCSE Science course.

Practical activities are an opportunity for you to apply your knowledge and understanding, while developing relevant practical skills and techniques.

You need to know how to:

- plan and carry out an investigation
- use apparatus correctly and safely
- take accurate measurements and record data appropriately
- analyse your findings
- evaluate your investigation.

Made a start | Feeling confident | Exam ready

# Multiple choice questions

Multiple choice questions give you several options to choose from. You must indicate the correct answer by marking your choice clearly.

## 1 Types of multiple choice question

- tick box
- linking boxes
- sentence completion

## 1 Exam focus

Bold words usually give important instructions. Read them carefully.

e.g. Tick **one** box.

## 5 Exam explainer

If you are unsure of the answer, use what you know to rule out the incorrect options.

A cricket ball is hit by a bat. The bat and ball exert a force on each other. Choose the correct statement about the two forces. Tick **one** box.

**[1 mark]**

**A** the force on the bat and the force on the ball are in the same direction ☐

**B** the bat has a larger mass so it exerts a larger force on the ball ☐

**C** the two forces are equal ☑

**D** the two forces give the bat and ball equal accelerations ☐

Clearly mark the answer you think is correct with a tick in the box. If you change your mind, draw a line through the incorrect answer and tick the correct answer.

Draw **one** line from each diagram to the name of the cell.

**[3 marks]**

Use a pencil to draw lines, so you can change your answer easily, if necessary.

**Diagram** | **Name of cell**

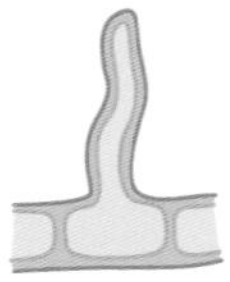

red blood cell

sperm cell

root hair cell

Read the question carefully. Here, you are instructed to only use words from the box provided. You would not be awarded marks for using similar words.

The pH scale is a measure of the acidity or alkalinity of a solution.

Use words from the box to complete the sentences. **[3 marks]**

| neutral | acidic | alkaline |
|---|---|---|

A solution with a pH value of 5 is ____________.

A solution with a pH value of 7 is ____________.

A solution with a pH value of 13 is ____________.



Made a start | Feeling confident | Exam ready

# Short-answer questions

Short-answer questions come in a variety of forms and are the most common type of questions.

## 5 Exam explainer

Underline key information, such as numbers and units. Make sure you include the correct units in your answer.

A power station has an efficiency of 0.45. Its energy comes from burning coal, which it uses at a rate of 300 MW.

**(a)** Calculate the useful output of electrical power. **[2 marks]**

**(b)** Describe the advantages and disadvantages of this type of power station compared to a wind turbine. **[3 marks]**

It is important to show your working when answering a calculation question. If done correctly, you will get method marks even if the answer is wrong.

For a sketch question, you only need to draw approximately. You should only use a ruler if it helps you to make your answer clear.

Sketch a reaction profile for an endothermic reaction. **[3 marks]**

You will need to be able to interpret information from a graph, photo, table or image in any of your exam papers.

A student investigated the rate of reaction between calcium carbonate and hydrochloric acid.

**Figure 1** The student's results for one concentration of hydrochloric acid.

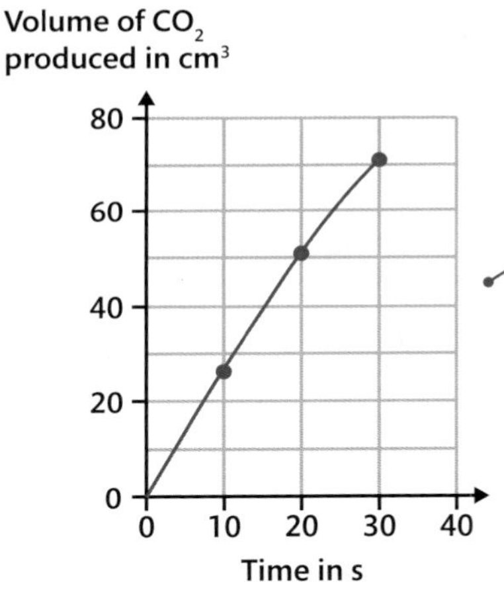


The table shows the student's results when the concentration was two times greater than the results shown in **Figure 2**.

| Time in s | Volume of $CO_2$ in $cm^3$ |
|---|---|
| 0 | 0 |
| 10 | 41 |
| 20 | 62 |
| 30 | 71 |

**(a)** Plot the results shown in the table on the grid in **Figure 1**. Draw a line of best fit. **[3 marks]**

**(b)** Give **one** conclusion about how the rate of reaction changed when the concentration of hydrochloric acid was changed. **[1 mark]**

# Extended-response questions

Some questions require a longer written response or a multi-step calculation. They are typically worth 4, 5 or 6 marks. You will need to give a coherent and sustained line of reasoning in your answer.

## ② Command words

- ☑ **explain** – set out purposes or reasons
- ☑ **evaluate** – consider evidence for and against and conclude
- ☑ **calculate** – use numbers provided to work out the answer
- ☑ **compare** – identify similarities and/or differences
- ☑ **describe** – recall some facts, events or processes

## ② Structure your answers

**1** Make a **point** – for example: *Embryo screening is an expensive procedure.*

**2** **Develop** your point – for example: *This means that the procedure is available only to people who can afford it.*

**3** **Link** your point back to the question – for example: *This is a socio-economic issue because the procedure is not accessible to everyone.*

## ⑤ Exam explainer

4 mark questions have **two** levels:
1. basic
2. clear.
A clear answer interprets, evaluates or analyses scientific information or resources.

> Aluminium can be extracted from its ore by electrolysis. Explain how aluminium is extracted from aluminium oxide by electrolysis.
>
> **[4 marks]**

For this question, you are expected to use your knowledge of electrolysis to explain how the process can be used to extract aluminium from aluminium oxide. You need to include reference to ions, electrodes and reduction in your answer.

For this type of question, you should provide specific examples for each of the issues mentioned, interpreting them in an objective way, and finishing with a reasoned conclusion.

> Evaluate the use of embryo screening for cystic fibrosis. In your answer discuss the economic, social and ethical issues.
>
> **[6 marks]**

6–9 mark questions have **three** levels:
1. basic
2. clear
3. detailed.
A detailed answer shows understanding of scientific topics and knowledge of specific information. It is presented in a clear and balanced way.

When asked to calculate something, always show your working. There are often some marks available for method and it also helps you to check your answer.

> Calculate the mass of calcium carbonate needed to produce 56 g of calcium oxide during thermal decomposition.
>
> **[5 marks]**

# Levels of organisation

You need to understand the principles of organisation within living organisms.

## 10 Organisation

Cells are the fundamental building blocks of all living things. Simple organisms, such as bacteria, consist of just one single cell (**unicellular**). **Multicellular** organisms have various levels of organisation within them, ranging from the individual cell to the entire organism. The levels of organisation range in complexity, from simplest to most complex, and in size, from very small to large.

Cells contain **organelles**, also known as sub-cellular structures, which perform specific functions within the cell. Individual cells can perform specific functions (page 6). Groups of specialised cells which all have a similar structure and function are called **tissues**. Groups of tissues that perform specific jobs are known as **organs**. Groups of organs form **organ systems**.

Cells are very small. You need a microscope to be able to examine them. Go to pages 4 and 5 to revise microscopy.

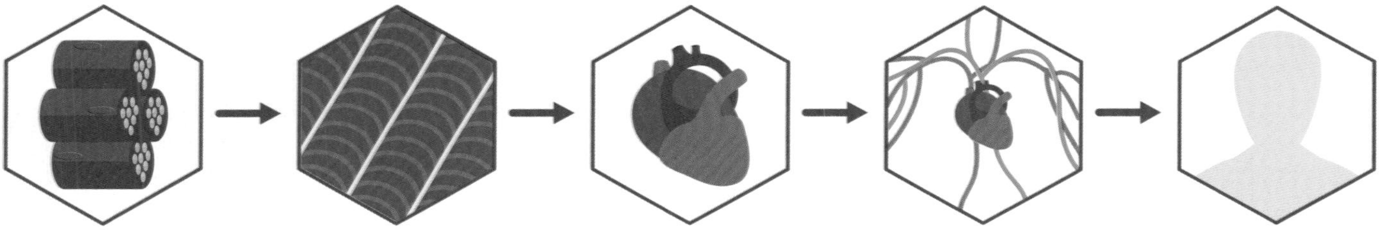

Some cells specialise to become muscle cells.

Groups of muscle cells form muscle tissue.

Cardiac muscle works with other types of tissue to form an organ called the heart.

The heart works with other organs to form the circulatory system.

The circulatory system works with other systems, such as the digestive and nervous systems, to form an organism.

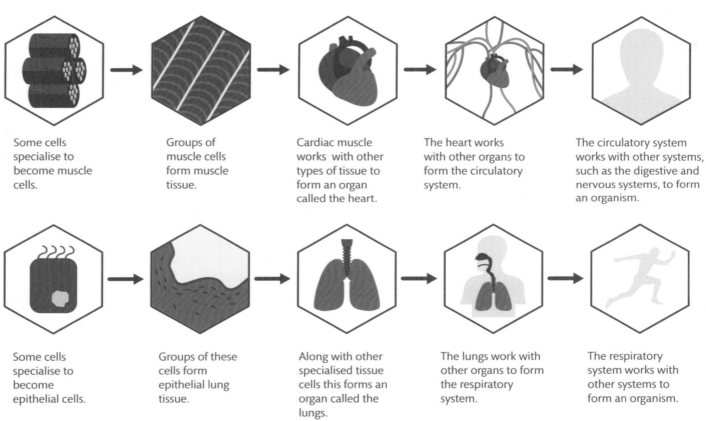

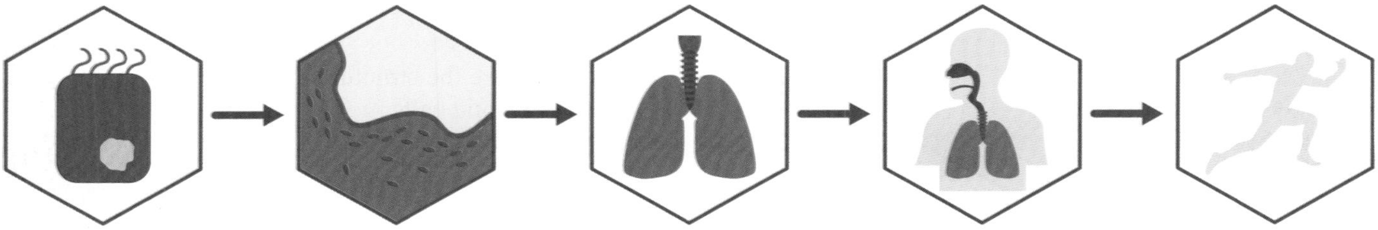

Some cells specialise to become epithelial cells.

Groups of these cells form epithelial lung tissue.

Along with other specialised tissue cells this forms an organ called the lungs.

The lungs work with other organs to form the respiratory system.

The respiratory system works with other systems to form an organism.

**Figure 1** The levels of organisation within the circulatory system

## 5 Worked example — Grade 4

Describe the levels of organisation within the human digestive system. **[4 marks]**

*The human digestive system is an organ system made up of several organs, including the stomach, liver and intestines, working together. The organs consist of different types of tissues, epithelial, muscle, nervous or connective tissues. The tissues are made up of cells.*

Go to page 21 for more about the human digestive system.

## 5 Exam-style practice — Grade 4

1. Describe what is meant by an organ system. **[2 marks]**
2. Describe the levels of organisation within the human respiratory system. **[4 marks]**

# Prokaryotic and eukaryotic cells

You need to know the differences in structure and function of prokaryotic and eukaryotic cells.

## 10 Prokaryotes and eukaryotes

Cells can be classified as either **prokaryotic cells** (prokaryotes) or **eukaryotic cells** (eukaryotes). Animals and plants consist of eukaryotic cells. Bacteria consist of prokaryotic cells. Eukaryotic cells are larger and more complex than prokaryotic cells.

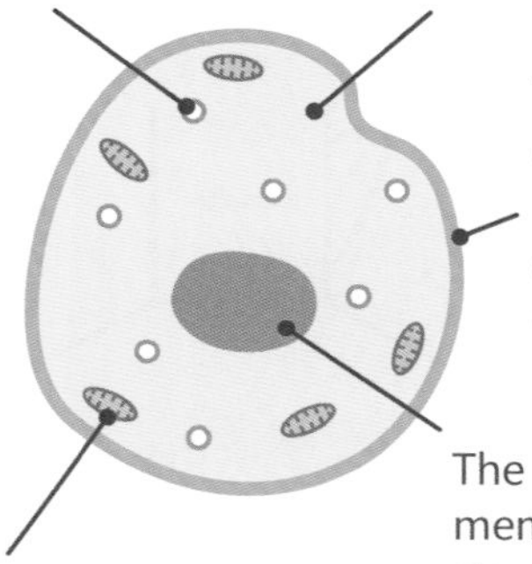
**Ribosomes** are tiny structures where proteins are made.
**Cytoplasm** is a jelly-like substance where chemical reactions take place.
The **cell membrane** controls the movement of substances into and out of the cell.
The **nucleus** is a large membrane-bound structure which contains DNA. DNA controls the growth and development of every living thing.
**Mitochondria** release energy for cell processes. The energy is a product of respiration.

**Figure 1** Eukaryotic cell

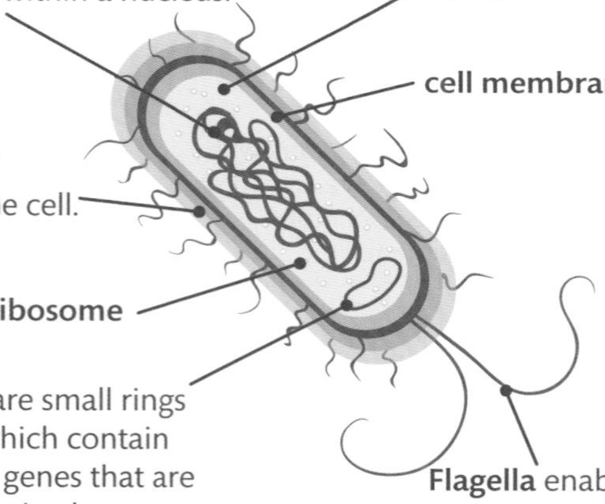
A **single loop of DNA** not contained within a nucleus.
**cytoplasm**
**cell membrane**
A **cell wall** protects the cell.
**ribosome**
**Plasmids** are small rings of DNA, which contain additional genes that are not present in chromosomes.
**Flagella** enable the cell to move.

**Figure 2** Prokaryotic cell

## 1 Working scientifically

Most cells are microscopic. You need to understand the scale and size of cells and use the correct prefixes.

The following are compared to one metre.

**centi**metre (cm) = one hundredth or $10^{-2}$

**milli**metre (mm) = one thousandth or $10^{-3}$

**micro**metre (μm) = one millionth or $10^{-6}$

**nano**metre (nm) = one billionth or $10^{-9}$

Remember, prokaryote means 'before nucleus'. Prokaryotic cells do not have a nucleus. They contain a single DNA loop and small rings of DNA called plasmids.

## 5 Worked example — Grade 6

**1** Where is DNA found in prokaryotic cells? **[1 mark]**

The single loop of DNA is found in the cytoplasm. It is not enclosed in a nucleus.

**2** Compare the structure of prokaryotic and eukaryotic cells. **[2 marks]**

Eukaryotes are larger and have more complex structures than prokaryotes. The main difference between eukaryotes and prokaryotes is that the genetic material in eukaryotes is enclosed in a nucleus.

Eukaryotic cells and prokaryotic cells are similar in that they both have:

- a cell membrane
- cytoplasm.

Prokaryotic cell structures differ to eukaryotic cells because:

- they don't have a nucleus.

## 5 Exam-style practice — Grade 6

**1** Describe the similarities and differences between prokaryotic and eukaryotic cells. **[3 marks]**

**2** Look at **Figure 1**, a diagram of a eukaryotic cell. Give the organelles in size order, starting with the smallest first. **[2 marks]**

# Animal and plant cells

You need to be able to describe and explain the differences in structure of animal and plant cells.

## Animal and plant cell structures

Although both animal and plant cells are eukaryotic, there are important structural differences between them. Plants stay in the same place and produce their own food. Animals move around in search of an external supply of food. These differences are the main reasons animal and plant cell structures differ.

Algal cells have a similar structure to plant cells. They also have a cellulose cell wall that strengthens the cell.

Go to page 2 to revise the functions of organelles.

| Organelle | Plant cell | Animal cell |
|---|---|---|
| nucleus | ✓ | ✓ |
| cytoplasm | ✓ | ✓ |
| cell membrane | ✓ | ✓ |
| cell wall | ✓ | ✗ |
| mitochondria | ✓ | ✓ |
| ribosomes | ✓ | ✓ |
| chloroplasts | ✓ | ✗ |
| permanent vacuole | ✓ | ✗ |

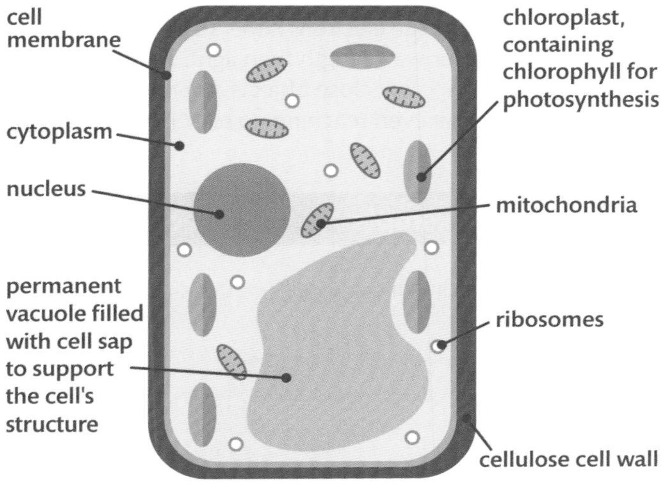


**Figure 1** A plant cell

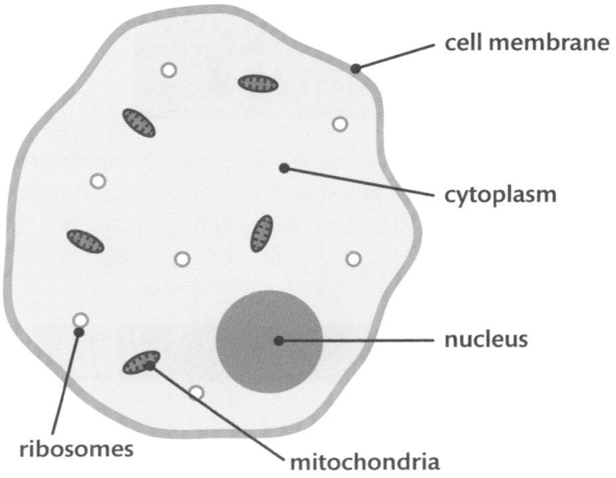


**Figure 2** An animal cell

Structure is often related to function. Think of how animals and plants function differently from one another.

## Worked example — Grade 6

Suggest how the structures of plant cells are adapted to carry out their function. **[4 marks]**

Plants must produce their own food as they cannot move. Plant cells contain chloroplasts, which use sunlight to convert water and carbon dioxide into glucose and oxygen (photosynthesis).

Unlike animals, plants do not have a skeleton, so they need another form of support and protection. Each cell has a cellulose cell wall and a sap-filled vacuole which makes the cell much firmer and helps support the plant.

## Exam-style practice — Grade 7

1 Look at **Figure 3**.

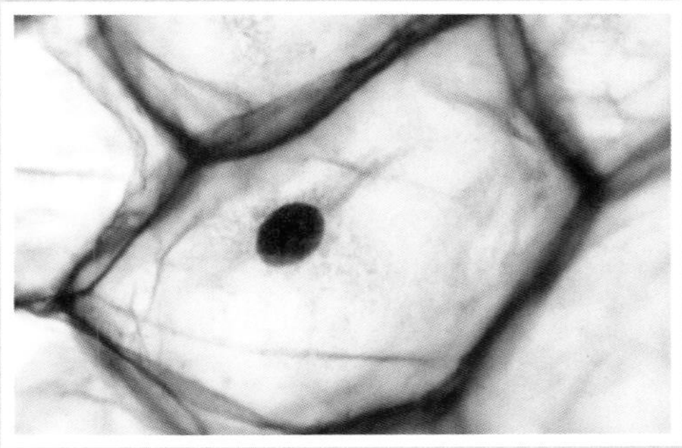

**Figure 3** A plant cell

(a) Label the nucleus. **[1 mark]**

(b) Estimate how many times wider a cell is than its nucleus. **[1 mark]**

2 Describe **three** differences between animal and plant cell structures. **[3 marks]**

# Microscopy

You need to know how microscopes have developed, allowing scientists to examine increasingly small cellular structures.

## 5 Types of microscope

Microscopes are used to study cells. Over time, different kinds of microscope have been developed. The first light microscope, which could be used to observe simple cell structures, was invented about 350 years ago. This was gradually improved upon and refined to give the compound light microscopes that we use today. More complex cell structures can be viewed with a compound light microscope. The electron microscope was invented in the 1930s.

**Figure 1** Tiny cell organelles can be observed with an electron microscope. Ribosomes can be seen with an electron microscope but they are too small to be seen with a light microscope. The nucleus and mitochondria can be seen with a light microscope. The nucleus is larger so can be seen more clearly.

## 1 Maths skills

You need to know how to work out magnification using the formula:

$$\text{magnification} = \frac{\text{size of image}}{\text{size of real object}}$$

Use a ruler to measure the size of the image.

## 2 Maths skills

When calculating the size of microscopic cells, you may need to use standard form. Standard form is an efficient way of writing very big or very small numbers. For example:

35 000 000 can be written as:

$3.5 \times 10 \times 10 \times 10 \times 10 \times 10 \times 10 \times 10$

or $3.5 \times 10^7$ in standard form.

## 10 Magnification and resolution

**Magnification** is the measure of how many times bigger the image is than the object.

If a microscope has an eyepiece lens of ×10 and an objective lens of ×50, the image looks 10 × 50 times bigger, that is, 500 times bigger.

Light microscopes use light to see an image. They can only magnify up to about ×1200, due to problems with resolution.

**Resolution** is the measure of how well a microscope can distinguish between two very close objects.

Above ×1200, light microscopes cannot distinguish between two close objects. This is due to the wavelength of light.

Electron microscopes use electrons rather than light. Electrons have a much shorter wavelength than light. This means they can resolve two very close objects at a much higher magnification, some even reaching up to ×10 000 000.

## 5 Worked example — Grade 5

**Figure 2** A scale drawing of a cell

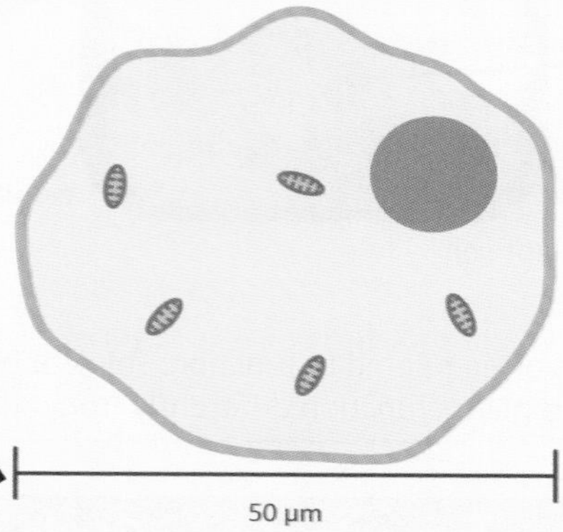


Calculate the magnification of the image in **Figure 2.** **[3 marks]**

size of image = 5 cm

5 cm = 50 000 µm

size of real object = 50 µm ← from scale bar

$$\text{magnification} = \frac{50\,000}{50} = \times 1000$$

## 5 Exam-style practice — Grade 7

1. A cell has a width of 100 µm. A scale drawing of the same cell has a width of 20 cm. Calculate the magnification of the drawing. Write your answer in standard form. **[2 marks]**
2. A microscope has an eyepiece lens of ×15 and an objective lens of ×50. Calculate how many times bigger the image is than the object. **[2 marks]**

# Using microscopes

You need to know how to set up and use a microscope to look at cells. You also need to be able to draw and label cells from a micrograph.

## 5 Using a microscope

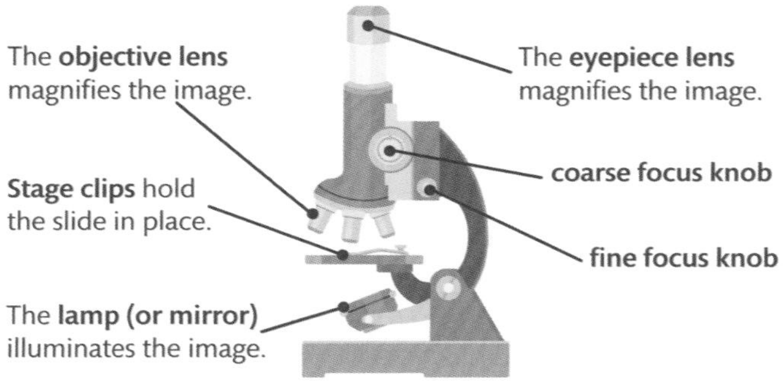


**Figure 1** A light microscope

## 2 Working scientifically

You need to be able to use appropriate measurements when answering questions about the size of microscopic cells.

megametre (Mm) = one million metres

kilometre (km) = one thousand metres

metre (m) = one metre

millimetre (mm) = one thousandth of a metre

micrometre (μm) = one millionth of a metre

nanometre (nm) = one billionth of a metre

## 10 Worked example — Grade 5

**(a)** Explain how you would prepare a slide of onion epidermal tissue. You may use a diagram to help you answer. **[4 marks]**

Drop a spot of water on a glass slide. Peel off a one-cell thick layer of cells and place on a glass slide. Add one drop of stain to the tissue. Use a mounted needle to lower the cover slip slowly and carefully to avoid trapping any air bubbles. Place the cover slip on top of the tissue, ensuring no air bubbles get trapped.

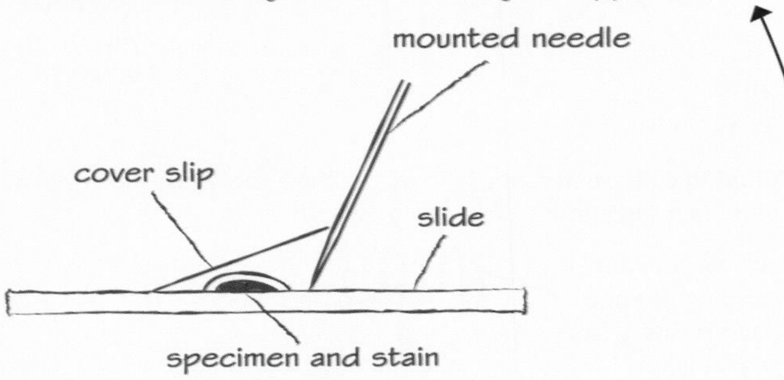


Tissue samples are stained to add contrast because most cells are colourless. Samples should be one cell thick so that cells can be seen clearly without different layers overlapping.

**(b)** Explain how you would view the slide under a microscope. **[4 marks]**

Place the prepared slide under the stage clips of the microscope. Use the coarse focus knob to lower the low power objective lens to just above the slide. Look through the eyepiece lens and raise the lens until the image is nearly in focus. Use the fine focus knob to get a clear sharp image.

**(c)** Look at **Figure 2**. Draw what you can see. **[2 marks]**

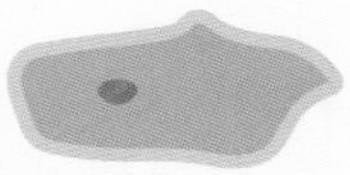

**Figure 2** An onion cell

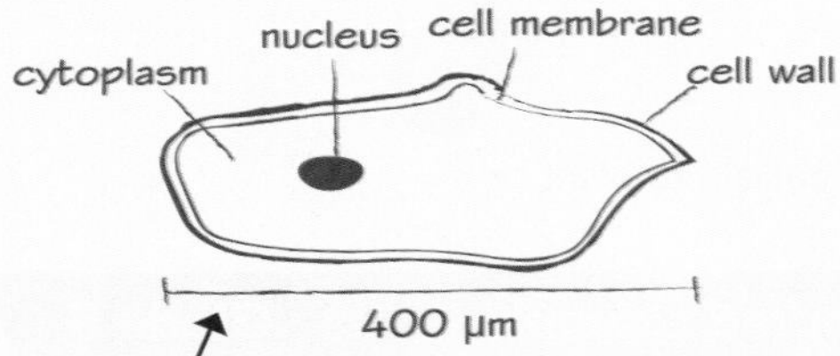


- You should only draw the things that you can see and not the things that you think should be there.
- Do not use shading.
- Keep the labels simple and clearly identified.
- Remember to include a scale bar on your drawing.

## 5 Exam-style practice — Grade 5

1. Suggest why tissue samples must be very thin to be viewed with a microscope. **[1 mark]**
2. Suggest why scientists often stain tissue samples before viewing them with a microscope. **[1 mark]**

# Specialised cells

Multicellular organisms are large organisms, like animals, made up of more than one type of cell. You need to know about the structural adaptations of specialised cells that enable them to perform specific functions.

## 5 Specialised plant cells

You need to know how the following plant cells are specialised to carry out a particular function.

**Xylem cells** transport water and minerals up from the roots to the rest of the plant. Go to page 20 to revise the functions of the plant organs in more detail.

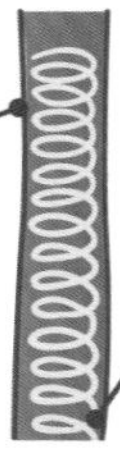


**Root hair cells** absorb water and minerals from the soil.

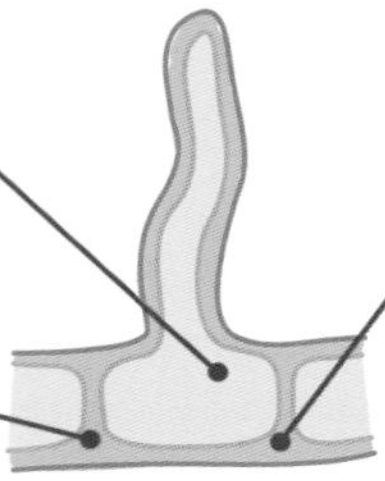


**Phloem cells** transport dissolved sugars from the leaves to the roots, where they are stored.

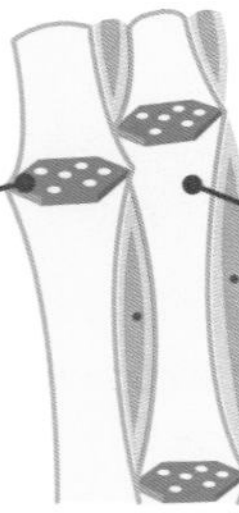


**Figure 1** Specialised plant cells

## 5 Worked example — Grade 5

**1** Describe **two** ways nerve cells are adapted for their function. **[2 marks]**

Nerve cells have long axons so they are able to transmit nerve impulses between distant parts of the body. They also have branched endings called dendrites that connect with other nerve cells.

**2** Why do muscle cells contain many mitochondria? **[1 mark]**

Mitochondria produce the energy needed for muscles to contract.

## 5 Specialised animal cells

You need to know how the following animal cells are specialised to carry out a particular function.

**Nerve cells** carry electrical impulses around the organism.

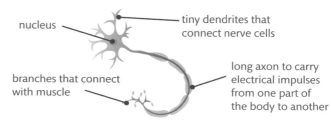

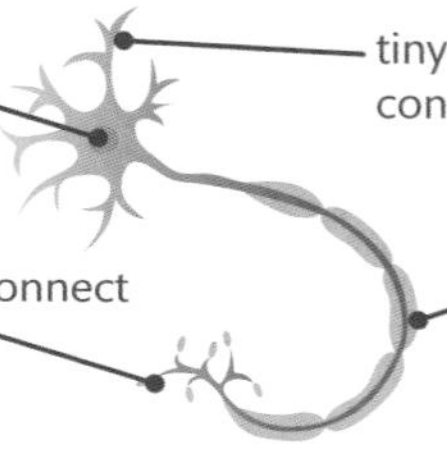


**Muscle cells** move causing the muscle to contract.

**Sperm cells** swim and fertilise an egg cell.

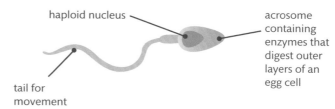

**Ciliated cells**, such as those in the trachea, move substances in a particular direction.

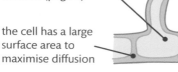

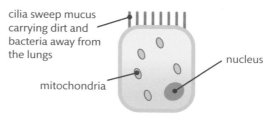

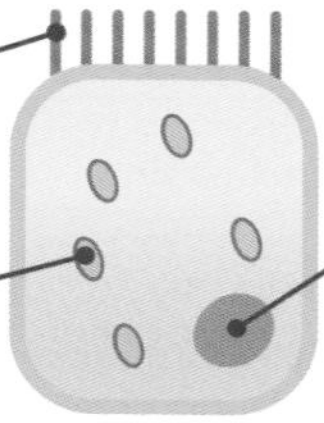


**Figure 2** Specialised animal cells

Red blood cells are another type of specialised cell. Go to page 24 to revise the function and adaptations of red blood cells.

## 10 Exam-style practice — Grade 5

Describe **two** ways muscle cells, sperm cells and phloem are each specialised to perform their functions. **[6 marks]**

# Cell differentiation

You need to understand the importance of cell differentiation in plants and animals.

## 5 Cell differentiation

As an organism develops, cells differentiate to form different types of specialised cells. When a cell differentiates, it acquires different sub-cellular structures to enable it to perform specific functions.

- Muscle cells need to be able to contract to cause movement.
- Nerve cells need to be able to transmit electrical impulses to communicate with other parts of the organism.
- Root hair cells need to have a large surface area to absorb water and nutrients from the soil.

Stem cells are able to differentiate into any kind of human cell. Human stem cells can come from human embryos or from adult bone marrow. Go to page 71 to revise stem cells.

Go to page 6 to revise how cells have become specialised to perform their function.

### Differentiation in animal cells

Most types of animal cell differentiate at an early stage in the life of an organism. In mature animals, cell division is restricted mainly to repair and replacement, such as generating new blood cells, healing skin cuts, hair and fingernail growth, and healing broken bones.

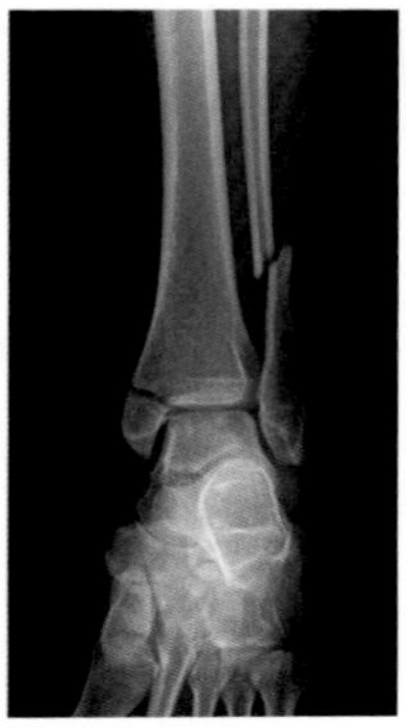

**Figure 1** An X-ray of a broken ankle

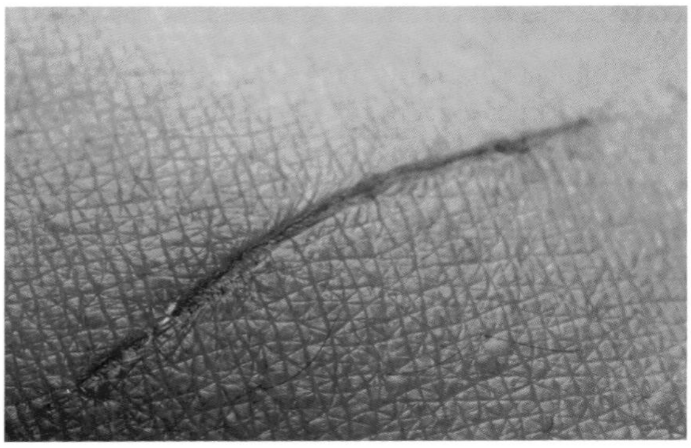

**Figure 2** A healing cut

### Differentiation in plant cells

Many types of plant cell retain the ability to differentiate throughout the life of an organism. Cells can differentiate to grow new leaves, flowers, branches, xylem and phloem. This is why plants can regrow branches that are cut off during pruning. Cells in meristems (page 19) in plants can differentiate into any type of plant cell, throughout the life of the plant.

## 5 Worked example — Grade 6

Describe **two** examples of cell differentiation in mature animals. **[4 marks]**

*In mature animals, cell division is mainly restricted to providing new cells to repair and replace damaged or lost tissue. For example, new red blood cells are constantly being generated to replace old and damaged red blood cells. Cell differentiation is also integral to the repair of skin and bone after injury.*

## 10 Exam-style practice — Grade 7

1. Describe **two** examples of repair and replacement in humans, not including the creation of red blood cells or the healing of cut skin. **[2 marks]**
2. Explain the advantage of cells retaining the ability to differentiate throughout the life of the organism. **[1 mark]**

# Diffusion

You need to know how certain factors affect the rate of diffusion and how multicellular organisms have adaptations to enable the effective exchange of substances.

## 5 Rate of diffusion

Diffusion is the **net movement** of particles of gas or particles in solution, down a **concentration gradient**, from an area of high concentration to an area of low concentration. Diffusion is an important process that occurs in both plants and animals. Useful substances such as oxygen and glucose diffuse into cells. Waste products diffuse out of cells. Carbon dioxide is a waste product, produced during gas exchange in fish gills, leaf cells and the lungs. Urea is a waste product, which diffuses into the blood plasma and is then excreted in the kidney.

Certain factors affect the rate of diffusion:

- **difference in concentrations** – the greater the concentration gradient, the greater the rate of diffusion
- **temperature** – the higher the temperature, the higher the rate of diffusion because molecules have more kinetic energy so move faster.

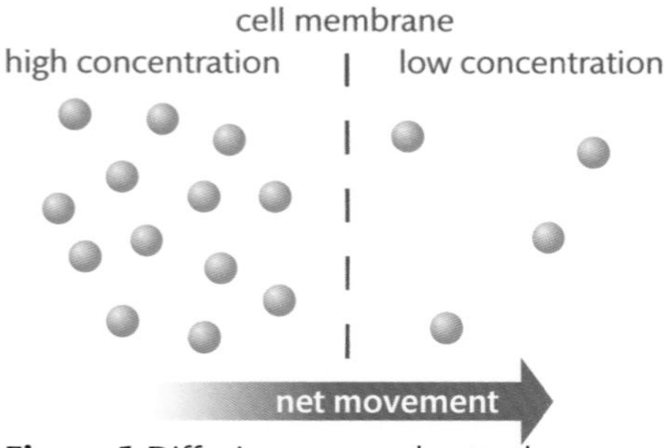


**Figure 1** Diffusion occurs due to the random movement of particles. Particles move into and out of cells by diffusion until they are evenly distributed in space.

## 2 Exchange surfaces

Small unicellular organisms have a large surface to volume ratio so diffusion can occur rapidly. Whereas, multicellular organisms have a small surface area to volume ratio, which slows down the rate of diffusion. Multicellular organisms have evolved to have specialised exchange surfaces and organ systems that maximise diffusion by having:

- a large surface area
- a thin membrane for a short diffusion path
- a good transport system to maintain maximum concentration gradients.

In animals, an efficient blood supply and continuous ventilation maintain the concentration gradient required for efficient gaseous exchange of oxygen and carbon dioxide.

Examples of specialised exchange surfaces include:

- air sacs in the lungs and filaments in fish gills, which provide a large surface area and thin membrane for gaseous exchange. Go to page 25 for more about adaptations within the lungs.
- villi in the small intestine, which have a good blood supply and a large surface area for absorbing digested food molecules. Go to page 21 for more about digestion in humans.
- palisade cells in the leaf, which have a large surface area for gas exchange. Go to page 19 to revise the adaptations within leaf cells and tissues.

## 5 Surface area to volume ratio

Think of a cube with sides of length 1 cm:

- the surface area is 6 $cm^2$
- the volume is 1 $cm^3$
- the ratio of surface area to volume is 6 : 1.

If the cube now has sides of length 2 cm:

- the surface area is 24 $cm^2$
- the volume is 8 $cm^3$
- the ratio of surface area to volume is 3 : 1.

There is a greater volume for more chemical reactions in the larger cube but proportionately less surface area for the molecules to diffuse through. This limits the maximum size of a cell.

## 5 Worked example — Grade 6

Give **three** factors that affect the rate of diffusion into and out of cells. **[3 marks]**

*The difference in concentration (i.e. the concentration gradient), the temperature and the surface area of the membrane.*

Another suitable answer is the thickness of the membrane.

## 5 Exam-style practice — Grade 6

1. Explain why a good blood supply increases the rate of absorption of oxygen in the lungs. **[2 marks]**
2. Air sacs in the lungs have a large surface area. Explain the effect this has on the rate of gas exchange. **[2 marks]**

# Osmosis

You need to understand the process of osmosis and be able to draw and interpret labelled diagrams that model the diffusion of water molecules.

## 10 Diffusion of water molecules

Osmosis is the diffusion of water molecules, from a **dilute solution** to a **concentrated solution**, through a **partially permeable membrane**.

The glucose molecules are too large to pass through the membrane. The water molecules are small enough to pass through.

Partially permeable membranes only allow certain molecules to move across. They don't allow ions or large molecules to cross. Cell membranes are partially permeable.

Concentrated solutions contain a low concentration of water molecules.

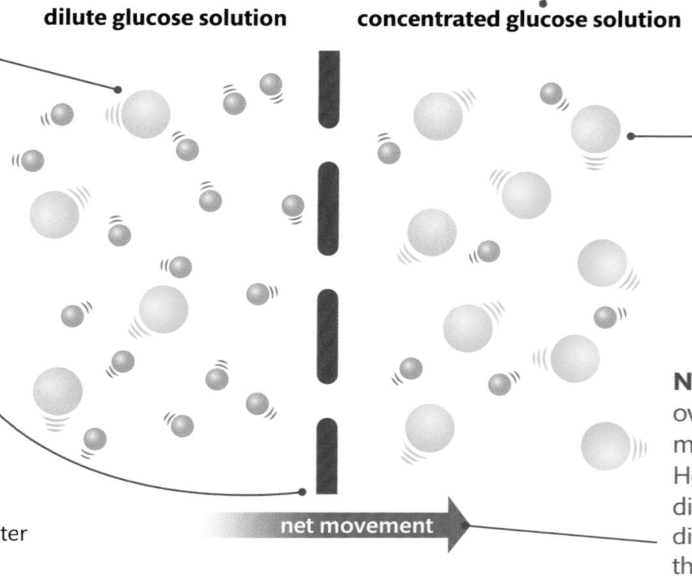


There are fewer water molecules and more glucose molecules on this side of the membrane. This means the water molecules will diffuse across to the right-hand side.

**Net movement** is the overall direction of movement of a substance. Here, water diffuses in both directions, but **more** water diffuses from left to right than from right to left.

glucose molecule

water molecule

net movement of water

**Figure 1** Osmosis model

## 5 Worked example — Grade 8

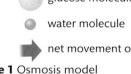

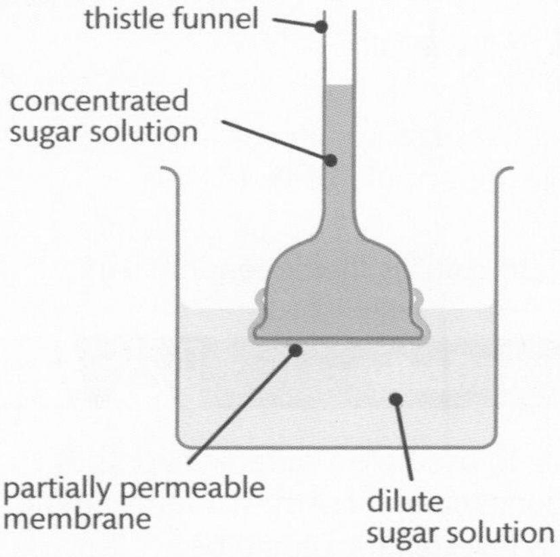


**Figure 2** Investigating osmosis apparatus

**Figure 2** shows the apparatus a student uses in an osmosis experiment.

**(a)** Describe the result that the student observes. **[1 mark]**

*The water level will rise up the tube.*

**(b)** Use your knowledge of osmosis to explain this result. **[3 marks]**

*In the dilute solution there are more water molecules than in the concentrated sugar solution. Sugar molecules are too large to pass through the partially permeable membrane. Water molecules are able to pass through the membrane and will move from the dilute solution to the concentrated solution. There will be a net movement of water molecules into the thistle funnel.*

Go to page 10 to revise the effect of a range of concentrations of sugar solutions on osmosis.

You need to think about how the concentration gradient will change. Go to page 8 for more about this topic.

## 5 Exam-style practice — Grade 8

1. Explain what happens to the rate of osmosis in **Figure 1** if the concentration of sugar on the right-hand side of the partially permeable membrane is increased. **[3 marks]**
2. The higher the temperature, the faster molecules move. Explain what happens to the rate of osmosis as the temperature is increased. **[2 marks]**

# Investigating osmosis

You need to know how to produce a hypothesis and investigate the effect of different concentrations of sugar solution on osmosis.

## 10 Worked example — Grade 9

A student placed equal-sized raw potato chips in different concentrations of sugar solution for two hours. The table shows the change in mass of each of the potato chips.

| Sugar solution concentration in $g/dm^3$ | Initial mass of chip in g | Final mass of chip in g | Percentage change in mass |
|---|---|---|---|
| 0.00 | 2.5 | 2.95 | +18 |
| 80 | 2.5 | 2.45 | −2 |
| 160 | 2.5 | 2.23 | |
| 240 | 2.5 | 2.05 | −18 |
| 320 | 2.5 | 1.98 | −21 |

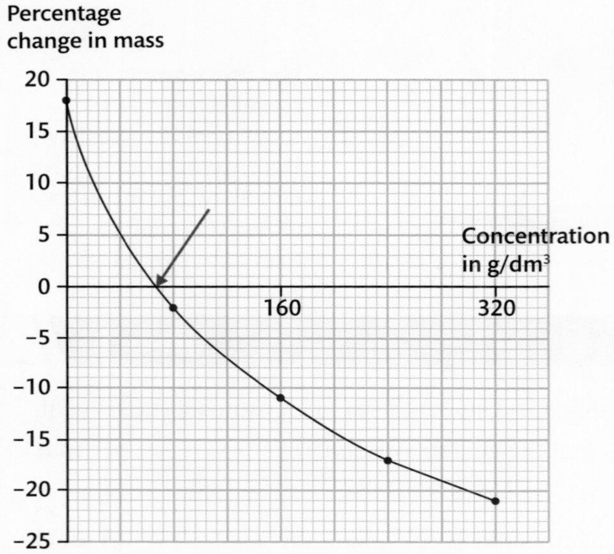


**Figure 1** A graph showing the student's results

**(a)** One of the results is missing from the table. Determine the missing result. **[2 marks]**

$$100 \times \frac{(2.23 - 2.5)}{2.5} = -11\%$$

**(b)** Explain how the student could improve the repeatability of their measurements. **[2 marks]**

The student could repeat the investigation several more times under the same conditions to see whether the results are similar.

**(c)** Use **Figure 1** to determine the concentration of sugar solution inside the potato cells. **[2 marks]**

The concentration of the cytoplasm will be the same as the sugar solution when there is no change in mass. From the graph, this is 72 $g/dm^3$.

## 2 Apparatus

- five equal-sized potato chips
- five different concentrations of sugar solution:
  - 0.00 $g/dm^3$
  - 80 $g/dm^3$
  - 160 $g/dm^3$
  - 240 $g/dm^3$
  - 320 $g/dm^3$
- ruler
- balance

### Maths skills

You can calculate percentage change in mass by subtracting the initial mass from the final mass, then dividing by the initial mass and multiplying by 100.

## 5 Method

1. Using the balance, measure five **equal-sized** potato chips.
2. Place each potato chip in a different concentration of sugar solution.
3. Leave the chips for several hours.
4. Remove each of the chips and measure their masses.
5. Record the data in a table of results.
6. Plot a line graph of the results.

The concentration of the sugar solution is the independent variable that should be varied in a controlled way.

The mass of the potato chips is the dependent variable.

## 1 Working scientifically

You need to be able to produce a suitable hypothesis based on your understanding of osmosis. For example, a hypothesis for this investigation could be:

*The higher the concentration of sugar solution, the greater the change in mass.*

## 5 Exam-style practice — Grade 5

1. What are the dependent and independent variables in this investigation? **[2 marks]**
2. Was the hypothesis proved or disproved? Give a reason for your answer. **[2 marks]**

# Active transport

You need to understand how substances are transported by active transport and be able to describe how it differs from osmosis and diffusion.

## 10 Active transport

**Active transport** is the movement of a substance from a dilute solution to a more concentrated solution against the **concentration gradient**. It requires energy from respiration.

Plants require mineral ions for healthy growth. The uptake of minerals in a plant requires active transport. Root hair cells absorb minerals from the soil, where the concentration is very low. Go to page 6 for more about specialised root hairs.

In humans, active transport allows glucose to be absorbed through the wall of the small intestine during digestion. The concentration of glucose is higher in the blood than in the gut so the glucose does not enter by diffusion. The glucose is then used for respiration.

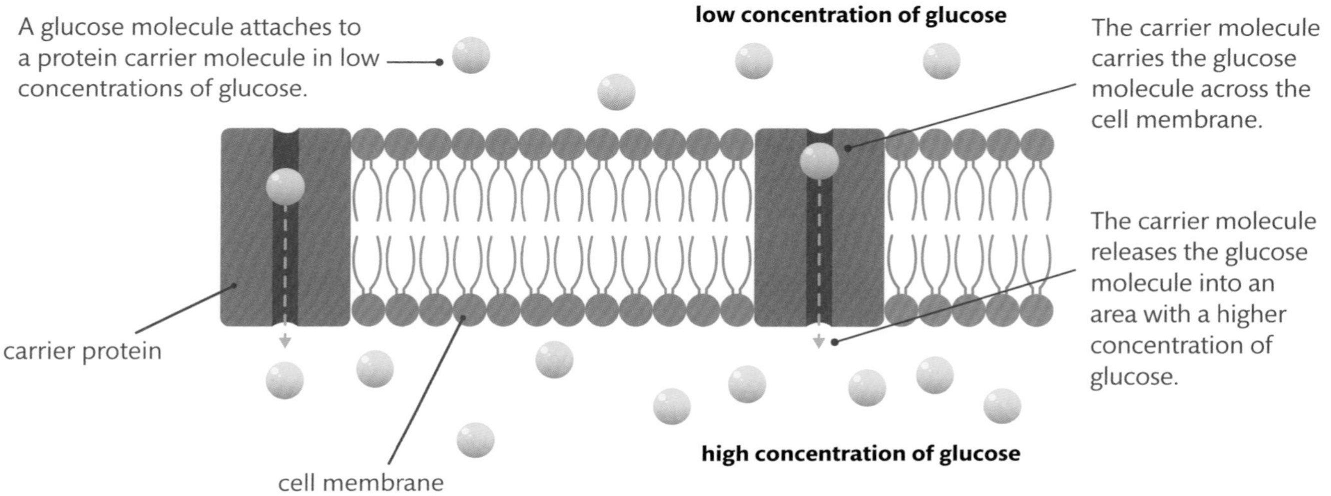

A glucose molecule attaches to a protein carrier molecule in low concentrations of glucose.
low concentration of glucose
The carrier molecule carries the glucose molecule across the cell membrane.
The carrier molecule releases the glucose molecule into an area with a higher concentration of glucose.
carrier protein
high concentration of glucose
cell membrane

**Figure 1** Active transport in the human gut

## 5 Worked example — Grade 6

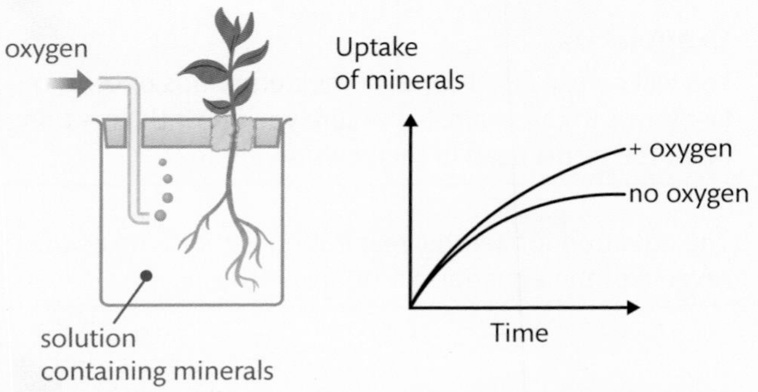


**Figure 2** The apparatus shows a plant growing in a solution of mineral ions. Oxygen is bubbled through the solution.

1 Explain the shape of the graph in **Figure 2**. **[2 marks]**

*The graph shows the increase in active transport when oxygen is bubbled through the solution. This is because oxygen is needed for respiration and respiration provides energy for the active transport of mineral ions.*

2 State the factor that slows down the rate of active transport. **[1 mark]**

*A reduction in the availability of oxygen*

## 1 Exam focus

You could be asked about the differences between diffusion and active transport in the exam. Unlike diffusion, active transport involves substances moving against the concentration gradient and requires energy.

## 5 Exam-style practice — Grade 6

1 Explain the differences between diffusion and active transport. **[3 marks]**

2 Describe **two** different examples of active transport in living organisms. **[2 marks]**

# Aerobic and anaerobic respiration

Respiration is a chemical reaction that takes place inside all living cells, releasing energy into and around the body. You need to know about two types of respiration – aerobic and anaerobic.

## 5 Respiration

Respiration is an **exothermic reaction** that releases energy needed for life processes.

The energy released by respiration has several different uses.

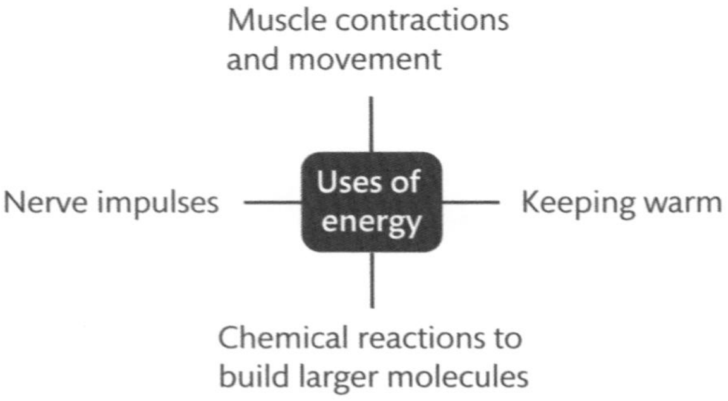


### Aerobic respiration

Aerobic respiration requires oxygen.

glucose + oxygen → carbon dioxide + water

$C_6H_{12}O_6 + 6O_2 \rightarrow 6CO_2 + 6H_2O$

Most of the reactions involving aerobic respiration happen inside mitochondria in cells.

The rate of aerobic respiration can be measured by how much oxygen is being used.

## 10 Anaerobic respiration

Anaerobic respiration does not require oxygen. Less energy is released by anaerobic respiration, the incomplete oxidation of glucose, than by aerobic respiration.

There are two forms of anaerobic respiration that you need to know for the exam.

Anaerobic respiration takes place in muscles when there is not enough oxygen available for aerobic respiration, such as when an animal is running away from a predator.

glucose → lactic acid

The muscle ache felt during exercise is due to a build up of lactic acid.

Anaerobic respiration also takes place in microorganisms and plant cells, such as in plant root cells in very wet soil.

### Anaerobic respiration in yeast

Anaerobic respiration in yeast can be shown by the following equation:

glucose → ethanol + carbon dioxide

Yeast is used to produce alcohol by a process called **fermentation**. This is how alcoholic drinks are made.

Yeast is also used to make bread, as the carbon dioxide released in respiration makes the dough rise.

## 5 Worked example — Grade 6

1. What does the term 'aerobic respiration' mean? **[1 mark]**

*Aerobic respiration is when glucose reacts with oxygen to release energy.*

2. Give the word equation and a balanced symbol equation to show aerobic respiration. **[3 marks]**

*glucose + oxygen → carbon dioxide + water*

$C_6H_{12}O_6 + 6O_2 \rightarrow 6CO_2 + 6H_2O$

**Exam focus**

You will be expected to recall the definitions of certain key terms in the exam. Make sure you know the meaning of all the terms used in this revision guide.

The equation for aerobic respiration is the same as the reverse of the equation for photosynthesis.

**Exam focus**

For the exam, you need to know:

- the word equations for aerobic and anaerobic respiration
- the chemical symbols for glucose, water, oxygen and carbon dioxide.

## 5 Exam-style practice — Grade 6

Compare aerobic and anaerobic respiration. **[5 marks]**

# Response to exercise

You need to know how the human body responds to the increased demand for energy during exercise.

## 2 Three responses

During exercise the human body responds to the increased demand for energy by supplying more glucose and more oxygen to the muscles. The human body responds to exercise in three ways:

1. The rate of breathing increases.
2. Breaths are deeper so the volume of each breath increases.
3. The heart rate increases.

The heart beats faster so glucose and oxygenated blood are pumped to the muscles more quickly, and carbon dioxide is removed more quickly.

## 2 Investigating the effects

There are various ways that you can investigate the effect of exercise on the human body. You can:

- Measure the number of breaths per minute before and immediately after exercise.
- Measure the volume of each breath, using a device called a spirometer before and immediately after exercise.
- Measure the heart rate by counting the pulse rate in the wrist before, during and after exercise.

## 5 Oxygen debt

After strenuous exercise, lactic acid builds up in the muscles due to anaerobic respiration. The body needs oxygen to react with the lactic acid to remove it from the cells. The oxygen required to do this is called the '**oxygen debt**'. The oxygen debt is the total amount of oxygen required to react with the accumulated lactic acid and remove it from the cells. This explains why the breathing rate and heart rate remain high immediately after exercise.

During long periods of vigorous activity, muscles become fatigued so they stop contracting efficiently. One cause of this is the build-up of lactic acid in the muscles from anaerobic respiration. Lactic acid is removed from the muscles by blood flowing through them.

Blood transports lactic acid from the muscles to the liver. The liver uses oxygen to convert the lactic acid into glucose.

**Figure 1** Runners continue to breathe deeply and rapidly after exercise because of an 'oxygen debt'.

## 5 Worked example — Grade 7

**1 (a)** Apart from fatigue, what other effect does lactic acid have on muscles? **[1 mark]**

*Pain, or stops the muscle from contracting easily*

**(b)** How is this waste product eventually disposed of? **[2 marks]**

*It is converted into glucose in the liver.*

**2** Explain why athletes gasp for breath after they have finished a race and are no longer running. **[2 marks]**

*They are repaying the oxygen debt so that the lactic acid produced during exercise can be converted into carbon dioxide and water.*

Breathing rate and pulse rate both remain elevated for a while after exercise because more oxygen is needed to convert lactic acid into carbon dioxide and water.

## 5 Exam-style practice — Grade 7

1. Some athletes run a 100 m race without taking any breaths. Explain how they can do this. **[2 marks]**
2. Marathon runners run for many miles. Explain why oxygen debt does not stop them from running for such long distances. **[2 marks]**

# Metabolism

Metabolism is the sum of all of the reactions, in which molecules are made or broken down, happening in a cell or organism.

## Forming new molecules

The energy that is transferred and released during respiration is used by organisms to build new, larger molecules. These processes are controlled and catalysed by enzymes. Metabolism includes:

### Converting glucose

Glucose can react in different ways to form:

- starch for storage in plants
- cellulose to strengthen plant cell walls
- glycogen for storage in muscles and the liver.

Amylase breaks down starch to form glucose. Go to page 21 to revise digestive enzymes.

### Converting glucose in anaerobic and aerobic respiration

Go to page 12 to revise respiration.

Glucose is used in both aerobic and anaerobic respiration.

glucose + oxygen → carbon dioxide + water (aerobic)

glucose → lactic acid (anaerobic)

### Forming lipids

Lipid molecules consist of a glycerol molecule and three fatty acids.

Lipids are fats and oils. They are used for storage in plants and animals, and insulation in animals.

fatty acids + glycerol → lipids

### Forming amino acids and proteins

Plants absorb nitrate ions through their roots. These ions combine with glucose to form amino acids in the reaction:
glucose + nitrate ions → amino acids

Different amino acids join together to form different proteins. Proteins include enzymes, collagen and keratin. Excess proteins are broken down to form urea which is then excreted by the kidney as urine.

## Worked example — Grade 4

1 Which of these statements is the correct definition of metabolism? Tick **one** box. **[1 mark]**

- **A** the synthesis of compounds in a cell ☐
- **B** all of the reactions in a cell or organism ☑
- **C** the movement of substances through the membranes in a cell ☐
- **D** some of the reactions in a cell or organism ☐

2 Give **three** types of digestive enzyme involved in metabolism. **[3 marks]**

Carbohydrase (such as amylase), lipase, protease

3 Give a food test that can be used to identify amylase. What would be observed for a positive reaction? **[3 marks]**

Biuret test – sodium hydroxide and copper sulfate solution. It turns purple for a positive test.

## Exam-style practice — Grade 7

1 Explain why metabolism is important in animals and plants. **[2 marks]**

2 Describe where the energy for metabolism comes from. **[1 mark]**

# Photosynthesis

You need to understand the process of photosynthesis, including the chemical equation for the reaction.

## 5 Photosynthesis

During the process of photosynthesis, plants use energy from sunlight to build large complex organic molecules from simple inorganic ones. Cells in green leaves contain small structures called chloroplasts. Chloroplasts contain chlorophyll, a green pigment that absorbs the energy from sunlight. This energy is needed for photosynthesis.

Photosynthesis is an **endothermic reaction**. This means that it absorbs energy.

### The chemical equation for photosynthesis

Water is absorbed by root hair cells. Go to page 20 for more about how this happens.

Go to page 17 to read about the uses of glucose in plants.

carbon dioxide + water $\xrightarrow[\text{chlorophyll in green leaves}]{\text{light from the Sun}}$ glucose + oxygen

$$6CO_2 + 6H_2O \xrightarrow[\text{chlorophyll in green leaves}]{\text{light from the Sun}} C_6H_{12}O_6 + 6O_2$$

Carbon dioxide diffuses from the air into the cell. Oxygen diffuses from the cell into the air. Go to page 8 to revise diffusion.

Light energy is absorbed by chloroplasts in plant cells.

## 10 Working scientifically

You should be able to balance simple equations.

Look at the equation for photosynthesis:

$$\square CO_2 + \square H_2O \rightarrow C_6H_{12}O_6 + \square O_2$$

You can balance the equation by looking at how many atoms of each type there are on each side of the arrow. The numbers on each side should balance.

For example:

There are 6 carbon atoms on the right-hand side. This can be balanced by putting a 6 in front of the carbon dioxide on the left-hand side. This gives you:

$$\boxed{6} CO_2 + \square H_2O \rightarrow C_6H_{12}O_6 + \square O_2$$

There are 12 hydrogen atoms in glucose. Put a 6 in front of the water to give a total of 12 hydrogen atoms on the left-hand side of the equation (6 × $H_2$). This gives you:

$$\boxed{6} CO_2 + \boxed{6} H_2O \rightarrow C_6H_{12}O_6 + \square O_2$$

Add up the number of oxygen atoms on the left and right-hand sides. There are 12 (6 × $O_2$) in $CO_2$ and 6 in $H_2O$, giving a total of 18 oxygen atoms on the left. On the right, there are 6 atoms in glucose and 2 in $O_2$, giving a total of 8. Put a 6 in front of the $O_2$ to give both sides 18 oxygen atoms.

$$\boxed{6} CO_2 + \boxed{6} H_2O \rightarrow C_6H_{12}O_6 + \boxed{6} O_2$$

Go to page 19 to revise the structure of plant tissues.

## 10 Worked example — Grade 7

**1** Most chloroplasts are found in cells towards the upper surface of leaves. Suggest why. **[1 mark]**

*More light reaches the upper surface of leaves, enabling more photosynthesis to take place.*

**2** Explain how animals and plants are interdependent. Use the processes of respiration and photosynthesis in your answer. **[2 marks]**

*Plants provide animals with oxygen and food. Animals provide plants with carbon dioxide.*

**3** Photosynthesis is an endothermic reaction. Explain what this means. **[1 mark]**

*It is a reaction that takes in energy.*

## 2 Exam-style practice — Grade 7

A student tells their teacher 'photosynthesis is the opposite of respiration'. Use the equations for photosynthesis and respiration to explain what the student means. **[2 marks]**

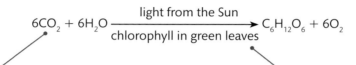

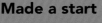

# Rate of photosynthesis

The rate of photosynthesis is determined by four factors: temperature, light intensity, carbon dioxide concentration and the amount of chlorophyll. You need to know how these factors affect the rate of photosynthesis.

## 10 Graphs of limiting factors

Limiting factors are environmental conditions that have an impact on the rate of a process. There are four factors that affect the rate of photosynthesis.

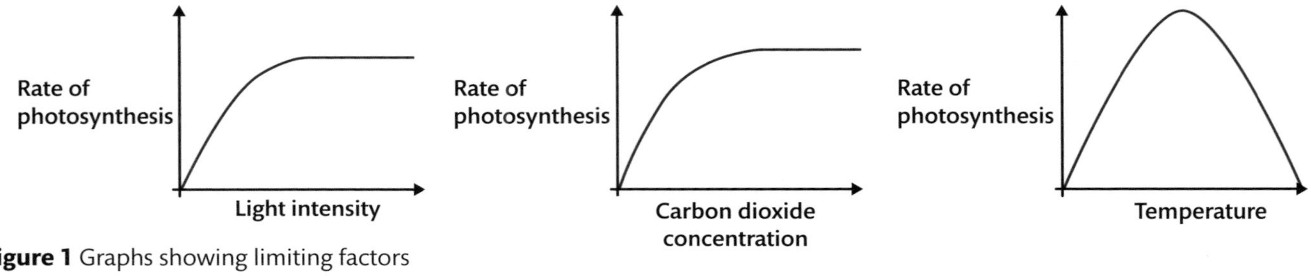


**Figure 1** Graphs showing limiting factors

When light levels are low, the rate of photosynthesis will be slow as it is limited by the lack of light. As light intensity increases, the rate of photosynthesis increases until it reaches an optimum level when any further increase in light intensity has no effect. As light cannot be a limiting factor when at a high intensity, there must be another factor affecting the rate of photosynthesis.

Carbon dioxide is a common limiting factor affecting the rate of photosynthesis because it is at a low level in the atmosphere. Plants cannot photosynthesise without carbon dioxide. The level of carbon dioxide can be increased if plants are grown in a greenhouse.

As the amount of chlorophyll increases, the rate of photosynthesis increases because more light is being absorbed.

As temperature increases, the rate of photosynthesis increases until it reaches a maximum and then begins to decrease until it reaches zero. This is because at high temperatures the enzymes that control photosynthesis are denatured.

### Working scientifically

Commercial growers can use knowledge of limiting factors to improve yields by raising temperature, carbon dioxide and light levels, although doing so costs money and they must find a balance between maximising photosynthesis and making a profit.

## 5 Worked example — Grade 5

**Figure 2** The apparatus shown can be used to measure the rate of photosynthesis in pondweed.

**1** How can the apparatus in **Figure 1** be used to work out the rate of photosynthesis? Give a reason for your answer. **[2 marks]**

*Count the bubbles over a certain period of time. Pondweed gives off bubbles of oxygen as it photosynthesises.*

**2** A student wants to investigate the effect of carbon dioxide on the rate of photosynthesis. Describe how they could do this. **[2 marks]**

*Dissolve different amounts of sodium hydrogencarbonate in the water to vary the concentration of carbon dioxide.*

## 10 Exam-style practice — Grades 5–7

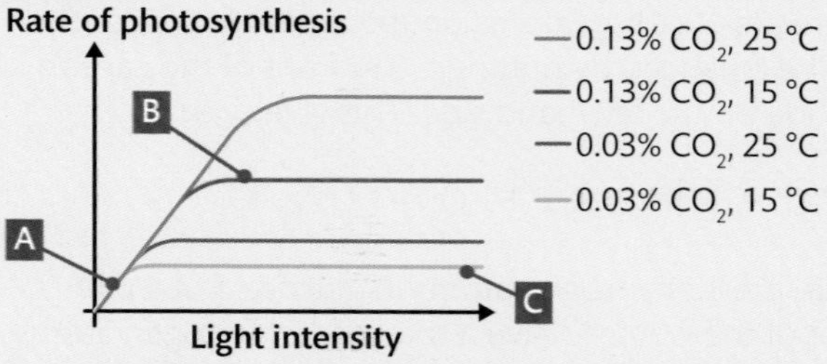


**Figure 3** The effect of limiting factors on growing tomatoes in a greenhouse.

Use **Figure 3** to answer the following questions.

**(a)** Write down the **three** limiting factors shown on the graph. **[3 marks]**

**(b)** What is the limiting factor at point A on the graph? Explain your answer. **[2 marks]**

**(c)** What is the limiting factor at point B on the graph? Explain your answer. **[2 marks]**

**(d)** Identify a factor that is definitely **not** limiting at point C. **[1 mark]**

# Uses of photosynthesis

You need to know how the glucose produced by photosynthesis is used by plants.

## Uses of glucose

The glucose produced by photosynthesis is transported around the plant as soluble sugars. Glucose has several different uses in a plant. It is used to make cellulose, a structural carbohydrate which forms cell walls, giving strength and support to the plant. Along with nitrate ions that are absorbed from the soil, glucose is used to make proteins for growth and repair. It is also used in respiration to release energy required for plant cells. The oxygen produced by photosynthesis is a waste product. Any glucose made by the plant that isn't required immediately can be converted and stored as:

- insoluble starch
- fat or oil.

Wheat plants store glucose as starch, while oilseed rape plants store glucose as rapeseed oil.

## Worked example — Grade 6

**1** Which **two** of the following statements about the uses of glucose are correct?
Tick **two** boxes. **[2 marks]**

- **A** used for photosynthesis ☐
- **B** used to make oils ☑
- **C** used to transport oxygen ☐
- **D** used to produce cellulose ☑
- **E** used to absorb light ☐

**2** Give the role of cellulose in plants. **[2 marks]**

It helps to make cell walls to support the plant.

## Respiration

One of the uses of glucose is respiration (page 12). Plants respire all the time, whereas they can only photosynthesise during daylight hours. At night, there is no sunlight so plants cannot photosynthesise, but they can respire so oxygen is taken in and carbon dioxide is given out.

In dim light, the rate of photosynthesis is equal to the rate of respiration so neither gas is taken in or given out, as they cancel each other out.

The maximum rate of photosynthesis occurs around midday, when sunlight is brightest. The rate of photosynthesis is greater than the rate of respiration so carbon dioxide is taken in and oxygen is given out.

During the day, plants make an excess of glucose.

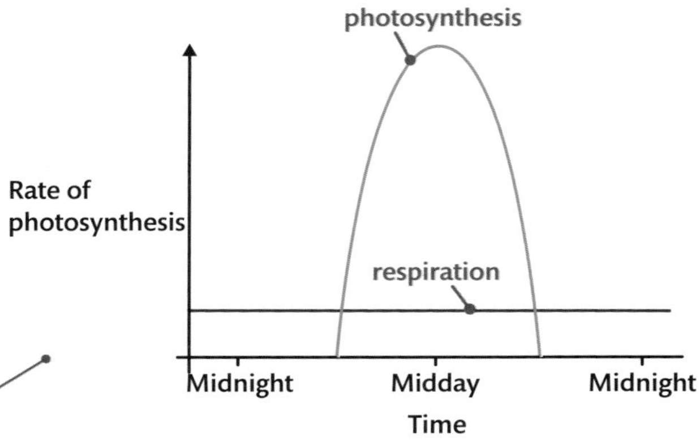


**Figure 1** The graph shows that the rate of respiration stays constant over a 24-hour period but the rate of photosynthesis varies.

Go to page 20 to revise transport and storage in plants.

## Exam-style practice — Grade 7

**1** Explain why it is important that plants can store glucose made during the day. **[1 mark]**

**2** Give **one** reason why plants store glucose as starch. **[1 mark]**

**3** State **three** locations in a plant where starch is stored. **[3 marks]**

# Investigating photosynthesis

You need to know how to investigate the effect of light intensity on the rate of photosynthesis.

## 5 Method

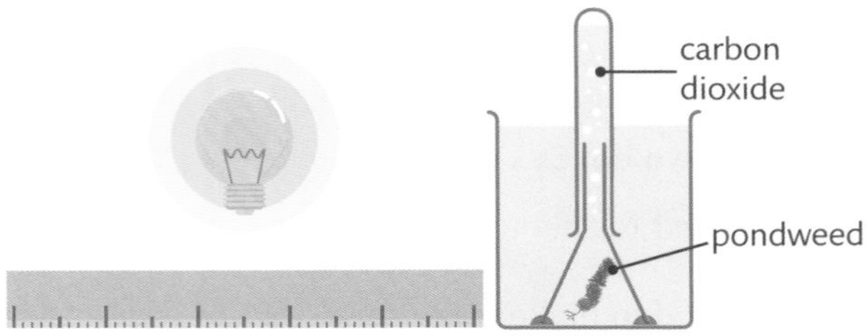


**Figure 1** Investigating light intensity

1. Control the light intensity by altering the distance of the lamp from the pondweed.
2. Record the distance and the number of bubbles counted in a minute in a table.

## 10 Worked example — Grade 7

The rate of photosynthesis is measured by counting the number of bubbles given off by pondweed each minute.

| Distance of pondweed from lamp in cm | Rate of photosynthesis in bubbles per minute |
|---|---|
| 10 | 63 |
| 20 | 16 |
| 30 | |
| 40 | 4 |
| 50 | 3 |

**(a)** Look at the table. There is a number missing. Use the inverse square law to estimate the missing number. Show your working. **[3 marks]**

Increasing distance from 10 cm to 30 cm (by a factor of 3), changes the intensity by a factor of $\frac{1}{3^2} = \frac{1}{9}$

Number of bubbles is directly related to intensity, so the estimate for number of bubbles $= \frac{1}{9} \times 63 = 7$ bubbles when lamp is at 30 cm from pondweed.

**(b)** Explain how the accuracy of this investigation could be improved. **[2 marks]**

Repeat it several times and calculate the mean.

**(c)** A student repeated the experiment but placed a sheet of glass between the beaker and the lamp. The glass absorbed the heat from the lamp. Suggest why the student did this. **[1 mark]**

To control the temperature

## 2 Variables

This practical investigates the effect of light intensity on the rate of photosynthesis. This means that light intensity is the **independent variable**.

The rate of photosynthesis is determined by counting oxygen bubbles in a given period of time. This is the **dependent variable**.

## 5 Key experimental skills

- Use of correct apparatus to record measurements accurately.
- Safe use of hot devices, such as a lamp.
- Consider ethical issues by removing any small invertebrates on the pondweed before starting the investigation.
- Use appropriate apparatus and techniques to observe and measure change.
- Measure rate of photosynthesis by counting oxygen bubbles.

## 2 Inverse square law

Light intensity is proportional to the inverse square of the distance.

$$\text{intensity} \propto \frac{1}{\text{distance}^2}$$

If you double the distance between the lamp and the plant, the light intensity is reduced by one quarter.

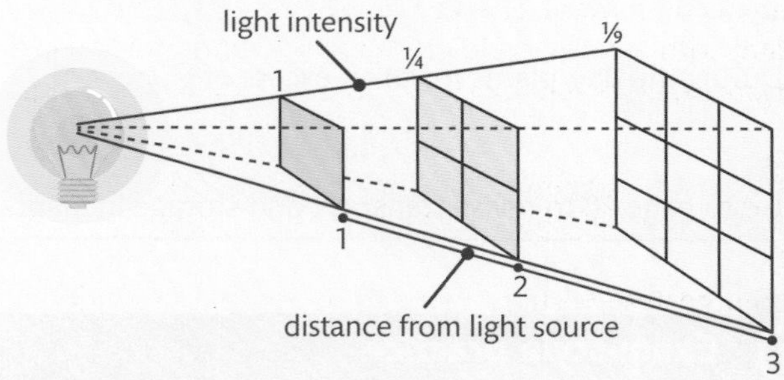


**Figure 2** Inverse square law

## 2 Exam-style practice — Grade 7

Suggest a more accurate method of measuring the gas produced than counting bubbles. **[2 marks]**

# The leaf

You need to know how the structures of plant tissues are related to their functions.

## 10 Plant tissues in the leaf

A tissue is a group of similar cells. Groups of different types of tissue can form an organ, such as a plant leaf.

**Xylem** and **phloem** are transport tissues. They are both long and tubular in shape. Xylem is hollow and transports water to the leaves from the roots. Phloem transports dissolved sugars from the leaves to other parts of the plant.

**Epidermal tissue** forms a tough boundary on the outside of the leaf, as well as secreting a waxy cuticle. Contains no chloroplasts so is transparent to allow light to reach mesophyll layers.

**Palisade mesophyll tissue** contains most chloroplasts. It is found near the upper surface of the leaf so it can trap as much energy from sunlight as possible. Orientation of palisade cells allows cells to receive both light from above and carbon dioxide from below.

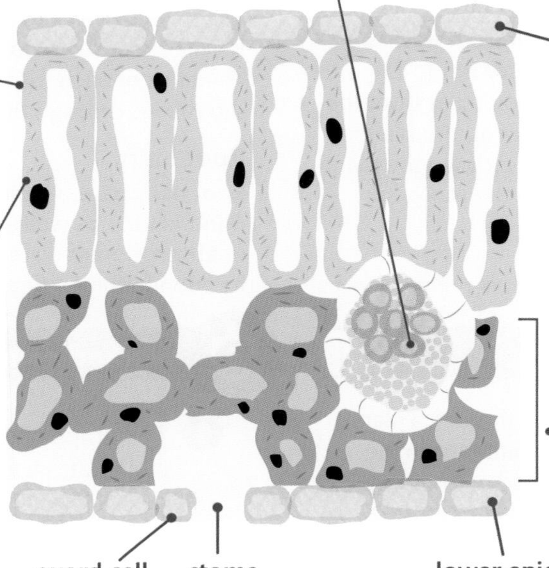


**Spongy mesophyll tissue** has a large exposed surface area surrounded by air spaces. This allows carbon dioxide to diffuse into the tissue and oxygen to diffuse out. Contains fewer chloroplasts for photosynthesis than palisade mesophyll tissue.

**Figure 1** Tissues in a leaf

## 2 Meristems

In animals, growth can occur anywhere in the body. Plants can only grow in certain areas. These areas are called **meristems**. Meristems consist of stem cells that can differentiate to form xylem and phloem cells. Growth can occur in meristems as they are the only points on the plant with actively dividing cells. Meristems are found, for example, at the tips of shoots and in the roots of plants.

## 2 Guard cells in a leaf

**Stomata** are small pores on the underside of the leaf. They allow carbon dioxide and oxygen to diffuse in and out of the leaf.

The stomata also control the loss of water through transpiration (page 20). Plants cannot photosynthesise at night, so guard cells (specialised cells in epidermal tissue) close the stomata. This prevents valuable water from evaporating from the leaf.

## 5 Worked example — Grade 7

Suggest why guard cells are found on the underside of the leaf and chloroplasts mostly near the upper surface. **[4 marks]**

*Guard cells open and close pores on the underside of the leaf called stomata. This prevents rain water entering through the leaf's pores. Chloroplasts are near the upper surface of the leaf to trap as much sunlight energy as possible.*

## 10 Exam-style practice — Grade 7

Suggest how the structure of a leaf is related to its function. Use ideas about tissues in the leaf in your answer. Do not refer to the distribution of cells. **[6 marks]**

# Plant tissues

You need to know how the roots, stem and leaves of a plant are adapted to transport substances, including water, by transpiration and food molecules by translocation.

## Transport in plants

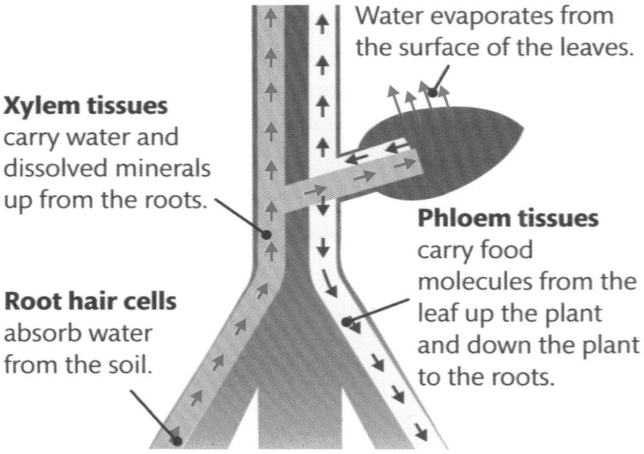

Water evaporates from the surface of the leaves.
**Xylem tissues** carry water and dissolved minerals up from the roots.
**Phloem tissues** carry food molecules from the leaf up the plant and down the plant to the roots.
**Root hair cells** absorb water from the soil.


**Figure 1** Plant organs involved in the transport of substances

### Xylem

Xylem tissue transports water and dissolved minerals. It is made of hollow tubes strengthened by a substance called lignin. Pits in the tubes allow water and ions to move out.

### Phloem

The movement of food molecules through phloem tissue is called **translocation**. Phloem tubes are elongated cells. The ends of each tube have a sieve plate with pores. Cell sap moves through the pores carrying dissolved sugars.

### Root hairs

Root hairs have a large surface area to absorb water and mineral ions, as well as a large vacuole to increase the rate of absorption of water by osmosis and many mitochondria to provide the energy needed for active transport.

## Transpiration

**Transpiration** is the movement of water through a plant from the roots to the leaves. Water evaporates from the surface of mesophyll cells in the leaves and diffuses out through open stomata. This causes more water to be drawn upwards against gravity in xylem cells through the plant. It is absorbed from the soil by osmosis in root hairs.

### Factors affecting the rate of transpiration

- **Temperature** – As temperature increases, water molecules have more kinetic energy. This means evaporation from the leaf increases, so transpiration is faster in higher temperatures.
- **Humidity** – As air humidity increases, the concentration gradient between the water vapour inside the air spaces of the leaf and the outside air decreases. This causes the rate of diffusion to decrease, slowing the rate of transpiration.
- **Air movement** – As wind speed increases, the water molecules which have just left the stomata get blown away. This maintains a greater concentration gradient so water molecules diffuse out of the leaf more rapidly, increasing the rate of transpiration.
- **Light intensity** – At night, the guard cells close the stomata to retain valuable water resources, so transpiration stops. In bright light, the stomata open wider to allow more carbon dioxide to enter the leaf for photosynthesis, so the rate of transpiration increases.

## Worked example — Grade 8

**1** The graph shows how the rate of transpiration in a plant changes as light intensity increases.

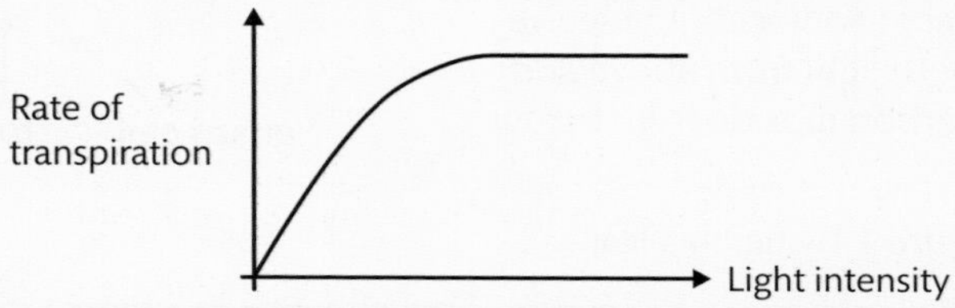


Explain the shape of the graph. **[3 marks]**

*The graph shows that rate of transpiration increases with light intensity until it reaches a maximum. This is because the stomata open wider at greater light intensities, up to a maximum width.*

**2** A student investigates the uptake of water using a piece of capillary tubing connected to a plant. The water uptake is measured by recording the time taken for a bubble to move a set distance in the capillary tubing. The bubble moves 34 mm in 15 minutes. Calculate the rate of water uptake. Give your answer in mm/minute. **[2 marks]**

$$\text{rate of water uptake} = \frac{\text{distance moved by bubble}}{\text{time}}$$

$$\frac{34}{15} = 2.3 \text{ mm/minute}$$

## Exam-style practice — Grade 6

**1** Describe the passage of water through plants from the root hairs to the stomata. **[3 marks]**

**2** Explain the special features a root hair cell has to allow it to function efficiently. **[4 marks]**

# Digestion in humans

You will have already studied the digestive system in Key Stage 3 science. For the GCSE exam, you need to know the function of bile and how the digestive enzymes, carbohydrase, protease and lipase act.

## Lock and key model

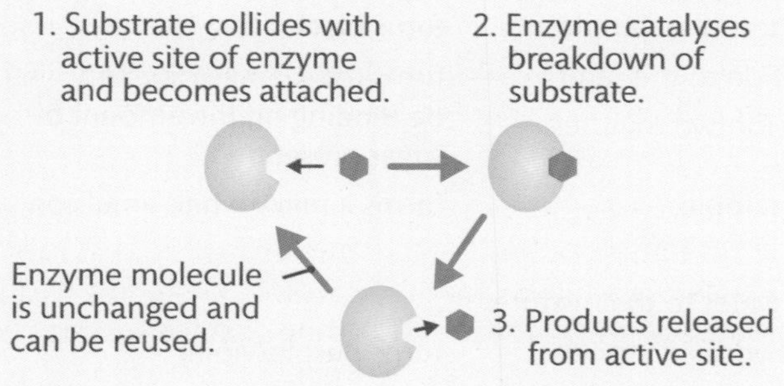


**Figure 1** The lock and key model helps explain how enzymes work. Each type of enzyme has a differently shaped active site so can only work with a specific shape of molecule.

## Worked example — Grade 5

Scientists use models to help to explain how things work. Which **two** of the following explain why **Figure 2** is called the lock and key model?
Tick **two** boxes. **[2 marks]**

- **A** Keys can be made from metal or plastic. ☐
- **B** Different keys can be kept on a key ring. ☐
- **C** Keys can open and close a lock. ✓
- **D** A key will only fit one specific lock. ✓
- **E** Keys can be different colours. ☐

## Enzymes and digestion

Digestion is the process of enzymes breaking down large food molecules into small simple molecules that can be absorbed into the bloodstream. Enzymes catalyse and speed up chemical reactions. They work best at specific temperatures and pH levels.

### Protease enzymes

- Proteases, such as pepsin, break down proteins into amino acids in the stomach and small intestine.
- They are produced in the stomach, small intestine and pancreas.

### Carbohydrase enzymes

- Carbohydrases, such as amylase and maltase, break down carbohydrates into simple sugars.
- Amylase is produced in the salivary glands, small intestine and pancreas. Amylase and maltase mixtures break down starch into glucose in the mouth and small intestine.

### Lipase enzymes

- Lipases break down fats and oils into fatty acids and glycerol in the small intestine.
- They are produced in the pancreas and the small intestine.
- They need alkaline conditions.

The products of digestion are used to build up new proteins, carbohydrates and fats in our body. Some of the glucose produced is used for respiration and the release of energy.

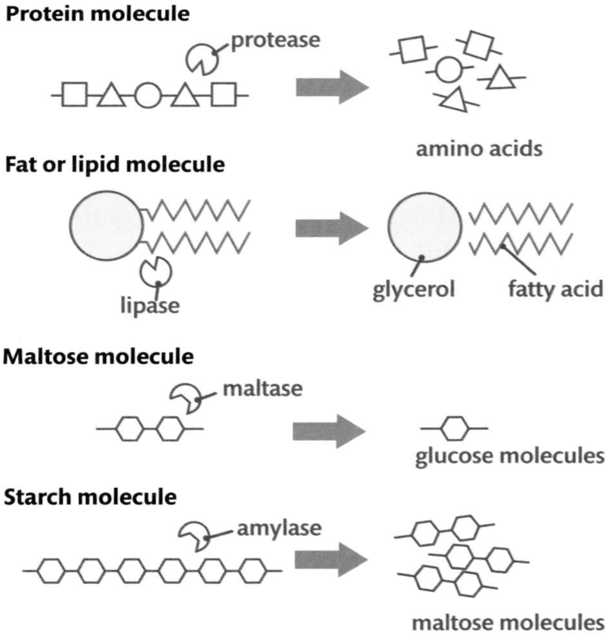


**Figure 2** Enzymes in digestion

### Bile

Bile is produced by the liver, stored in the gall bladder, and then released into the small intestine. It is alkaline, so it neutralises hydrochloric acid from the stomach. It also emulsifies fats by breaking them down into smaller droplets with a larger surface area, which can be broken down more quickly by lipase.

## Exam-style practice — Grade 7

Suggest why acid from the stomach must be neutralised before it enters the small intestine. **[2 marks]**

# Food tests

You need to know how food can be tested to see whether it contains carbohydrates, lipids or proteins.

## 10 Testing for lipids, proteins and carbohydrates

| Type of food | Reagent used | Method | Positive result |
|---|---|---|---|
| starch | iodine solution | Drop iodine solution onto the sample. | turns black |
| simple sugars | Benedict's solution | 1. Add Benedict's solution to the sample.<br>2. Boil in a water bath for two minutes. | turns red-orange or green depending on the amount of sugar present |
| lipids (fats) | ethanol | 1. Add ethanol to the sample.<br>2. Shake the mixture.<br>3. Add a few drops of water to the mixture. | forms a milky white emulsion |
| proteins | Biuret reagent – sodium hydroxide and copper sulfate solution | 1. Add dilute sodium hydroxide to the sample.<br>2. Add copper sulfate solution to the mixture. | turns purple/violet |

### Working scientifically

The results of a test involving Benedict's solution are **semi-quantitative**. They give you an approximation of how much sugar is present in each sample.

The results of tests involving iodine solution and the Biuret reagent are **qualitative**. They only indicate whether the type of food is present but they do not indicate how much is present.

## 10 Worked example — Grade 6

A student carries out food tests on an unknown sample of food.

**Table 1**

| Test | Result |
|---|---|
| iodine solution | turns black |
| Benedict's solution | no change |
| Biuret reagent | no change |

**(a)** What is present in the food in **Table 1**? **[1 mark]**

Starch

The student adds an enzyme to the food and waits 30 minutes before testing the food again.

**(b)** Look at **Table 2**.

**Table 2**

| Test | Result |
|---|---|
| iodine solution | no change |
| Benedict's solution | turns orange |
| Biuret reagent | turns purple/violet |

**(i)** What is now present in the food? **[2 marks]**

Sugar and protein

**(ii)** Suggest what enzyme was added to the food. **[1 mark]**

Amylase

**(iii)** Suggest why protein was detected in the second stage of food testing. **[2 marks]**

The enzyme amylase was added – enzymes are proteins.

Go to page 21 to revise enzymes.

## 5 Exam-style practice — Grade 6

A student carries out a test on a sample of food, thought to contain lipids. Explain the test the student should carry out and describe the appearance of a positive result obtained for a sample containing lipids. **[3 marks]**

# Investigating enzymes

You need to know how to investigate the effect of pH on the rate of reaction of an enzyme. Most enzymes will only work efficiently within a narrow pH range.

## Apparatus

- four beakers containing the same amount of water
- four test tubes containing starch solution
- four test tubes containing amylase solution
- water bath
- spotting tile with iodine solution
- thermometer
- pipette

### Working scientifically

You must control temperature during this investigation, as it affects the behaviour of enzymes.

## Worked example — Grade 7

1. Look at **Figure 1**. Which pH is the optimum condition for the enzyme amylase to break down starch? Justify your answer. **[3 marks]**

*pH 7 – at pH 7 the drops go from black to brown the quickest, showing that the starch is easier to break down at pH 7*

2. Explain why it is difficult to decide how long it takes for amylase to break down the starch at pH 8. **[2 marks]**

*The drops change from black to brown gradually over a period of 2–3 minutes.*

3. A student investigated the time taken for amylase to break down starch at different pH values. Calculate the rate of reaction for each pH value. Give your answers to two significant figures. **[3 marks]**

| pH | Time taken for starch to disappear in s | Rate of reaction per second |
|---|---|---|
| 4 | 474 | *0.0057* |
| 6 | 110 | *0.0091* |
| 8 | 272 | *0.0037* |

## Maths skills

You need to know how to calculate the rate of a reaction. The rate of a reaction is inversely proportional to the time taken for it to complete.

$$\text{rate} \propto \frac{1}{\text{time}}$$

## Method

1. Add one drop of iodine solution to each well in the spotting tile.
2. Make up four beakers of water, each containing a test tube of starch solution and a test tube of amylase solution in a buffer solution. Each buffer solution should be at a different pH, for example: pH 7, pH 8 and pH 9.
3. Using a water bath, heat the four beakers to 25 °C.
4. Pour the test tube of amylase solution into the test tube of starch solution.
5. Starting at 0 seconds, take a drop from each test tube every 30 seconds and add it to the iodine using a pipette.

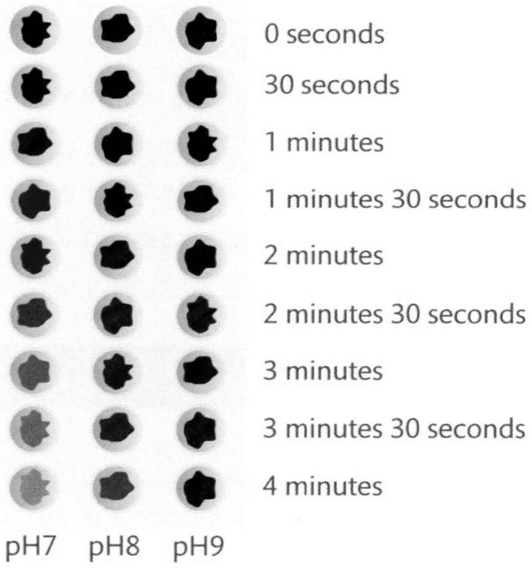


**Figure 1** Results

### Working scientifically

Interpreting these results is tricky. Iodine solution turns from yellow to black in the presence of starch. When the spots on the tile no longer turn black, all the starch has been broken down into maltose by the amylase.

You need to make a sensible judgement of when all the starch has been broken down.

## Exam-style practice — Grade 6

1. Explain why temperature must be controlled during this experiment. **[3 marks]**
2. Suggest **one** way the experiment could be improved. **[1 mark]**

Made a start | Feeling confident | Exam ready

# The blood

You need to be able to recognise the different components of blood and describe their functions. You also need to know how blood is transported around the body by three different types of blood vessel.

## 15 Key components of the blood

Blood is a tissue. It consists of a fluid called plasma in which red blood cells, white blood cells and platelets are suspended. Platelets help blood to clot.

### Plasma

Plasma transports carbon dioxide, water, dissolved food, urea, hormones and heat around the body.

### Red blood cells

Red blood cells absorb oxygen from the lungs and carry it to muscles and tissue around the body. They are adapted for this function in several ways.

- They have no nucleus, which increases the space available for haemoglobin.
- They have a biconcave shape to increase the surface area for oxygen to diffuse in and out.
- They are small, which allows them to pass easily through the smallest capillaries.
- They have a large surface area to volume ratio.

You can calculate the rate of blood flow using the following equation: rate of blood flow = $\frac{\text{volume of blood}}{\text{time}}$

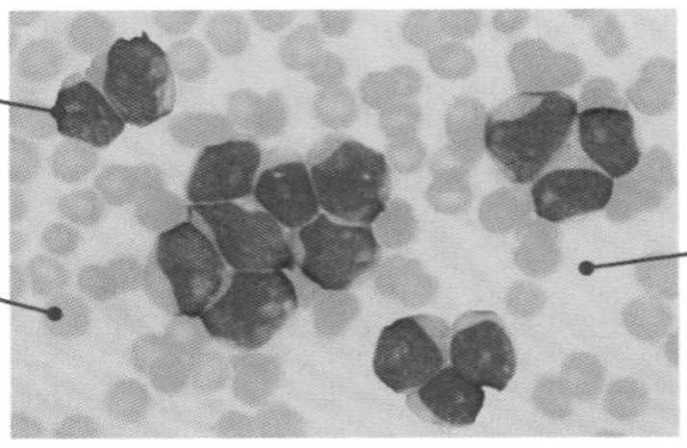


**Figure 1** Blood viewed through a light microscope.

### White blood cells

White blood cells fight disease by producing antibodies and destroying bacteria and viruses. White blood cells have three main roles.

- Many of them are **phagocytes**, which ingest and destroy pathogens (phagocytosis).
- They produce **antibodies**, specialised proteins produced in response to an **antigen**. An antigen is a substance that induces an immune response. Antibodies recognise when an antigen is foreign to the body and produce an immune response.
- They produce **antitoxins**. Bacteria produce harmful toxins, and white blood cells can produce antitoxins to neutralise specific toxins.

## 10 Worked example — Grade 8

1. Complete the table with the rate of blood flow in each of the blood vessels over a period of one minute. **[3 marks]**

| Vessel | Volume of blood in $cm^3$ | Rate of blood flow in $cm^3/s$ |
|---|---|---|
| Artery | 24 | 0.4 |
| Capillary | 4.5 | 0.075 |
| Vein | 3.3 | 0.055 |

The lumen is the space inside the vein. Skeletal muscle contracts causing blood to be squeezed through veins back to the heart.

2. Explain how each blood vessel is adapted to its function. **[3 marks]**

Arteries have thick walls containing muscle and elastic tissue, enabling them to stretch and then return to their original shape, maintaining blood pressure.

Capillaries have very thin walls, usually one cell thick, to allow oxygen, carbon dioxide, glucose and urea to diffuse to and from tissues.

Veins have valves to prevent the blood flowing backwards, and keep it flowing in one direction towards the heart. They have a large lumen to maximis blood flow.

## 2 Working scientifically

Health care workers often come into contact with blood and products related to blood. It is important that they evaluate the risks of working with them. Risks include using sharp objects such as syringe needles and scalpels, and infection from contaminated blood.

## 5 Exam-style practice — Grade 7

1. Explain how the structure of a red blood cell is adapted to its function. **[4 marks]**
2. Describe the function of phagocytes. **[2 marks]**

# The heart and lungs

You need to know how the structures of the heart and lungs are adapted to their functions within the circulatory system.

## 5 The heart

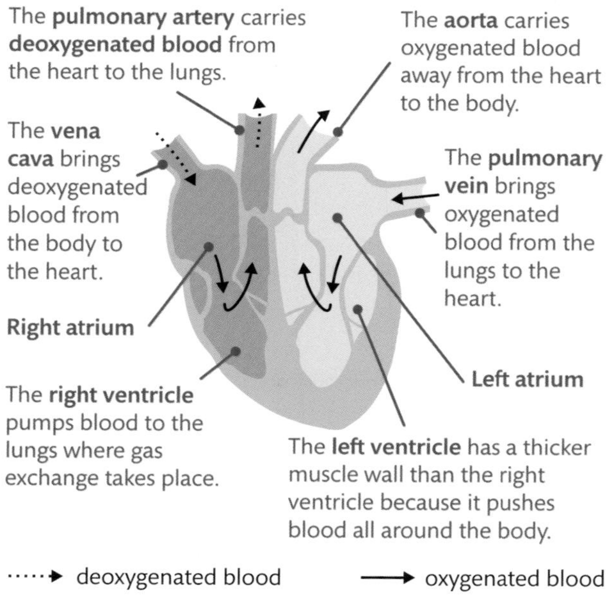
The **pulmonary artery** carries **deoxygenated blood** from the heart to the lungs.
The **aorta** carries oxygenated blood away from the heart to the body.
The **vena cava** brings deoxygenated blood from the body to the heart.
The **pulmonary vein** brings oxygenated blood from the lungs to the heart.
**Right atrium**
**Left atrium**
The **right ventricle** pumps blood to the lungs where gas exchange takes place.
The **left ventricle** has a thicker muscle wall than the right ventricle because it pushes blood all around the body.
deoxygenated blood
oxygenated blood

**Figure 1** Structure of the heart

The coronary arteries supply **oxygenated blood** to the heart from the lungs. The blood enters the right and left atria, which contract, forcing blood into the ventricles. The left and right ventricles contract, forcing blood into the arteries.

## 5 The double circulatory system

**Figure 2** The heart pumps blood around the body in a double circulatory system.

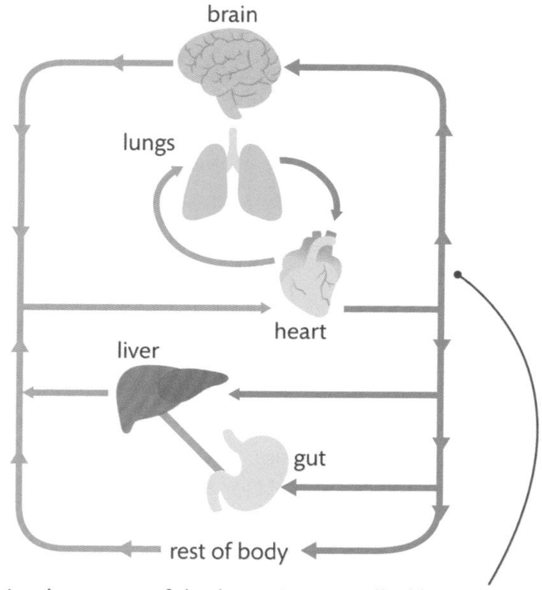
brain
lungs
heart
liver
gut
rest of body

The resting beat rate of the heart is controlled by a group of cells in the wall of the right atrium. This group of cells is called the **pacemaker**. An artificial pacemaker may be installed when the body's natural pacemaker fails.

## 5 The lungs

The lungs consist of several different structures that are adapted for gas exchange. Air enters the lungs via the **trachea** (the windpipe). The trachea leads from the nose to the two **bronchi**, one **bronchus** for each lung. Bronchus branch into **bronchioles** and at the end of each bronchiole are **alveoli**.

Alveoli, the small air sacs in the lungs, have:

- a large surface area to absorb $O_2$ and remove $CO_2$
- thin, moist membranes to allow gases to diffuse
- a capillary network, which provides a good blood supply to transport the gases to and from the rest of the body.

The trachea contains rings of cartilage in its walls, which enables it to stay open, allowing air to pass through.

The cells lining the trachea and bronchus are covered in cilia. Cilia are tiny hair-like structures that help to remove dust and microorganisms before they enter the lungs.

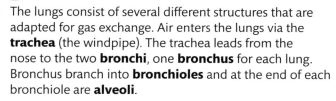

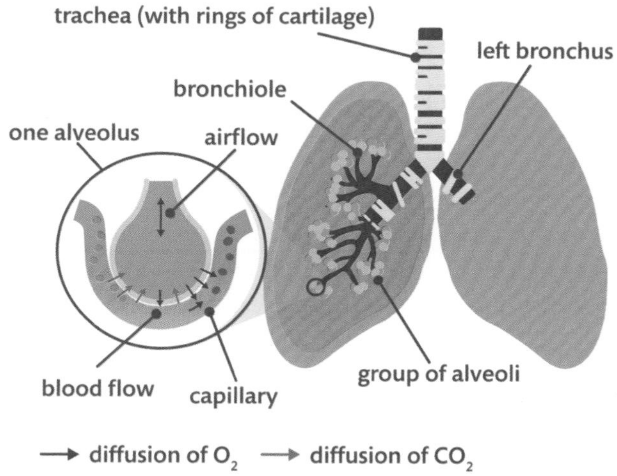
trachea (with rings of cartilage)
left bronchus
bronchiole
one alveolus
airflow
blood flow
capillary
group of alveoli
diffusion of $O_2$
diffusion of $CO_2$

**Figure 3** The lungs

## 2 Worked example — Grade 4

Give the names of the four chambers of the heart. **[2 marks]**

*Left and right atria, left and right ventricles*

## 10 Exam-style practice — Grade 7

1. Describe the path taken by a red blood cell from the left ventricle to the left atrium. **[4 marks]**
2. Explain how alveoli and capillaries are adapted to their function. **[4 marks]**

# The human nervous system

The nervous system senses a stimulus (a change in the environment) and coordinates the body's response. You need to know the structure and function of the human nervous system.

## ⑤ Coordination ✓

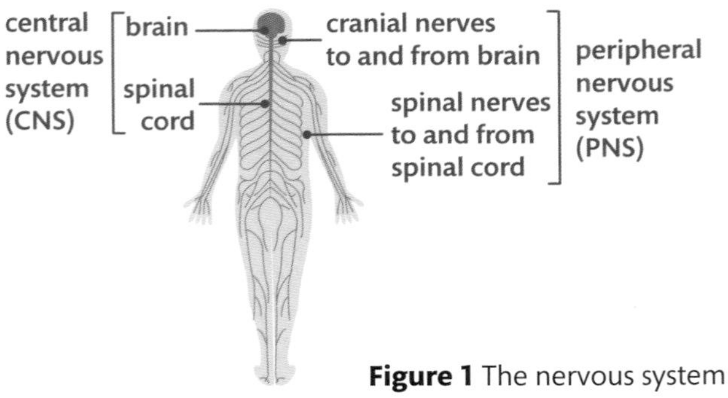

**Figure 1** The nervous system

When receptors are stimulated, information in the form of electrical impulses is passed from the receptor along a sensory neurone to the central nervous system (CNS).

The CNS consists of the brain and spinal cord. The brain coordinates the information and passes instructions along motor neurones to an effector such as a muscle or gland.

stimulus→receptor→coordinator→effector→response

Examples include: touch, substances in food, temperature and light.

## ⑤ Types of neurone ✓

**a sensory neurone**

myelin sheath

dendrites

axon

cell body

**a motor neurone**

myelin sheath

cell body

axon

dendrites

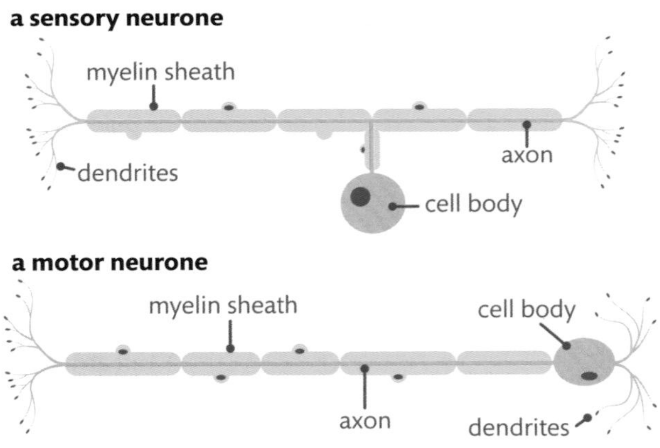

**Figure 2** Neurones

Neurones are cells in the nervous system. **Sensory neurones** carry information from a receptor, such as light receptors in the retina and touch receptors in the skin, to the CNS. **Motor neurones** carry instructions from the CNS to an effector, such as a muscle or a gland. **Synapses** are gaps between each neurone where chemical messengers called **neurotransmitters** diffuse from one neurone to the next.

## ⑤ Worked example — Grade 6 ✓

**Figure 3** A graph showing how reaction times are affected by alcohol and caffeine

Reaction time in ms

Amount of caffeine in mg

— alcohol
— no alcohol

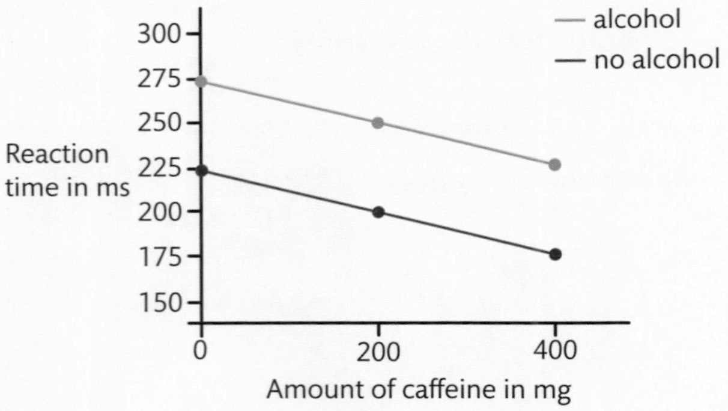

Look at **Figure 3**.

**(a)** What conclusions can be made about the effects of alcohol and caffeine on reaction times?

Use data in your answer. **[3 marks]**

When no alcohol is drunk 400 mg of caffeine speeds up reaction time from 225 ms to 175 ms. Alcohol slows reaction times.

**(b)** To interpret the graph fully, what other information do you need? **[2 marks]**

To know whether the graph shows the effects on one person or the mean for a group of people, and what the amount of alcohol was.

## ⑤ Reflex arcs ✓

spinal cord

pain receptor in skin

sensory neurone

pin

relay neurone

motor neurone

muscle, e.g. in arm

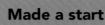

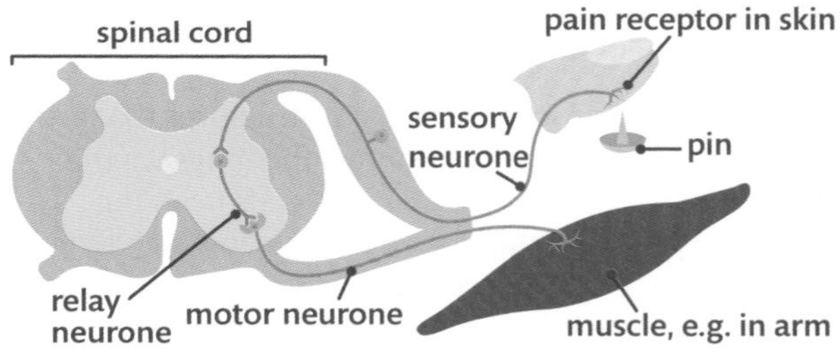

**Figure 4** A reflex arc

Reflex arcs are automatic and do not involve the concious part of the brain. They are important because they speed up reaction times.

Instead of an impulse being sent via the CNS to the brain, the impulse just goes into the spinal cord and straight back out to an effector. The sensory neurone and motor neurone are connected by a relay neurone.

receptor→sensory neurone→relay neurone→motor neurone→effector

## ⑤ Exam-style practice — Grade 6 ✓

Give **two** examples of each of the following:

**(a)** a receptor **[2 marks]**

**(b)** an effector **[2 marks]**

Page 26 LINKS

# Reaction times

You need to know how to plan and carry out an investigation into factors that affect human reaction times.

## 5 Method

This method requires two students: one who is doing the testing (student A) and one who is being tested (student B).

1. Student B rests their elbow on a table so that their hand extends over the side.
2. Student A holds a metre ruler vertically between student B's thumb and index finger, but not touching. The zero mark on the ruler is lined up with student B's fingers.
3. Student B indicates that they are ready.
4. Without warning, student A releases the ruler and lets it drop.
5. Student B catches it as quickly as possible.
6. Record the distance the ruler falls.
7. Repeat three times and calculate the mean score.
8. Repeat the test again, but with student B performing a task, such as counting to 100 or saying the alphabet backwards.

## 2 Factors affecting reaction times

There are many factors that can affect human reaction time. Reaction time is the length of time taken for a person to respond to a given stimulus.

Factors known to affect reaction times include: distraction, physical fitness and fatigue.

## 2 Working scientifically

You could repeat this investigation to test how a range of factors affect reaction time. For example, have student B drink coffee (the effect of caffeine) or do physical exercise (the effect of fatigue) before the second test.

### Maths skills

You can calculate reaction time using

$$\text{time} = \sqrt{2 \times \frac{\text{distance travelled by ruler}}{\text{acceleration due to gravity}}}$$

$$t = \sqrt{\frac{2s}{a}}$$

Acceleration due to gravity, $a$, is 9.8 $m/s^2$.
Distance, $s$, must be measured in metres for this equation to provide a reaction time in seconds.

Go to page 237 to revise handling data.

## 10 Worked example — Grade 5

**1** State the equipment needed to perform this investigation. **[1 mark]**

A metre ruler

**3** The method used does not actually measure reaction times, but only how far the ruler falls before being caught.

Describe **two** ways you could improve the investigation to measure actual reaction times. **[2 marks]**

Use a reaction time chart or formula to convert distance fallen into reaction time.

Use a computer program to measure reaction times.

**4** Look at **Figure 1**.

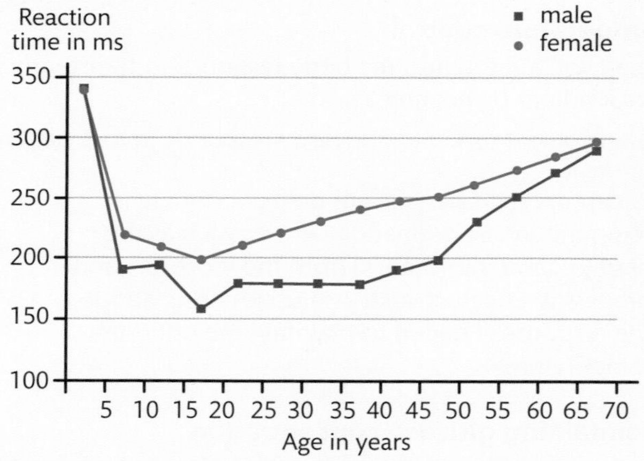


**Figure 1** A graph showing the effect of age on reaction time

What conclusions can you make from the data? **[3 marks]**

Reaction time decreases between the ages of five and seventeen.

Reaction time increases after the age of twenty.

The reaction time of men is usually lower than that of women.

## 5 Exam-style practice — Grade 5

Six students are tested in the practical. The distances travelled by the ruler for each student are given below.

103 110 113 101 121 113

Calculate:

**(a)** the mean distance traveled by the ruler **[1 mark]**
**(b)** the median distance traveled by the ruler **[1 mark]**
**(c)** the mean reaction time. **[1 mark]**

# Homeostasis

You need to know how homeostasis regulates the internal conditions of a cell or an organism to maintain a constant internal environment.

## Homeostasis and enzymes

Enzymes in the cells of your body only work within very specific conditions. They need a constant temperature of about 37 °C and a constant pH of around pH 7.

Homeostasis is the regulation of conditions such as temperature and pH to maintain optimum conditions.

### Homeostatic control systems

Homeostatic control systems are either electrical (the nervous system) or chemical (hormones).

All control systems use:

- a receptor which detects a stimulus, such as a change in temperature
- a coordination centre such as the brain or a hormone gland, such as the pancreas, which receives and processes information from receptors
- an effector such as a muscle or a gland that releases a hormone, which brings about a response which restores conditions to a normal optimum level.

## Regulating temperature, glucose and water

### Temperature control

When you are too hot, the body responds to transfer more energy to the surroundings by heating.

When you are too cold, the body responds to lose heat more slowly.

Receptors such as skin cells detect a change in temperature. Coordination centres such as the brain receive information from the receptors and process it. Effectors such as muscles bring about the responses needed to maintain the optimum temperature.

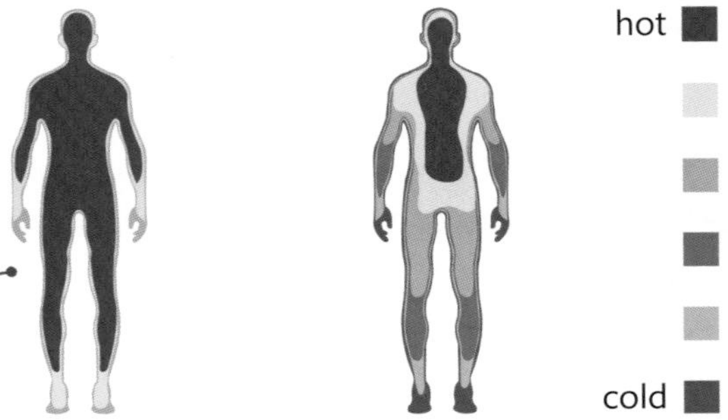


**Figure 1** Thermograms of the human body when hot (left) and cold (right)

### Maintaining glucose concentration

Glucose is produced by the digestion of carbohydrates in food. Soon after a meal, levels of glucose in the blood rise. During fasting, the levels of glucose in the blood fall. Blood glucose levels are controlled by the hormones **insulin** and **glucagon** to provide cells with a continuous supply of glucose for respiration. Go to page 30 for more about insulin.

### Controlling water levels

When you eat, drink or respire your body gains water. When you sweat, breathe or urinate your body loses water.

The kidneys regulate the levels of water within our body. If you drink too much water, the kidneys produce a large amount of dilute urine. If you do not drink enough, the kidneys produce small amounts of very concentrated urine.

## Worked example — Grade 7

Write down one example of a nervous and one example of a hormonal control system. **[2 marks]**

*Hormonal system: controlling blood glucose*
*Nervous system: controlling heartbeat*

Another suitable answer is controlling secondary sexual characteristics in males and females (page 31).

Another suitable answer is controlling muscle contraction (page 26).

## Exam-style practice — Grade 7

1. The body needs to maintain a constant temperature. Explain why. **[2 marks]**
2. Describe how the body reacts to a change in water levels. **[4 marks]**

# Human endocrine system

You need to know how the release and distribution of hormones is controlled by the human endocrine system.

## 10 Hormones

Hormones are sometimes called chemical messengers. They are secreted by glands and released directly into the blood. The blood carries the hormone to a target organ where the hormone produces an effect. The effects of the hormone system are much slower than the nervous system as it takes time for hormones to be transported around the body by the blood. The effects of the hormone last longer than an impulse sent by the nervous system.

### Hormonal glands

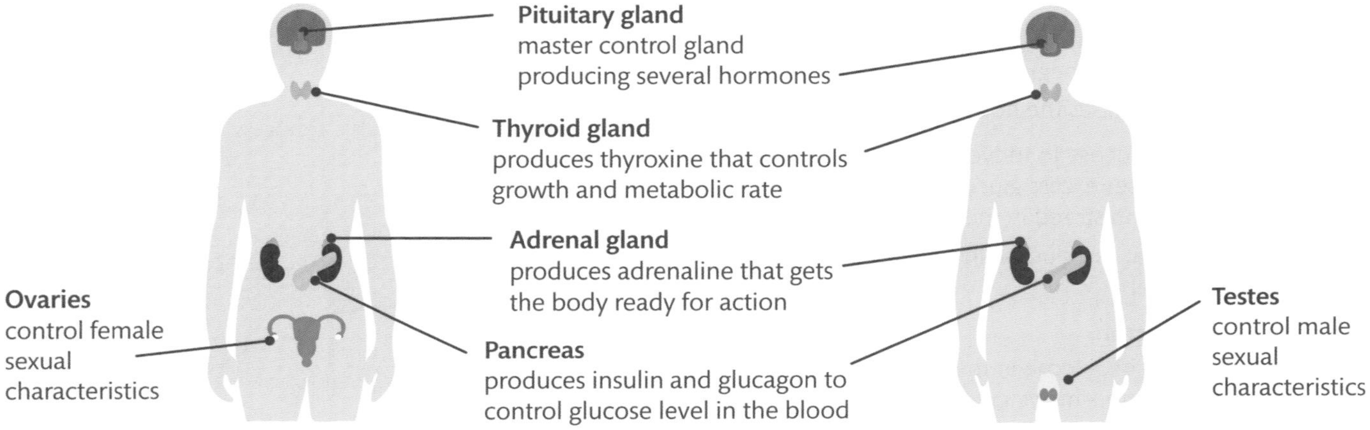


**Figure 1** The hormonal glands

### The pituitary gland

The pituitary gland is located in the brain and is sometimes called the master gland. It secretes several different hormones. Some of these hormones control other hormonal glands by stimulating the gland to release its own hormone. It does this as the concentration of the hormone from the gland begins to fall.

This system that involves two different hormones controlling each other is an example of **negative feedback**.

## 5 Worked example — Grade 5

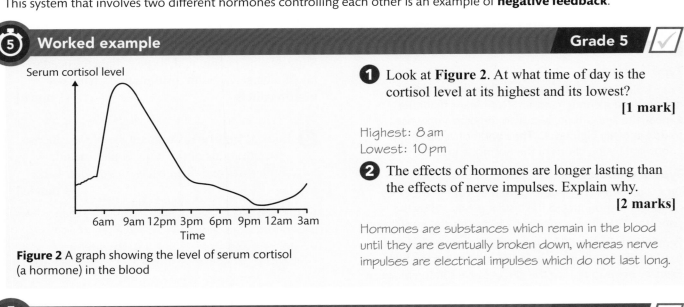

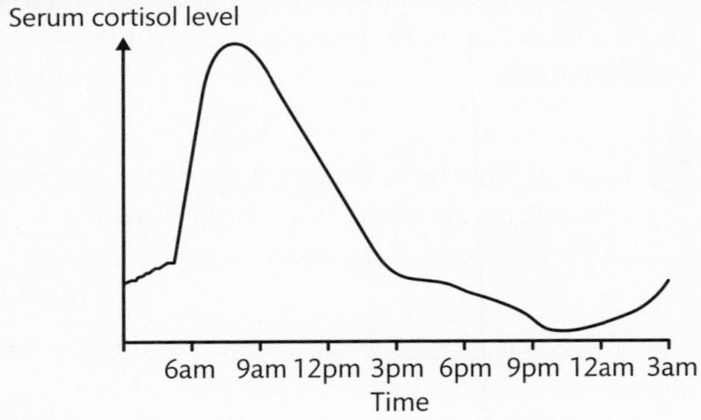


**Figure 2** A graph showing the level of serum cortisol (a hormone) in the blood

**1** Look at **Figure 2**. At what time of day is the cortisol level at its highest and its lowest? **[1 mark]**

*Highest: 8 am*
*Lowest: 10 pm*

**2** The effects of hormones are longer lasting than the effects of nerve impulses. Explain why. **[2 marks]**

*Hormones are substances which remain in the blood until they are eventually broken down, whereas nerve impulses are electrical impulses which do not last long.*

## 5 Exam-style practice — Grade 7

**1** Where is the hormone insulin produced? Tick **one** box. **[1 mark]**

**A** Brain ☐ **B** Pituitary ☐ **C** Pancreas ☐ **D** Thyroid ☐

**2** Describe what is meant by a hormone. **[3 marks]**

# Control of blood glucose

Controlling the level of glucose in the blood is very important as glucose is needed for respiration. You need to know how glucose levels are controlled in the human body.

## 10 Blood glucose

After a meal, carbohydrates are digested into simple sugars, such as glucose. Glucose is important as it is used during respiration. Go to page 12 to revise the importance of respiration.

### The role of insulin

1. When glucose enters the blood after a meal, the blood glucose levels begin to rise.
2. The pancreas releases the hormone insulin.
3. Insulin causes glucose to move from the blood into cells. It also causes excess glucose to be converted into glycogen and stored in muscles and the liver.

   This ensures that the glucose in the blood remains at the correct level.

### The role of glucagon

If the concentration of glucose in the blood is too low, the pancreas releases the hormone glucagon.

Glucagon causes glycogen, which is stored in the liver and muscles, to be converted back into glucose. The glucose is then released into the blood stream, bringing the concentration back to a normal level.

The control of blood glucose by insulin and glucagon is an example of negative feedback.

## 5 Diabetes

### Type 1 diabetes

Type 1 diabetes is a disease caused by the pancreas not producing enough insulin. This means that after a meal, the amount of glucose in the blood may rise to dangerously high levels. The condition is normally controlled by injections of the hormone insulin.

### Type 2 diabetes

Type 2 diabetes is a disease caused by cells in the body no longer responding to the insulin produced by the pancreas. Obesity is a major risk factor for this condition.

People with Type 2 diabetes must eat a controlled diet to prevent glucose levels in their blood rising too high. Exercise helps to reduce the glucose levels in the blood. It is not possible to treat people with Type 2 diabetes with insulin injections.

## 5 Worked example — Grade 4

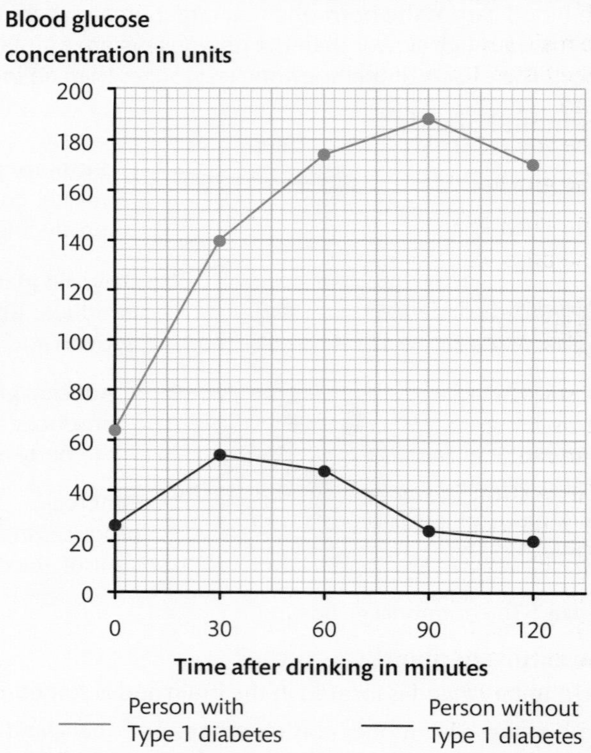


**Figure 1** A graph showing the changing blood glucose concentration of two people after they each drank a sugar solution

1. The hormone insulin is a protein.

   Suggest why people with Type 1 diabetes need to inject themselves with insulin rather than take insulin tablets. **[1 mark]**

   *The insulin protein would be digested.*

2. Look at **Figure 1**. Compare the blood glucose concentrations of the two people. Include similarities and differences in your answer. **[4 marks]**

   *The blood glucose concentration rises and falls in the person with Type 1 diabetes and the person without it. At the start, the blood glucose concentration is higher in the person with Type 1 diabetes and rises higher and more rapidly than the person without diabetes. The concentration stays high for longer in the person with diabetes.*

## 5 Exam-style practice — Grade 4

Describe **three** of the differences between Type 1 and Type 2 diabetes. **[3 marks]**

# Hormones in reproduction

During puberty, hormones cause secondary sexual characteristics to develop. These include the production of sperm in males and the beginning of the menstrual cycle in females. You need to know the roles of different hormones in the menstrual cycle.

## 2 Male reproduction

The main sex hormone in men is testosterone. It is produced in the testes. Testosterone levels increase during puberty and cause:

- the voice to break and get deeper
- the growth of facial and pubic hair
- muscle growth
- the production of sperm.

## 2 Female reproduction

One of the main sex hormones in women is oestrogen. It is produced in the ovaries. Oestrogen levels increase during puberty and cause:

- the growth of pubic hair
- breast development
- the start of menstruation.

## 10 The menstrual cycle

The **menstrual cycle** is a recurring process in which the uterus lining is prepared for pregnancy. There are several hormones involved in this cycle.

**Follicle stimulating hormone (FSH)** is secreted by the pituitary gland. It stimulates the ovaries to release oestrogen and it causes an egg to mature.

**Oestrogen** is secreted by the ovaries. It affects the pituitary gland where it inhibits the production of FSH, causing only one egg to mature during each monthly cycle. It stimulates the pituitary gland to release **luteinising hormone (LH)**, which triggers **ovulation**, the release of the mature egg from the ovary.

**Progesterone** builds up and maintains the uterus lining during the middle part of the cycle and pregnancy.

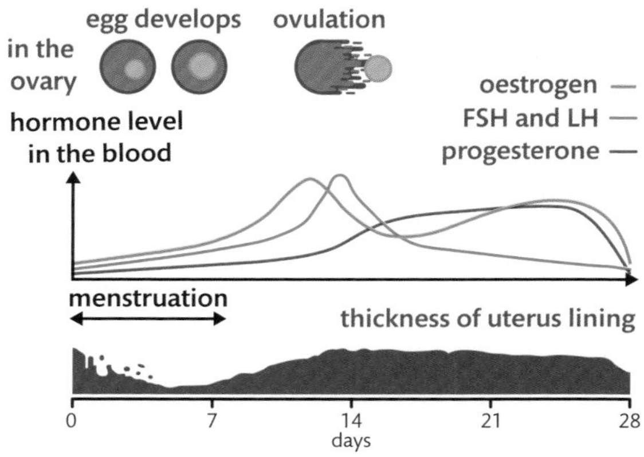


**Figure 1** The interaction of hormones during the menstrual cycle

## 5 Worked example — Grade 8

During puberty, eggs begin to mature in the ovaries. One egg is released about every 28 days. This is called ovulation. The whole 28-day cycle is called the menstrual cycle. Hormones play an important part in the menstrual cycle.

Explain the roles of the hormones oestrogen, progesterone, and pituitary hormones FSH and LH. **[5 marks]**

Oestrogen repairs and thickens the lining of the uterus.

Progesterone stimulates the wall of the uterus to thicken even more and prevents menstruation from starting.

FSH stimulates the production of an egg in the ovaries.

LH triggers ovulation, causing the egg to be released from the ovaries ready for fertilisation.

## 10 Exam-style practice — Grade 8

1. Explain how hormones ensure that usually only one egg is released every 28 days. **[2 marks]**
2. Describe one example of negative feedback in the hormones involved with the menstrual cycle. **[2 marks]**
3. Menstruation, a 'period', is the monthly breakdown of the uterus lining. It stops during pregnancy. Suggest which hormone prevents menstruation from happening. **[1 mark]**

# Hormones to treat infertility

You need to know how reproductive hormones can be used to treat **infertility** (where it isn't possible to conceive a child naturally).

## 5 Fertility treatments

Some women have difficulty releasing eggs from their ovaries. This means they are unable to become pregnant.

Drugs containing follicle stimulating hormone (FSH) and luteinising hormone (LH) can be used to stimulate ovulation, which increases a woman's chance of becoming pregnant.

### In-vitro fertilisation

Some women produce eggs but still cannot become pregnant.

*In-vitro* fertilisation (IVF) is sometimes used to help these women become pregnant. *In vitro* means 'in glass'. The woman's eggs are fertilised in a Petri dish before being placed back into her uterus to develop.

## 5 IVF process

1. The woman is injected with hormones to make her ovaries release eggs.
2. The eggs are collected and mixed with her partner's sperm in a Petri dish.
3. The eggs are fertilised and begin to divide and form tiny embryos.
4. The most viable embryos are selected and transplanted back into the woman's uterus.
5. The embryos are then left to develop into foetuses in the mother's uterus.

Developments in microscopes (page 4) have enabled IVF treatments to develop.

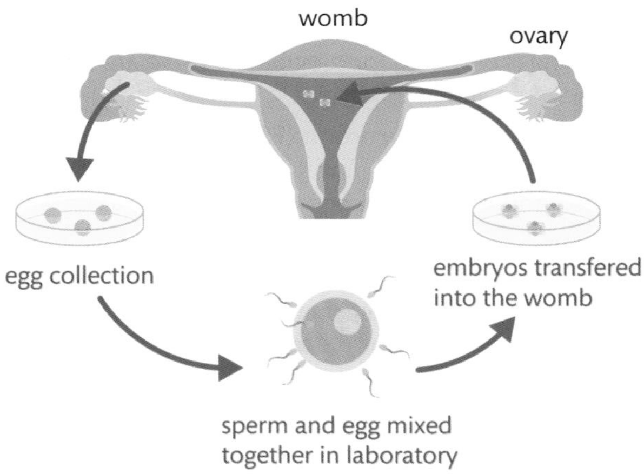


**Figure 1** The stages in IVF

## 5 Working scientifically

You need to know some of the social and ethical issues associated with fertility treatments like IVF.

- Sometimes, this can lead to multiple pregnancies which can reduce the chances of any one embryo developing and is a risk to the health of the mother.
- Some people think it is wrong to 'play God' and create life in a test tube.
- It is very emotionally and physically stressful for the potential parents.
- The success rate is not very high.
- If several embryos are implanted it can lead to multiple pregnancies.
- Some of the embryos are discarded and not used, which some people think is unethical.

## 2 Worked example — Grade 6

People undergoing IVF often find the experience very stressful. Suggest why. **[2 marks]**

It can be stressful because success is not guaranteed. Additionally, the procedure is invasive, requiring injections of hormones and the collection of eggs.

## 5 Exam-style practice — Grade 6

1. Compare the similarities and differences between fertility drugs and IVF. **[3 marks]**
2. Write down the names of **two** hormones that are used to treat fertility and explain what they do. **[2 marks]**

# Contraception

You need to know how both hormonal and non-hormonal methods of contraception can be used to prevent pregnancy.

## 5 Methods of contraception

### Hormonal

- Oral contraceptives such as 'the pill' contain hormones that inhibit FSH production and therefore stop eggs maturing and being released ready for fertilisation.
- Injections, skin patches or implants contain slow release progesterone to prevent the maturation and release of eggs for months or years.

### Non-hormonal

- Barrier methods such as the condom and diaphragm act as a physical barrier between the sperm and egg.
- Intrauterine devices (IUDs) prevent the fertilised egg from implanting and growing in the uterus. They may also release a hormone.
- Spermicides kill or disable sperm.
- Abstaining from intercourse during the time in the menstrual cycle when an egg could be fertilised reduces the chances of pregnancy. This is sometimes called the rhythm method.
- Male and female sterilisation is a surgical method of preventing conception.

## 5 Working scientifically

### Ethics

There are some questions that science can answer, such as: 'How can you stop a sperm fertilising an egg?'

There are some questions that science cannot answer, such as: 'When should we stop a sperm from fertilising an egg?'

Individuals have to decide whether or not to use contraception to prevent pregnancy. They also have to decide which methods of contraception to use.

Science can provide data to help you decide which methods are the most reliable, and understand the advantages and disadvantages of each method.

However, some people think that contraception is wrong.

Each person should evaluate personal, social, economic and religious implications, and make a decision about contraception based on evidence and argument.

## 5 Worked example — Grade 6

The table summarises different methods of contraception.

| | The contraceptive pill | Diaphragm | Rhythm method | Sterilisation |
|---|---|---|---|---|
| **Reliability** | very reliable | reliable | not very reliable | very reliable |
| **Level of risk to health** | some risk | little risk | no risk | some risk |
| **Are effects reversible?** | reversible | reversible | reversible | may not be reversible |

A young, newly married couple want children but decide to postpone having them for ten years.

Which methods of contraception would not be suitable? Explain your answer. **[4 marks]**

The rhythm method is unsuitable because it is unreliable and may fail over the next ten years. Sterilisation may not be reversible in ten years' time so it would not be suitable.

**Exam focus**

Always read exam questions carefully. This question asks which contraceptive methods are **not** suitable.

You could also comment on the health risk associated with different methods of contraception. The contraceptive pill and sterilisation are less suitable because they pose some risk to health.

## 10 Exam-style practice — Grade 6

1. Science can help people decide which method of contraception to use. Explain how science can help. **[4 marks]**
2. When deciding whether to use contraception, suggest **two** questions that science cannot answer. **[2 marks]**

Made a start | Feeling confident | Exam ready

# Negative feedback

You need to know how negative feedback works and how it controls hormone levels within the body.

## 5 Negative feedback

Negative feedback happens where an output of a process feeds back into the system to reverse changes and bring them back to a set level.

### Thyroxine

Thyroxine is a hormone produced in the thyroid gland. It does several different jobs:

- It increases the basal metabolic rate.
- It plays an important role in growth and development, for example in the manufacture of proteins and the growth of the long bones in the arms and legs.

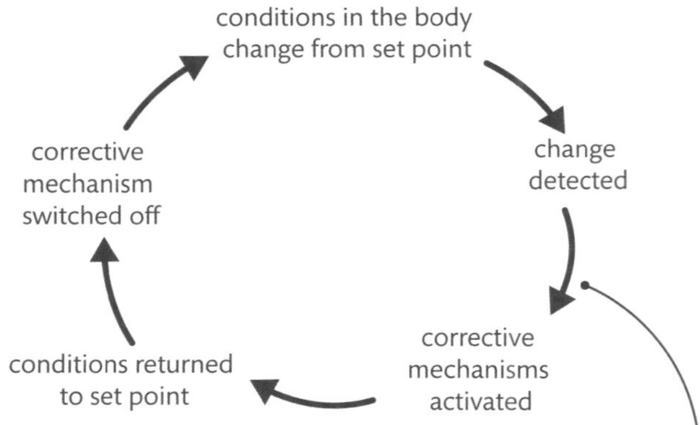


**Figure 1** Thyroxine levels are controlled by negative feedback.

**Working scientifically**
You need to be able to interpret and explain simple diagrams of negative feedback control

## 5 Adrenaline

Adrenaline is sometimes called the fight, flight or fright hormone. It is the hormone that causes the feeling of 'butterflies in your stomach' when you are frightened.

Adrenaline prepares the body for rapid action.

Adrenaline has several effects:

- It increases the heart rate, pumping blood containing oxygen and glucose more rapidly to the brain and muscle cells.
- It increases the level of glucose in the blood.
- It diverts blood from the gut to the muscles.
- It increases sweating.
- It dilates the pupils of the eyes.

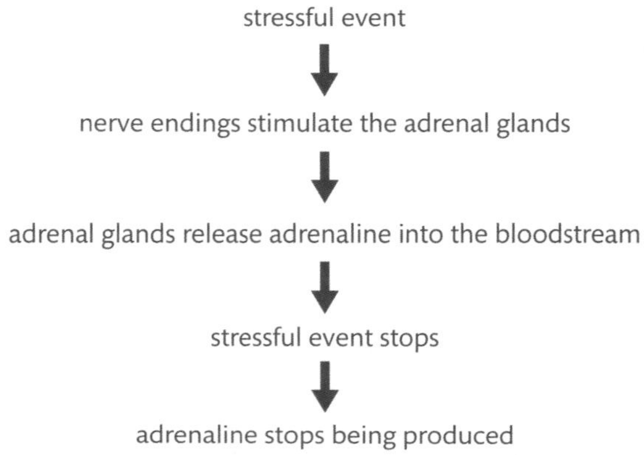


**Figure 2** How levels of adrenaline are controlled

## 10 Worked example — Grade 7

**1** Tomatoes can be grown in a greenhouse. To keep the greenhouse at a constant temperature, farmers use a thermostatic heater and windows that automatically open and close.

The thermostat controls the heater and the windows to maintain a constant temperature using negative feedback. Explain how this works. **[4 marks]**

When the temperature drops, the thermostat turns the heater on and closes the windows. This causes the temperature to rise. When the temperature rises too much the thermostat turns the heater off and opens the windows, making the temperature fall.

**2** Why does adrenaline increase heart rate? **[2 marks]**

Adrenaline increases the heart rate so blood containing oxygen and glucose is transported to the brain and muscles more quickly.

## 5 Exam-style practice — Grade 7

1. Explain why thyroxine is needed by the body. **[2 marks]**
2. Describe what is meant by negative feedback. **[2 marks]**
3. Name the site of adrenaline production. **[1 mark]**

# Health issues

Health is the state of physical and mental well-being, including being free from disease. You need to know about the things that can affect health.

## 5 Types of disease

Some diseases are communicable and some are not.

### Communicable diseases

Communicable diseases are diseases that can be spread from one person to another. They are often called infectious diseases. They are caused by pathogens - microorganisms which cause disease. Examples of pathogens are:

- bacteria
- viruses
- fungi
- protists.

Examples include flu, measles and food poisoning.

### Non-communicable diseases

Non-communicable diseases are diseases that cannot be passed on from one person to another.

They are usually caused by lifestyle factors, such as diet, stress, drinking and smoking, and/or failures within the body's own systems, such as auto immune diseases and old age.

Examples include cardiovascular disease, cancer and diabetes.

## 2 Disease interaction

Some diseases are more complex and may be caused by multiple factors. Different types of disease may interact.

- Defects in the immune system mean a person is more likely to suffer from infectious diseases.
- Viruses living inside cells can sometimes be the cause of cancer.
- The immune system, which is designed to destroy invading pathogens, can sometimes be the cause of allergies and asthma.
- Severe illnesses can lead to depression and other mental illnesses.

## 5 Worked example — Grade 4

The table shows the number of cases of Ebola and the number of deaths caused in four different countries during a recent outbreak.

| Country | Number of cases of Ebola | Number of deaths caused by Ebola | Case fatality rate |
|---|---|---|---|
| Guinea | 2871 | 1876 | 0.65 |
| Liberia | 8478 | 3605 | 0.43 |
| Mali | 8 | 6 | 0.75 |
| Sierra Leone | 10 340 | 3145 | |

The case fatality rate is calculated using the formula

$$\text{case fatality rate} = \frac{\text{number of deaths}}{\text{number of cases}}$$

**(a)** The case fatality rate for Sierra Leone is missing.
Calculate the case fatality rate for Sierra Leone. **[2 marks]**

$\frac{3145}{10\,340} = 0.30$ (2 decimal places)

**(b)** One newspaper reported that three quarters of all the people who catch Ebola die. Does the data support this conclusion? Explain your answer. **[2 marks]**

In countries with a substantial number of cases the death rate is much lower than three quarters, so this conclusion is not supported.

## 1 Exam focus

In the exam, you could be expected to interpret data from a table, graph or chart. Before answering any questions, make sure you know what the data is, what its units are, and if there are any trends.

Go to page 39 to revise how the spread of infections can be reduced.

## 10 Exam-style practice — Grade 7

**1** **(a)** Explain the difference between communicable and non-communicable diseases. **[2 marks]**

**(b)** Suggest **two** ways that the spread of communicable diseases can be prevented. **[2 marks]**

**2** **(a)** Describe what is meant by a pathogen. **[1 mark]**

**(b)** Give **three** ways pathogens can be spread. **[3 marks]**

# Coronary heart disease

You need to know how different diseases of the heart occur and how they can be treated.

## 10 Diseases of the heart

### Blocked coronary arteries

The coronary arteries supply the heart muscle with blood containing oxygen and glucose.

The build up of fatty deposits, such as cholesterol, in the coronary arteries can narrow or even block them, starving the heart muscle of oxygen. This can cause a heart attack. A heart attack occurs when the supply of blood to the heart is suddenly blocked, which can seriously damage the heart muscle or cause it to die from lack of oxygen. A heart attack can be life threatening.

### Faulty valves

Sometimes the valves in the heart become faulty, preventing the valve from opening fully, or the valve may develop a leak. This makes it harder for the heart to pump blood around the body. The valves prevent blood from flowing backwards when the muscles of the heart contract.

### Heart failure

Heart failure occurs when the heart is unable to pump blood around the body properly.

Go to page 25 for more about the heart.

## 5 Treatment

### Treating blocked coronary arteries

- Stents can be inserted into the artery to keep the artery open.
- Drugs such as statins can be used to lower the blood cholesterol.

### Treating faulty valves

- Biological or mechanical valves can be used to replace a faulty one.

### Treating heart failure

- Heart or heart and lung transplants can be performed.
- If the damage is extensive the whole heart can be replaced with an artificial heart. These are sometimes used to keep patients alive while they are waiting for a heart transplant or to allow the heart to rest to help it recover.

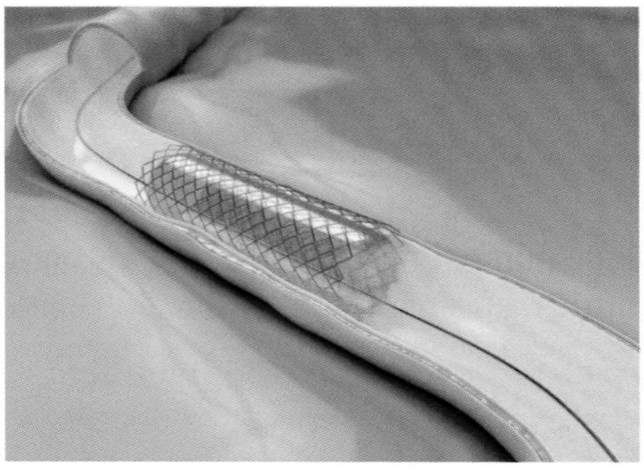

**Figure 1** A stent used to keep arteries open

## 5 Working scientifically

### Evaluation of treatments

- Heart surgery is risky and not all surgery is successful.
- Sometimes the patient's body rejects the new heart or valve.
- Artificial hearts need a source of power, such as batteries, to make them work.
- Treatment using drugs such as statins may have unwanted side effects in some people.
- Mechanical replacement valves can wear out.

**Figure 2** Heart surgery

## 2 Worked example — Grade 6

What are the main drawbacks to having a valve replacement operation? **[1 mark]**

*The main drawbacks include the risk of blood clots and the fact that it involves major surgery.*

## 5 Exam-style practice — Grade 7

1. No surgery is 100 per cent safe. Explain what this statement means. **[2 marks]**
2. Give **two** treatments for a blocked artery. **[2 marks]**

# Effects of lifestyle

You need to know how lifestyle can effect whether or not people develop some non-communicable diseases.

## 5 Risk factors

### Lifestyle risk factors

- Smokers are more likely to develop lung cancer.
- Heavy drinkers are more likely to suffer from cirrhosis of the liver.
- Smoking and drinking during pregnancy increases the risk of growth and development impairments in embryos.
- Obese people are more likely to develop Type 2 diabetes.
- Lack of exercise and eating fatty foods can lead to coronary heart disease.

### Environmental risk factors

- People who live in houses in areas affected by radioactive radon gas are more likely to develop cancer.
- People who have worked with asbestos are more likely to develop lung cancer.

### Interaction of risk factors

Many risk factors interact to increase the risk of non-communicable diseases. For example the chances of getting coronary heart disease increase dramatically for someone who smokes, drinks heavily, is obese and takes little exercise.

## 5 Implications

### Impact of lifestyle

Having a poor lifestyle can affect an individual, their family and the wider community.

### Cost implications

Local and national authorities must plan their spending on new hospitals, doctors and surgeries.

Non-communicable diseases which are contributed to by lifestyle factors also affect the government's spending on the National Health Service.

Type 2 diabetes can seriously limit the life of an individual and is extremely expensive to treat. In 2016, prescribing drugs to treat diabetes cost the NHS nearly £1 billion, and 89 per cent of diabetics have been diagnosed with Type 2 diabetes, which is heavily influenced by lifestyle. These costs are rising and unsustainable. Stopping smoking, regular exercise and eating a healthy balanced diet can hugely reduce the risk of developing the disease.

**Maths skills**

A scatter diagram is a graph where the values of two variables are plotted and the pattern of the plots shows any correlation present between them.

## 5 Worked example — Grade 4

Look at **Figure 1**.

**(a)** What conclusions can be made from the data? **[2 marks]**

*There is a positive correlation between blood cholesterol levels and Body Mass Index.*

**(b)** Suggest what type of non-communicable disease the risk factors in the diagram could lead to. **[1 mark]**

*Heart disease*

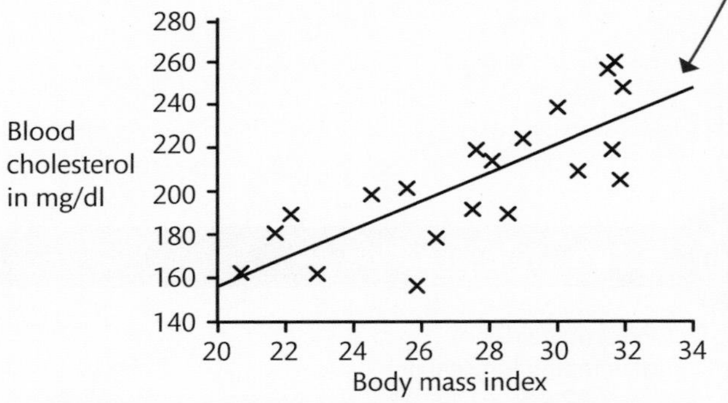


**Figure 1** Scatter diagram showing the correlation between body mass index and blood cholesterol levels

## 2 Causal mechanisms

A causal mechanism is a process which explains how a risk factor can cause a particular disease. For example, it is the carcinogens in tobacco smoke that cause lung cancer. For many years it was thought that smoking caused lung cancer but no one had found a causal mechanism to link the two together. However, people now know that carcinogenic substances in tobacco smoke can cause cells to become cancerous.

## 10 Exam-style practice — Grade 7

1. Suggest a causal mechanism for Type 2 diabetes. **[2 marks]**
2. Type 2 diabetes is usually a preventable disease. Suggest **two** ways that the NHS could save large amounts of money by preventing Type 2 diabetes. **[2 marks]**
3. Describe how poor diet affects health. **[2 marks]**

# Cancer

Cancer is caused by changes inside cells that lead to uncontrolled cell division and tissue growth. You need to know the lifestyle and genetic risk factors linked to some cancers.

## 2 Genetic risk factors

Cancer is caused by changes to genes in the DNA in cells that control cell growth. A change in the DNA of a cell is called a **mutation** (page 55).

Some people inherit genes that are more likely to mutate (change) than other genes.

This means that people are born with certain genetic risk factors which make them more or less likely to develop cancer later in life.

## 5 Lifestyle risk factors

**Carcinogens** are substances or agents that cause cancer.

- **sunbathing** – risk factor for skin cancer
- **smoking** – risk factor for lung cancer
- **heavy drinking** – risk factor for liver and other cancers
- **working with carcinogenic materials such as asbestos** – risk factor for lung and other cancers
- **living in unventilated buildings** in areas where **radioactive radon** is released from the ground.

## 2 Types of tumour

**Benign tumours** are growths of abnormal cells. They usually grow slowly and in one area. They are not cancerous and usually do not spread to other parts of the body.

**Malignant tumours** are growths of abnormal cells called cancers. They often grow rapidly, spreading to neighbouring tissues in the body. Cancerous cells can break free from the tumour and get carried by the blood to other parts of the body. These cells then continue to divide and produce secondary tumours. This makes malignant tumours much harder to treat than benign tumours.

## 5 Worked example — Grade 5

Tumours can either be malignant or benign.

Describe the difference between malignant and benign tumours. **[4 marks]**

*Benign tumours are growths of abnormal cells. They are usually enclosed inside a membrane in one specific area of the body. They do not invade other parts of the body. This makes them much less dangerous and easier to treat and remove than malignant tumours. Malignant tumours consist of cancerous cells. These tumors invade neighbouring tissues and spread, via the blood, to different parts of the body where they form secondary tumours.*

## 10 Exam-style practice — Grade 5

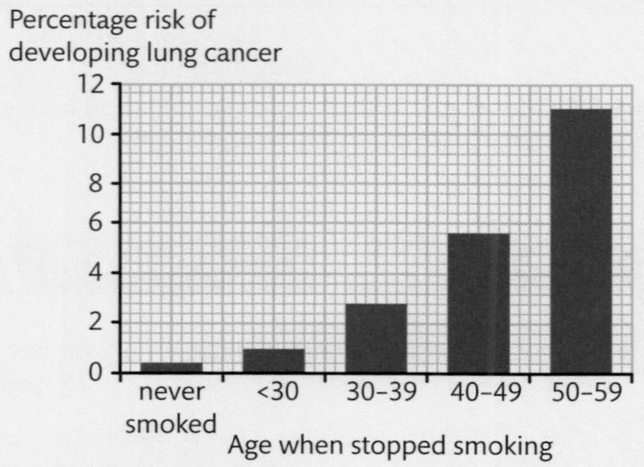


**Figure 1** A chart showing the risk of cancer for people who stop smoking

Look at **Figure 1**.

**(a)** Explain what is meant by <30 on the *x*-axis. **[1 mark]**

**(b)** Suggest what conclusions can be made from the data shown by the graph. **[2 marks]**

**(c)** Give the risk of getting cancer for people who have:

**(i)** never smoked **[1 mark]**

**(ii)** stopped smoking at the age of 45 years old. **[1 mark]**

# Infections

Communicable diseases are diseases that can be spread from one person to another. They are sometimes called infectious diseases. You need to know how infections spread.

## Pathogens

**Pathogens** are microorganisms such as bacteria and viruses that cause infectious diseases.

Once inside the body they reproduce rapidly.

Viruses enter cells, and force them to make more copies of the virus.

This causes the cells to die and other cells are then invaded by the viruses.

Go to page 40 to revise viral diseases.

Bacteria produce poisonous waste products called toxins. These toxins damage tissue and can make you feel ill.

## Four types of pathogen

1. viruses
2. bacteria
3. fungi
4. protists

## Spread of communicable diseases

Communicable diseases can be spread by:

1. **Direct contact** which involves touching or coming into contact with the diseased person.
2. **Indirect contact** which involves touching objects that have been contaminated with the disease-causing organism, breathing in airborne disease-causing organisms, or eating or drinking contaminated food or water.

The spread of communicable diseases can be reduced or prevented by:

- reducing contact with the microorganism which causes the disease
- using physical barriers such as surgical masks
- using the immune system to destroy the pathogen
- using drugs such as antibiotics to destroy bacteria
- vaccination.

Go to page 44 to revise human defence systems.

## Worked example — Grade 7

| Time in minutes | Number of bacteria |
|---|---|
| 20 | 2 |
| 40 | 4 |
| 60 | 8 |
| 80 | 16 |
| 100 | 32 |
| 120 | |
| 140 | 128 |
| 160 | 256 |
| 180 | 512 |

Some bacteria can divide once every 20 minutes.

Look at the table. It shows the number of bacteria produced from a single bacterium after 180 minutes.

**(a)** The number of bacteria for 120 minutes is missing.
Calculate the missing number. **[1 mark]**

*64*

**(b)** Calculate the number of bacteria a single bacterium could produce in 4 hours. **[1 mark]**

*4096*

**(c)** Suggest why it is important to treat infectious diseases at an early stage. **[2 marks]**

*Fewer bacteria are present at an early stage of an infectious disease so it is easier to treat.*

## Exam-style practice — Grade 6

1. Explain the meaning of the word 'infectious'. **[1 mark]**
2. Airborne diseases spread much faster than diseases which are spread through contact. Suggest why. **[2 marks]**

# Viral diseases

A virus is an infective agent that is too small to be seen using a light microscope. You need to know the characteristics and some examples of viruses.

## 5 Viruses

Viruses are much smaller than bacteria. They are so small that for many years scientists did not know that they existed.

They consist of small fragments of DNA enclosed by protein.

They invade other cells and the DNA in the virus takes over the cell. The DNA instructs the cell to make more copies of the virus.

This kills the cell and millions more viruses are released into the body to invade other cells.

## 10 Viral diseases

### Measles

Measles is a viral disease which affects humans. It is spread by breathing in airborne droplets from sneezes and coughs.

Symptoms include a fever, sore eyes and a red skin rash. Most people recover from the disease but fatal complications can sometimes arise. These complications include swelling of the brain, called encephalitis, and ear and eye infections. One in 20 children who get measles also get pneumonia. This is why most young children are vaccinated against measles.

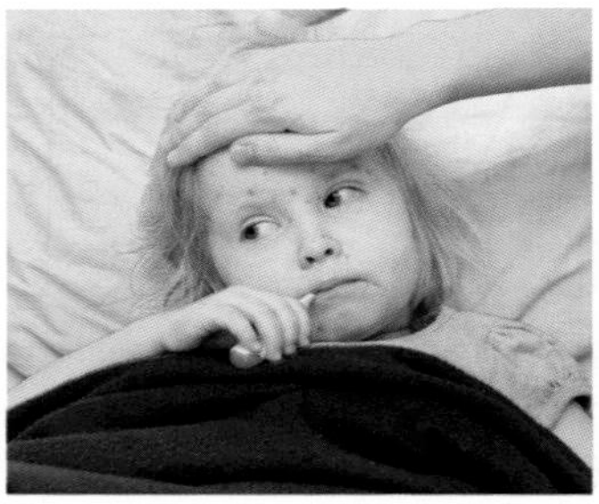

**Figure 1** Measles is usually accompanied by a fever and a red skin rash.

### Human Immunodeficiency Virus (HIV)

HIV causes flu-like symptoms. The virus attacks the human immune system which is why the body cannot destroy the virus.

In the final stage of HIV infection, when the immune system is badly damaged, it can no longer protect the body from other pathogens or cancers. This is called Acquired Immune Deficiency Syndrome (AIDS). The infected person will develop other diseases. It is these diseases that normally kill a person with HIV.

People infected with HIV can take antiviral drugs to prevent the virus from damaging their immune system.

HIV is spread by sexual contact or other exchanges of bodily fluids, such as blood when drug users share needles.

### Tobacco Mosaic Virus (TMV)

Tobacco Mosaic Virus is a disease which commonly affects some types of plants, such as tomato plants.

It produces a characteristic mosaic pattern on the leaves. The TMV-affected leaves can no longer photosynthesise. This causes the plant to die because it can no longer manufacture its own food.

**Figure 2** Plant leaves with TMV

## 2 Worked example — Grade 6

Describe the differences between how HIV and the measles virus are spread. **[2 marks]**

*HIV can only be passed from one person to another through the transfer of body fluids. Measles can be spread by droplets coughed or sneezed out by an infectious person.*

## 5 Exam-style practice — Grade 6

Give **three** characteristics of viruses. **[3 marks]**

# Bacterial diseases

You need to know about the different kinds of bacteria. Most are harmless, some are very useful and some can cause diseases in humans.

## 2 Bacteria

Bacteria are microscopic organisms. Once they have entered the body, they reproduce rapidly.

Some produce toxins that kill tissues and make us feel unwell.

Unlike viruses, bacteria can be treated with antibiotics. However, many strains of bacteria have become resistant to antibiotics. Scientists are trying to find new antibiotics that will be effective against disease-causing bacteria.

## 5 Bacterial diseases

### Salmonella

Salmonella is a bacterium that is spread through contaminated food such as chicken and eggs.

It can be spread through a lack of proper food hygiene, particularly through food not being cooked thoroughly, which can cause the person eating the food to get food poisoning. Symptoms include vomiting, diarrhoea, fever and abdominal pain.

In the UK, chickens are vaccinated against salmonella to help control the spread of the disease.

### Gonorrhoea

Gonorrhoea is a sexually transmitted disease (STD). Symptoms include a thick yellow or green discharge from the penis or vagina and pain when urinating.

The disease used to be treated using the antibiotic penicillin. However, new strains of gonorrhoea have appeared which are resistant to penicillin so new types of antibiotic now have to be used.

The spread of the disease can be reduced by using a barrier method of contraception such as a condom.

## 10 Worked example — Grade 7

Look at **Figure 1**.

**(a)** Compare the incidence of gonorrhoea in males and females for the different age groups. **[2 marks]**

Before the age of 25, more females have gonorrhoea than males. After the age of 25, more males have gonorrhoea than females.

**(b)** Suggest why the incidence of gonorrhoea is greater in 15–24 year olds than it is in people over 60 years old. **[2 marks]**

People aged 15–24 are more likely to have many different sexual partners, so they are more likely to get gonorrhoea.

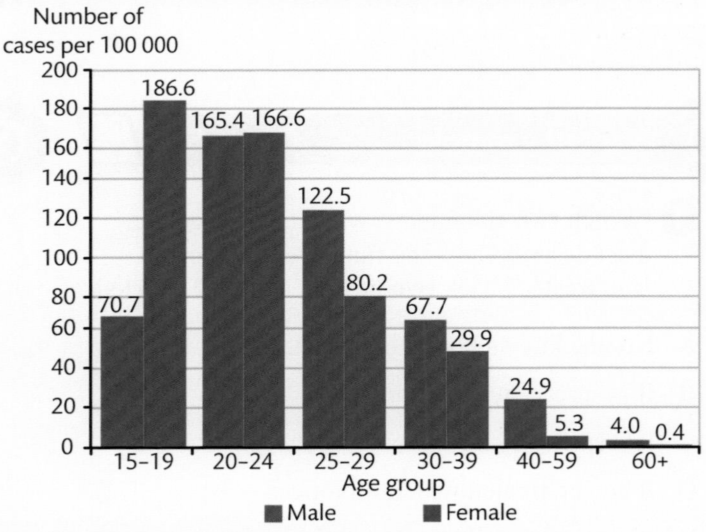


**Figure 1** Cases of gonorrhoea in Canada during 2008

**(c)** Gonorrhoea is a sexually transmitted disease. Explain what this means and how this knowledge could be used to reduce the incidence of the disease. **[2 marks]**

The disease can be transmitted from one person to another by sexual intercourse. Therefore, barrier methods of contraception can reduce the spread of the disease.

## 5 Exam-style practice — Grade 6

1. Explain how bacteria cause the symptoms of a disease. **[2 marks]**
2. Suggest how the spread of gonorrhoea can be prevented. **[3 marks]**

# Fungal diseases

You need to know about fungal diseases and how they affect both animals and plants.

## 5 Fungus

A fungus is a living organism, but it is neither a plant nor an animal. Fungi include moulds, yeast, mushrooms and toadstools.

Unlike plants, they do not contain chlorophyll so cannot make their own food. Instead they secrete enzymes onto organic matter, and then absorb the digested organic products. Fungi can live on dead organisms or invade living ones.

### How are fungal diseases spread?

Fungi reproduce by producing microscopic spores, which can grow into a new fungus. The spores can be spread in droplets of rain water or may be blown by the wind.

## 5 Rose black spot

Rose black spot is a fungus which attacks rose plants. It produces purple or black spots on the rose's leaves.

The leaves then turn yellow and fall from the plant, which greatly affects the health and vigour of the plant.

It also affects the plant's growth as the rate of photosynthesis is reduced because of the reduction in the number of leaves.

Rose black spot is spread by water or wind. It can be treated by removing the affected leaves and burning or burying them, and by spraying the plant with a fungicide, a substance that destroys the fungus.

**Figure 1** Rose black spot

## 5 Worked example — Grade 5

**1** Which **two** statements, when taken together, best describe how the fungus can be spread and treated? Tick **two** boxes. **[2 marks]**

- **A** No one knows how it is spread. ☐
- **B** It is spread by water or wind. ☑
- **C** It is spread by direct contact between plants. ☐
- **D** It can be treated with antibiotics. ☐
- **E** It can be treated by composting the affected plants. ☐
- **F** It can be treated with a fungicide. ☑

**2** Suggest why it is likely that roses not treated with a fungicide will eventually get infected with rose black spot. **[2 marks]**

*The fungal spores are released into the air, so it is likely that healthy roses will be infected as the wind blows the spores to them.*

## 1 Exam focus

Multiple-choice questions can be more difficult when you are expected to choose two statements which relate to each other.

Check your answer is correct by using a process of elimination to rule out the other options.

> Think about the structure of plant and animal cells (page 3) compared with fungal cells.

## 5 Exam-style practice — Grade 6

**1** Suggest why fungi are classified as neither a plant nor an animal. **[3 marks]**

**2** Explain why the rose leaves infected with rose black spot should be removed from the plant and burned. **[2 marks]**

# Protist diseases

Protists are a group of organisms that are usually unicellular (made of just one cell) and have a nucleus. You need to know how protist diseases like malaria are spread.

## 10 Malaria

Malaria is spread from person to person by mosquitos. If left untreated, malaria can be fatal.

The spread of malaria can be controlled by preventing mosquitos from breeding and by people using nets to avoid being bitten.

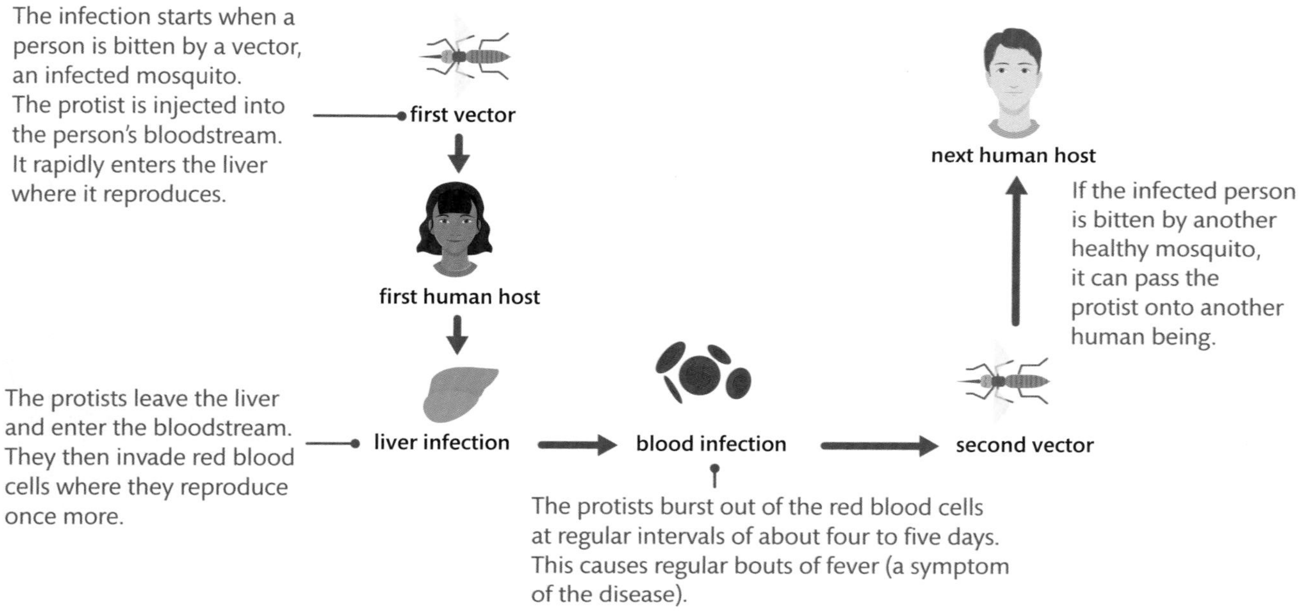

The infection starts when a person is bitten by a vector, an infected mosquito. The protist is injected into the person's bloodstream. It rapidly enters the liver where it reproduces.
first vector
first human host
next human host
If the infected person is bitten by another healthy mosquito, it can pass the protist onto another human being.
The protists leave the liver and enter the bloodstream. They then invade red blood cells where they reproduce once more.
liver infection
blood infection
second vector
The protists burst out of the red blood cells at regular intervals of about four to five days. This causes regular bouts of fever (a symptom of the disease).

**Figure 1** The life cycle of the malarial protist

## 10 Worked example — Grade 6

**Figure 2** shows malarial protists invading human blood.

**(a)** Draw straight lines and label:

**(i)** a malarial protist **(ii)** a red blood cell. **[2 marks]**

**(b)** Explain what is meant by 'protist'. **[2 marks]**

An organism made of a single cell with a nucleus.

**(c)** A person suffering from malaria gets regular bouts of fever. Explain why. **[2 marks]**

The fever is caused by the protists bursting out of red blood cells every four to five days.

**(d)** The malarial protist is transferred from one person to another. Explain how. **[2 marks]**

An infected person is bitten by a mosquito, which then bites another person, infecting them with the protist.

malarial protist

red blood cell

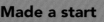

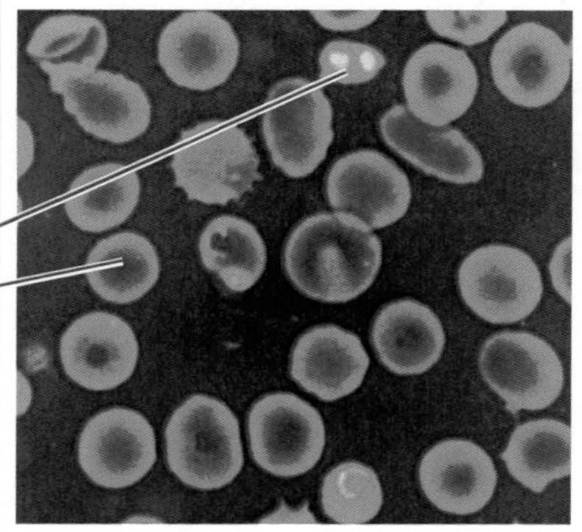

**Figure 2** A photomicrograph of malarial protists in human blood

When labelling diagrams always make sure your lines are straight and start and finish at the correct points.

## 5 Exam-style practice — Grade 6

1. Name the vector involved with the transfer of malaria. **[1 mark]**
2. Explain why it is incorrect to say that mosquitos cause malaria. **[2 marks]**

# Human defence systems

You need to know about the human body's defence mechanisms and how they protect us from invading pathogens.

## Physical defences

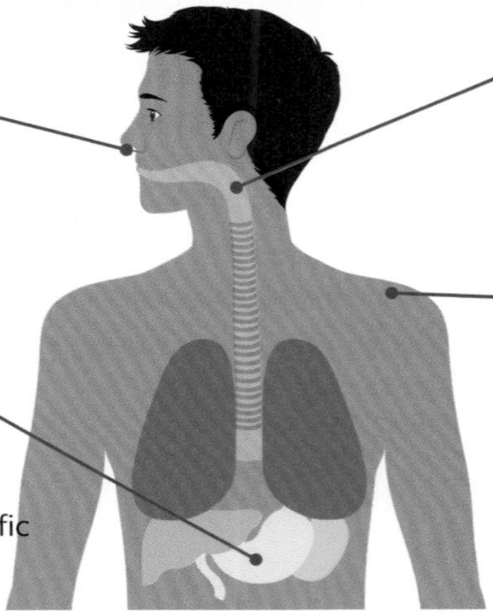

The nose is lined with hairs and mucus to trap pathogens to stop them getting to the lungs.
The stomach produces hydrochloric acid to help kill any pathogens in food.
Sticky mucus in the trachea and bronchi traps pathogens. Cilia on the cells lining these passages move in a wave-like motion, moving mucus and trapped pathogens out of the lungs towards the back of the throat where they are swallowed.
The skin is the organ that covers the outer surface of the body. It acts as a barrier to pathogens and has other features that defend against them. It secretes antimicrobial substances that kill pathogenic bacteria or inhibit their growth. Many species of non-pathogenic bacteria live on the skin. They secrete substances that kill pathogenic bacteria, and compete with them for nutrients. Scabs form over damaged skin, keeping pathogens out while the skin repairs itself.

**Figure 1** The body's non-specific defences make it difficult for pathogens to enter the body.

## The immune system

When a person is infected with a pathogen, the pathogen starts to reproduce. Symptoms of the illness only appear after there are a large number of pathogens present in the body producing toxins and killing cells.

When a pathogen enters the body the **immune system** tries to destroy it. There are several ways it does this:

- **Phagocytosis** – some white blood cells engulf the pathogen and digest it.
- **Antibody production** – some white blood cells produce antibodies. These are proteins that recognise and target specific antigens on the pathogen and destroy it. When the infection has passed, some white blood cells remain in the blood as 'memory cells'. If a person is re-infected by the same pathogen, the memory cells enable the immune system to react more rapidly, which reduces the risk of the symptoms.
- **Antitoxin production** – some white blood cells produce **antitoxins**. Antitoxins are proteins that attach to the poisonous toxins produced by pathogens and neutralise them.

## Worked example — Grade 5

Look at **Figure 2**.

**(a)** How long did it take for the body to start producing the antibody after infection? **[1 mark]**

7.5 hours

**(b)** How many hours did the person feel ill for? **[1 mark]**

23 hours

**(c)** What was the concentration of antibodies in the blood when the pathogen started being destroyed faster than it was reproducing? **[1 mark]**

34 au

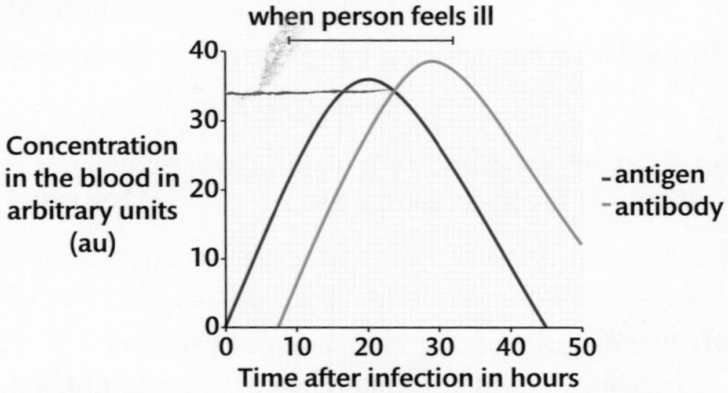


**Figure 2** The concentration of antigens of a pathogen in the blood and the concentration of antibodies that the body produces in response.

## Exam-style practice — Grade 6

1. White blood cells help to protect the body against disease-causing microorganisms. Explain how. **[2 marks]**
2. A person who has had an infectious disease is less likely to get the same disease again. Explain why. **[2 marks]**

# Vaccination

You need to know how a vaccination can build up immunity to a disease.

## 5 Vaccination

Vaccination is the process of using dead or inactive pathogens to ensure that the immune system can recognise and quickly respond to the live pathogen if they become infected with the disease.

1. Dead or inactive pathogens are injected into the body.
2. The body responds by white blood cells producing antibodies specific to the pathogen.
3. If the live pathogen infects the body in the future, cells in the blood rapidly produce large quantities of antibodies to destroy the pathogen.

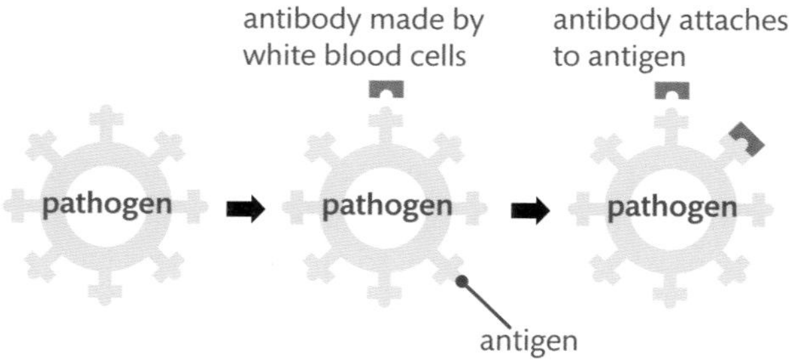


Go to page 44 for more about antibodies.

**Figure 1** How antibodies attack pathogens

## 2 Working scientifically

To prevent a disease from spreading, not everyone in the population needs to be vaccinated.

This is because the more people that are vaccinated, the less chance there is of an infected person meeting and passing on the infection to someone who has not been vaccinated. This is called **herd immunity**.

## 2 Smallpox

Smallpox is a disease that has killed millions of people around the world. The World Health Organisation organised a global vaccination programme. In 1977, Ali Maow Maalin had the last recorded case of smallpox. No one has had the disease since that date. Smallpox is the only disease that has been totally eradicated by science and vaccination. Millions of lives have been saved.

## 10 Worked example — Grade 8

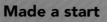

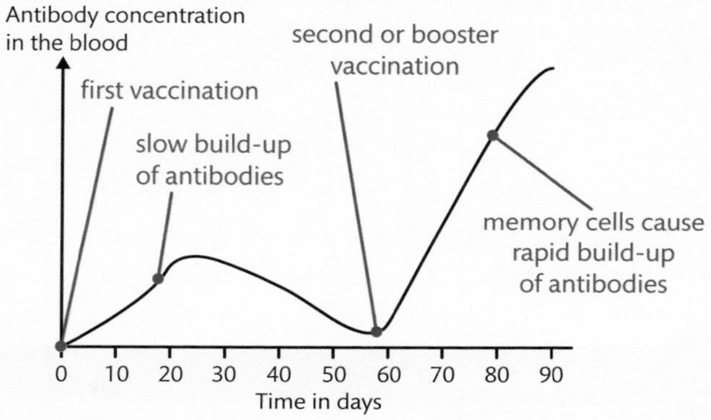


**Figure 2** A graph showing antibody build up after vaccination.

Look at **Figure 2**.

**(a)** Explain how the body responds after a vaccine is injected. **[2 marks]**

*White blood cells produce antibodies to destroy the antigens in the vaccine.*

> Use information in the graph to help you answer the question. The graph shows the concentration of antibodies increasing after the first vaccination.

**(b)** Describe the difference in response when a second or booster dose of vaccine is injected. **[2 marks]**

*Memory cells in the blood produce the antibodies much faster and in greater quantities.*

> The graph shows that the concentration of antibodies increases more quickly and significantly following the second vaccination.

## 10 Exam-style practice — Grade 7

1. Some people think that it is their social responsibility to have their children vaccinated. Suggest why. **[1 mark]**
2. Explain what is meant by 'herd immunity'. **[2 marks]**
3. Give **two** reasons why some people prefer to not have vaccinations. **[2 marks]**
4. Describe the function of memory cells. **[1 mark]**

# Antibiotics and painkillers

You need to know how drugs can be used to treat diseases and reduce symptoms.

## 2 Antibiotics: Key facts

- Antibiotics are a group of drugs that kill bacteria.
- Specific bacteria should be treated using specific antibiotics.
- Antibiotics do not destroy viruses.
- Antibiotics have significantly reduced deaths from infectious bacterial diseases since their discovery.
- However, many bacteria are now developing strains which are resistant to antibiotics. This has serious implications for treating bacterial diseases.

## 2 Antivirals: Key facts

- Antivirals are drugs used to treat diseases caused by viruses.
- Viruses enter cells, making it very difficult to kill the viruses without also killing the cells. This is why there are not many antiviral drugs.
- New antiviral drugs are being developed to help destroy the virus which causes AIDS, HIV.

## 1 Working scientifically

At present, the majority of new drugs are synthesised by scientists in the lab. However, some drugs and substances are still extracted from natural sources, such as plants.

## 2 Development of drugs

**Painkillers** are a group of drugs that are used to relieve pain. Painkillers do not kill pathogens and so do not cure the disease. They only alleviate the painful symptoms.

Aspirin was one of the first painkillers to be used. It can be extracted from the bark of the willow tree. Aspirin is now made synthetically in laboratories.

Another drug extracted from plants is digitalis. It comes from foxgloves and is used for treating heart conditions.

## 5 Worked example — Grade 5

Penicillin was the first antibiotic to be discovered.

The discovery was made by Alexander Fleming.

Fleming was growing bacteria in a Petri dish.

The Petri dish was contaminated by the mould *Penicillium*.

Describe and explain how looking at this Petri dish led to Fleming discovering penicillin. **[3 marks]**

Fleming noticed that no bacteria were growing near the mould. He realised that the mould must be producing a substance that killed bacteria. He isolated the substance which was called penicillin. This substance became the first antibiotic.

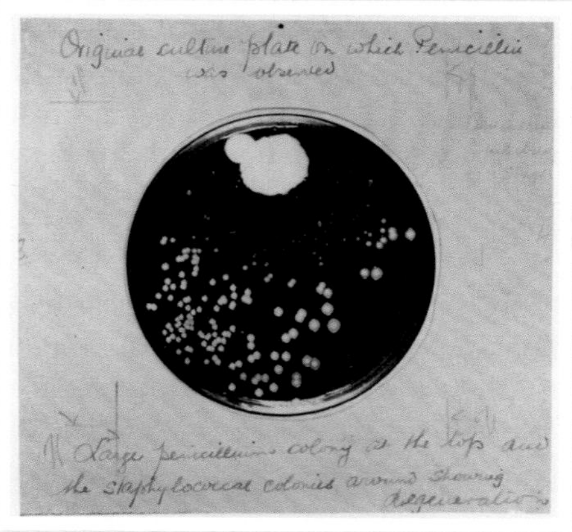

**Figure 1** Fleming's Petri dish

## 10 Exam-style practice — Grade 5

1. Antibiotics do not kill viruses. Suggest a reason why. **[1 mark]**
2. Write down the name of a drug that is used to cure a disease and the name of a different drug that just alleviates the symptoms of a disease. **[2 marks]**
3. Conserving plants in rainforests is very important for drug companies. Suggest why. **[1 mark]**

# Resistant bacteria

More and more strains of bacteria are developing resistance to antibiotics. You need to know the effects this has on the treatment of bacterial diseases.

## 10 Bacterial resistance

Bacteria can develop resistance to antibiotics by evolution and natural selection (page 67).

- They reproduce very rapidly.
- Some bacteria have mutations which make them resistant to an antibiotic.
- Bacteria that are susceptible to the antibiotic get killed.
- Bacteria that are resistant to the antibiotic survive and reproduce rapidly.
- Soon all the surviving bacteria are resistant to the antibiotic.
- Resistant strains can then spread because people are not immune to them and there are no effective treatments.

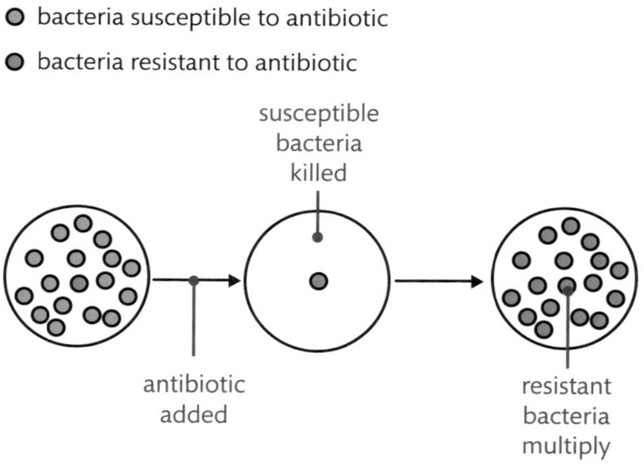


**Figure 1** Bacteria developing resistance to an antibiotic

## 5 MRSA

MRSA is a type of bacteria that is now resistant to many known antibiotics and is therefore difficult to treat.

To reduce the chances of other types of pathogen developing antibiotic resistance:

- Doctors should not prescribe antibiotics for viral diseases or diseases which are not serious.
- Any patient prescribed a course of antibiotics should complete the course to reduce the chances of any bacteria surviving and forming a resistant strain.
- The use of antibiotics in agriculture to increase growth rates in animals should be restricted.

## 5 The future of antibiotics

Producing new drugs is very expensive.

After a potential new drug is discovered, it takes a very long time for the drug to become available to doctors and the general public.

Drug companies will only invest in developing new drugs if they know that they can make a profit in the long term.

Because microorganisms can evolve so rapidly it is unlikely that the discovery and production of new antibiotics will keep up with the emergence of new resistant strains of bacteria.

Go to page 48 for more about developing new drugs.

## 2 Worked example — Grade 7

Describe the measures that doctors and patients can take to reduce bacterial resistance to new drugs. **[2 marks]**

*They should only use antibiotics when necessary, and patients should make sure they finish their course of treatment.*

Antibiotics are often prescribed, inappropriately, for minor viral infections. The misuse of antibiotics is speeding up the process of antibiotic resistance, resulting in some commonly used antibiotics becoming ineffective.

## 2 Exam-style practice — Grade 7

1. Describe how antibiotic resistance develops. **[4 marks]**
2. Bacteria can become resistant to an antibiotic very quickly. Explain why. **[2 marks]**

# Development of drugs

You need to know how drugs are discovered and tested over time.

## 10 Timescale for drug development

| Research & development 3–6 years | Pre-clinical studies 1 year | Clinical trials 4–7 years | Review & approval 1–2 years |
|---|---|---|---|
| This is when potential new drugs are made or discovered. | This is when the drug is tested in the laboratory. | This is when the drug is tested on healthy human volunteers, starting with very low doses for toxicity and efficacy. | This is when new drugs are approved to be used on patients. |
| Scientists first decide what drugs are needed. | In vitro ('in glass') tests on cells and tissues (the drug is tested in Petri dishes and test tubes) | **Phase 1** It is tested on about 50 people to check for side effects and to see how quickly the body breaks down the drug. | If the drug is effective it is sent to regulating bodies for approval. |
| Scientists then look for compounds that might do the job they are looking for. | Testing in animals | **Phase 2** It is tested on about 200 patients with the condition. | The governing body fast tracks drugs that are desperately needed. If the benefits outweigh the risks it is approved. |
| Thousands of chemical compounds are then tested or modified to improve their action. | Testing in mammals | **Phase 3** If the drug is found to be safe, it is tested on about 2000 people to see how well the drug works and its optimum dose. | When the drug is available for doctors to use it is monitored for side effects indefinitely. |

## 5 Worked example — Grade 5

New drugs are tested using double blind trials and placebos.

**(a)** Which of these statements best describes a double blind trial? Tick **one** box. **[1 mark]**

**A** Only the doctor knows if the patient is getting the drug or a placebo. ☐

**B** Only the patient knows if they are getting the drug or a placebo. ☐

**C** Both the patient and the doctor know if they are getting the drug or a placebo. ☐

**D** Neither the patient nor the doctor know if they are getting the drug or a placebo. ☑

**(b)** Placebos are used in double blind trials. Explain what a placebo is and why it is used. **[2 marks]**

*A placebo is a substance that does not contain the drug. It is used to check if the effects are caused by the drug or by something else.*

A placebo is designed to appear exactly the same as the drug itself, but it does not actually contain any of the drug.

## 2 Working scientifically

All the results from testing and trialling new drugs are published. Other scientists then peer review the data.

The other scientists check the results and the theories suggested. They may also carry out further tests to check the data provided is correct. Peer review in this way helps to ensure new drugs and the results of trials are as safe and effective as possible.

## 5 Exam-style practice — Grade 5

1. Explain what is meant by peer review. **[2 marks]**
2. Give the approximate time needed for a new medical drug to be developed. **[1 mark]**

# Asexual and sexual reproduction

You need to know how living organisms can reproduce by either asexual reproduction or sexual reproduction.

## 10 Sexual reproduction

Sexual reproduction requires male (sperm) and female (ova or egg) gametes. A **gamete** is a sex cell which contains genetic information. Gametes in reproductive organs are produced by a type of cell division called meiosis (page 51).

During fertilisation, the nuclei of the male and female gametes fuse together to make a fertilised egg cell called a **zygote**. The zygote divides many times by a type of cell division called mitosis (page 50), eventually forming an embryo.

In sexual reproduction, genetic information from the male and the female parent is mixed together. This provides variation in the offspring.

Go to page 55 to revise variation.

Nuclei is the plural of nucleus.

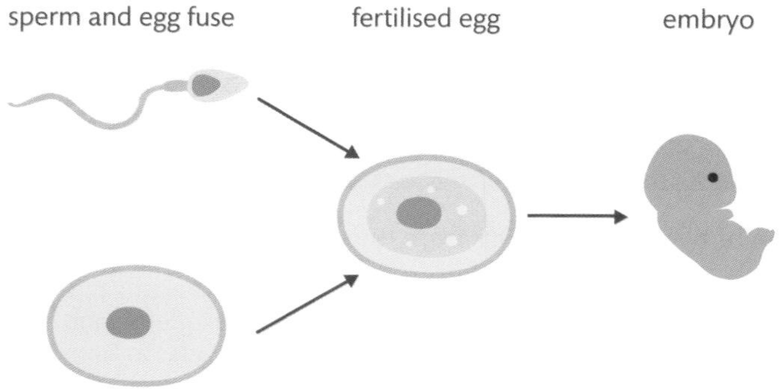


**Figure 1** Fertilisation

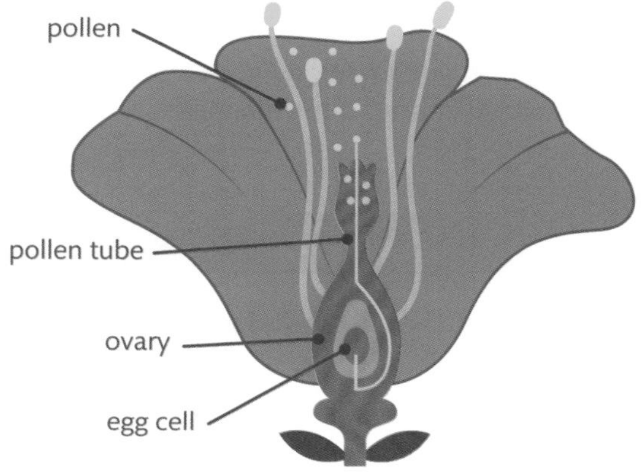


**Figure 2** In plants, pollen is used to fertilise the egg cell in the ovary.

## 5 Asexual reproduction

Asexual reproduction only involves one parent. There is no fusion of male and female gametes.

This means that there is no mixing of genetic information, so when the cells divide, all the offspring are genetically identical to the parent.

The type of cell division involved in asexual reproduction is called mitosis. These offspring are called clones. Organisms which can produce asexually include bacteria, fungi, potatoes and daffodils.

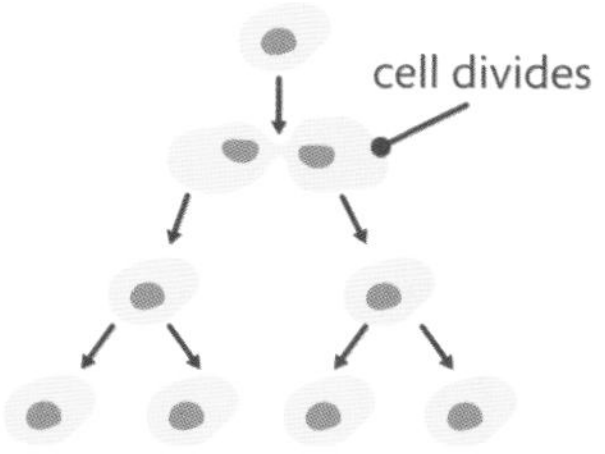


**Figure 3** Asexual reproduction involves only mitosis.

## 2 Worked example — Grade 5

Compare sexual and asexual reproduction. **[4 marks]**

Sexual reproduction involves two parent cells dividing by meiosis, whereas asexual reproduction involves one parent cell diving by mitosis. Sexual reproduction produces variety in offspring but asexual reproduction leads to genetically identical clones. This is because sexual reproduction involves the mixing of genetic information from male and female gametes.

### Exam skills

You could be asked to compare sexual and asexual reproduction in the exam. Make sure you know the differences between the two types of cell division.

## 5 Exam-style practice — Grade 6

1. Describe **one** difference between asexual and sexual reproduction. **[2 marks]**
2. Define the term 'gamete'. **[1 mark]**

# Chromosomes, mitosis and the cell cycle

Multicellular organisms grow and develop using a type of cell division called mitosis. You need to know how this occurs.

## 5 Key facts: Chromosomes

- Chromosomes are found in the nucleus of nearly all types of cell.
- There are two copies of each chromosome in nearly all body cells. In humans, there are 23 pairs of chromosomes giving a total of 46 chromosomes in each cell (but not in the sex cells – see page 56 **Sex determination**).
- Chromosomes consist of long strands of DNA coiled up.
- Chromosomes carry many **genes**, sections of DNA which control our characteristics.

## 5 Mitosis

**Mitosis** is the process of cell division involved in asexual reproduction. The products of mitosis are genetically identical clone cells produced for growth, repair and replacement of damaged body cells.

Before a cell can divide, it needs to grow and increase the number of sub-cellular structures such as ribosomes and mitochondria.

During the cell cycle the genetic material is doubled and then divided into two identical cells. Mitosis takes place after the cell contents have been replicated.

## 10 Stages in the cell cycle

The cell cycle consists of **three stages** that lead to the production of two daughter cells from one parent cell.

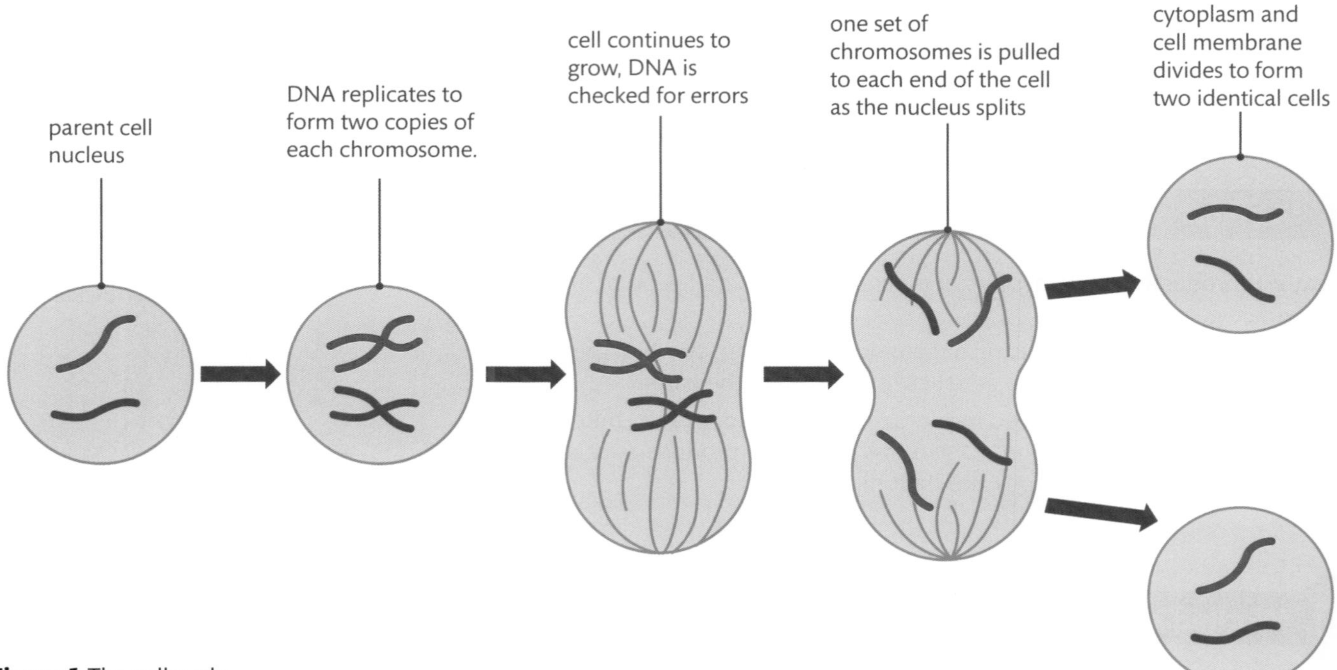


**Figure 1** The cell cycle

## 5 Worked example — Grade 6

Explain the process of mitosis, where it takes place and the kind of products that are made. **[4 marks]**

Mitosis is an asexual process that occurs in body cells. It enables an organism to grow and repair. One division occurs to produce two cells. The cells produced are genetically identical copies.

## 5 Exam-style practice — Grade 6

1. Describe what must happen to a cell before it can divide. **[1 mark]**
2. Explain the three stages of the cell cycle. **[4 marks]**
3. Give the number of chromosomes in a body cell from a human baby. **[1 mark]**

# Meiosis

You need to know how meiosis produces the cells required for sexual reproduction. Meiosis is the type of cell division that produces gametes, which are needed for sexual reproduction. You need to know how this occurs.

## 10 The stages of meiosis

**Meiosis** results in sperm and egg cells (**gametes**).

Although similar to mitosis, it is a two-stage cell division process, resulting in the production of four cells, each containing a single set of chromosomes.

The gametes produced by meiosis are genetically different from each other.

During fertilisation, one male gamete and one female gamete join up to form a cell with the typical number of chromosomes in a body cell (46 chromosomes arranged in 23 pairs).

This cell will then divide by mitosis as the embryo develops. As the embryo develops, cells differentiate.

The final stage of division during meiosis will always produce cells containing half the number of chromosomes as the parent cell. The chromosomes can be either chromosome from each pair of chromosomes contained in the parent cell.

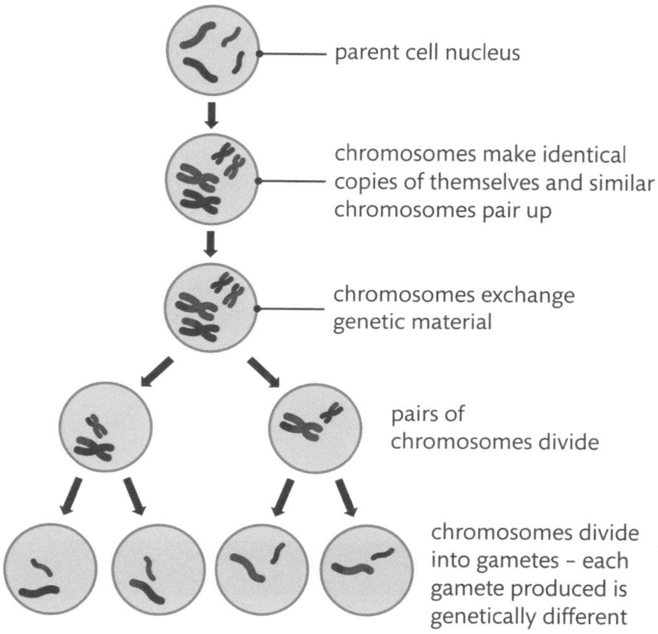
parent cell nucleus
chromosomes make identical copies of themselves and similar chromosomes pair up
chromosomes exchange genetic material
pairs of chromosomes divide
chromosomes divide into gametes – each gamete produced is genetically different

**Figure 1** The stages of meiosis

## 5 Worked example — Grade 8

**(a)** Describe what happens to the chromosomes when a cell divides by meiosis. **[4 marks]**

The chromosomes duplicate; the cell then divides twice to form four gametes, each with a single set of chromosomes.

**(b)** Complete the diagram to show the nucleus of a parent cell. **[1 mark]**

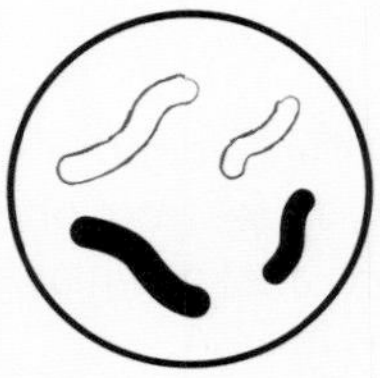

**(c)** Complete the diagram to show one of the four nuclei produced from the cell above during meiosis. **[1 mark]**

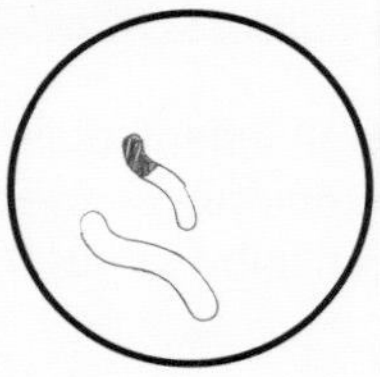

The first cell division occurs after chromosomes have made identical copies of themselves and paired up. Before the division takes place the chromosomes swap sections of DNA, which ensures that there will be variation in the gametes.

The second round of cell division splits the 46 chromosomes in one cell into two cells, each containing only half the number of chromosomes (23).

## 2 Key terms

- **gametes** – sex cells: sperm and egg cells
- **diploid** – a cell containing two sets of chromosomes
- **haploid** – a cell containing a single set of unpaired chromosomes

## 1 Exam focus

You need to know the differences between meiosis and mitosis (page 50) for the exam.

## 5 Exam-style practice — Grade 7

1. Describe how variation occurs due to meiosis and sexual reproduction. **[3 marks]**

2. **(a)** Describe how the number of chromosomes in a human sex cell differs from the number of chromosomes in a human body cell. **[1 mark]**

   **(b)** Give the number of chromosomes found in a human egg cell. **[1 mark]**

# DNA and the genome

The whole genetic material of an organism is called its genome. You need to know about the substance that makes up all genetic material, DNA – deoxyribonucleic acid.

## 10 The structure of DNA

The whole genetic material of an organism is called its genome.

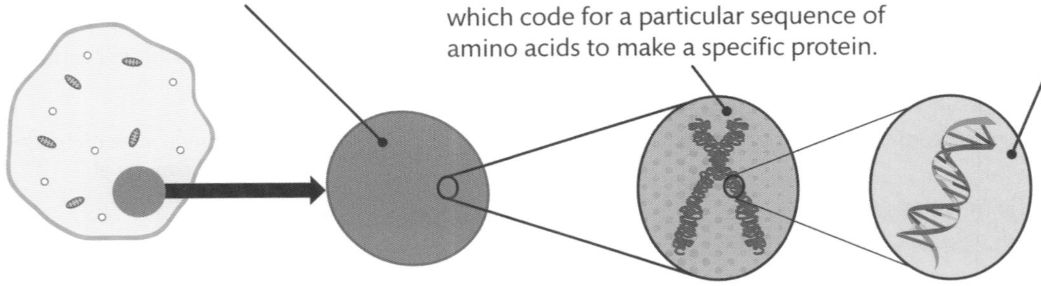

The nucleus contains chromosomes.
DNA is a polymer, which is tightly coiled to form structures called chromosomes. Genes are small sections of DNA on a chromosome which code for a particular sequence of amino acids to make a specific protein.
DNA is the genetic material. It consists of two strands coiled into a double helix structure.
cell
nucleus
chromosome
DNA

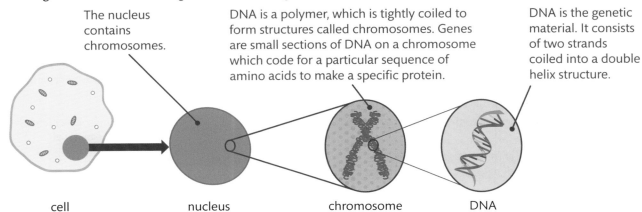

**Figure 1** DNA in a cell

## 5 The Human Genome Project

Completed by 2003, the purpose of the Human Genome Project was to map and identify all the genes in the human genome.

Information about DNA can be very useful for forensic science, tracing human migration patterns, and for the understanding and treatment of inherited genetic disorders. The project enables scientists to:

- diagnose diseases before symptoms develop
- identify the genetic changes that are responsible for an already diagnosed disease
- help doctors to determine the best treatment
- identify genetic mutations that may increase the risk of developing a disease
- identify gene changes that could be inherited
- screen babies for treatable conditions.

## 5 Worked example — Grade 8

**1** Describe the role of a gene. **[1 mark]**

A gene codes for a sequence of amino acids to make a protein.

**2** Explain how the human genome and genetic markers have enabled scientists to trace human migration back to Africa. **[3 marks]**

Genetic markers are areas of variation in the sequence of human DNA. Mapping the occurrence of these markers around the world shows the movement of human population. As human populations migrated their genome mutated, showing small changes in different populations. These changes can be traced back, showing that it is most likely that all humans descended from people in Africa.

Virtually all human DNA is identical – only around 1 in 1000 DNA base pairs varies from one individual to the next. These variations are known as genetic markers, caused by mutations in DNA.

## 10 Exam-style practice — Grade 7

**1** Cystic fibrosis is an inherited disorder. Explain how the human genome can be used to identify whether or not an unborn baby carries the disorder. **[3 marks]**

**2** Describe how an understanding of the human genome is useful for developing treatments for diseases caused by mutations in genes. **[2 marks]**

**3** Give **three** ways in which knowledge of the sequence of the human genome can be used. **[3 marks]**



Made a start | Feeling confident | Exam ready

# Genetic inheritance

Many of our characteristics are controlled by the genes we inherit. You need to know how alleles, the different forms of each gene, cause variation between individuals.

## 5 Key terms

- **gene** – a short section of DNA which codes for a protein
- **allele** – different version of a gene
- **dominant** – only one dominant allele is needed for a characteristic to be expressed
- **recessive** – two recessive alleles are needed for the characteristic to be expressed
- **homozygous** – both alleles for a gene are identical
- **heterozygous** – the alleles for a gene are different
- **genotype** – the alleles present for genes
- **phenotype** – the physical characteristics, determined by the alleles

## 5 Genes

Some characteristics are controlled by a single **gene**, such as red-green colour blindness in humans, and fur colour in mice.

Most characteristics are controlled by multiple genes interacting. For example, multiple genes affect eye colour and skin colour.

The different forms of a gene are called **alleles**; alleles for each gene are inherited from each parent.

The combination of alleles present (**genotype**) operates at a molecular level to develop a person's observable characteristics (**phenotype**).

The appearance of a characteristic is dependent on both the type of alleles present and whether they are dominant or recessive.

## 10 Worked example Grade 7

The allele **m** causes a rare blood-linked condition.

**(a)** What type of allele is responsible for the disease? **[1 mark]**

A recessive allele

**(b)** Two parents produce offspring. Parent A has the alleles **Mm** and parent B has the alleles **mm**.

Produce a Punnett square to calculate the percentage chance of their offspring inheriting the disease. **[3 marks]**

| | | Parent A | |
|---|---|---|---|
| | | M | m |
| Parent B | m | Mm | mm |
| | m | Mm | mm |

There is a 50% chance of having a child with the disease.

## 2 Working scientifically

You need to know how to draw genetic cross diagrams, or Punnett squares, to predict the probability of the results of a single gene cross. The results of genetic crosses are usually represented as either a ratio or a percentage.

One mark is awarded for correctly separating the alleles for the axes. The second mark is for four correct crosses. The final mark is for the correct percentage given.

Dominant alleles are represented by a capital letter, while recessive alleles are shown by a lowercase letter.

## 2 Exam focus

In the exam, you are expected to know how to construct genetic cross diagrams and make predictions about the inheritance of particular genes based on the theory of probability.

Go to page 54 to read about the inheritance of polydactyly.

## 5 Exam-style practice Grade 7

Polydactyly is an inherited condition which causes the sufferer to have extra fingers or toes. It is caused by a dominant allele.

**(a)** Draw a Punnett square to show the inheritance of polydactyly between a mother who is homozygous for polydactyly, and a father who does not have the polydactyly gene.

Use D for the polydactyly allele and d for the normal allele. **[3 marks]**

**(b)** Give the percentage of the offspring that will inherit the condition. **[1 mark]**

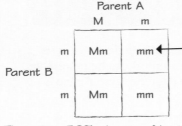

# Inherited disorders

You need to know how genetic disorders like polydactyly and cystic fibrosis are inherited.

## 5 Polydactyly and cystic fibrosis

Polydactyly is a disorder where the person has extra fingers or toes. It is caused by a dominant allele.

Cystic fibrosis is a disorder of the cell membranes leading to the production of a thick sticky mucus which affects organs, particularly the lungs. It is caused by a recessive allele.

This means that people will only have cystic fibrosis if they inherit two copies of the recessive allele. Go to page 53 for more about alleles.

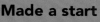

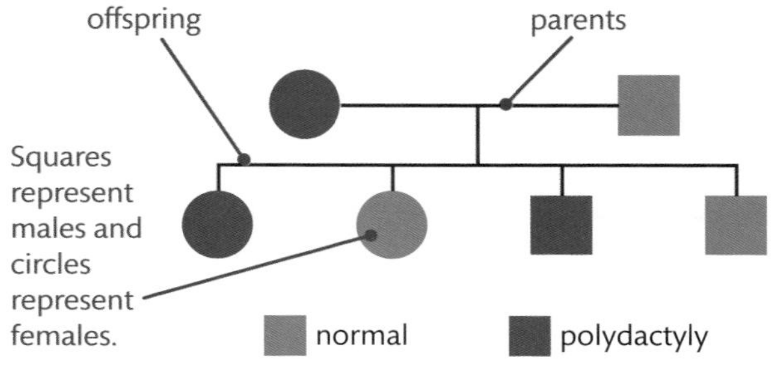

**Figure 1** This family tree shows the inheritance of polydactyly within a family.

## 10 Worked example — Grade 8

**1** Polydactyly is an inherited disorder.

**(a)** Explain what is meant by 'an inherited disorder'. **[1 mark]**

*An inherited disorder is a genetic disorder that has been passed on from either one or both parents.*

**(b)** Explain how **Figure 1** shows that polydactyly is caused by a dominant allele. **[2 marks]**

*One parent has polydactyly, so must be homozygous or heterozygous for the allele. The other does not have polydactyly, so must not have the allele. If some of the children have polydactyly, the allele must be dominant.*

**2** Evaluate the use of embryo screening for cystic fibrosis. In your answer discuss the economic, social and ethical issues. **[6 marks]**

*Economic issues relating to the use of embryo screening include the fact that it is a very expensive procedure. However, the cost of bringing up a child with cystic fibrosis could be much more expensive.*

*Social issues include the possibility that the embryo might be damaged during the testing, causing social issues when born. Wider social issues include the possibility that testing for genetic disorders may cause people to become prejudiced against anyone with a disorder, but by using embryo screening the child is more likely to be born healthy and is unlikely to pass on the CF gene to its offspring.*

*Ethical issues related to embryo screening include the fact that some people believe it is wrong to kill an embryo as it is a living thing. However, it may mean that a child won't be born who would have to suffer a life-limiting illness.*

## 1 Exam focus

In the exam, you could be asked to:

- complete a Punnett square diagram
- extract and interpret information from genetic crosses and family trees.

## 2 Working scientifically

Embryo screening can take place either during IVF or by taking a sample of DNA from the embryo while in the womb. Embryo screening cannot be used to treat the problem but it will allow parents to make an informed decision as to whether it is fair to have the child if the condition causes a lot of pain.

## 10 Exam-style practice — Grade 7

**1** Cystic fibrosis is caused by a defective gene. The allele for cystic fibrosis can be represented by f, while the allele for the normal gene is represented as F.

**(a)** Give the genotype of a person who is unaffected and is not a carrier of the condition. **[1 mark]**

**(b)** Will a person who has cystic fibrosis be heterozygous or homozygous for the condition? Explain your answer. **[2 marks]**

**(c)** Determine the probability of the offspring being affected if both parents are unaffected carriers. Use a genetic diagram to show your answer. **[3 marks]**

**2** Give **one** ethical advantage and **one** ethical disadvantage of embryo screening. **[2 marks]**

# Variation and mutation

You need to know how both variation and mutation occur in a species.

## Causes of variation

Although a lot of characteristics are inherited, the interaction of genes with the environment will also influence the phenotype (physical features) of an individual.

Variation between individuals occurs due to differences in:

- inherited genes
- the environment in which the person grew up
- the interaction of genes with the environment.

Some characteristics brought about by genetic variation include Down's syndrome, blood group and eye colour.

Some characteristics brought about by environmental variation include weight and language spoken.

Many kinds of variation are influenced by both environmental and genetic factors. For example, a person may have the potential to be tall, but an unhealthy diet can cause poor growth.

There is usually a lot of genetic variation within a population of a species.

Genetic variation in individuals is caused by mutations. Most mutations will have no effect on the phenotype; only rarely do mutations lead to a new phenotype. Mutations occur continuously. If the new phenotype is suited to an environmental change it can lead to a relatively rapid change in the species.

## Mutations: key facts

- A mutation is a change in genetic material (DNA).
- Mutations occur naturally and continuously, usually when DNA is being copied before cell division takes place.
- Mutations usually have no effect on the individuals' characteristics. However, sometimes they can be harmful or useful.
- Mutations cause variation within a species, which is vital to ensure the survival of the species.
- Some mutations are caused by substances such as tar from cigarettes.
- Radiation, including gamma rays, X-ray and UV rays, can also cause genetic mutations.

Mutations can have positive or negative effects:

- improve chances of survival
- increase genetic diversity
- can lead to diseases, such as cancer (page 38)
- can lead to genetic disorders (page 54).

Remember, the phenotype (appearance) is determined by a combination of factors.

## Worked example — Grade 7

**1** Use the correct word from the box to complete the sentence to explain how extensive variation occurs within a species. **[4 marks]**

| phenotype | rapid | variation | mutations |
|---|---|---|---|

Differences in the characteristics of individuals in a population is called variation. This arises as mutations occur continuously. Only rarely does a mutation lead to a change in the phenotype but if the change is beneficial for survival then it can lead to a rapid change in the species.

**2** Identical twins are individuals who developed from a single fertilised ovum. As a result, they have almost identical DNA. Explain why identical twins may or may not be identical when they reach adulthood. **[3 marks]**

Phenotype is controlled by genetic inheritance, environmental factors and the interaction between them. Identical twins will inherit the same DNA and so are genetically identical. However, environmental factors such as their diet will also affect their phenotype so their appearance could be different.

## Exam-style practice — Grade 7

**1** Give **two** forms of genetic variation and **two** forms of environmental variation. **[2 marks]**

**2** Describe what is meant by a mutation. Give **two** ways in which mutation can occur. **[3 marks]**

**3** Give **one** way in which a mutation can be beneficial. **[1 mark]**

Made a start | Feeling confident | Exam ready

# Sex determination

You need to know how sex is determined by chromosomes.

## Formation of sex chromosomes

Human body cells each contain 23 pairs of chromosomes, 22 of which control a person's characteristics.

The 23rd pair carry the genes that determine whether a person is male or female.

The female sex chromosomes are XX. The male sex chromosomes are XY.

Female sex cells (gametes) only contain an X chromosome. The male sex cells (gametes) can either contain an X or a Y, depending on how the chromosomes are separated during meiosis. Therefore an X chromosome is always inherited from the egg but there is a 50% chance of inheriting an X or a Y chromosome from the sperm, which determines the sex of the offspring.

## Genetic diagrams

A genetic diagram can be used to determine the sex of offspring.

1. To construct a genetic diagram, the phenotype of each parent must be given on the top line.
2. The next stage is to provide the genotype for each parent, underneath their phenotype.
3. The next line shows the genotype of all the gametes which can be passed on to the offspring.
4. The final stage in the genetic cross diagram is to show all of the combinations of gametes which could occur which gives the different genotypes possible.

You are expected to know the genotype for a male and a female:

- In males, the two sex chromosomes are different. They are XY.
- In females, the two sex chromosomes are the same. They are XX.

## Worked example — Grade 7

There is a 1:1 chance of a child being a boy or a girl. Draw a suitable diagram to explain this.

**[4 marks]**

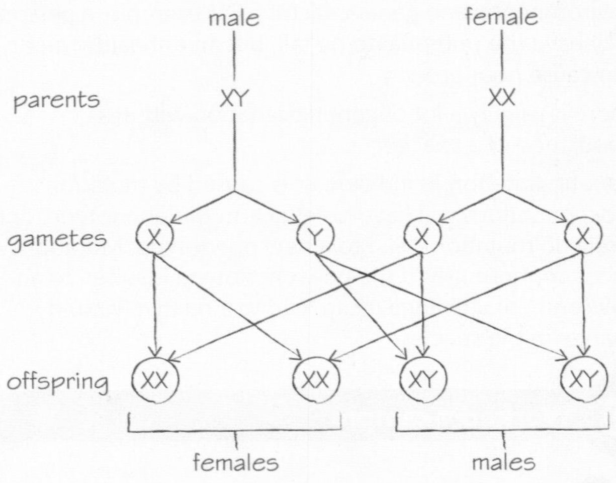


The diagram shows that there is a 2 : 2 chance of female : male offspring which equates to a 1 : 1 ratio.

You could also show your answer as a Punnett square diagram:

| | | Male | |
|---|---|---|---|
| | **gametes** | **X** | **Y** |
| **Female** | **X** | **XX** | **XY** |
| | **X** | **XX** | **XY** |

## Working scientifically

Although it is possible to identify the sex of an unborn baby, it is illegal to choose the sex of a baby unless you have a serious genetic condition which could put a child at risk if inherited, such as haemophilia or muscular dystrophy.

## Exam-style practice — Grade 5

Humans have two different sex chromosomes: X and Y.

**(a)** Give the genotype of a female. **[1 mark]**

**(b)** Give the number of chromosomes, passed on from the egg, that determine the sex of a baby. **[1 mark]**

**(c)** Give the probability of having a male child. Explain your answer. **[2 marks]**

# Communities

A community is all the populations of living organisms within an ecosystem. You need to know how the species within a community depend on one another.

## 5 Features of an ecosystem

A **population** is all the **organisms** of one species within an ecosystem.

A **community** consists of all the populations of different species living in the same habitat. A **habitat** is the place where organisms live.

An **ecosystem** is the interaction of a community of living organisms (**biotic factors**, page 59) with the non-living (**abiotic factors**, page 58) parts of their habitat.

Plants in a community may compete for:

- light
- water
- space
- minerals.

Animals in a community may compete for:

- food
- a mate
- water
- territory.

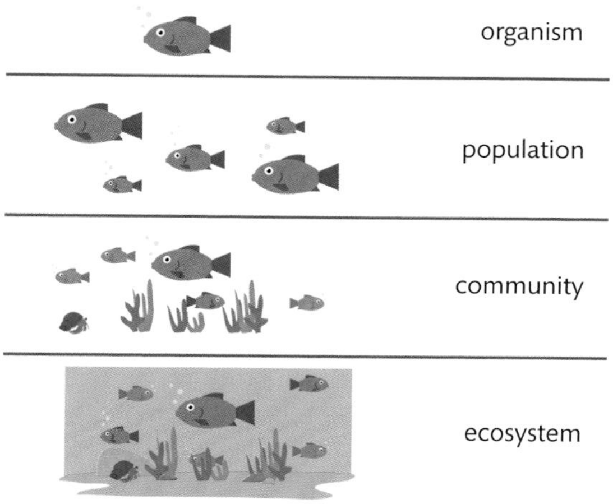


**Figure 1** The different levels of organisation in an ecosystem

## 10 Worked example Grade 6

**Figure 2** A food web for a grassland ecosystem

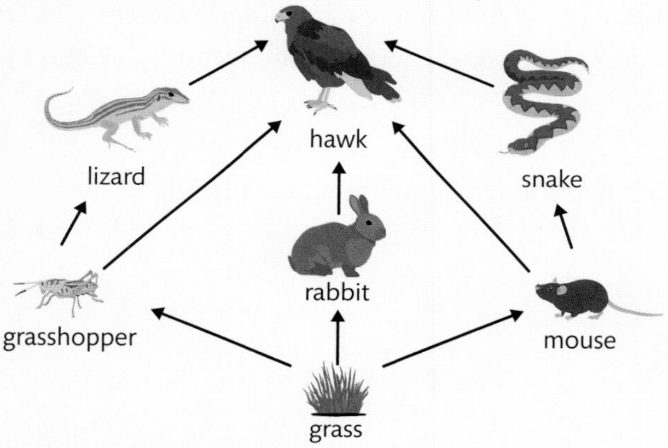


**Figure 2** shows interdependence and competition between species.

**(a)** Name **three** organisms that are competing for grass as a source of food. **[3 marks]**

*Grasshopper, rabbit and mouse*

**(b)** Suggest how the populations of the lizards and the rabbits would be affected if the grasshoppers were all killed by a disease. **[3 marks]**

*The number of lizards would decrease as there would be less food available for them.*

*As the number of lizards decreases, the hawks would need an alternative source of food and so would start to eat more rabbits, causing the population of rabbits to decrease.*

## 5 Interdependence

Within a community, each species depends upon other species for the things they need, including food, shelter, pollination and seed dispersal. This is known as **interdependence**.

If a change occurs, such as the removal of a species, then the whole community could be affected. If all the species and environmental factors in a community are balanced, then the community is stable and the size of populations remains fairly constant.

## 10 Exam-style practice Grade 6

**Figure 3** The changing populations of snails and algae

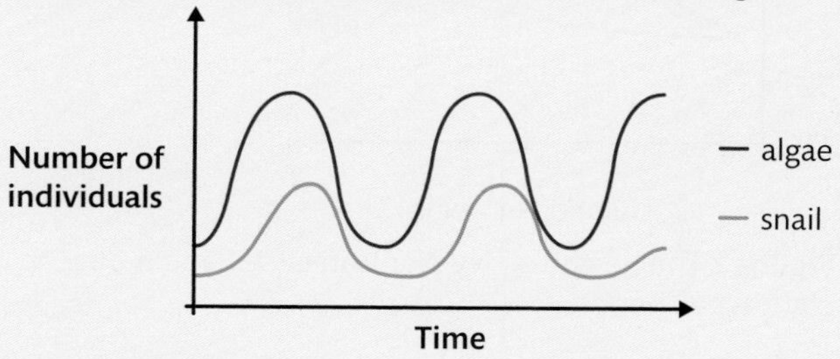


Look at **Figure 3**.

**(a)** Describe how changes in the population of algae affect the population of snails. **[4 marks]**

**(b)** Suggest how the appearance of the graph would alter if a new predator (of the snails) was introduced to the ecosystem. Explain your answer. **[2 marks]**

# Abiotic factors

You need to know how abiotic (non-living) factors can affect a community and its survival.

## 10 Abiotic factors

**Abiotic factors** are non-living factors, including:

- temperature
- pH and mineral content of soil
- wind intensity and direction
- light intensity
- carbon dioxide levels (mainly affects plants)
- oxygen levels (for aquatic animals)
- moisture levels.

The oxygen content of the water can be greatly reduced if it is polluted by sewage or nitrates from farming. The amount of dissolved oxygen usually determines the number and types of organisms living in that body of water. For example, mayfly larvae need water with a high oxygen content, whereas rat tailed maggots can thrive in low oxygen levels.

**Figure 1** Changes in abiotic factors, such as temperature, can have a serious impact on the environment. Rising temperatures are causing sea ice in the Arctic to melt, which is having a negative effect on polar bears who are adapted to hunt and breed there.

## 10 Worked example — Grade 6

A study into the growth of ivy plants in different habitats was conducted. The pH of the soil was different in each habitat.

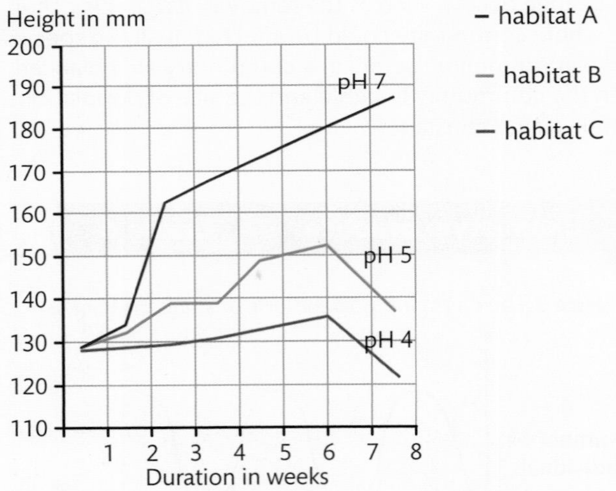


**Figure 2** The heights of ivy plants in each habitat over an eight-week period

**(a)** Soil pH is an example of an abiotic factor. What is meant by the term abiotic factor? **[1 mark]**

*Abiotic factors are the non-living factors that can affect a community.*

**(b)** Using **Figure 2**, interpret how pH affects the growth of ivy. **[3 marks]**

*The graph shows that as the pH becomes more acidic, the growth of the ivy plant decreases. For example, after 6 weeks the ivy plant in pH 7 soil had grown to a height of 180 mm, whereas the plant in pH 5 had only grown around 152 mm and in soil of pH 4 the ivy plant had reduced in height to 135 mm.*

When you are asked to 'use data' you will need to refer to specific data from a chart or table and explain the pattern it shows.

## 1 Exam focus

In the exam, you could be expected to extract and interpret information from charts, tables and graphs in order to comment on the effect of abiotic factors on organisms within a community.

## 5 Exam-style practice — Grade 6

1. Give **three** abiotic factors in the rainforest. **[3 marks]**

2. Explain, giving an example, how a change in an abiotic factor could affect the stability of an ecosystem in the Arctic. **[2 marks]**

# Biotic factors

You need to know how biotic (living) factors can affect a community and its survival.

## 5 Biotic factors

Biotic factors are living factors, including:

- availability of food
- new predators arriving
- pathogens
- competition for food, mates and territory.

There are many biotic factors within a coral reef (**Figure 1**). These include consumers, such as coral, turtles and fish. Producers such as algae and some types of plankton can also be found within the coral reef ecosystem. Competition occurs between predatory animals, like sharks, eels and dolphins. Coral reefs also contain many types of bacteria.

If one species outcompetes another it can lead to insufficient numbers for breeding.

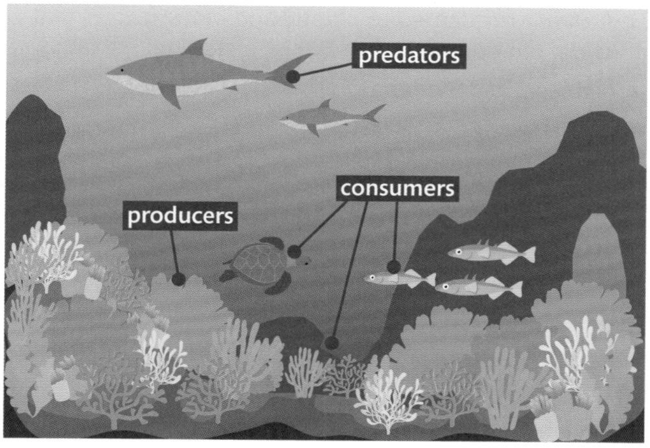


**Figure 1** Biotic factors in a habitat

## 5 Interspecies competition

Different species also compete for things like food and habitat. This can lead to different species trying to outcompete one another, which can result in a species' rate of reproduction decreasing or even its survival being threatened because of the presence of a competitor.

### Working scientifically

The presence of a pathogen called 'white band disease' in aquatic communities is killing coral. The coral is being replaced by algae which in turn is attracting new predators into the ecosystem.

## 10 Worked example — Grade 7

A hedgerow is an example of an ecosystem.

**(a)** Suggest **one** biotic factor that could affect this ecosystem. How could a change in this biotic factor affect the community within the hedgerow? **[4 marks]**

If a new insect-eating species was introduced into the ecosystem, this would affect the stability of the ecosystem as the number of organisms preying upon the insects would increase. This could cause a dramatic drop in the population of a species. It could also affect several species, as there would be less food available for the original predators in the ecosystem and so they may starve and die out.

A biotic factor could have a positive effect on the hedgerow, for example a new species of plant growing could provide more food and allow populations to thrive.

**(b)** Explain how clearing the rainforest for biofuel production is affecting communities of birds within the rainforest. **[3 marks]**

Deforestation removes habitat for insects and small organisms. This leads to a decline in the population sizes of prey for birds. Therefore, the populations of birds will also decrease.

## 10 Exam-style practice — Grade 5

1. Give **three** biotic factors affecting an Arctic ecosystem. **[3 marks]**
2. Draw lines to show whether each factor is biotic or abiotic. **[4 marks]**

| | |
|---|---|
| temperature | |
| carbon dioxide levels | abiotic factors |
| new pathogens | |
| wind intensity | biotic factors |
| food availability | |
| predators | |

3. Suggest how the introduction of the grey squirrel has caused the red squirrel to become endangered. **[2 marks]**

Made a start | Feeling confident | Exam ready

# Adaptations

You need to know how organisms are adapted to enable them to survive the conditions of their natural environment.

## 10 Types of adaptation

Organisms are adapted to abiotic and biotic factors that affect the environment they live in, including:

- high and low temperatures
- lack of water
- lack of sunlight
- predators.

These adaptations enable them to survive. Adaptations can be classed as structural, behavioural or functional.

### Structural adaptations

These are physical features, e.g. structural adaptations of polar bears include:

- They have a thick layer of blubber to keep them warm.
- Their paw pads have special bumps to help to grip ice.
- They have sharp teeth and claws to catch prey.

Structural adaptations of desert hares:

- They have large ears to provide a large surface area for heat loss, and have a good sense of hearing.

### Behavioural adaptations

These are ways in which an organism's behaviour is adapted for survival:

- Polar bears can dig deep into the snow to gain shelter, and they move slowly to prevent overheating.
- Desert hares are active at dawn and dusk to avoid the hot sun during the day.

### Functional adaptations

These are functions that an organism carries out to survive, e.g. functional adaptations of polar bears include:

- They have an incredible sense of smell to detect prey over long distances.
- They have good long sight vision to spot prey.

Functional adaptations of desert hares:

- They produce only small amounts of urine and sweat to conserve water.

## 2 Extremophiles

Some organisms have adaptations that allow them to survive in extreme conditions, such as:

- high temperatures and pressure in volcanoes and deep sea vents
- areas with high acid, alkali or salt concentration like hot springs and salt marshes.

These organisms are known as **extremophiles**.

Many bacteria are examples of extremophiles.

They can survive in different extreme conditions.

## 10 Worked example — Grade 6

**1** Plants and animals have adaptations to survive in their habitats.
Give **two** adaptations of a cactus and explain how these adaptations help it to survive in desert conditions. **[4 marks]**

*Cacti have spines instead of leaves, so they have a smaller surface area through which to lose water by transpiration. They can also store water within their trunks, so water is available when needed.*

> You could also describe how the roots of the cactus are located near the surface of the ground to quickly collect any surface water.

**2** Explain why animals which live in cold places have a low surface area to volume ratio. **[1 mark]**

*A low surface area to volume ratio ensures that the organism retains body heat.*

## 5 Exam-style practice — Grade 6

1. Give a behavioural adaptation of birds for coping with changes in environmental temperature. **[1 mark]**
2. Some animals, such as hedgehogs, hibernate over winter. This can be classed as a functional adaptation. Explain the advantage of hibernation as a functional adaptation. **[1 mark]**
3. Suggest why the fur of an Arctic fox changes from brown in the summer to white in the winter. **[2 marks]**

# Organisation of an ecosystem

You need to know about some of the feeding relationships that exist within an ecosystem.

## Food chains

Feeding relationships within an ecosystem can be represented by food chains.

Experimental methods, including transects and quadrats, can be used to determine the population size and distribution of different species within an ecosystem.

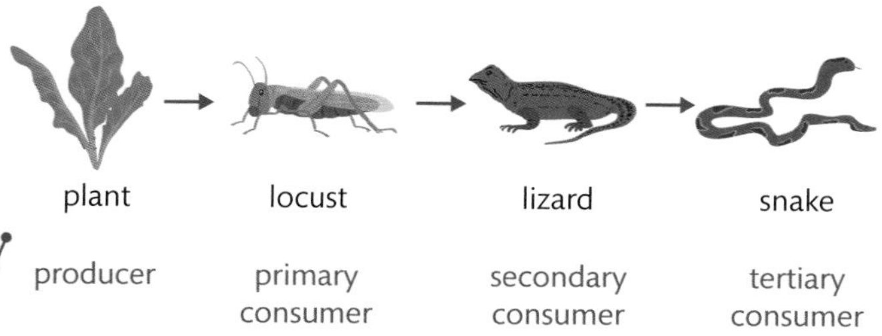


**Figure 1** A simple food chain

All food chains must begin with a producer and end with a consumer.

## Key terms

- **biomass** – the total dry mass of one animal or plant in a food chain. For this measurement to be taken, all water must be removed from organisms, which can be a difficult process.
- **producer** – usually a photosynthesising green plant or algae
- **consumer** – an organism which cannot make its own food; eats producers or other consumers
- **primary consumer** – eats the producer; the first consumer in the food chain
- **secondary consumer** – eats the primary consumer; the second consumer in the food chain
- **tertiary consumer** – eats the secondary consumer in the food chain; the third consumer
- **predator** – kills and eats other animals
- **prey** – animal that is hunted and killed by a predator

## Worked example — Grade 7

**Figure 2** The changing population size of lynx and hares

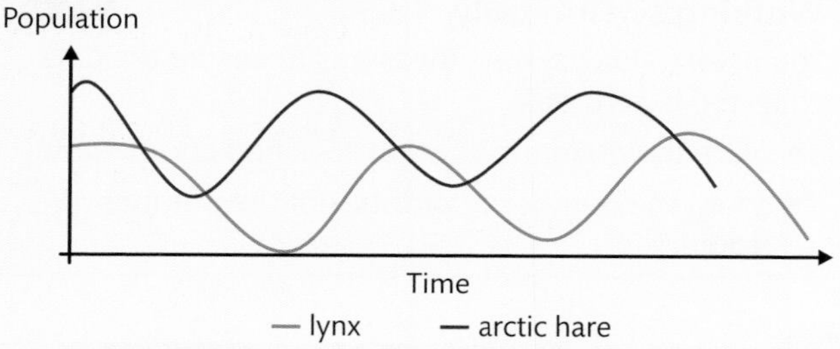


Look at **Figure 2**.

**(a)** What happens to the number of lynx after the number of hares decreases? **[1 mark]**

*The number decreases.*

**(b)** Suggest a reason for this. **[2 marks]**

*There is less food available so the lynx starve and die.*

Besides stating that the lynx die of starvation, you could also explain that they do not have enough food to enable them to breed successfully and that is why numbers are decreasing.

## Maths skills

You are expected to understand the terms:

- **mean** – the average of all the values
- **mode** – the most commonly occurring value
- **median** – middle value when put in value order.

### Calculating the arithmetic mean

If three quadrats are thrown and the numbers of dandelions in each quadrat were 5, 9 and 13 then the mean is:

$$\frac{5 + 9 + 13}{3} = \frac{27}{3} = 9 \text{ dandelions}$$

number of quadrats

## Exam-style practice — Grade 7

1. Suggest why it is necessary for consumers to eat producers or other consumers. **[2 marks]**
2. Give the type of producer for most food chains. **[1 mark]**
3. Suggest why biomass is usually an estimation. **[1 mark]**
4. Describe what is meant by the term 'tertiary consumer'. **[1 mark]**

# Investigating population size

You need to know how the size of a population in a habitat can be measured, using the method of quadrat random sampling. Quadrats can also be used along a transect line to investigate the effect of an abiotic factor on the distribution of a species.

## 10 Using a transect and quadrats

This method describes the process of sampling the number of plants in an area of trampled grass and an area of untrampled grass.

1. Set up a transect line, across the trampled grass area, using a tape measure (or string marked out with the required distances).
2. Place the quadrat against the transect line, ensuring the corner of the quadrat is lined up with 0 on the tape measure.
3. Count how many plants are within the quadrat and record the number in a suitable table.
4. Place the quadrat 5 metres along the transect; count and record the number of plants.
5. Repeat the steps above until you have values for 0, 5, 10, 15, 20, 25 and 30 metre distances.
6. Move to an area of untrampled grass, set up a new transect line and repeat the steps given above.

## 2 Maths skills

You will need to calculate the mean number of plants in both the trampled and untrampled areas.

The mean is calculated by:

$$\frac{\text{total number of plants}}{\text{number of quadrats}}$$

## 1 Key terms

- A **quadrat** is a square frame, usually 1 $m^2$; they are mainly used to sample the distribution of plants or animals.
- A **transect** is a line across a habitat.

## 5 Worked example — Grade 6

The table shows the number of buttercups found in four different areas of a habitat.

| Quadrat number | 1 | 2 | 3 | 4 |
|---|---|---|---|---|
| Number of buttercups | 12 | 14 | 17 | 13 |

**(a)** Calculate the mean number of buttercups per quadrat. **[1 mark]**

$$\text{mean} = \frac{\text{total number of buttercups}}{\text{number of quadrats}}$$

$$= \frac{56}{4} = 14$$

**(b)** Using your answer from **(a)**, estimate the population of buttercups in the field. The quadrat has an area of 0.5 $m^2$ and the field has an area of 125 $m^2$. **[2 marks]**

$\frac{125}{0.5}$ = 250 quadrats for the whole field

14 × 250 = 3500 buttercups in the field

First, work out the number of quadrats it would take to cover the whole field.

There are an average of 14 buttercups per quadrat.

## Working scientifically

You need to take certain measures to ensure the data collected is accurate:

- place the quadrats down at specified coordinates
- count the number of **plants**, not the number of **flowers**.

## 5 Exam-style practice — Grade 6

A student used random sampling to estimate the number of daisy plants in a field. The student placed a quadrat in eight random positions in the field and counted the number of daisy plants in each quadrat. The quadrat measured 1 $m^2$; the field was 2000 $m^2$. The table shows the student's results.

| Quadrat number | 1 | 2 | 3 | 4 | 5 | 6 | 7 | 8 |
|---|---|---|---|---|---|---|---|---|
| Number of daisy plants | 3 | 5 | 3 | 1 | 3 | 5 | 2 | 2 |

**(a)** Calculate the mean number of daisy plants per quadrat. **[1 mark]**

**(b)** Calculate the estimated number of daisy plants in the field. **[1 mark]**

# Biodiversity

Biodiversity refers to the variety of plant and animal species within a habitat, in a larger area or on Earth. You need to be able to discuss the benefits of and threats to biodiversity.

## 5 Advantages of biodiversity

The greater the number of species in a community, the greater the biodiversity.

An ecosystem (page 61) is much more stable if there is greater biodiversity because organisms can depend upon multiple species for food and shelter. This gives them a greater chance of survival compared with relying on one species.

### Working scientifically

Human activities have major negative impacts on biodiversity, leading to some species becoming extinct and many others becoming endangered. The future of the human species on Earth relies on maintaining a good level of biodiversity. Measures are now being taken to protect and maintain biodiversity.

## 2 Key threats to biodiversity

- deforestation
- pollution
- climate change
- destruction of habitats
- landfill
- changes in agricultural methods
- increasing human population
- over-exploitation, e.g. fishing
- introduction of new species

## 10 Worked example — Grade 7

**1** What is meant by the term biodiversity? **[1 mark]**

The variety of all the different species in an ecosystem

**2** Suggest **two** ways in which deforestation is leading to a decrease in biodiversity. **[3 marks]**

Loss of habitat, food and shelter will lead to smaller populations, which makes species more vulnerable.

**3** Explain how human waste is reducing biodiversity. **[2 marks]**

Human waste is often disposed of at landfill, which destroys habitats and therefore has a negative impact on biodiversity. Landfill sites can also release toxic gases or substances into the environment. Sewage and substances can be washed into rivers and water supplies, harming plants, animals and even humans.

Deforestation is the destruction of forests. Go to page 75 for more about deforestation and the impacts it has on biodiversity.

**4** **Figure 1** shows the harlequin ladybird, which was introduced in the USA as a predator to control whitefly on crops.

**Figure 1** This species of ladybird is particularly competitive and aggressive.

Suggest why scientists are concerned that the appearance of this ladybird in the UK would have severe detrimental effects on biodiversity. **[3 marks]**

All species of ladybird are competing for similar food sources. The more aggressive species will take all the food available, leaving the less competitive species to starve and die, reducing biodiversity.

## 5 Exam-style practice — Grade 6

**1** Over-exploitation of cod has led to vastly reduced cod supplies in the ocean. Suggest **two** methods that can be employed to reverse this. **[2 marks]**

**2** Explain why biodiversity is vital for the stability of ecosystems. **[2 marks]**

# Maintaining biodiversity

It is important to reverse the negative effect the growing human population has had on biodiversity to improve the stability of ecosystems. You need to know the methods used and the difficulties involved with maintaining biodiversity.

## 10 Maintaining biodiversity

- **Captive breeding programmes** increase the population of endangered organisms until they are no longer vulnerable and can be released to re-establish wild populations.
- **Reducing the rate of deforestation** reduces the negative impacts on the climate, habitats and food supply which aids organisms' survival.
- **Reducing carbon dioxide emissions** slows down global warming which is already reducing the populations of Arctic and Antarctic animals.
- **Recycling waste** reduces the use of landfill and saves energy. Landfill sites produce 'landfill gas', a mixture of greenhouse gases which contribute to climate change. Dumping waste at landfill also wastes land and destroys ecosystems.
- **Protecting and regenerating habitats** prevents harm to the ecosystem. Coral reefs are protected to prevent further damage and to allow the coral to recover.
- **Reintroducing field margins and hedgerows** to the edges of fields of crops increases biodiversity in these areas, especially where farmers grow only one type of crop.

**Figure 1** A giant panda, born and raised in a captive breeding programme, being released into the wild

## 5 Conflicting pressures

Running programmes to maintain biodiversity effectively can be very expensive – national parks and protected habitats all cost money to maintain.

Some revenue can be generated by opening protected areas to the public and charging them for entry.

Governments may offer incentives to businesses to reduce their carbon emissions and reduce their waste, or they may tax heavily polluting industries.

Farmers may be offered benefits for replanting hedgerows such as an increased price for their crops and livestock.

Go to page 74 to revise the different ways that humans use land and how it affects the environment.

## 5 Worked example — Grade 6

Why is it important to prevent organisms from becoming extinct? **[3 marks]**

*Species should be preserved so future generations can see them. Extinctions can have a dramatic effect on food chains, causing other species to become endangered.*

*Most species directly or indirectly impact our food supply.*

Another suitable answer is that certain plants are sources of vital medical treatment. It may be difficult or even impossible to find replacements.

## 5 Exam-style practice — Grade 6

1. Give **two** methods that can be used to reduce carbon emissions. **[2 marks]**
2. Describe **one** advantage and **one** disadvantage for reintroducing hedgerows in farmland. **[2 marks]**

# Cycling materials

You need to know how materials in the living world are recycled to provide the building blocks for future organisms. The carbon cycle and the water cycle are two examples of how substances are cycled through an ecosystem.

## 5 The carbon cycle

Carbon dioxide ($CO_2$) is removed from the atmosphere by photosynthesis in plants and algae.
$CO_2$ is stored in fossil fuels and as carbon compounds in animals and plants, such as glucose, carbohydrate, protein and fat.

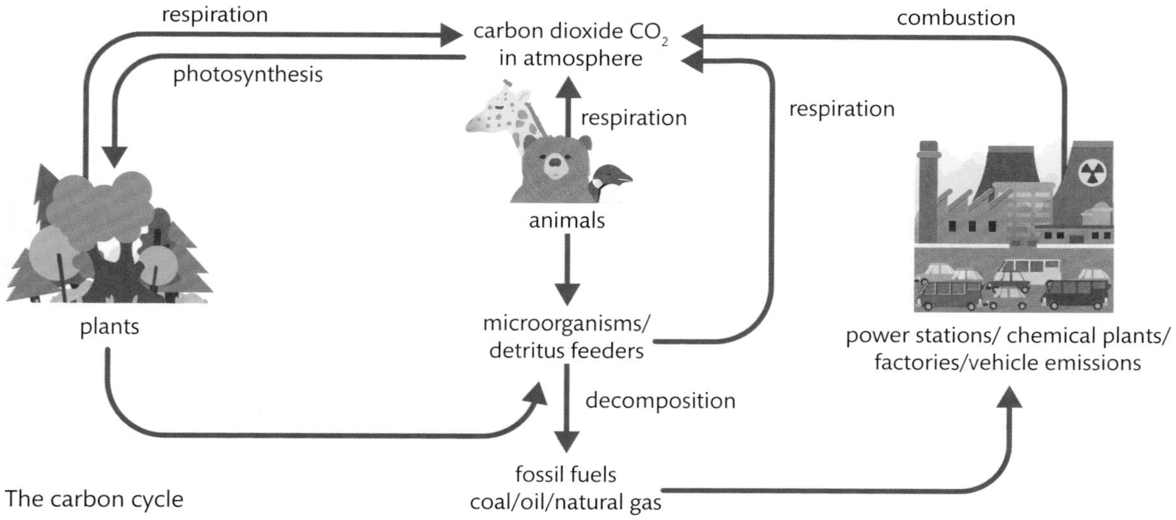


**Figure 1** The carbon cycle

## 5 The water cycle

The water cycle is important because every living organism on Earth depends on water to survive. Without water, all living organisms would die very quickly. The water cycle recycles water and nutrients, bringing fresh water to people, animals and plants all around the world. There are four main stages to the water cycle.

1. **Evaporation** – the (heat) energy from the Sun causes water in the oceans, lakes and rivers to evaporate, forming water vapour in the atmosphere.
2. **Condensation** – as the water vapour cools high up in the atmosphere it condenses to form clouds.
3. **Precipitation** – as the clouds become more condensed water falls as rain, snow, ice or hail.
4. **Collection** – the water may fall straight into rivers, lakes and oceans ready for the process to begin again, or it may be absorbed into the soil and taken up by vegetation to eventually evaporate from the leaves (by **transpiration).** Water that isn't absorbed (surface run-off) will flow across the ground until it reaches a river or other area of water.

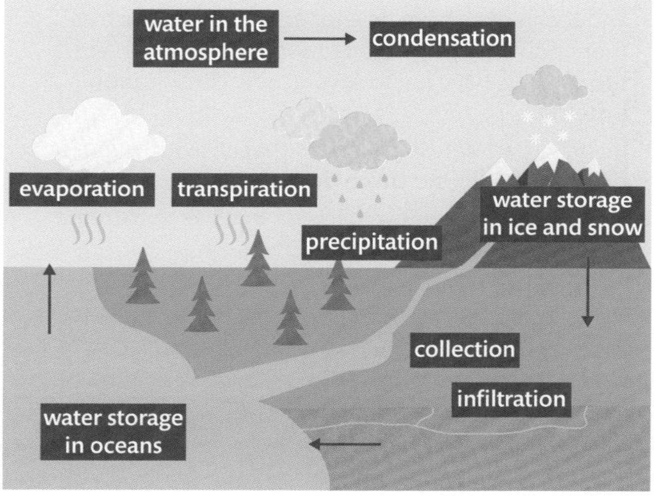


**Figure 2** The water cycle

Plants produce more water when they respire.

## 5 Worked example — Grade 6

How do microorganisms help to fertilise the soil? **[2 marks]**

Microorganisms feed on dead plant matter.

As they break down the plant waste they return mineral ions to the soil.

## 5 Exam-style practice — Grade 6

1. When an animal dies, the carbon it contains is recycled through the carbon cycle. Explain how the carbon is released back into the atmosphere. **[2 marks]**
2. Describe why the water cycle is vital to life on Earth. **[2 marks]**

# Classification

Classification is the process used to arrange living organisms into groups based on their similar structures and characteristics. You need to know how species are classified and how the process of classification has changed over time.

## 15 Classifying organisms

In the 18th century, Carl Linnaeus introduced a hierarchical system for classifying living organisms and giving them scientific names. Linnaeus divided all living things into large **kingdoms** according to the features of organisms' cells. Then he divided them into smaller and smaller groups, as shown in **Figure 1**.

You need to know about five kingdoms:

1. Animals
2. Plants
3. Fungi
4. Prokaryotes
5. Protists

| | |
|---|---|
| **Kingdom** | animal |
| **Phylum** | chordate |
| **Class** | mammal |
| **Order** | primate |
| **Family** | hominid |
| **Genus** | *Pongo* |
| **Species** | *albelii* |

As the classification groups get smaller, the organisms have more characteristics in common.

**Figure 1** Classification of a Sumatran orangutan

### Naming species

It is important for a species to have a unique scientific name as it allows scientists to identify and refer to individual species quickly and accurately. Organisms are named after the genus and species that they belong to. This double name is called the **binomial system** of naming. The scientific name for the Sumatran orangutan is *Pongo albelii*.

## 2 Working scientifically

Over time, scientists' understanding of biochemistry and cell structure has changed as scientific equipment and techniques have developed. Advances, such as more powerful microscopes and DNA analysis and sequencing, have led to several new classification systems.

In 1977, Carl Woese proposed that all living organisms can be divided into **three domains**:

- **archaea** – primitive bacteria that live in extreme environments
- **bacteria** – true bacteria
- **eukaryota** – protists, fungi, plants and animals.

## 1 Exam focus

This mnemonic can help you remember the classification system for the exam.

**K**ing **P**hilip **c**ame **o**ver **f**rom **g**reat **S**pain

## 5 Worked example — Grade 5

Look at **Figure 2**. Which **two** organisms are more closely related to humans than orangutans? Explain your answer. **[3 marks]**

Gorillas and chimpanzees – they have evolved from the line that leads to humans more recently than orangutans.

## 5 Evolutionary trees

**Evolutionary trees** show how scientists think organisms are related to one another. The evidence for evolutionary trees comes from classification data for living organisms and the fossil record for extinct organisms.

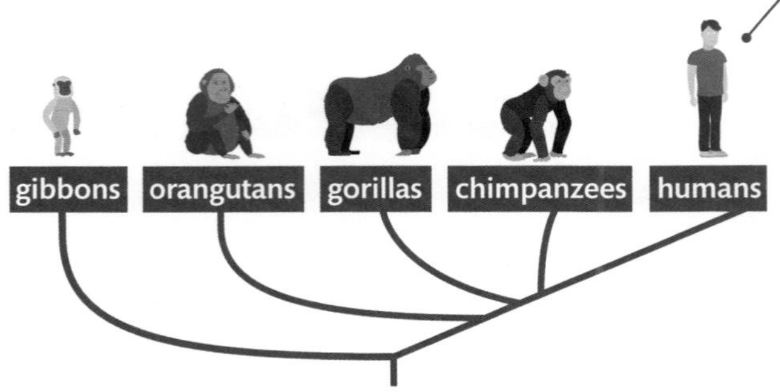


**Figure 2** An evolutionary tree of orangutans and humans

This evolutionary tree shows that these organisms all have a common ancestor. A **common ancestor** is an ancestor which two or more species have descended from. An **ancestral species** is a species that the species in question has evolved from. The more recent the common ancestor, the more closely related the species are.

## 5 Exam-style practice — Grade 5

1. Give **two** advantages of using the binomial system of classification. **[2 marks]**
2. Give **two** reasons why we now have more information to classify organisms. **[2 marks]**



Made a start — Feeling confident — Exam ready

# Evolution

You need to know how the theory of evolution explains the development of species over time.

## 5 Natural selection

The theory of evolution states that all species of living things have evolved, over more than three billion years, from simple life forms, through a process called natural selection. **Natural selection** is the theory that organisms which are best suited to their environment are more likely to survive and reproduce. Therefore, their offspring are more likely to inherit genes that give rise to phenotypes (page 55) most suited to the environment, causing changes to the population over time and ensuring the survival of the species.

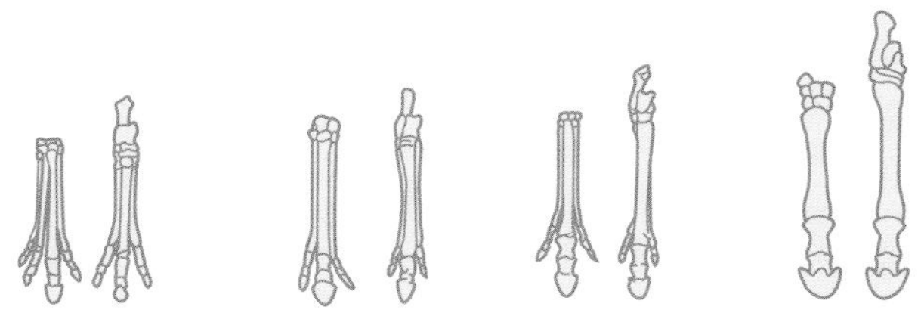


**Figure 1** All the main stages of the horse's evolution have been preserved in fossil records.

## 5 Working scientifically

Alongside other scientists, Charles Darwin developed the theory of natural selection after observing variation between species of tortoises and finches while voyaging around the Galapagos islands.

Darwin realised that the animals that exhibited a variation that made them more successful were more likely to survive and breed, passing on the genes for this feature to their offspring. As more generations reproduce, the successful feature is passed on to the next generation.

As more evidence surrounding genetic inheritance (page 53) has been discovered and the fossil record continues to grow, the theory of evolution by natural selection is now widely accepted by scientists. There is further evidence for evolution in the process by which bacteria become resistant to certain antibiotics over time (page 47).

The theory of evolution by natural selection was only gradually accepted because:

- The theory challenged the idea that God made all the animals and plants that live on Earth.
- There was insufficient evidence at the time the theory was published to convince many scientists.
- The mechanism of inheritance and variation was not known until 50 years after the theory was published.

## 10 Worked example — Grade 4

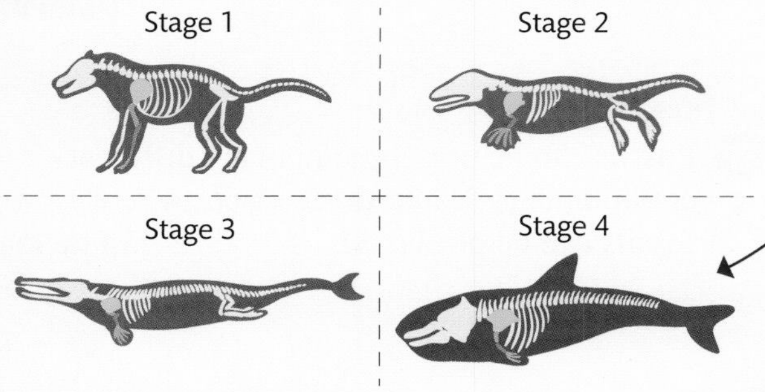


**Figure 2** Evolution of the whale

**Figure 2** shows how the whale is thought to have evolved from its early ancestors.

Give **two** ways in which the whale has adapted since Stage 1. **[2 marks]**

*The early ancestor had four limbs, and the whale alive today doesn't.*

*The whale has a fin on its back unlike its ancestors.*

New species can form when the genes of individuals within a species become so different that their phenotype changes and they can no longer interbreed to form fertile offspring. This is known as **speciation**.

You are not expected to recall evolutionary stages in the development of species; you need to use the information provided in the question.

You could also be asked to explain why the feature has evolved. For example, the whale's fin developed so that the whale could swim efficiently.

## 5 Exam-style practice — Grade 7

1. Describe the process of natural selection suggested by Darwin. **[3 marks]**
2. Some organisms have evolved to look like another species; for example, the scarlet king snake, which is harmless, has evolved to look like the deadly coral snake. Explain why this is considered to be a successful adaptation. **[2 marks]**
3. Define the theory of evolution. **[2 marks]**

# Fossils

A fossil is the preserved remains of an organism that lived millions of years ago. You need to know how fossils can be analysed to show us how different organisms have changed as life has developed on Earth.

## 10 Formation of fossils

Fossils are found preserved in rocks, amber (hardened tree resin), ice, acidic peat bogs (page 74) and tar pits. Fossils can be formed in a number of ways.

- Parts of the organism have not decayed: hard parts of an organism such as bone, shells and claws do not decay easily and can fossilise. Soft tissue is less likely to be preserved, so the majority of fossils tend to be of species with hard skeletons.
- Parts of the organism have been replaced by minerals as they decayed: any hard parts such as bones and teeth that don't decay easily may slowly become mineralised.
- Traces of organisms may be preserved: these include footprints, burrows, droppings and rootlet traces.

**Figure 1** A fossil of a fish preserved in rock

Fossils are able to form if one or more of the conditions needed for decay is absent: if there is no oxygen or moisture present, if there are toxic gases or it is an acidic environment, or if it is too cold, the microorganisms that cause decay cannot function or may be killed.

## 5 The fossil record

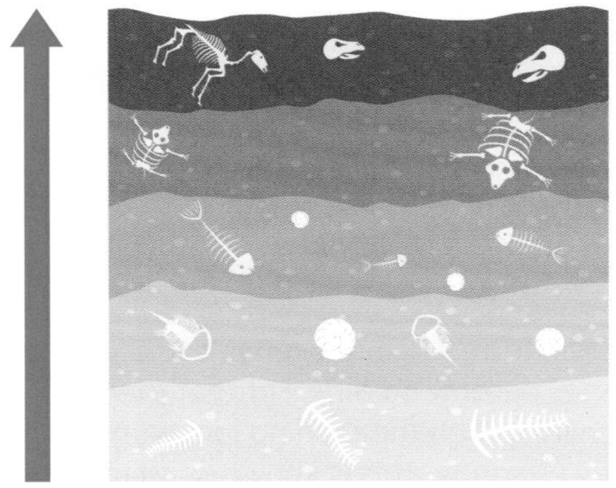


**Figure 2** Fossils have been found in rocks of all ages. The older the fossil, the less complex the organism. This evidence supports the theory of evolution (page 67).

Fossils provide some evidence for evolution, but they are not the only (or even the main) source of evidence. Many early forms of life had soft bodies, so they left few traces behind. In addition, some of these traces have since been destroyed by geological activity. This is why scientists cannot be certain about how life began on Earth.

### Working scientifically

There are gaps in the fossil record because:

- Fossilisation itself is a rare occurrence. The organism has to die, and lie undisturbed in just the right conditions.
- Many fossils have just not been found yet.
- Many have been formed but have been destroyed by erosion and other geological changes.

Branching occurs where **speciation** has taken place. A group of organisms has evolved into a new species from its common ancestor.

## 10 Worked example — Grade 7

Look at **Figure 2**.

1. What do fossils show? **[1 mark]**

   *Fossils show the progression of how a species has evolved.*

2. Why do evolutionary trees have branches? **[1 mark]**

   *The branches show where one species splits into two.*

3. Fossils can be preserved in many different environments. Name **three** places where fossils can be preserved. **[3 marks]**

   *Amber, ice, peat bogs*

## 5 Exam-style practice — Grade 7

1. Suggest a reason why it is impossible to know for sure how life began on Earth. **[1 mark]**
2. Give the evidence we have that fossils have formed when bones and skeletons have been replaced by minerals. **[1 mark]**
3. Explain how fossils support Darwin's theory of evolution. **[3 marks]**

# Selective breeding

You need to know about selective breeding and the positive and negative impacts it can have.

## Positive and negative impacts

Selective breeding is like natural selection (page 67), but humans choose the desired characteristics to produce the best offspring. Selective breeding is also called artificial selection. It involves selecting and breeding together parents with the desired characteristic from a mixed population. Those offspring that have the desired characteristic are then bred together. This continues over many generations, until all the offspring show the desired characteristic. Selective breeding can lead to inbreeding, where problems are caused by inherited defects or being prone to certain diseases.

### Impacts of selective breeding

| Positive | Negative |
|---|---|
| **plants**<br>• improved crop yield<br>• improved disease resistance<br>• large or unusual flowers.<br>**animals**<br>• improved quality of meat<br>• increased milk production<br>• increased meat production<br>• sociable domesticated animals<br>• large eggs. | • A new disease could put the whole species at risk as the lack of genetic diversity makes them all equally vulnerable.<br>• The reduction in the stock of different genes in the population would restrict the ability to produce new varieties in the future.<br>• Inbreeding can lead to inherited defects or susceptibility to disease. |

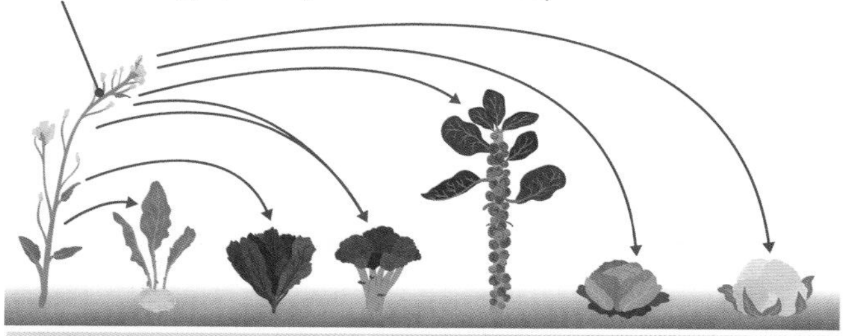


| Strain | Modified trait |
|---|---|
| kohlrabi | stem |
| kale | leaves |
| broccoli | flower buds and stem |
| Brussels sprouts | lateral leaf buds |
| cabbage | terminal leaf bud |
| cauliflower | flower buds |

**Figure 1** Artificial selection of wild cabbage

## Worked example — Grade 7

1. Describe the stages of selective breeding in cattle to produce an increased milk yield. **[4 marks]**

Choose cows that have a high milk yield and a bull that is the offspring of females with high milk yield. Breed them together. Select the highest milk-yielding offspring that are produced and breed them together. For each generation, select the males from the highest milk-yielding females and the highest milk-yielding females and breed them together. Continue this over many generations until all offspring show the desired characteristic.

2. Selective breeding leads to a reduction in variety in genetic material. Why is this beneficial for cattle farming? **[1 mark]**

A reduction in the variety of genetic material in cattle would increase the chance of inheriting the desired feature.

Remember, selective breeding and artificial selection are the same thing: inheritance of genes is controlled to give offspring with desired traits.

In this case, the desired livestock would be a cow that produces a high yield of milk and a bull that is healthy (free from any genetic diseases).

## Exam-style practice — Grade 7

1. One reason domestic animals are bred is to be sociable. Suggest another reason. **[1 mark]**
2. Describe **two** ways in which selective breeding differs from natural selection. **[2 marks]**
3. Suggest **two** issues which could be caused by selective breeding. **[2 marks]**
4. Selective breeding is used for crops. Suggest **two** reasons why. **[2 marks]**

# Genetic engineering

You need to know how genetic engineering is used to change the genome of an organism.

## 5 What is genetic engineering?

Genetic engineering is a process used to alter the genetic material (genome) of an individual, by inserting a gene from another organism to give a desired characteristic. Bacterial cells are genetically modified to produce substances that are useful to humans, such as insulin for the treatment of diabetes. Scientists are working on cures for genetic disorders based on genetic engineering. However, there are ethical concerns linked to genetic engineering. For example, some people have concerns about animal welfare and believe that it is unethical to clone animals.

### Genetically modified (GM) crops

GM crops are crops that have had genes inserted into them to alter their characteristics.

Plant crops have been genetically engineered to produce higher quality and increased yield, and be disease, herbicide and insect resistant. Crops can also be engineered to grow containing added nutrients, such as golden rice, which has higher levels of vitamin A. This is useful for countries where vitamin deficiencies are common.

## 10 Stages in genetic engineering

1. The required gene is isolated from the DNA, using enzymes, and removed from the cell.
2. The gene is inserted into a vector, such as a bacterial plasmid or a virus.
3. The vector is then put into the cells of the desired organism (animal, plant or microorganism) at an early stage of their development.
4. The organism develops exhibiting the desired characteristics.

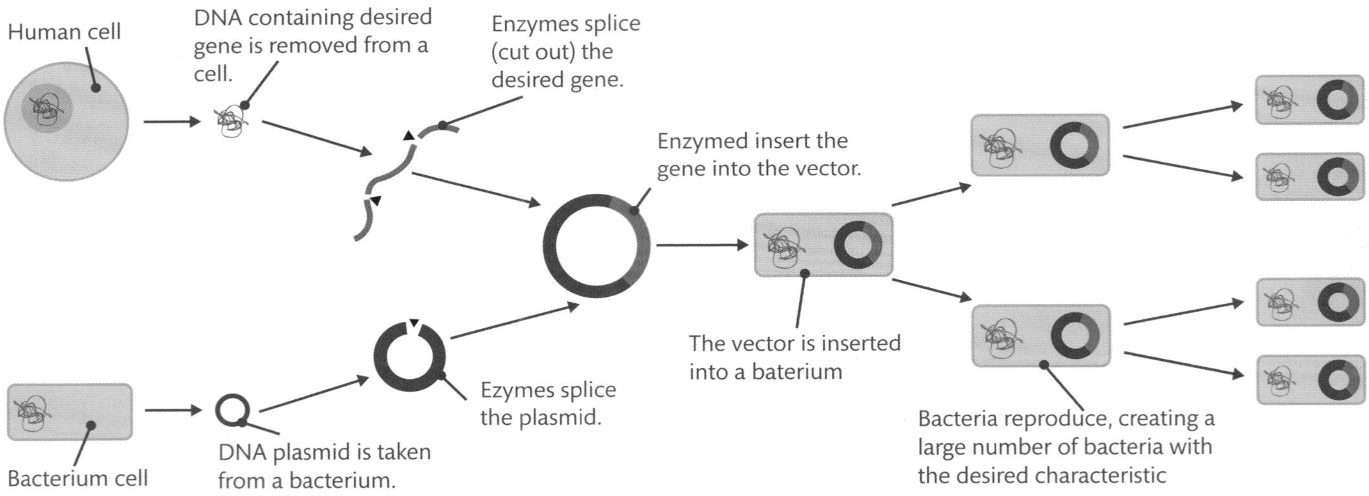


**Figure 1** An example of genetic engineering bacteria

## 5 Worked example — Grade 7

1. Give **two** reasons why people are against the growth of GM crops. **[2 marks]**

They might cross pollinate with wild plants. We don't know if there are potential health risks for humans. They may pass on their herbicide resistance to wild plants or weeds.

This answer could also be developed to include concerns about the effect of GM crops on the ecosystem and how insects feeding off the crops might be affected.

2. Give **one** advantage to growing herbicide resistant crops. **[1 mark]**

Farmers can spray the crops with herbicide as the crops won't be harmed (only the weeds).

## 5 Exam-style practice — Grade 7

1. Explain the ethical concerns linked to genetically engineering animals. **[3 marks]**
2. Give **two** ethical issues associated with GM crops being herbicide resistant. **[2 marks]**

# Stem cells

Stem cells are undifferentiated cells. They can develop into different types of body cell. You need to know how stem cells are obtained and how they can be used.

## 10 Stem cell applications

Stem cells may one day be used to cure diseases by replacing faulty cells. They could cure diseases such as diabetes, paralysis, hearing and vision loss, and Parkinson's disease.

### Therapeutic cloning

An embryo can be produced by cloning the cells of the patient who is suffering an illness. The embryo will contain the same genes as the patient, therefore embryonic stem cells can be used to treat the condition as they will not be rejected by the patient's body because they contain the same genetic information. The stem cells will differentiate and replace the damaged cells. However, there is some risk of viral infection with stem cell treatment.

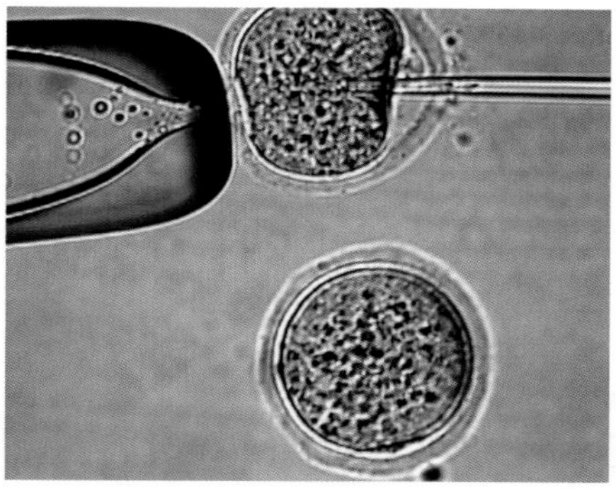

**Figure 1** Stem cell research – an adult cell nucleus being injected into an egg cell

### Embryonic stem cells

Stem cells from embryos can be cloned and made to differentiate into most types of human cells when instructed. They have the potential to cure many genetic conditions by replacing damaged cells. However, embryos cannot choose to donate and they are destroyed in the process. Unwanted embryos from fertility clinics are often used.

### Adult stem cells

Adult stem cells can be taken from bone marrow. They can form many, but not all, types of cells, as they are used in the body for repair and replacement of cells. Adult stem cells are useful in the treatment of people suffering blood disorders as they can form new blood cells.

An advantage is that donation of adult stem cells is a choice and no life is destroyed, but it can be a painful procedure.

### Meristem tissue in plants

Stem cells in the meristems (areas of growth in plants) can differentiate into any type of plant cell throughout the life of the plant. They can be used to quickly and cheaply produce cloned plants (by taking cuttings) and are useful for growing rare species of plants to protect them from extinction. They can be used to grow lots of identical crops exhibiting desired traits such as disease resistance.

## 1 Working scientifically

Stem cell research is very controversial. Some people have ethical and religious objections to the process. Some people say it shouldn't be allowed as human embryos are being destroyed in the process, but others believe the advantages of using stem cells to cure diseases or injured people outweighs the rights of an embryo.

## 1 Exam focus

You don't need to know details about stem cell techniques for the exam, but you are expected to be able to evaluate the risks and benefits. You also need to know about the social and ethical issues involved in the use of stem cells in medical research.

## 5 Worked example — Grade 7

1. Scientists are developing a treatment for paralysis using embryonic stem cells.
   Why are stem cells used? **[2 marks]**

   *Stem cells are unspecialised, so they can differentiate into any type of cell. Therefore, they can differentiate and replace the damaged cells causing the paralysis.*

2. Suggest an advantage of using adult stem cells. **[1 mark]**

   *An embryo isn't used against its consent.*

## 5 Exam-style practice — Grade 7

1. Give **one** advantage for commercial growers using cloned plants. **[1 mark]**
2. Describe the ethical considerations involved with embryonic stem cell therapy. **[2 marks]**

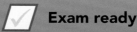

# Extinction

Extinction of a plant or animal species occurs when there are no more individuals of that species alive and the loss of the species is permanent. You need to know how and why species can become extinct.

## 5 Key factors contributing to extinction

- **New predators** – if a new species is introduced or a predator moves in to the territory, it may wipe out a species which isn't adapted to protecting itself.
- **New diseases** – if a species' defences against pathogens (e.g. immune system in mammals) cannot protect it against a viral or bacterial disease, it could become extinct.
- **Mutations** – if another species evolves as a result of mutation, it could become a more successful competitor.
- **Temperature change** – global warming is causing changes in habitats which could leave species without shelter or food.
- **Environmental change** – destruction of habitat can leave organisms without food or shelter.
- **Catastrophic event** – an asteroid colliding with Earth, a comet strike or a tsunami could wipe out an entire community.
- **Speciation** – a species evolves and the original species dies out.

## 10 Human influence

The following human activities have a major effect on extinction:

- hunting
- increasing levels of pollution
- destruction of habitats.

The fossil record shows species that have become extinct.

The dodo is thought to have become extinct because of new competitors being introduced to the island where it lived and because it was hunted by humans.

Many animals are critically endangered, including the giant panda and Sumatran tiger.

**Figure 1** The golden toad became extinct in 1989. Scientists believe global warming was instrumental in its extinction.

## 5 Worked example — Grade 5

**1** Give **two** physical factors and **two** biological factors that may have caused a species to become extinct. **[4 marks]**

*Physical factors – volcanoes and earthquakes*

*Biological factors – lack of food and mates*

> You could also suggest an ice age, climate change or an asteroid collision for physical factors.

> You could suggest disease, speciation or lack of habitat for biological factors.

**2** Why do scientists not always know what extinct species looked like? **[1 mark]**

*They may not be present in the fossil record.*

> You could also say that nobody has ever seen one.

## 5 Exam-style practice — Grade 7

**1** Give **three** strategies which can be used to try to prevent the extinction of a species. **[3 marks]**

**2** Define the term 'extinct'. **[1 mark]**

**3** Describe how an ice age could lead to the extinction of a species. **[2 marks]**

# Waste management

You need to know how unprecedented human population growth is causing an increase in waste production.

## 10 Pollution

Pollution created by humans can occur in water (e.g. from fertiliser), in the air (e.g. from smoke) and on land (e.g. from landfill). Pollution destroys habitats, and kills animals and plants. A reduction in the numbers of animals and plants leads to a reduction in biodiversity. A reduction in biodiversity will cause further species to become extinct and could lead to food shortages.

**Why is there an increase in the waste humans are producing?**

An increase in the human population is leading to more water pollution from sewage, fertilisers and substances from industry and farming entering water supplies. This has a negative effect on aquatic life.

Air pollution, such as smoke and toxic gases, is being produced from burning fossil fuels and other substances. This is causing global warming, acid rain and smog.

Landfill and toxic substances are polluting land, making it uninhabitable for plants and animals.

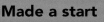

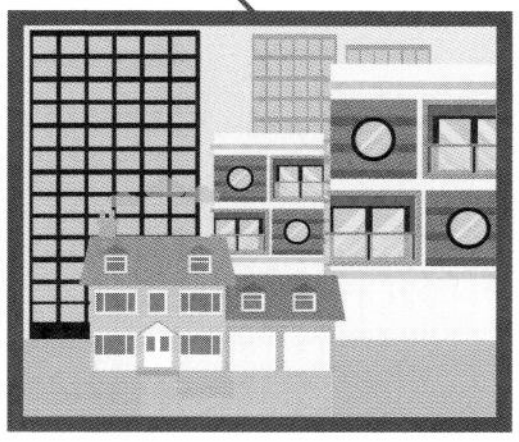

An increase in the standard of human living means more resources are being used, which in turn, produces more waste.

## 1 Waste substances

- sewage
- smoke and gases
- herbicides, pesticides and fertilisers
- paper and cardboard
- plastic

## 1 Working scientifically

Pollution has a negative impact on the environment, as well as plant and animal species. Some species are unable to survive as a result. Humans need to find a way to balance development with sustaining other organisms and protecting the environment for future generations.

## 5 Worked example — Grade 7

Give **two** reasons why the mass of household waste is increasing. **[2 marks]**

*The global population is increasing in size. Increases in the standard of living are resulting in more resources being used and waste being produced.*

## 5 Exam-style practice — Grade 7

1. As the human population increases, the amount of waste produced also increases. Explain why human waste is harming the environment. **[2 marks]**
2. Give **two** reasons why levels of carbon dioxide in the atmosphere are increasing. **[2 marks]**

# Land use

You need to know how the use of land by humans is reducing the habitats available for plants and animals.

## 5 Examples of land use

Human activity is having significant effects on the environment and on biodiversity (page 63). As the world's population continues to grow rapidly, these effects are increasing in severity and becoming more widespread.

**Human land use**

**Buildings**
As our population increases, more land is needed for houses, shops and factories.

**Farming**
An increased demand for food has led to more land being used for agriculture.

**Open cast mining**
Rocks and minerals are extracted from the ground. When all the minerals have been extracted from an area, it is usually used for landfill.

**Landfill**
Disposal of waste in landfill sites has a negative effect on the environment. A lot of industrial waste is also disposed of on land.

**Quarrying**
There is a huge demand for the products of quarrying, such as limestone. However, it can destroy wildlife habitats and it creates pollution.

## 5 Peat bogs

Peat is an important store of carbon. Humans are destroying peat bogs, which take thousands of years to form, and other areas of peat, to produce compost for food production. This is reducing areas of habitat for plants, animals and microorganisms. This will lead to a decrease in the biodiversity of these species. When the peat decays or is burned, carbon dioxide is released into the atmosphere, leading to increased greenhouse gas emissions and contributing to global warming.

Peat bogs are formed from partially decomposed vegetation. Full decomposition cannot take place due to the acidity and high levels of water, which prevents the microorganisms from fully decomposing the organic matter. When peat bogs are drained, the decomposition process can be completed, and so carbon dioxide is released into the atmosphere (by respiration of the microorganisms).

## 10 Worked example — Grade 7

Areas of marshland surrounding the Thames river are being converted every year for human use.

**(a)** Give **three** ways in which marshland is being converted and used by humans. **[3 marks]**

*Housing, farming and industry*

**(b)** What effect will these changes have on the environment, and the plants and animals that use the marshlands for their habitats? **[4 marks]**

*The number of habitats will be reduced. This could lead to a reduction in the biodiversity of the marshlands, which could affect food chains and lead to the eradication of other species. Human use of the land for housing is also likely to lead to more waste.*

You could also mention roads, transport, quarries, and leisure uses such as sports centres and tennis courts.

There are many factors you could discuss in this question. Both housing and industry will cause an increase in waste and pollution. Use of land for farming will probably result in an increase in the levels of herbicides, pesticide and fertilisers present in the environment.

## 10 Exam-style practice — Grade 6

1. Describe the effect of the destruction of peat bogs on the gases in Earth's atmosphere. **[1 mark]**
2. Many farmers are reducing the numbers of hedgerows between their fields to increase crop yield. Describe how this will affect the animals that live in the hedgerows. **[1 mark]**
3. Describe the effect of increasing areas of housing on the environment. **[2 marks]**
4. Give **one** advantage and **one** disadvantage to using the peat from peat bogs for compost. **[2 marks]**

# Deforestation

You need to know how deforestation in tropical areas is causing harm to the environment.

## 2 Reasons for deforestation

Vast areas of forest are being destroyed to:

- provide land for cattle and rice fields
- provide land for the growth of crops for biofuels
- create fuel, furniture and paper
- clear land to produce palm oil and coffee
- clear land for housing.

A lot of the rainforest has been cleared by burning, a method of land clearance called slash and burn.

The ash provides nutrients for the crops and the land is weed-free from the burning. When the soil becomes less fertile and weeds begin to grow, the farmers move on to a new patch of land and begin the process again, leaving the land barren and unusable.

## 10 Impacts of deforestation

Deforestation has a series of negative effects on the environment:

- **Flooding** – trees absorb the rain, releasing it back into the atmosphere as water vapour. Fewer trees will absorb less water, leading to flooding.
- **Climate change** – trees absorb carbon dioxide for photosynthesis. Fewer trees means more carbon dioxide in the atmosphere. Trees also affect the levels of water vapour in the atmosphere, which contributes to global warming.
- **Loss of species** – the more trees that are destroyed, the less habitat there is available for species to live in, so some species may gradually become extinct.
- **Soil erosion** – tree roots anchor soil. Without them, the soil can be eroded quickly making it difficult to grow crops.
- **Water pollution** – soil erosion can lead to silt entering water sources, which decreases the quality of the water and can affect human health.

There is a conflict between the need for deforestation to increase the land available for food production and the need to conserve forests to prevent the impacts listed above.

## 5 Worked example — Grade 6

Evaluate the environmental implications of deforestation. **[6 marks]**

Vast areas of forest have been destroyed by deforestation. Deforestation can have a negative impact on the environment. For example, many plant and animal species live in forests and cannot survive the deforestation that destroys their habitats. This can lead to species becoming extinct, reducing biodiversity. Additionally, the loss of vegetation means less rain water is absorbed, which increases the risk of flooding. Deforestation also causes soil erosion. Tree roots anchor soil, so with fewer tree roots, soil may blow or wash away, leading to water pollution and making it difficult to grow crops. Furthermore, felling or burning trees releases carbon dioxide into the atmosphere, and reduces the number of trees which can absorb carbon dioxide from the atmosphere during photosynthesis, thus acting as carbon 'sinks'.

However, deforestation makes more land available for housing and for the growth of food crops and biofuels. It also provides areas of grassland for feeding cattle. Forests are also cleared to make way for palm oil and coffee plantations, the products of which are particularly valuable exports. In addition, the timber from trees has many different uses, including paper, furniture and buildings.

There is a huge conflict between the need for deforestation to make land available for the production of food and biofuels and the need to reduce greenhouse gas emissions and conserve biodiversity. Ultimately, I think the negative impacts of deforestation outweigh its benefits.

## 10 Exam-style practice — Grade 6

1. Deforestation in rainforest areas has led to an increase in atmospheric carbon dioxide. Give **three** factors contributing to this. **[3 marks]**
2. Describe **three** environmental impacts of deforestation. **[3 marks]**

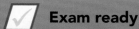

# Global warming

You need to be able to describe some of the ways that global warming affects living things in their environments.

## 5 The greenhouse effect

Greenhouse gases, such as carbon dioxide and methane, trap heat from the Sun, keeping Earth a suitable temperature to support life. This is known as the **greenhouse effect**.

Human activities, such as burning fossil fuels and industrial processes, have increased the amount of greenhouse gas emissions. This has led to global warming. **Global warming** is the increase in the mean temperature of the Earth. The Earth's temperature has risen by about 1 °C in the last century.

Go to pages 160–164 for more about the causes of global warming.

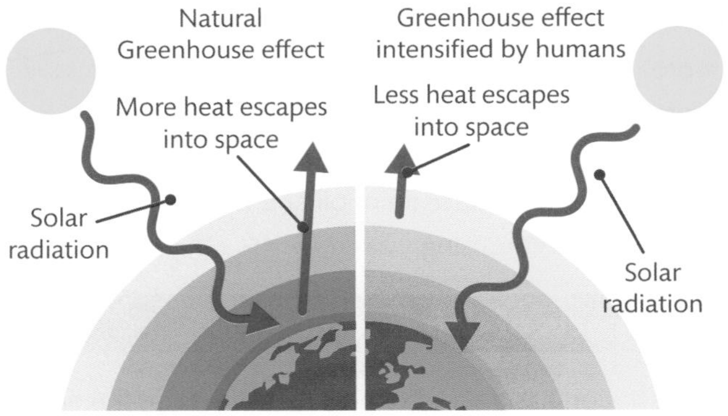


**Figure 1** Some causes of global warming

## 10 Effects of global warming

Climate change continues to cause Earth to dramatically transform in many ways:

- **Changes in biodiversity** – some species could become extinct leading to gaps in the food chain.
- **Changes in migration patterns** – migration timings are altering which could have an impact on food availability.
- **Changes in habitats** – animals may move to new habitats that are more suitable to their needs.
- **Increased adaptation** – species will have to adapt to cope with the changes in the environment.
- **Increase in pests and disease** – pests and disease can survive in warmer conditions.
- **Changes in the timings of plant and animal reproduction** – reproduction may happen at different times of the year affecting food supplies for humans and animals.
- **Rising sea levels** – melting ice and snow in polar regions could lead to flooding. During the past 100 years, global sea levels have risen 10–20 cm.
- **Increase in ocean temperature and air temperature** – rising temperatures affect habitats and plant growth possibly leading to a decrease in biodiversity.

## 10 Worked example — Grade 7

In most species, sex is determined during fertilisation. However, the sex of some reptiles such as sea turtles is determined after fertilisation. The temperature of the eggs determines whether the offspring will be male or female. Lower nest temperatures result in males and higher nest temperatures result in females.

**(a)** Look at **Figure 2**. Calculate the percentage increase in the female population of sea turtles from 1990–1995 to 2002–2007. **[1 mark]**

86 − 50 = 36%

**(b)** Suggest a reason for this increase. **[2 marks]**

Global warming is increasing the temperature of the turtle's nests so a higher proportion of the offspring are born female.

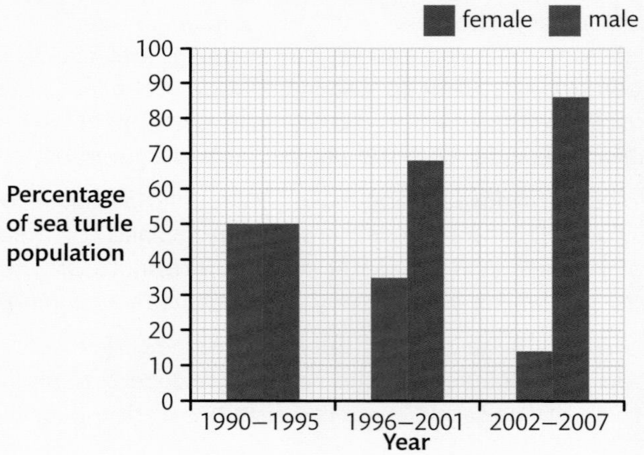


**Figure 2** The changing population of sea turtles from 1990 to 2007

## 5 Exam-style practice — Grade 7

Describe **three** biological effects of global warming. **[3 marks]**

# States of matter

You need to be able to predict the states of substances at different temperatures and explain changes of state using the particle model.

## Changing state

The three states of matter, solid, liquid and gas, can be represented by the **particle model**. This simple model shows the changes of state that occur during melting, boiling, freezing and condensing. When substances are heated or cooled the forces **between** particles change. The density, arrangement and motion of particles change when a substance changes state.

Particles in a substance **gain energy** when the substance turns from a solid to a liquid (**melting**) or from a liquid to a gas (**boiling**).

- The distance between particles increases.
- The strength of the forces between particles decreases.
- The particles have more energy so move faster.

Particles in a substance **lose energy** when the substance turns from a gas to a liquid (**condensing**) and from a liquid to a solid (**freezing**).

- The distance between particles decreases.
- The strength of the forces between particles increases.
- The particles have less energy so move more slowly.

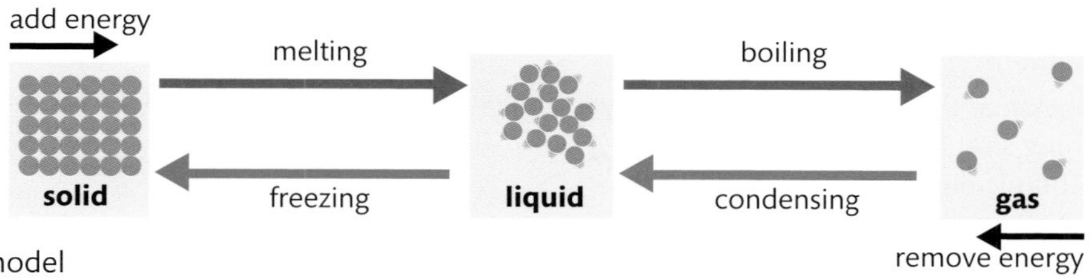


**Figure 1** The particle model

The amount of energy needed to change state from a solid to a liquid and from a liquid to a gas varies. The energy must be great enough to overcome the forces of attraction **between** the particles. The strength of forces varies according to the type of bonding and structure of the substance. The stronger the forces between the particles, the higher the **melting point** and **boiling point** of the substance.

## Exam focus

For the Higher Tier exam, remember that the following limitations mean that the particle model does not show collisions or change in forces.

- It shows particles as solid, inelastic spheres.
- It does not show the forces between the particles.
- It does not show what type of particles are present.

## State symbols

Symbols are used in a chemical equation to represent states of matter:

- (s) for solids, e.g. ice
- (l) for liquids, e.g. water
- (g) for gases, e.g. steam
- (aq) for aqueous solutions, e.g. NaCl in water.

For example:

$2Na(s) + 2H_2O(l) \rightarrow 2NaOH(aq) + H_2(g)$

## Worked example — Grade 5

**1** Explain, in terms of particles and energy, how a liquid evaporates. **[3 marks]**

*The particles in a liquid have different energies. An increase in energy (boiling) causes the forces of attraction between some particles to break. These particles will escape from the surface of the liquid and form a gas.*

**2** Why is more energy required to change the state of a solid than to change the state of a liquid? Explain your answer. **[2 marks]**

*The forces of attraction are much greater in a solid due to the regular lattice arrangement. The particles in a solid are much closer together than in a liquid so the forces of attraction are greater and more difficult to overcome.*

## Exam-style practice — Grade 7

| Compound | Melting point in °C | Boiling point in °C |
|---|---|---|
| LiCl | 610 | 1382 |
| $BeCl_2$ | 405 | 488 |
| $CCl_4$ | −23 | 77 |
| $NCl_3$ | −40 | 71 |
| $OCl_2$ | −20 | 4 |

**1** Look at the table. For each of the compounds, identify whether they are a solid, liquid or gas at room temperature (25 °C). **[2 marks]**

**2** Predict the state of LiCl at 900 °C. **[1 mark]**

**3** Predict whether $OCl_2$ is solid or liquid at −19 °C. **[1 mark]**

# Atoms, elements and compounds

You need to be able to apply your knowledge of atoms, elements and compounds to name substances and write balanced chemical equations.

## 5 Elements and compounds

Everything, whatever its state of matter, is made of atoms. An **atom** is the smallest part of an **element** that can exist. Go to page 85 to revise the structure of the atom.

### Elements

There are over 100 different elements, which are shown in the **periodic table**. Each element is made of atoms that have the same atomic number (number of protons). Each type of atom can be represented by an atomic symbol, e.g. Na for an atom of sodium.

An element is a pure substance that cannot be chemically broken down into anything simpler. The atoms of a particular element are chemically identical to each other.

Go to page 86 to find out about protons and atomic number.

Atoms do not have the bulk properties of molecular substances.

### Compounds

**Compounds** form when two or more elements chemically combine in fixed proportions. The name or symbol of a compound is derived from the elements reacting. For example, sodium and chlorine form sodium chloride.

Compounds can only be separated into elements by chemical reactions. Chemical reactions always involve the formation of new substances. The reactions also often involve an energy change.

If only a metal element and a non-metal element react, the compound name ends in **-ide**.

If a compound also contains oxygen, its name will end in **-ate**.

## 2 Key skills

- Use the names and symbols of the first 20 elements in the periodic table, and the elements in Groups 1 and 7.
- Name compounds from given formulae or symbol equations.
- Write word equations and produce balanced chemical equations for given reactions.

## 5 Worked example — Grade 4

**1** Name the compounds formed by the combination of the following elements.

**(a)** Cu and F **[1 mark]**

Copper fluoride

**(b)** Cu, O and F **[1 mark]**

Copper fluorate

**2** Write a word equation for the reaction between magnesium and oxygen. **[1 mark]**

magnesium + oxygen → magnesium oxide

## 5 Exam-style practice — Grade 5

**1** Complete the sentence. **[1 mark]**

Aluminium is an element because it is made of only one type of ______________.

**2** Give the correct atomic symbol for aluminium. **[1 mark]**

**3** Look at **Figure 1**, a section of the periodic table.

**(a)** Give the name of the labelled element in Group 1. **[1 mark]**

**(b) (i)** Give the name and symbol of the element in the blue box. **[1 mark]**

**(ii)** Write a word equation showing this element reacting with chlorine. **[1 mark]**

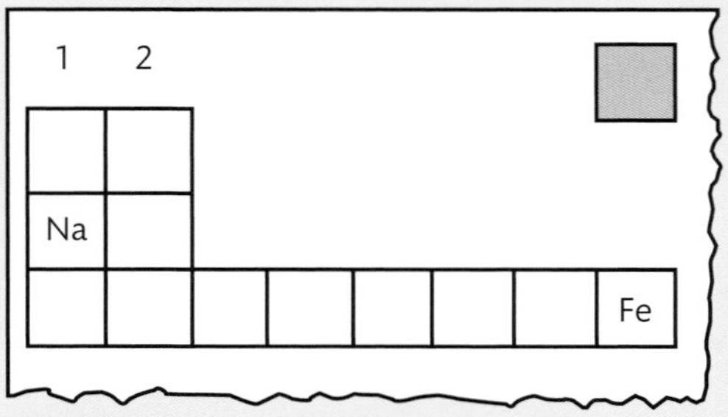


**Figure 1** A section of the periodic table

# Pure substances

You need to be able to distinguish pure from impure substances using melting and boiling points.

## 5 What is a pure substance?

In everyday language, a pure substance is a substance that has had nothing added to it, for example, pure milk.
In Chemistry, it is a substance that contains only atoms or molecules of that particular substance, for example, pure water must contain only $H_2O$ molecules.

Impure substances can be mixtures of elements, compounds, or mixtures of elements and compounds.

Pure substances cannot be separated by physical methods, such as filtration. Impurities in a substance will affect its properties. The values for melting point, boiling point and density obtained for a sample can be compared with data to identify its purity.

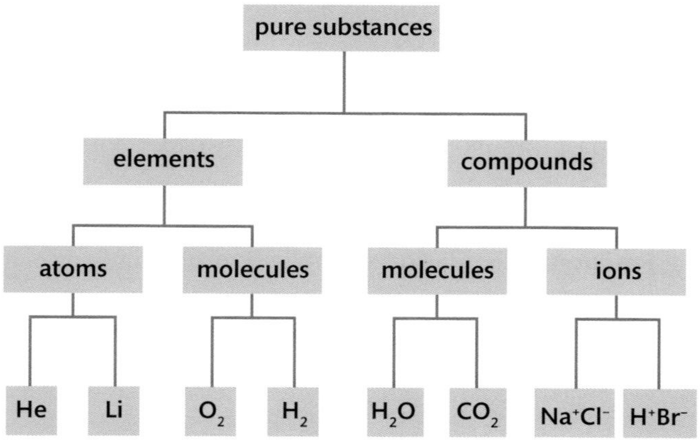


**Figure 1** Examples of pure substances

## 1 Working scientifically

It is important to manufacture drugs to be as pure as possible. This reduces the risk of side effects and helps to ensure an accurate dose.

## 10 Worked example Grade 6

The table shows the boiling points of three samples of water.

| Sample | Boiling point in °C |
|---|---|
| A | 98 |
| B | 100 |
| C | 103 |

**(a)** Which sample is pure water? Explain your answer. **[2 marks]**

Sample B is pure water because it boils at 100 °C, which is the boiling point of water.

If a substance is pure, every sample of that substance will have the same properties, including:

- melting point
- boiling point
- density.

**(b)** Suggest why the other two samples do not boil at the expected temperature. **[1 mark]**

They contain impurities.

**(c)** When manufacturing pharmaceutical drugs, the drugs need to be as pure as possible to reduce the chance of side effects.

Suggest one method that could be used to check the purity of a sample of aspirin. **[2 marks]**

Measure the melting point of the sample and compare it to the known melting point of pure aspirin.

Other possible methods involve measuring the boiling point or the density, and then comparing them with known data.

## 5 Exam-style practice Grade 6

1. Describe how you could prove that a sample of ethanol is pure. **[2 marks]**
2. Purity is important when developing pharmaceutical drugs. Describe what is meant by the term 'pure'. **[2 marks]**
3. The boiling point of pure ethanol is 78 °C. A student measures the boiling point of a sample of ethanol and records a value of 79 °C. State whether the sample is pure or impure. **[1 mark]**

# Mixtures

You need to know the different types of mixtures and how they can be separated using physical methods.

## Separating mixtures

A mixture contains two or more substances that are not chemically bonded together, which means they can be separated by physical methods. The chemical properties of the substances in the mixture are unchanged as they haven't reacted with each other.

- **Filtration** separates an insoluble solid from a liquid. A mixture is passed through filter paper in a filter funnel. The liquid can pass through the gaps in the filter paper but the solid cannot.
- **Simple distillation** separates a solvent from a solution. A mixture is heated and the liquid evaporates, re-condenses and is collected.
- **Fractional distillation** separates a mixture of liquids. It is covered in more detail on page 152.
- **Crystallisation** separates a soluble solid from a liquid. A mixture is heated until the solvent evaporates, leaving a crystallised solid behind.
- **Chromatography** separates a mixture of several liquids. It is covered in more detail on page 82.

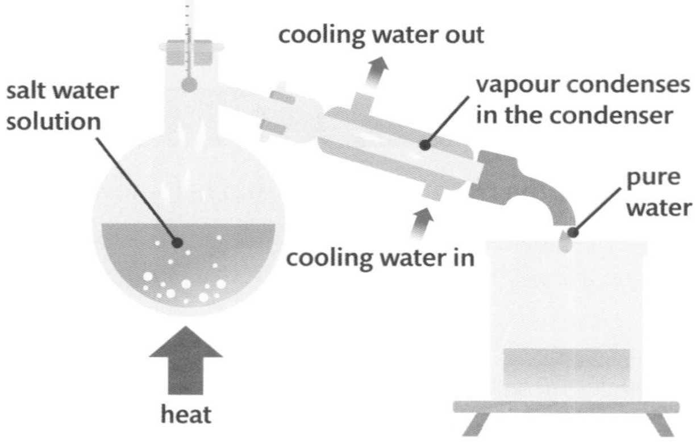


**Figure 1** Simple distillation

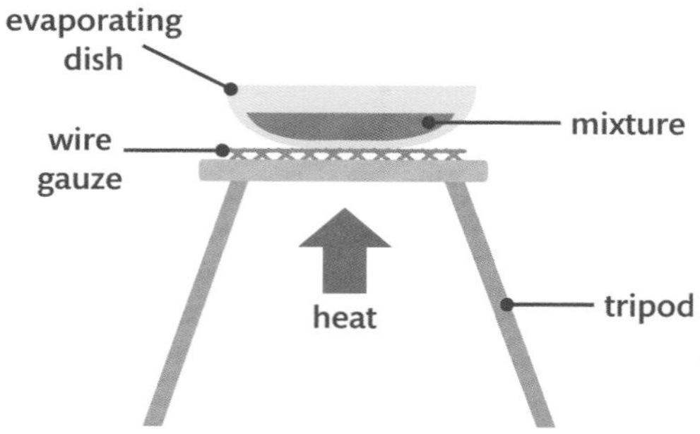


**Figure 2** Crystallisation

## Worked example — Grade 5

A student is given a mixture containing a liquid that evaporates at 65 °C, a soluble solid and a second liquid that evaporates at 98 °C. Explain the steps the student should follow to separate the soluble solid. **[4 marks]**

Step 1: The two liquids can be separated by fractional distillation. The liquid with a boiling point of 65 °C will evaporate first and be collected in the beaker.

Step 2: The remaining mixture should be heated in an evaporating dish to evaporate the liquid. It is then left to cool to allow crystals to form.

## Exam-style practice — Grade 4

**1** Match the mixtures to the methods of separation. **[4 marks]**

| Mixture | Separation method |
|---|---|
| ink and water | filtration |
| sand and water | simple distillation |
| crude oil | evaporation |
| sugar and water | fractional distillation |

**2** Name the apparatus labelled **W**, **X** and **Y** in **Figure 3**. **[3 marks]**

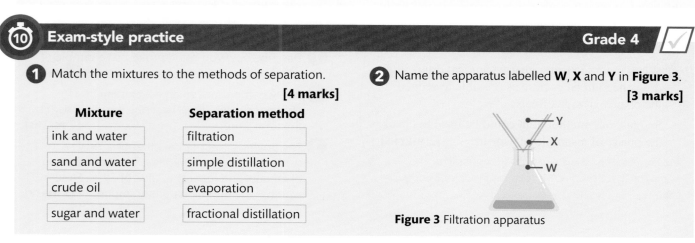

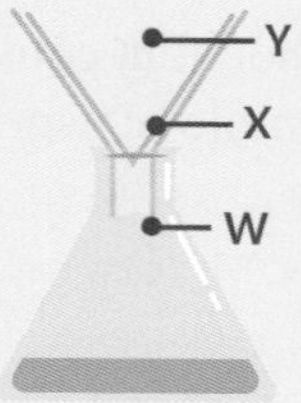


**Figure 3** Filtration apparatus



Made a start · Feeling confident · Exam ready

# Formulations

Formulations are mixtures designed to be useful products. They contain a combination of components with specific purposes.

## 5 What is a formulation?

A formulation is a product that contains a mixture of useful components. The components are added in carefully measured quantities to give the product its required properties.

### A soap formulation

| Ingredients | Percentage of total by weight |
|---|---|
| surfactants | 30–70 |
| plasticisers and binders | 20–50 |
| lather enhancers | 0–5 |
| fillers and binders | 5–30 |
| water | 5–12 |
| fragrance | 0–3.0 |
| opacifying agents | 0–0.3 |
| dyes and pigments | <1 |

## 2 Examples of formulations

Soap is an example of a formulation. An acid, such as coconut oil, is reacted with an alkali, such as potassium hydroxide. This formulation creates a salt, which is the basic soap. Preservatives are then added with any further additives for skin care or fragrance. Other examples of formulations include:

- medicines
- food
- fertilisers
- alloys
- paints
- cleaning agents
- fuels.

**Maths skills**

1. Divide the total volume by 100 to get 1% volume.
2. Multiply the volume for 1% by the percentage by volume.

## 10 Worked example — Grade 6

The table shows the typical formulations for gloss and emulsion paint.

| Component | Emulsion paint (percentage by volume) | Gloss paint (percentage by volume) |
|---|---|---|
| binder | 20 | 54 |
| pigment | 20 | 25 |
| extenders | 25 | 0 |
| solvent | 30 | 17 |
| additives | 5 | 4 |

A **solvent** is the liquid in which other substances are dissolved.

1. A consumer purchases 200 litres of emulsion paint. What volume of solvent will it contain? **[2 marks]**

$200 \div 100 = 2$

$2 \times 30 = 60$ litres of solvent used

2. One ingredient in paint is the binder, which is a resin that holds the pigment in place.

How much more binder is present in gloss than emulsion paint? Give your answer as a percentage. **[3 marks]**

Binder in emulsion = 20%

Binder in gloss = 54%

$54 - 20 = 34\%$

## 10 Exam-style practice — Grade 5

1. Paint is a mixture of liquids that has been designed as a useful product.
   **(a)** Give the name of this type of mixture. **[1 mark]**
   **(b)** Suggest the use of the pigment in a paint formulation. **[1 mark]**
2. Explain why it is important for cosmetic manufacturers to use specific quantities of ingredients in a formulation. **[2 marks]**
3. Give an example of a type of formulation used in everyday life. **[1 mark]**

# Chromatography

Chromatography is a technique used to separate the components of a mixture so they can be identified. You need to understand how chromatography works and be able to calculate $R_f$ values using chromatograms.

## 10 Paper chromatography

Chromatography is usually used to separate coloured substances, such as inks, food colourings and dyes. It can also be used to separate colourless mixtures with the use of a locating agent, which adds pigment to otherwise colourless substances. Chromatography is important in the manufacturing of pharmaceutical drugs. The process can be used to assess the purity of drugs and medicines, enabling scientists to reduce the risk of unnecessary side effects. Go to page 83 to revise how to set up chromatography apparatus to produce a chromatogram.

Paper chromatography involves two phases:

- the chromatography paper, which contains a spot of the unknown mixture, is the **stationary phase**.
- the liquid solvent, which moves through the chromatography paper carrying the components of the mixture, is the **mobile phase**.

Mixtures are separated because different substances travel different distances depending on their attractions to the stationary phase or the mobile phase.

### $R_f$ values

The **$R_f$ value** is the ratio of the distance moved by a substance (from the centre of its spot at the base line) to the distance moved by the solvent.

The $R_f$ value of a particular substance will always be the same if the same type of chromatography paper and solvent are used. This means that $R_f$ values can be used to identify unknown substances.

The more soluble a substance, the further it will travel up the chromatography paper and the higher the $R_f$ value will be. The less attracted the substance is to the paper, the further it will travel up the paper and the higher the $R_f$ value will be.

Pure compounds produce a single spot on the chromatogram.

Mixtures separate into several spots in different positions on the chromatogram.

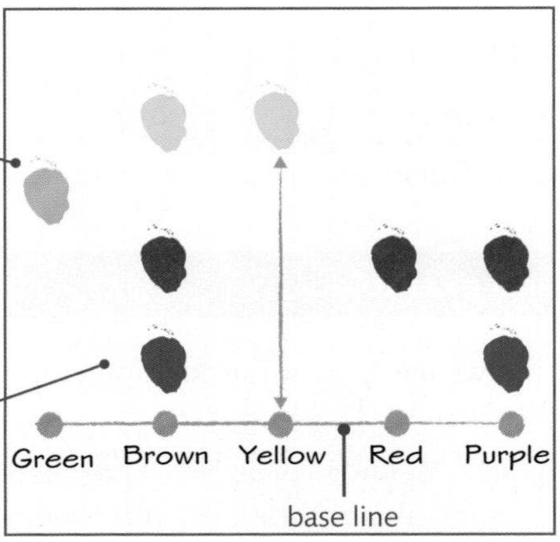


**Figure 1** A chromatogram of different food colourants

**Maths skills**

$R_f$ values can be worked out using the formula:

$$R_f = \frac{\text{distance moved by substance}}{\text{distance moved by solvent}}$$

Use a calculator to work out the answer. Remember to give your answer to 2 significant figures.

## 5 Worked example — Grade 7

A substance travels 78 mm from the base line while the solvent travels 150 mm.

What is the $R_f$ value for this substance?
Give your answer to 2 significant figures.

**[3 marks]**

$$R_f = \frac{78}{150}$$

$$R_f = 0.52$$

## 5 Exam-style practice — Grade 7

1. A scientist uses chromatography to see what mixture of colours a brown food colourant contains. The results are shown in **Figure 1.** Describe what the chromatogram tells you about the food colourant. **[2 marks]**
2. Describe what an $R_f$ value is. **[1 mark]**
3. Explain why $R_f$ values are not given units. **[1 mark]**

# Paper chromatography

The aim of this practical is to identify an unknown substance within a mixture, using paper chromatography to find the $R_f$ value.

## 2 Apparatus

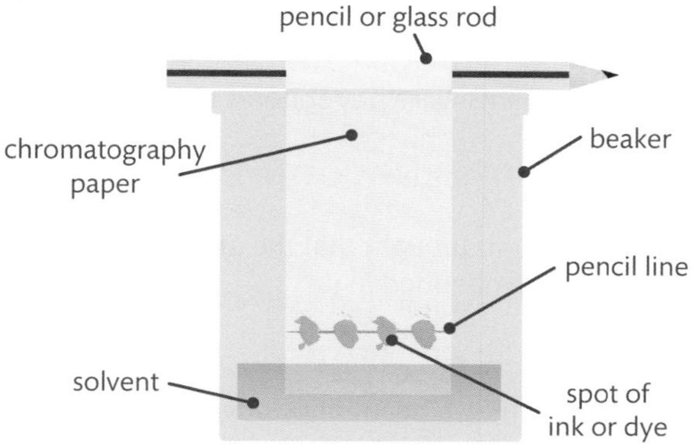


## 5 Investigating an unknown mixture

1. Use a ruler to draw a horizontal pencil line 2 cm from the bottom of the chromatography paper (the base line).
2. Using glass capillary tubes, put a small spot of each of the known colourings on the pencil line, 1 cm apart. Make sure each spot is no more than 5 mm in diameter.
3. Using another glass capillary tube, put a small spot of the unknown mixture on the paper.
4. Label each spot in **pencil**.
5. Tape the end edge of the chromatography paper to the glass rod so that the paper hangs with the base line at the bottom.
6. Pour water into the beaker so that the water level is **below** the base line.
7. Rest the rod on the top edge of the beaker. The bottom edge of the paper should dip into the water.
8. Use a ruler to measure the distance the solvent has moved up the paper (from the bottom edge of the paper) and the distance the spot has moved (from the base line).

## 10 Worked example — Grade 7

**Figure 1** shows a paper chromatogram of three food colourants and an unknown sample, **M**.

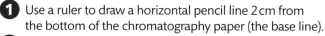

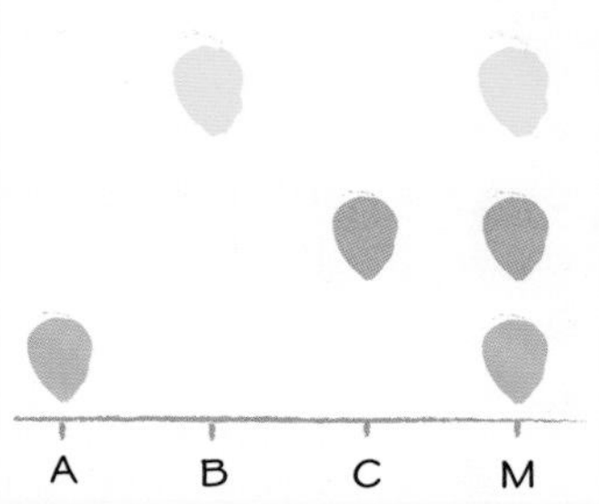


**Figure 1** Food colourant chromatogram

**(a)** How do the results prove that all the food colourants are present in sample **M**? **[1 mark]**

There are three spots in the column labelled M and they match the spots travelled by colourants A, B and C.

**(b)** Complete the table by using the data provided to calculate the $R_f$ values for each of the colourants. **[4 marks]**

| Food colourant | Distance travelled in mm | | $R_f$ value |
|---|---|---|---|
| | Solvent | Spot | |
| **A** | 52 | 8 | 0.15 |
| **B** | 52 | 42 | 0.81 |
| **C** | 52 | 17 | 0.33 |

**(c)** Explain how paper chromatography is used to separate substances. **[3 marks]**

As the solvent travels up the paper, it carries substances different distances. The distance a substance travels depends on its solubility and attraction to the paper.

## 2 Working scientifically

You need to be able to choose suitable apparatus and describe how it should be used for a particular purpose. For example, in paper chromatography:

- A pencil is used to draw the base line because ink may run and interfere with the chromatogram.
- The chromatography paper should sit above the solvent level so that the substance isn't dissolved in the solvent.
- You should wear eye protection to protect your eyes from harmful substances.

Go to page 82 to revise how $R_f$ values are calculated.

## 5 Exam-style practice — Grade 7

1. Suggest why the base line must be above the level of solvent at the start of the experiment. **[1 mark]**
2. Suggest why the base line should be drawn using a pencil and not a pen. **[1 mark]**
3. A substance travels 23 mm from the base line while the solvent travels 74 mm. Calculate the $R_f$ value for this substance. Give your answer to 2 significant figures. **[3 marks]**

# The model of the atom

The work of many scientists has led to our current model of the atom. You need to know the theories (outlined below) that have developed over time due to improving scientific methods.

## 10 Developing the model of the atom

1. Before electrons were discovered, it was thought that atoms were tiny spheres that could not be divided into anything else.

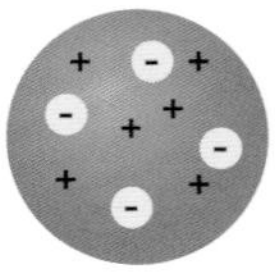

2. The **plum pudding model** was proposed by scientists who thought that the atom was like a positively charged 'pudding', with electrons like 'plums' embedded in it.

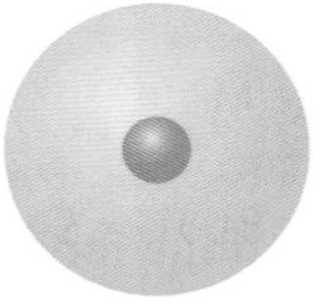

3. Ernest Rutherford tested the plum pudding model by aiming a beam of positively charged alpha particles at a very thin sheet of gold foil (scattering experiment). Some of the alpha particles were repelled by positively charged particles that were concentrated in the centre of the atom (the nucleus). Most alpha particles passed through unaffected, showing that the nucleus was only a very small part of the atom. This evidence gave rise to the **nuclear model**.

4. Niels Bohr adapted the nuclear model. Using theoretical calculations alongside experimental observations, Bohr suggested that electrons travel in circular orbits around the nucleus. Further research showed that the nucleus was actually composed of smaller particles with equal amounts of positive charge. These became known as protons.

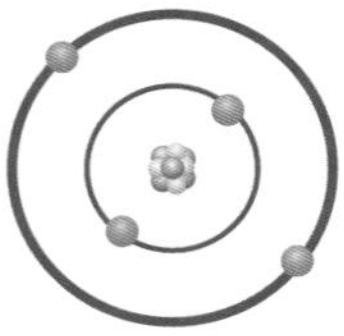

5. Approximately 20 years after the nuclear model became accepted, James Chadwick discovered that neutrons also existed in the nucleus.

## 5 Scientific theory

You need to know how scientific theories develop over time. New experimental evidence may lead to a scientific model being changed or replaced. The **scientific method** is a systematic, logical approach used to discover how science works. It may be modified but ultimately it is used to gather experimental and theoretical evidence and observations to solve a problem.

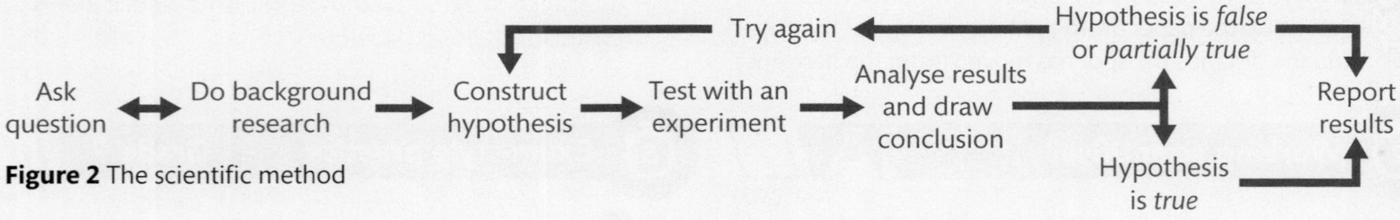


**Figure 2** The scientific method

## 2 Worked example — Grade 6

Describe the differences between the plum pudding model and the nuclear model of the atom.

**[2 marks]**

The electrons orbit a positive central nucleus in the nuclear model, whereas, in the plum pudding model, the electrons are dotted around the nucleus 'like plums in a pudding'.

## 5 Exam-style practice — Grade 8

Explain how evidence from Ernest Rutherford's scattering experiment changed ideas about the atomic model.

**[3 marks]**

# Subatomic particles

You need to know about the size and structure of atoms.

## Structure of an atom

Everything is made of atoms. Atoms contain subatomic particles, some of which are charged.

Within the atom, there is a central **nucleus** that contains the protons and neutrons. As the number of protons (the atomic number) identifies the element, all atoms of the same element must have the same number of protons.

The **atomic number** is the number of protons the atom contains. The number of electrons in an atom is equal to the number of protons in its nucleus.

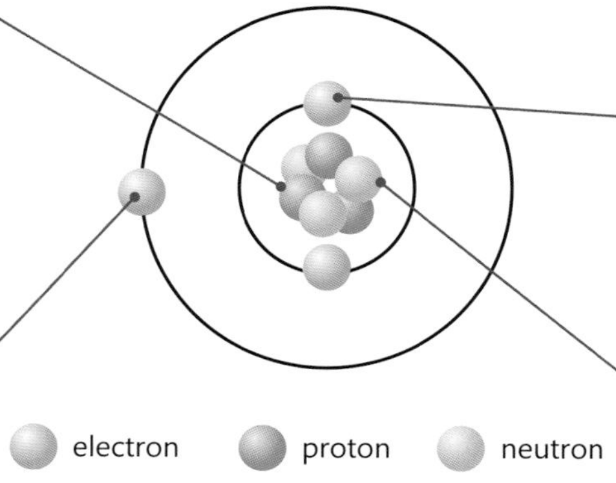


The tiny negatively charged electrons are found in electron shells (or energy levels) surrounding the nucleus. They are attracted to the positively charged protons.

Atoms are electrically neutral as they have an equal number of protons and electrons and neutrons are not charged.

**Figure 1** The nuclear model of the atom

## Size of an atom

The atom is the smallest part of an element. Atoms have a radius of about 0.1 nanometres (nm), which is equivalent to one-billionth of a metre ($1 \times 10^{-10}$ m). The nucleus of an atom has a radius of about 0.00001 nm ($1 \times 10^{-14}$ m).

Go to page 86 for more about the size of an atom.

### Maths skills

You need to know how to convert nanometres to metres using standard form.

$1 \text{ nm} = 1 \times 10^{-9}$ m

## Worked example — Grade 6

Convert the following units.

**(a)** 15 nm to m **[1 mark]**

$1.5 \times 10^{-8}$ m

**(b)** $3.4 \times 10^{-6}$ m to nm **[1 mark]**

$3.4 \times 10^{3}$ nm

## Exam-style practice — Grade 6

1. The nucleus of an atom has radius $1 \times 10^{-14}$ m. Given that one nanometre is $1 \times 10^{-9}$ m, calculate how many nanometres the radius of the nucleus is. **[2 marks]**
2. State the electrical charge of the nucleus of an atom. **[1 mark]**
3. Name the subatomic particles found in the nucleus of an atom. **[1 mark]**
4. Look at **Figure 2**, a diagram of a helium atom.
   **(a)** Give the atomic number of helium. **[1 mark]**
   **(b)** Explain why an atom of helium has no overall charge. **[2 marks]**
   **(c)** Use the diagram to explain the nuclear model of helium. **[2 marks]**

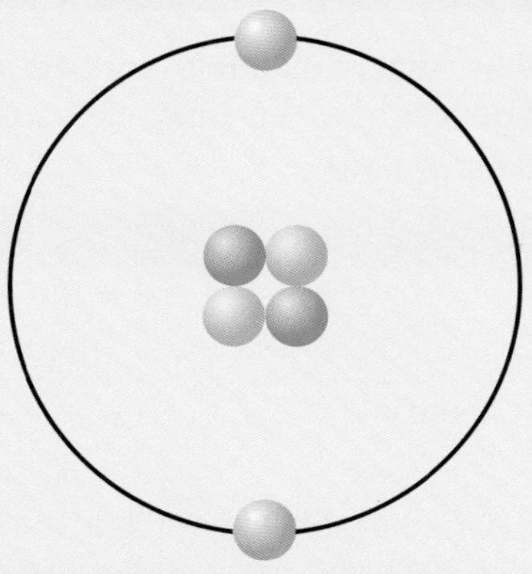

**Figure 2** An atom of helium

# Size and mass of atoms

The information given in the periodic table (page 89) can be used to explain the size and the mass of each type of atom.

## 5 Representing atoms

The **atomic symbol** is the short-hand name for the element.

The **atomic number** is the number of protons in an atom. Atoms contain the same number of protons and electrons.

12
C
carbon
6

The sum of the number of protons and neutrons in an atom is its **mass number**. Almost all the mass of an atom is in the nucleus.

This is the name of the element.

## 10 Worked example — Grade 5

**(a)** Name the three subatomic particles in an atom of aluminium and give their relative charge and relative masses. **[3 marks]**

Protons have a relative mass of 1 and a charge of +1.
Electrons have a very small relative mass and a charge of −1.
Neutrons have a relative mass of 1 and a charge of 0.

**(b)** Using the periodic table, explain why the mass number of aluminium is 27. **[3 marks]**

The mass number is the total number of protons and neutrons in an atom.
Aluminium has 13 protons and 14 neutrons. The relative mass of each proton and neutron is 1.
Therefore, the mass of an atom of aluminium is 13 + 14 = 27.

**(c)** Each oxygen atom gains 2 electrons to form an $O^{2-}$ ion. Work out the number of protons, electrons and neutrons in an $O^{2-}$ ion. **[3 marks]**

number of protons = atomic number = 8
number of electrons = 8 + 2 = 10
number of neutrons = 16 − 8 = 8

In an atom, the number of electrons is equal to the number of protons. In a negatively charged ion, there are more electrons than protons. In a positively charged ion, there are more protons than electrons. In this case, there are two more electrons than protons.

mass number − atomic number

## 1 Maths skills

You need to know how to use mass number and atomic number to work out the number of protons, neutrons and electrons.

For aluminium:

number of protons = atomic number = 13

number of electrons = number of protons = 13

number of neutrons = mass number − atomic number = 27 − 13 = 14

### Exam focus

When giving the mass of an atom in an exam you do not need to state the units.

## 15 Exam-style practice — Grade 6

**(a)** Atoms have different atomic numbers and mass numbers. In terms of subatomic particles, describe the differences between an atom's atomic number and its mass number. **[4 marks]**

**(b)** Complete the table. **[6 marks]**

| Subatomic particle | Relative mass | Relative charge |
|---|---|---|
| | $\frac{1}{1840}$ | |
| neutron | | |
| | 1 | |

**(c)** Use the periodic table to complete the table. **[1 mark]**

| Atom | Number of protons | Number of neutrons | Number of electrons |
|---|---|---|---|
| fluorine | 9 | | 9 |

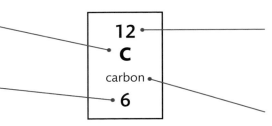

# Isotopes and relative atomic mass

Isotopes are atoms of the same element that have different numbers of neutrons. You need to be able to calculate relative atomic mass given the percentage abundance.

## 10 Isotopes

Isotopes have the same atomic number but a different atomic mass. Most elements have two or more isotopes. This means they have the same number of protons and electrons but a different number of neutrons. Isotopes of an element have the same chemical properties. Isotopes of the same element are usually specifically identified by their mass number, e.g. hydrogen-3.

### Isotopes of hydrogen

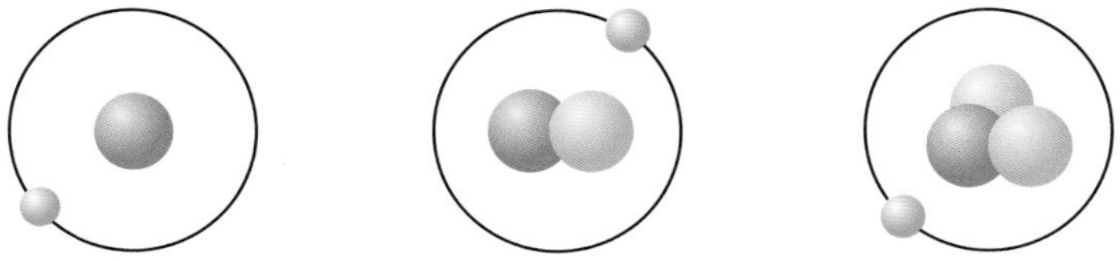

| | Hydrogen $^{1}_{1}H$ | Deuterium $^{2}_{1}H$ | Tritium $^{3}_{1}H$ |
|---|---|---|---|
| **Number of protons** | 1 | 1 | 1 |
| **Number of electrons** | 1 | 1 | 1 |
| **Number of neutrons** | 0 | 1 | 2 |

Atoms can be represented in this way. The top number is the mass number. The bottom number is the atomic number.

### Radioactive isotopes

Some radioactive isotopes have useful applications. For example, cobalt-60 is used in cancer treatment.

Fluorine-18 is used as a tracer for detecting cancers and in cardiac and brain imaging.

## 10 Worked example — Grade 8

**1** Two isotopes of lithium are $^{7}_{3}Li$ and $^{8}_{3}Li$. Describe the similarities and differences between them, referring to the number of subatomic particles in each isotope. **[3 marks]**

*The atoms of both isotopes possess the same number of protons and electrons – three of each. They have a different number of neutrons – $^{7}_{3}Li$ has four neutrons and $^{8}_{3}Li$ has five neutrons.*

**2** The percentage abundances of three lithium isotopes are:

$^{7}_{3}Li$ 55%

$^{8}_{3}Li$ 25%

$^{6}_{3}Li$ 20%.

Calculate the relative atomic mass of lithium. **[3 marks]**

$$A_r = \frac{(7 \times 55) + (8 \times 25) + (6 \times 20)}{100}$$

$$A_r = \frac{(385 + 200 + 120)}{100}$$

$$A_r = 7.05$$

## 2 Relative atomic mass

The relative atomic mass ($A_r$) is the average mass of one atom of an element compared with $\frac{1}{12}$ of a carbon-12 atom. The relative atomic mass of an element is the average value of the mass of all isotopes of the element, taking into account their abundance.

The percentage abundance of an element's isotopes is needed to calculate the $A_r$.

**Maths skills**

To calculate the relative atomic mass ($A_r$):

**1.** Multiply the atomic mass of each isotope by its percentage abundance.

**2.** Add these values together and divide by 100.

## 5 Exam-style practice — Grade 6

Look at the atomic symbols below. The letters are **not** the symbols for these elements.

$^{6}_{3}R$ $^{7}_{3}S$ $^{23}_{11}T$ $^{39}_{19}U$ $^{85}_{37}V$

**(a)** Show which **two** atoms are isotopes of the same element. Explain your answer fully. **[3 marks]**

**(b)** Name the element that they are isotopes of. **[1 mark]**

# Electronic structure

You need to be able to recognise and represent the electronic structures of the first 20 elements of the periodic table.

## 10 Electronic structure

Negatively charged electrons are held in electron shells surrounding the positively-charged nucleus of an atom. Electron shells are also referred to as energy levels.

Electrons occupy the lowest available electron shell first, starting with the innermost energy level. The innermost electron shell is very small and can only hold two electrons. Each subsequent shell can hold up to eight electrons.

The electronic structure of an atom can be represented by a diagram or by listing the number of electrons in each shell, starting with the innermost shell.

- The atomic number is the number of electrons in an atom.
- The number of electrons in the outermost electron shell is the same as the element's group number in the periodic table. The exception to this is elements in Group 0 which have complete outer shells.
- The number of electron shells is the same as the element's period number in the periodic table.

### Examples of electronic structures

| **Element** | fluorine | neon | sodium |
|---|---|---|---|
| **Electronic structure** | 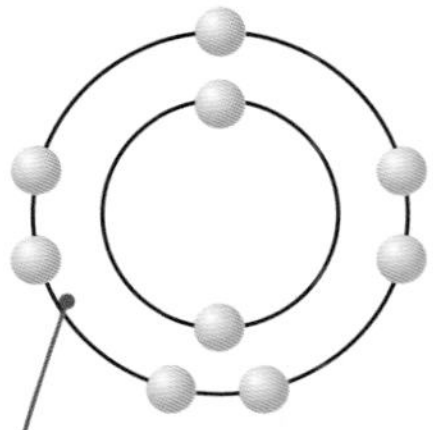 2,7 | 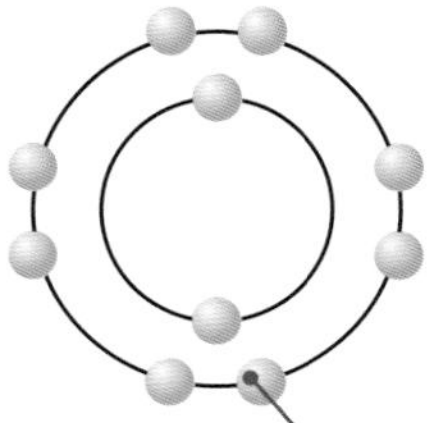 2,8 | 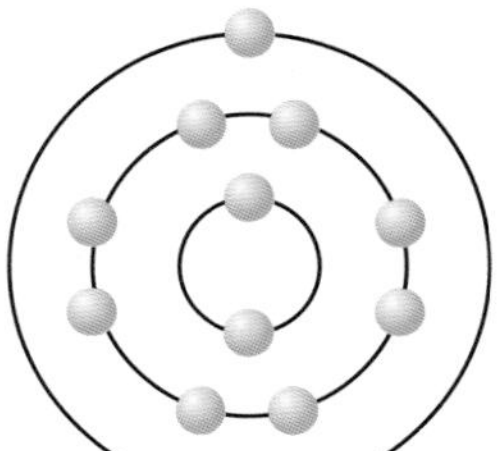 2,8,1 |
| **Periodic table group** | 7 | 0 | 1 |

Although electrons repel each other, and should be spread evenly around the shell, it is helpful to pair the electrons up so that you can clearly see how many are in each shell.

Go to page 85 for more about the properties of electrons.

## 5 Worked example — Grade 6

**(a)** Write down the electronic structure of nitrogen (atomic number 7). **[1 mark]**

2,5

Nitrogen is in Group 5 so it has five electrons in its outer electron shell.

**(b)** Complete the diagram to show the electronic structure of nitrogen. **[2 marks]**

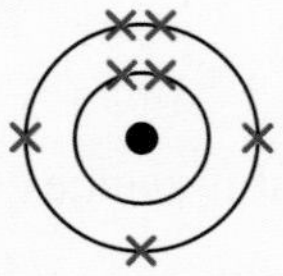

The number of electron shells is equal to the period the element is in (2). The number of electrons in the outer shell is equal to the group (5).

## 5 Exam-style practice — Grade 6

The electronic structures of four elements are:

**A** 2,5 **B** 2,7 **C** 2,8,8 **D** 2,8,8,1

Use the periodic table to answer these questions.

Identify which element, **A, B, C** or **D**:

**(a)** is a Group 0 gas **(b)** is fluorine **(c)** is found in Group 1 **(d)** is in Period 3. **[4 marks]**

# The periodic table

The periodic table contains all known elements arranged in order of their atomic number. You will be given a copy of the periodic table in your exam.

## 10 Groups and periods

The periodic table is so-called because similar properties occur at regular intervals. An element's position in the periodic table indicates how it reacts and how reactive it is likely to be.

alkali metals

Hydrogen is a non-metal but has the same electronic structure as the alkali metals and so is often put in the top middle area of the periodic table.

halogens

noble gases

The zigzag line divides the metals and the non-metals, with the metals to the left of the line.

| 1 | 2 | | | | | | | | | | | 3 | 4 | 5 | 6 | 7 | 0 |
|---|---|---|---|---|---|---|---|---|---|---|---|---|---|---|---|---|---|
| | | | | | | 1 H Hydrogen 1 | | | | | | | | | | | 4 He Helium 2 |
| 7 Li Lithium 3 | 9 Be Beryllium 4 | | | | | | | | | | | 11 B Boron 5 | 12 C Carbon 6 | 14 N Nitrogen 7 | 16 O Oxygen 8 | 19 F Fluorine 9 | 20 Ne Neon 10 |
| 23 Na Sodium 11 | 24 Mg Magnesium 12 | | | | | | | | | | | 27 Al Aluminium 13 | 28 Si Silicon 14 | 31 P Phosphorus 15 | 32 S Sulfur 16 | 35.5 Cl Chlorine 17 | 40 Ar Argon 18 |
| 39 K Potassium 19 | 40 Ca Calcium 20 | 45 Sc Scandium 21 | 48 Ti Titanium 22 | 51 V Vanadium 23 | 52 Cr Chromium 24 | 55 Mn Manganese 25 | 56 Fe Iron 26 | 59 Co Cobalt 27 | 59 Ni Nickel 28 | 63.5 Cu Copper 29 | 65 Zn Zinc 30 | 70 Ga Gallium 31 | 73 Ge Germanium 32 | 75 As Arsenic 33 | 79 Se Selenium 34 | 80 Br Bromine 35 | 84 Kr Krypton 36 |
| 85 Rb Rubidium 37 | 88 Sr Strontium 38 | 89 Y Yttrium 39 | 91 Zr Zirconium 40 | 93 Nb Niobium 41 | 96 Mo Molybdenum 42 | 98 Tc Technetium 43 | 101 Ru Ruthenium 44 | 103 Rh Rhodium 45 | 106 Pd Palladium 46 | 108 Ag Silver 47 | 112 Cd Cadmium 48 | 115 In Indium 49 | 119 Sn Tin 50 | 122 Sb Antimony 51 | 128 Te Tellurium 52 | 127 I Iodine 53 | 131 Xe Xenon 54 |
| 133 Cs Caesium 55 | 137 Ba Barium 56 | 139 La Lanthanum 57 | 178 Hf Hafnium 72 | 181 Ta Tantalum 73 | 184 W Tungsten 74 | 186 Re Rhenium 75 | 190 Os Osmium 76 | 192 Ir Iridium 77 | 195 Pt Platinum 78 | 197 Au Gold 79 | 201 Hg Mercury 80 | 204 Tl Thallium 81 | 207 Pb Lead 82 | 209 Bi Bismuth 83 | [210] Po Polonium 84 | [210] At Astatine 85 | [222] Rn Radon 86 |
| [223] Fr Francium 87 | [226] Ra Radium 88 | [227] Ac Actinium 89 | [261] Rf Rutherfordium 104 | [262] Db Dubnium 105 | [266] Sg Seaborgium 106 | [264] Bh Bohrium 107 | [277] Hs Hassium 108 | [268] Mt Meitnerium 109 | [271] Ds Darmstadtium 110 | [272] Rg Roentgenium 111 | [285] Cn Copernicium 112 | [286] Uut Ununtrium 113 | [289] Fl Flerovium 114 | [289] Uup Ununpentium 115 | [293] Lv Livermorium 116 | [294] Uus Ununseptium 117 | [294] Uuo Ununoctium 118 |

### Groups

Elements with similar properties are found in vertical columns known as **groups**. The group number is given on the periodic table above each column. All elements in the same group have the same number of electrons in their outer shell, for example, oxygen is in Group 6 and has six electrons in its outer shell (2,6).

### Periods

Rows of elements are called **periods**. All elements in the same period have the same number of electron shells. For example, sodium is in Period 3 and has three electron shells. Across a period, the number of outer shell electrons increases by 1. For example, lithium (Period 2) has the electronic structure of 2,1. The next element in the period, beryllium, has the electronic structure of 2,2 and so on.

## 5 Worked example — Grade 5

**(a)** The electronic structure of lithium is 2,1 and of sodium is 2,8,1. Explain how these electronic structures can be used to determine their position in the periodic table. **[3 marks]**

The number of electrons in an element's outer shell is the same as its group number, so both lithium and sodium must be in Group 1.

The number of occupied shells is the same as an element's period number, so lithium must be in Period 2 and sodium must be in Period 3.

**(b)** When lithium metal is added to water it fizzes, producing lithium hydroxide and hydrogen gas. Predict the reaction between sodium and water. Name the products formed. **[2 marks]**

Sodium would fizz more violently and produce sodium hydroxide and hydrogen.

Find sodium and lithium in the periodic table above or on the back cover of this book and compare their position with the answer. When counting rows, remember that the first row (or period) only contains two elements, H and He.

## 10 Exam-style practice — Grade 5

**1** An element has an electronic structure of 2,8,5.

**(a)** State which group the element is in. **[1 mark]**

**(b)** State which period the element is in. **[1 mark]**

**(c)** Name another element which would react in a similar way to this element. **[1 mark]**

**2** An element has 12 electrons.

**(a)** State which group the element is in. **[1 mark]**

**(b)** State which period the element is in. **[1 mark]**

**3** Explain the arrangement of the first 20 elements in the periodic table. You should answer in terms of atomic structure. **[2 marks]**

# Developing the periodic table

You need to be able to describe the development of the periodic table over time, in terms of the scientific theories and instruments available.

## 5 Early periodic tables

In the 19th century, scientists attempted to classify elements using a system based on the knowledge available at the time. In 1817, Johann Dobereiner noticed similar properties in small groups of elements – **the law of triads**.

In 1864, John Newlands arranged the elements in order of their atomic weight (similar to relative atomic mass). He proposed **the law of octaves** – every eighth element had similar properties.

Early periodic tables were incomplete and some atomic weights had been calculated incorrectly. This meant that some elements were placed in the wrong groups.

Later discoveries and knowledge of isotopes explained why it was not possible to arrange atoms solely according to their atomic weight.

| Group | | | | | | |
|---|---|---|---|---|---|---|
| **1** | **2** | **3** | **4** | **5** | **6** | **7** |
| H | Li | Be | B | C | N | O |
| F | Na | Mg | Al | Si | P | S |
| Cl | K | Ca | | | | |

**Figure 1** Part of Newlands' table

## 5 Mendeleev's periodic table

In 1869, Mendeleev correctly identified trends between elements and grouped them accordingly. Mendeleev arranged his table based on increasing relative atomic mass. Mendeleev realised there was a link between relative atomic mass and how elements reacted. In some cases, he changed the order of the elements to fit the trend better. He also left gaps for elements that had not yet been discovered.

Over the next 20 years more unknown elements were discovered and their properties were found to match Mendeleev's predictions.

| Row | Group | | | | | | | |
|---|---|---|---|---|---|---|---|---|
| | **1** | **2** | **3** | **4** | **5** | **6** | **7** | **8** |
| **1** | H | - | - | - | - | - | - | - |
| **2** | Li | Be | B | C | N | O | F | - |
| **3** | Na | Mg | Al | Si | P | S | Cl | - |
| **4** | K | Ca | ? | Ti | V | Cr | Mn | Fe, Co, Ni, Cu |
| **5** | (Cu) | Zn | ? | ? | As | So | Br | - |
| **6** | Rb | Sr | Yt | Zr | Nb | Mo | ? | Ru, Rh, Pd, Ag |

**Figure 2** The periodic table developed by Dmitri Mendeleev

## 2 Working scientifically

To develop new scientific ideas, predictions need to be tested. If the evidence supports the prediction, a scientific idea will develop.

The development of the periodic table is an example of how scientific ideas develop. Many scientists suggested possible arrangements of the elements but others rejected them as they weren't supported by evidence.

## 5 Worked example — Grade 6

In Dobereiner's law of triads, the elements lithium, sodium and potassium are grouped together.

Give **two** properties of these elements that support the idea that they should be grouped together. **[2 marks]**

*They are all very reactive – especially with water.*
*They all lose an electron when they react.*

## 5 Exam-style practice — Grade 4

Look at **Figure 1**.

**(a)** Give the names of the elements Newlands put into Group 4. **[1 mark]**

**(b)** Choose the property Newlands used to arrange his periodic table. Tick **one** box. **[1 mark]**

**A** atomic mass ☐

**B** atomic number ☐

**C** atomic size ☐

**(c)** Explain why the elements that Newlands put in Group 2 are now positioned in Group 1. **[2 marks]**

# Metals and non-metals

You need to know about the electronic structure, reactivity and properties of non-metals and metals.

## Differences between metals and non-metals

An element can be classified as a metal or a non-metal based on the electronic structure of its atoms.

- Metals lose electrons when they react, forming positive ions. Go to pages 105–107 to revise ionic bonding and compounds.
- Non-metals gain electrons when they react, forming negative ions or covalent compounds (page 114).

As you move across the periodic table, from left to right, the number of outer electrons increases. The elements become less metallic as they are more likely to share or gain electrons. The more electron shells an element has the easier it is to lose outer electrons. The outer electrons are further from the positive charge of the protons in the nucleus, so less energy is needed to remove them.

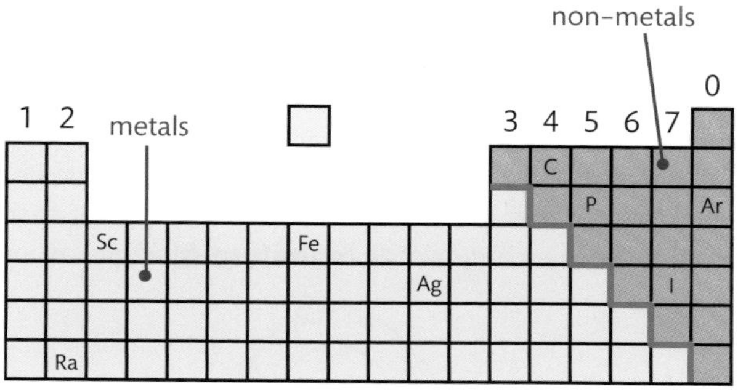


**Figure 1** Metals are on the left of the periodic table and non-metals are on the right.

## Properties of metals and non-metals

| | Metals | Non-metals |
|---|---|---|
| **State** | Solid at room temperature (except mercury) | • Usually liquids or gases at room temperature<br>• Some non-metals have giant structures so are solid at room temperature |
| **Conduction of heat and electricity** | Good conductors | • Usually poor conductors<br>• Some forms of carbon conduct electricity |
| **Strength** | Strong | Weak |
| **Melting point** | High | Usually low |
| **Appearance** | Shiny when cut | Dull |
| **Malleability** | Malleable (can be hammered into shape) | Brittle |

## Worked example — Grade 7

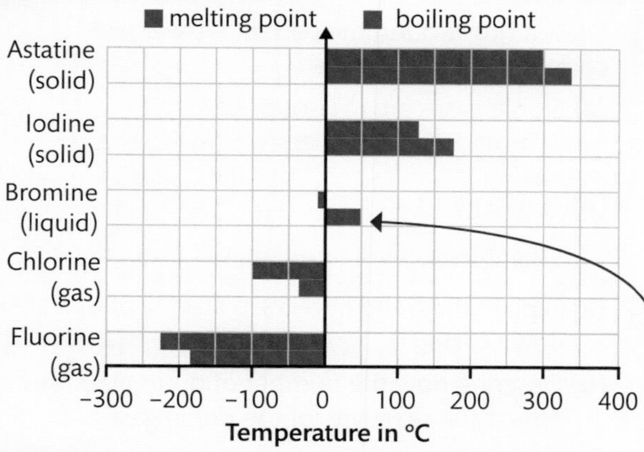


**Figure 2** A graph showing the approximate melting and boiling points of some Group 7 elements

Look at **Figure 2.**

**(a)** At what temperature does fluorine melt? **[1 mark]**

−225 °C

**(b)** Calculate the difference between the melting and boiling points of bromine. **[2 marks]**

50 °C − −10 °C = 60 °C

You need to take into account that melting point is a negative value and boiling point is a positive value. The melting point is about $\frac{1}{5}$ of a square so −10 °C and the boiling point is just over one square, so about 50 °C. The overall difference is 60 °C.

## Exam-style practice — Grade 5

Aluminium has a low density, conducts electricity and is resistant to corrosion. State which **one** of these properties makes aluminium suitable to use as kitchen foil. Give a reason for your answer. **[2 marks]**

# Group 0

You need to know the electronic structures of Group 0 elements, such as helium and argon, and the trends in their physical and chemical properties.

## 10 Electronic structure

The elements in Group 0 are known as the **noble** or **inert gases** due to their characteristic lack of reactivity. This is due to their stable electron arrangement. They all have a full outer shell – eight electrons in their outermost energy level (except helium which has two). They do not easily form molecules but exist as **monatomic** (single) atoms.

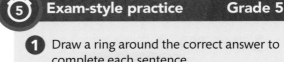

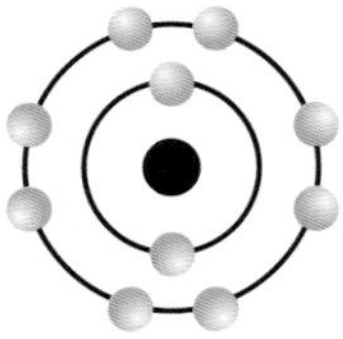

**Figure 1** Neon has the electronic structure 2,8

## 2 Physical and chemical trends

Trends are observed in the properties of Group 0 elements.

He
Ne
Ar
Kr
Xe

The boiling points increase. As the atoms get bigger they have more electrons, which leads to increased intermolecular forces between the atoms.

The relative atomic mass increases. There are more protons and neutrons in each atom down the group.

The size of the atoms increases due to the number of electron shells increasing.

## 10 Worked example — Grade 6

1. Explain why the noble gases are said to be monatomic. **[2 marks]**

*Their outer shell is full so they do not need to gain or lose any electrons. Therefore, they do not react with any other atoms.*

Go to page 88 to revise electronic structure.

2. Why are Group 0 elements used as the atmosphere for some chemical reactions? **[2 marks]**

*Group 0 elements are inert so they do not affect chemical reactions.*

3. Describe how the boiling point of Group 0 elements changes down the group. Explain this trend. **[3 marks]**

*The boiling point increases down the group. As the size of the atoms increases down the group, there are more electrons leading to increased intermolecular forces between the atoms.*

4. The radius of a neon atom is 154 pm. Predict whether the radius of a xenon atom will be larger or smaller than a neon atom. Justify your answer. **[2 marks]**

*The radius of a xenon atom will be larger than the radius of a neon atom, because xenon has 3 more occupied electron shells than neon.*

## 1 Exam focus

Make sure you know the trends in Group 0 and Group 1 of the periodic table. You need to be able to predict the properties of the elements in these groups.

## 5 Exam-style practice — Grade 5

1. Draw a ring around the correct answer to complete each sentence
   **(a)** Noble gases are in Group: ______

   | 0 | 1 | 7 |
   |---|---|---|

   **(b)** Noble gases are: ______

   | slightly reactive | unreactive | very reactive |
   |---|---|---|

2. **(a)** Explain the trend in relative atomic mass down Group 0. **[2 marks]**
   **(b)** Describe how the number of outer electrons affects the reactivity of the noble gases. **[1 mark]**

3. Draw the electronic structure of an argon atom. **[2 marks]**

# Group 1

You need to know the electronic structures of Group 1 elements, such as sodium and potassium, and the trends in their chemical properties.

## 5 Properties of Group 1 elements

Group 1 elements are known as the **alkali metals** due to the fact that they form alkaline solutions when they react with water.

All Group 1 elements have one outer electron. When they react, they lose this outer shell electron and form a positively charged ion.

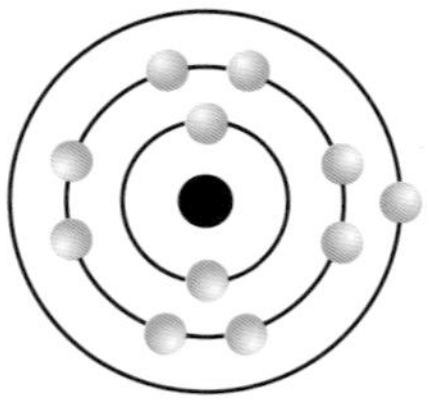

**Figure 1** Sodium has the electronic structure 2,8,1

## 2 Oxygen, chlorine and water

The first three Group 1 metals are lithium, sodium and potassium. The following table shows how these metals react with oxygen, chlorine and water.

| Element | Oxygen | Chlorine | Water |
|---|---|---|---|
| Li | red flame | red flame, white powder | fizzes |
| Na | yellow-orange flame | yellow flame, white powder | fizzes rapidly, may ignite |
| K | lilac flame | lilac flame, white powder | ignites, may be a small explosion |

## 5 Reactivity of Group 1 elements

Group 1 elements react with non-metals to form ionic compounds. The elements become more reactive further down the group, as the outer electron is further from the positive nuclear charge and less attracted to the nucleus. When the first three alkali metals react with water they fizz and move about the surface. They are releasing increasing amounts of energy to the surroundings. Potassium bursts into a lilac flame in the reaction:

potassium + water → potassium hydroxide + hydrogen

## 15 Worked example Grade 7

1 Write word and balanced symbol equations to show the reaction of lithium with oxygen. **[3 marks]**

lithium + oxygen → lithium oxide

$4Li + O_2 \rightarrow 2Li_2O$

> Group 1 elements all react with oxygen to form an oxide layer on their surface.

2 Write word and balanced symbol equations to show the reaction between sodium and water. **[3 marks]**

sodium + water → sodium hydroxide + hydrogen

$2Na + 2H_2O \rightarrow 2NaOH + H_2$

> Alkali metals react vigorously with water to produce an alkaline solution containing a metal hydroxide that turns universal indicator purple. Hydrogen gas is also produced. You should know the test for hydrogen – a lit splint produces a squeaky pop.

3 When sodium and chlorine react, a salt is formed. Give the word and balanced symbol equations for this reaction. **[3 marks]**

sodium + chlorine → sodium chloride

$2Na + Cl_2 \rightarrow 2NaCl$

> This reaction is vigorous, producing a metal chloride salt, a white crystalline solid. NaCl is the salt used in cooking.

4 The size of the atom increases down Group 1. How does this affect the reactivity of the atom? Explain your answer. **[3 marks]**

Reactivity increases down the group. The outer electron is further from the positively charged nucleus and so can be lost more easily.

## 10 Exam-style practice Grade 7

1 Explain why there is an increase in reactivity of elements down Group 1. **[4 marks]**

2 Lithium reacts with water. Explain why bubbles of gas are seen. **[1 mark]**

3 Lithium has a melting point of about 190 °C, sodium has a melting point of about 100 °C and potassium has a melting point of about 65 °C. Suggest the melting point of rubidium. **[1 mark]**

# Group 7

You need to know the electronic structures of Group 7 elements, such as chlorine, and their physical properties and reactivity.

## 5 Bonding

Group 7 elements, also known as the **halogens**, have seven outer electrons. It would take too much energy to try to remove such a large number of electrons. Therefore they either gain electrons by reacting with a metal, forming an ionic compound, or they share electrons with non-metals, forming a covalent bond.

The halogens exist as **diatomic molecules** (pairs of atoms), sharing electrons in a covalent bond (see page 114).

## 2 Properties

Group 7 elements share similar properties, including:

- non-metals
- low melting and boiling points
- brittle when solid
- poor conductors of heat and electricity
- coloured vapours
- molecules each contain two atoms (diatomic).

The outer shell is closest to the nucleus in fluorine. This means that an electron will be gained more easily, as there is stronger attraction to the nucleus.

## 10 Worked example — Grade 7

1. Explain, in terms of electrons, why fluorine is the most reactive halogen. **[3 marks]**

*Fluorine is the most reactive halogen because its outer electron shell is closest to its nucleus. This makes it easier for fluorine to attract electrons. The easier it is to gain an electron, the more reactive the halogen is.*

2. Explain why the boiling points of the halogens change down the group from fluorine to iodine. **[3 marks]**

*The boiling points increase down Group 7 because as the atoms get larger there are more intermolecular forces to overcome.*

3. The size of the atoms increases down Group 7. Explain how this affects the reactivity of Group 7 elements. **[3 marks]**

*The reactivity decreases down the group. As the size of the atom increases, the outer electron shell is further from the positively-charged nucleus and so there is less attraction to gain electrons.*

Larger molecules have more electrons so more intermolecular forces, which must be overcome to boil the molecule.

## 5 Reactivity

Halogens react vigorously with metals to form halide ions with a charge of −1. They react with non-metals to form small molecules (page 115).

As you go down Group 7:

- reactivity decreases
- relative molecular mass increases
- melting and boiling points increase.

### Displacement reactions

A more reactive halogen will displace (push out) a less reactive halogen from an aqueous solution of its salt.

Chlorine is more reactive than iodine, so chlorine will displace iodine from an aqueous solution of an iodide salt.

chlorine + magnesium iodide → magnesium chloride + iodine

Bromine is less reactive than chlorine, so bromine cannot displace chlorine – no reaction takes place.

bromine + sodium chloride → sodium chloride + bromine

The table shows the results of the reactions between halogens and aqueous solutions of halide salts.

| | Chloride | Bromide | Iodide |
|---|---|---|---|
| **Chlorine** | no reaction | bromine forms (turns orange) | iodine forms (turns brown) |
| **Bromine** | no reaction | no reaction | iodine forms (turns brown) |
| **Iodine** | no reaction | no reaction | no reaction |

## 10 Exam-style practice — Grade 6

1. Complete the word equation. **[2 marks]**
   bromine + potassium iodide → _____ + _____
2. Give a reason why chlorine displaces iodine from silver iodide. **[1 mark]**
3. Suggest which halogen produces bromine when it reacts with lithium bromide. **[1 mark]**
4. Fluorine atoms have two occupied shells but iodine atoms have five occupied shells. Explain how this affects the relative reactivity of these two elements. **[4 marks]**

# Conservation of mass

The law of conservation of mass enables scientists to make predictions about chemical reactions before carrying them out.

## Conservation of mass and balanced chemical equations

You need to know the law of conservation of mass:

> *In a closed system, the mass of the products equals the mass of the reactants.*

This means that no atoms are lost or made during a chemical reaction - only their arrangement changes. For example, hydrogen and oxygen react to form water (**Figure 1**). The total number of hydrogen and oxygen atoms is unchanged in the reaction. There are four hydrogen atoms and two oxygen atoms before the arrow (reactants) and after the arrow (products).

For mass to be conserved the reaction must take place in a **closed system** where none of the reactants or products can escape.

You can write the law as an equation and use it to find missing masses in chemical reactions:

mass of A + mass of B → mass of AB

total mass of reactants = total mass of products

The law of conservation of mass applies to changes of state (page 77). This includes sublimation. **Sublimation** is the process by which a solid turns directly into a gas.

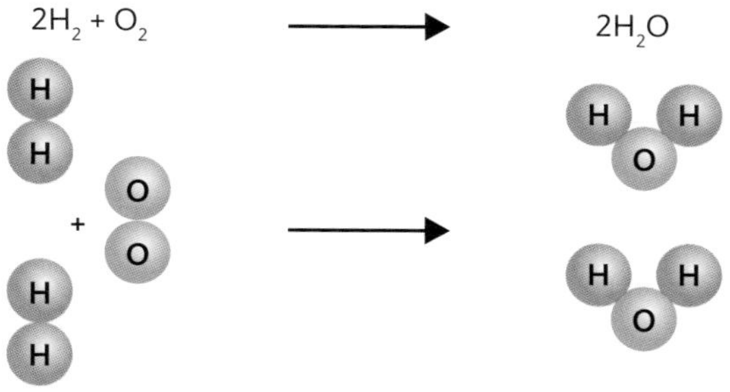


**Figure 1** Hydrogen reacts with oxygen to form water in a balanced chemical equation.

## Worked example — Grades 5–7

**1** 112 g of iron reacts with oxygen to produce 160 g of iron oxide. Calculate the mass of oxygen used in this reaction. **[2 marks]**

iron + oxygen → iron oxide

112 g    ?    160 g

160 − 112 = 48 g

**2** Magnesium and chlorine react to produce magnesium chloride in the following reaction.

$Mg + Cl_2 \rightarrow MgCl_2$

Show that mass is conserved in this reaction.

(Atomic masses: Mg = 12; Cl = 35.5) **[3 marks]**

$Mg + Cl_2 \rightarrow MgCl_2$

$12 + (2 \times 35.5) \rightarrow 12 + (2 \times 35.5)$

83 → 83

### Exam focus

In the exam, you may need to use the law of conservation of mass to work out the unknown mass of a substance in a reaction.

1. Write the word equation for the reaction.
2. Write the masses provided in the question under the correct substance.
3. Rearrange the masses to calculate the missing substance. Don't forget to include units in your answer.

Conservation of mass can be shown by adding up the relative atomic mass (see pages 87 and 96) each of the atoms either side of a balanced symbol equation.

The total mass of the atoms on the left hand side (the reactants) will always equal the total mass of the atoms on the right hand side, in a balanced equation.

## Exam-style practice — Grade 5

**1** When iodine is heated, it sublimes (changes from a solid to a gaseous state). If 50 g of iodine is heated, calculate the mass of the iodine vapour produced. **[2 marks]**

**2** When heated, magnesium carbonate thermally decomposes, producing magnesium oxide and carbon dioxide.

**(a)** Write a word equation for this reaction. **[1 mark]**

**(b)** If 84 g of magnesium carbonate is used and 40 g of magnesium oxide is produced, calculate the mass of carbon dioxide produced in the reaction. **[2 marks]**

# Relative formula mass

The relative formula mass of a compound is found by adding together the relative atomic masses of all the atoms in the compound.

## 5 Relative formula mass

**Relative formula mass** ($M_r$) is the sum of the relative atomic masses of all the atoms in a compound. For example, to find the $M_r$ of sodium hydroxide (NaOH), you add together the $A_r$ values of all the atoms in its formula:

$A_r$ of Na is 23

$A_r$ of O is 16

$A_r$ of H is 1

so the $M_r$ of NaOH is 23 + 16 + 1 = 40.

In a balanced equation, the sum of the $M_r$ of the reactants is equal to the sum of the $M_r$ of the products.

## 10 Worked example — Grades 6–7

**1** Calculate the relative formula mass of carbon dioxide. **[2 marks]**

$CO_2 = C + (2 \times O)$

$= 12 + (2 \times 16)$

$= 44$

**2** Calculate the relative formula mass of zinc nitrate.

The formula for zinc nitrate is $Zn(NO_3)_2$.

($A_r$ values: Zn = 65; N = 14; O = 16) **[2 marks]**

$A_r$ of Zn = 65

$M_r$ of $(NO_3)_2$ =

$2 \times N + 2 \times O_3$

$2 \times 14 + 2 \times (3 \times 16)$

$28 + 2 \times 48$

$28 + 96$

$= 124$

$M_r$ of $Zn(NO_3)_2 = 124 + 65 = 189$

Go to page 87 to revise relative atomic mass.

Look at the periodic table to find the relative atomic mass of each atom.

The relative formula mass has no units.

When there are brackets, the subscript number that follows means everything inside the brackets is multiplied by that number.

The '2' in $O_2$ refers to a pair of atoms that are joined together. Whereas, the '2' in $(NO_3)_2$ means there are two separate $NO_3$ ions, so you need to multiply each atom in $NO_3$ by two.

## 10 Exam-style practice — Grades 6–7

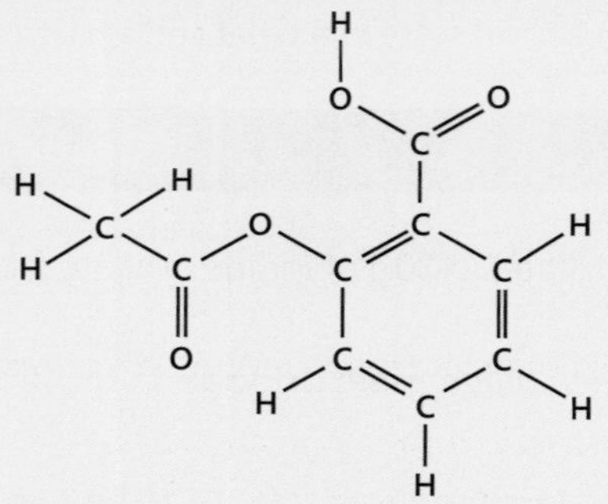


**Figure 1** Aspirin

**1** **Figure 1** represents a molecule of aspirin.
Calculate the relative formula mass of aspirin.
($A_r$ values: C = 12; H = 1; O = 16) **[2 marks]**

**2** Calculate the relative formula mass of aluminium sulfate. The formula for aluminium sulfate is $Al_2(SO_4)_3$.
($A_r$ values: Al = 27; S = 32; O = 16) **[2 marks]**



Made a start / Feeling confident / Exam ready

# Balancing equations

You need to be able to balance a chemical equation given the masses of reactants and products, using the law of conservation of mass.

## 5 Balancing equations

Chemical reactions can be represented by balanced symbol equations. In a balanced chemical equation, there must always be the same number of each element on either side of the arrow. This is because no atoms are lost or made in a chemical reaction.

Chemical equations can only be balanced by putting multipliers in front of the formulae of elements or compounds. You cannot change the formulae of elements or compounds to balance an equation.

**$H_2O$**

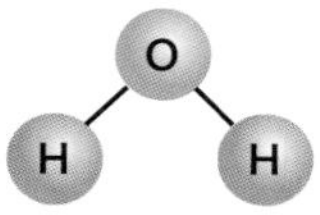


**Figure 1** $H_2O$ is a molecule with one oxygen and two hydrogens.

If you tried to balance an equation by adding a 2 to the end of the formula you would end up with a new substance – hydrogen peroxide $H_2O_2$.

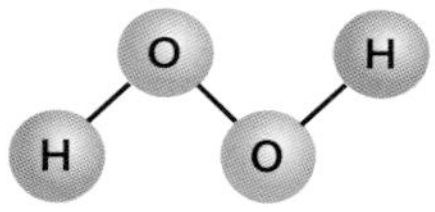


**Figure 2** Hydrogen peroxide, $H_2O_2$

## 5 Checking balanced equations

You can check that an equation is balanced using the law of conservation of mass. For example, aluminium reacts with bromine to create aluminium bromide in the equation:

$2Al + 3Br_2 \rightarrow 2AlBr_3$

To check that the equation is balanced, use relative formula mass ($M_r$) to find the total mass of the reactants and products.

| Reactants | | |
|---|---|---|
| 2Al | $2 \times 27$ | $= 54$ |
| $3Br_2$ | $3 \times (80 \times 2)$ | $= 480$ |
| $2Al + 3Br_2$ | $54 + 480$ | $= 534$ |

| Products | | |
|---|---|---|
| $AlBr_3$ | $2 \times (27 + (3 \times 80))$ | $= 267$ |
| $2AlBr_3$ | $2 \times 267$ | $= 534$ |

The total masses for the reactants and products are equal, so the equation is balanced.

Go to page 95 for more about the law of conservation of mass.

## 5 Worked example — Grade 6

Balance the following equations.

**(a)** $CH_4 + \underline{2}O_2 \rightarrow CO_2 + \underline{2}H_2O$ **[1 mark]**

Carbon: $1 \rightarrow 1$

Oxygen: $2 \rightarrow 1$

Hydrogen: $4 \rightarrow 2$

**(b)** $\underline{2}Na + \underline{2}H_2O \rightarrow \underline{2}NaOH + H_2$ **[1 mark]**

Sodium: $1 \rightarrow 1$

Hydrogen: $2 \rightarrow 3$

Oxygen: $1 \rightarrow 1$

Symbol equations show the balanced chemical formulae of reactants and products. Word equations show names of the reactants and products but are not balanced.

Work out how many atoms of each element are present on each side of the equation.

Adding a 2 before $H_2O$ balances the hydrogen atoms. There are now 4 oxygen atoms on the right side of the reaction and 2 on the left. Adding a 2 before $O_2$ balances the oxygen atoms.

## 10 Exam-style practice — Grade 7

1. Iron reacts with oxygen to produce iron(III) oxide, $Fe_2O_3$. Write a balanced symbol equation to show the reaction that takes place. **[2 marks]**
2. Give **two** reasons why a balanced equation is more useful than a word equation for describing a reaction. **[2 marks]**
3. Give a reason why chemical equations always balance. **[1 mark]**

# Mass changes

Some chemical reactions seem to involve a change in mass. This is usually because one of the reactants or products is a gas.

## 5 Change in mass

If a reactant or a product is a gas, its mass is often not included in calculations. This occurs when a reaction does not take place in a **closed system**. There are two possibilities:

1. A gaseous product escapes while the reaction takes place. The product mass will be lower than the reactant mass.
2. Gases from the air enter a reaction. They have not been measured with the reactants so the mass will appear to increase.

Change in mass can be calculated using the law of conservation of mass (page 95). For example, after heating 6.2 g of copper carbonate (**Figure 1**), the product (copper oxide) has a mass of 4 g. This means that 2.2 g of gas was produced and lost to the atmosphere during the reaction.

Go to page 123 to revise the tests for different gases.

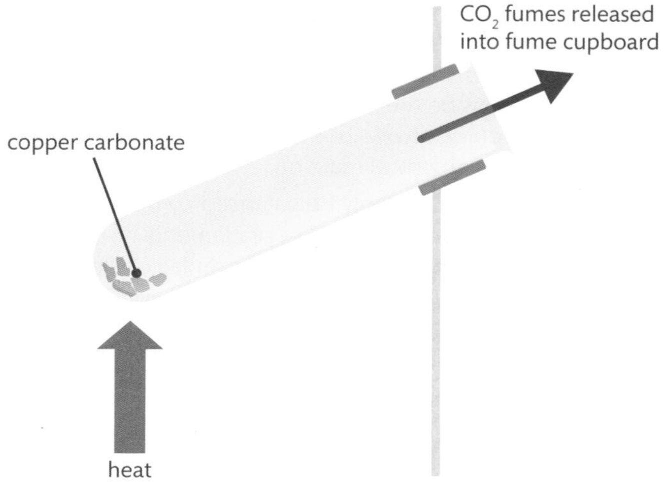


**Figure 1** Heating copper carbonate will cause it to decompose and release carbon dioxide. If the gas is not collected, there will appear to be a loss in mass during the reaction.

## 5 Worked example — Grade 5

For each of the following reactions, explain how and why the mass may appear to change during each reaction.

**(a)** magnesium + oxygen → magnesium oxide **[2 marks]**

The mass appears to increase because oxygen from the air is gained in the reaction.

**(b)** calcium carbonate → calcium oxide + carbon dioxide **[2 marks]**

The mass appears to decrease because carbon dioxide is given off in the reaction.

When a metal is heated, it may react with oxygen from the air. The mass of the magnesium oxide will be greater than the mass of the magnesium.

When a substance undergoes thermal decomposition, the mass of the products may appear to have decreased as the gas produced can escape, leaving only the metal oxide as the product.

Think about the conditions required for the law of conservation of mass (page 95).

## 10 Exam-style practice — Grade 7

1. When heated, zinc carbonate decomposes to produce zinc oxide and carbon dioxide.
   **(a)** Give the word equation for this reaction. **[1 mark]**
   **(b)** A student decomposed 50 g of zinc carbonate in unsealed container. After the reaction, there was only 32 g of product. Give a reason why. **[1 mark]**
   **(c)** Explain how a closed system could be used to improve accuracy when measuring the mass of the products. **[2 marks]**
2. When ethanol, $C_2H_5OH$, burns it reacts with oxygen from the air to produce carbon dioxide and water.
   **(a)** Write a balanced symbol equation, with state symbols, to show the reaction. **[2 marks]**
   $C_2H_5OH(l)$ + _____ → _____ + _____
   **(b)** Explain why the mass appears to increase during the reaction. **[1 mark]**

# Chemical measurements

You need to know the factors that affect the uncertainty of measurements and be able to make estimations about uncertainty.

## 10 Uncertainty of measurements

All measurements have a degree of uncertainty regardless of the **precision** and **accuracy** involved. Measurements are precise if they are very similar to each other. The accuracy of a set of results is a measure of how close they are to the true value. Accuracy of measurements can be improved by taking averages of a series of trials.

There are three main factors affecting uncertainty:

- the limitation of the measuring instrument
- the skill of the experimenter taking the measurements
- changes in the environment, e.g. temperature.

Go to page 240 to revise planning practicals and choosing suitable apparatus.

**Human error** in measurement is not classed as a factor. **Anomalous results** are results that do not fit the trend; they should be ignored when taking the mean of a set of results.

| Systematic error | Random error |
|---|---|
| If a measuring cylinder measures 9.8 $cm^3$ at the 10 $cm^3$ mark, every measurement will be out by about 0.2 $cm^3$. | Random errors are variable; they could fall either side of the true value. |
| Taking the mean value is unlikely to give a more accurate value as each measurement will have the same error. | Taking a series of readings and then finding the mean of these results will increase the accuracy of the value. |
| The error is reproducible. | The error is not reproducible. |

## 10 Worked example — Grade 7

**1** A student measures the volume of gas produced in 30 seconds. Calculate the mean, range and uncertainty of the results. **[3 marks]**

| Trial | 1 | 2 | 3 |
|---|---|---|---|
| Volume of gas produced in $cm^3$ | 55.2 | 48.4 | 58.4 |

mean $= \frac{(55.2 + 48.4 + 58.4)}{3} = 54.0\ cm^3$

range $= 58.4 - 48.4 = 10.0\ cm^3$

uncertainty $= \frac{10}{2} = 5.0\ cm^3$

the uncertainty of the mean is $54.0 \pm 5.0\ cm^3$

### Working scientifically

- To calculate the mean add up the results for each trial and divide by how many trials there are.
- To calculate the range find the difference between the highest and the lowest values.
- To calculate uncertainty divide the range by two.

**2** Two students carried out the same experiment three times. Their results are shown in the table.

| Student 1: time for X to dissolve in s | Student 2: time for X to dissolve in s |
|---|---|
| 62 | 59 |
| 87 | 67 |
| 53 | 63 |

**(a)** Suggest which student's results were more precise. Explain your answer. **[2 marks]**

Student 2 – the measurements are closer together

**(b)** How could the students reduce the effect of random errors on their results? **[1 mark]**

By calculating the mean

**(c)** Calculate the uncertainty of Student 1's results. **[2 marks]**

Range of results $= 87 - 53 = 34$

Uncertainty $= \frac{\text{range}}{\text{number of trials}} = \frac{34}{2} = 17$

## 5 Exam-style practice — Grade 7

The table shows the time it takes to dissolve magnesium ribbon in hydrochloric acid. Use the results to calculate the mean, range and uncertainty. **[5 marks]**

| Trial number | 1 | 2 | 3 | 4 | 5 |
|---|---|---|---|---|---|
| Time taken to dissolve in s | 154.4 | 167.7 | 162.1 | 171.3 | 159.4 |

# Moles

It is impossible to weigh a single atom because they are too small, so scientists measure amounts of substances in moles. This enables scientists to compare the amount of each substance in a reaction.

## 10 Measuring substances

Chemical amounts are measured in **moles**. The symbol for mole is **mol**. One mole of a substance has the same number of particles as one mole of another substance, regardless of their different properties. Moles can refer to the number of particles, atoms, ions or molecules in a substance. For example, one mole of helium (He) has the same number of atoms as the number of molecules in one mole of water ($H_2O$).

One mole (mol) of a substance contains $6.02 \times 10^{23}$ particles. This numerical value is known as the **Avogadro constant**. Using this constant means one mole of a substance will have a mass in grams equal to the relative formula mass of the atoms or molecules.

## 15 Worked example — Grade 7

The relative atomic masses ($A_r$) of hydrogen, oxygen and helium are: H = 1; O = 16; He = 4.

**1** What is the mass of one mole of helium? **[1 mark]**

4 g

**2** **(a)** Calculate the relative formula mass ($M_r$) of water ($H_2O$). **[1 mark]**

16 + 1 + 1 = 18

**(b)** What is the mass of one mole of water? **[1 mark]**

18 g

**3** Calculate the number of moles of water in 99 g. **[3 marks]**

$$\text{moles} = \frac{m}{M_r} = \frac{99}{18} = 5.5\ \text{mol}$$

**4** How many atoms are there in one mole of helium? **[1 mark]**

$6.02 \times 10^{23}$

**5** Calculate the mass, in grams, of lithium oxide ($Li_2O$) in 5 moles. **[3 marks]**

Li = 7 $Li_2 = 2 \times 7 = 14$

O = 16

$M_r = 30$

mass = $5 \times 30 = 150$ g

The mass of one mole of an element is equal to its relative atomic mass ($A_r$) in grams.

**Maths skills**

You can use this formula triangle to calculate number of moles, mass or relative formula mass by substituting in the known values.

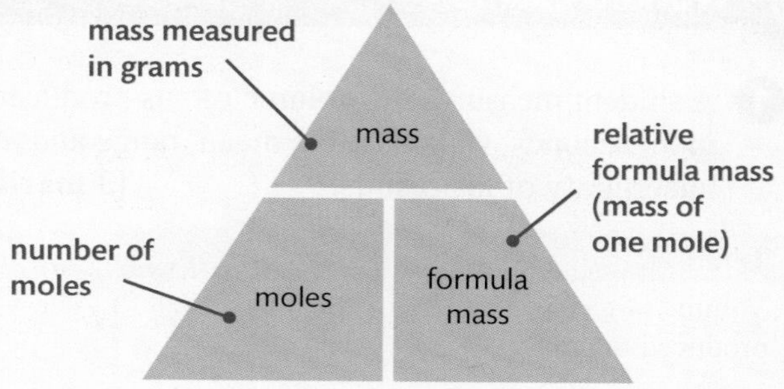


The mass of one mole of a molecule is equal to its relative formula mass ($M_r$) in grams.

One mole of any atom contains $6.02 \times 10^{23}$ particles. This is the Avogadro constant.

Calculate the $M_r$ of $Li_2O$.

## 5 Exam-style practice — Grade 7

**1** State the mass of one mole of $O_2$. **[1 mark]**

**2** State how many moles of each reactant are in the equation given below. **[2 marks]**

$Mg + 2HCl \rightarrow MgCl_2 + H_2$

**3** Calculate the number of moles in 10 000 g of calcium carbonate ($CaCO_3$). **[3 marks]**

$A_r$: Ca = 40; C = 12; O = 16

# Amounts of substances

You need to know how to calculate the mass of products and reactants from balanced symbol equations.

## 5 Balanced equations

Balanced equations show how many moles of substances react to make a product. Go to page 100 to revise moles.

$2Cu(s) + O_2(g) \rightarrow 2CuO(s)$

This equation tells you that two moles of copper (solid) react with one mole of oxygen (gas) to produce two moles of copper oxide (solid).

You can calculate the mass of reactants and products from a balanced equation and a given mass using the following steps:

1. Balance the given equation.
2. Calculate the relative formula mass, $M_r$.
3. Rearrange the mole calculation triangle to find mass from the $M_r$ and number of moles.

## 10 Worked example — Grade 8

What mass of sodium chloride is produced by 0.35 g of sodium hydroxide reacting with an excess of hydrochloric acid?

**[4 marks]**

($A_r$: Na = 23, Cl = 35.5, O = 16, H = 1)

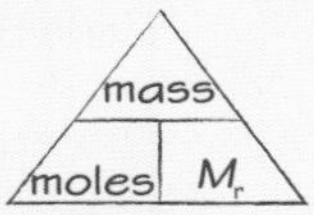


$NaOH(aq) + HCl(aq) \rightarrow NaCl(aq) + H_2O(l)$

1 mole : 1 mole

40 : 58.5

$0.35 \div 40 = 0.00875$ mol

1 : 1 so NaCl = 0.00875 mol

$0.00875 \times 58.5 = 0.511875$

$= 0.51$ g

It is common for an excess of one of the reactants to be used in a reaction to ensure all of the other reactant is used up. Go to page 125 to revise limiting reactants.

**Maths skills**

Draw a formula triangle, and cover up the quantity you need to find. For example, to find mass, you multiply the number of moles by the relative formula mass ($M_r$).

Write out the balanced equation and work out the ratio of moles reacting and work out the $M_r$ for the molecules involved, i.e. the mass of one mole.

Divide the given mass of sodium hydroxide by the relative formula mass of sodium hydroxide.

As one mole of sodium hydroxide reacts to give one mole of sodium chloride, 0.00875 moles of sodium hydroxide produces 0.00875 moles of sodium chloride.

## 10 Exam-style practice — Grade 8

1. **(a)** Balance this equation.
   $Mg(s) + O_2(g) \rightarrow MgO(s)$ **[1 mark]**
   **(b)** If 55 g of magnesium reacts with excess oxygen, calculate how much magnesium oxide will be produced.
   ($A_r$ : Mg = 24, O = 16) **[4 marks]**
2. Calculate how much calcium reacts with excess hydrochloric acid to produce 0.5 g of calcium chloride.
   ($A_r$: Ca = 40, Cl = 35.5, H = 1)
   $Ca(s) + 2HCl(aq) \rightarrow CaCl_2(aq) + H_2(g)$ **[4 marks]**

# Concentrations of solutions

Many chemical reactions take place in solutions. The concentration of a solution depends on the mass of solute and the volume of solution.

## 5 Calculating concentrations

A solution is prepared by dissolving a solute (solid) in a solvent (liquid).
The concentration of a solution is how much solute is dissolved into the solvent.

Concentration can be calculated using the formula given below:

$$\text{concentration (g/dm}^3\text{)} = \frac{\text{mass (g)}}{\text{volume (dm}^3\text{)}} \qquad c = \frac{m}{v}$$

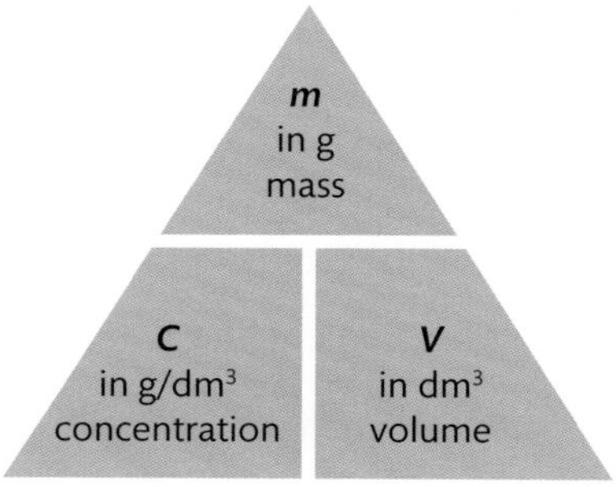


To find the mass of solute, you need to rearrange the formula:

mass (g) = concentration (g/dm$^3$) × volume (dm$^3$)

If the mass of solute is increased but the volume of solvent stays the same, the concentration of the solution will increase.

If the volume of solvent is increased but the mass of solute stays the same, the concentration of the solution will decrease.

## 10 Worked example — Grade 7

**1** Calculate the mass of solute needed to be dissolved in 1.5 dm of a solvent to produce a concentration of 3 g/dm$^3$. **[3 marks]**

mass = concentration × volume

3 × 1.5 = 4.5 g

Use the formula triangle to rearrange the calculation for mass.

**2** 58 g of sodium hydroxide was dissolved in water. What volume of solution was used to produce a concentration of 16.11 g/dm$^3$? **[3 marks]**

You can use the units as a clue to work out the formula. The units of concentration are g/dm$^3$. This tells you that concentration = mass ÷ volume.

$$v = \frac{m}{c} = \frac{58}{16.11} = 3.6 \text{ dm}^3$$

**3** Calculate the concentration of a solution of sodium carbonate, when 37 g of sodium carbonate is dissolved in 4.25 dm$^3$ of solvent. **[3 marks]**

Give your answer to no more than 2 or 3 significant figures.

$$c = \frac{m}{v} = \frac{37}{4.25} = 8.70588235$$
$$= 8.71 \text{ g/dm}^3$$

Remember to give the correct units.

## 2 Maths skills

You need to know how to convert units from cm$^3$ to dm$^3$ and vice versa.

1 dm$^3$ = 1000 cm$^3$ (multiply by 1000)

1 cm$^3$ = 0.001 dm$^3$ (divide by 1000)

## 10 Exam-style practice — Grade 7

**1** A student dissolves 60 g of sodium chloride in 1.5 dm$^3$ of water.
Calculate the concentration of the solution of sodium chloride produced. **[2 marks]**

**2** Calculate the mass of calcium chloride needed to produce a solution with a concentration of 10 g/dm$^3$ when dissolved into 5 dm$^3$ of water. **[3 marks]**

**3** Explain how increasing the mass of solute used affects the concentration of the solution produced, when the same volume of solvent is used. **[1 mark]**

# Using mass to balance equations

You need to know how to calculate the masses of reactants and products from the balanced symbol equation for a reaction.

## Using reacting masses to balance equations

If you have the masses of all the reactants and products in an equation, you can use these values to balance the equation and show how many moles of each substance react.

To balance equations using given masses you should follow these steps:

1. Calculate the relative formula mass, $M_r$.
2. Rearrange the mole calculation triangle and calculate the number of moles of each substance.
3. Use the ratio of moles to balance the equation.

Divide the given mass, in grams, of each substance by its $M_r$ to get the number of moles of each substance.

## Worked example — Grade 8

**1** 12 g of magnesium reacts completely with 8 g of oxygen to produce 20 g of magnesium oxide. Give the balanced equation for the reaction. **[4 marks]**

$M_r$: Mg = 24; $O_2$ = 32; MgO = 40

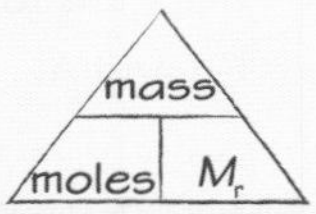


Mg = 12 ÷ 24 = 0.5 mol

$O_2$ = 8 ÷ 32 = 0.25 mol

MgO = 20 ÷ 40 = 0.5 mol

0.5 ÷ 0.25 = 2Mg

0.25 ÷ 0.25 = $1O_2$

0.5 ÷ 0.25 = 2MgO

$2Mg + O_2 \rightarrow 2MgO$

The lowest value is 0.25. Dividing the highest values (0.5) by the lowest value gives the ratio 2 : 1 : 2. This means two moles of magnesium react with one mole of oxygen to form two moles of magnesium oxide.

**2** 7 g of $N_2$ reacts with 1.5 g of hydrogen to produce 8.5 g of $NH_3$. Write a balanced equation for the reaction. **[4 marks]**

$M_r$: $N_2$ = 28; $H_2$ = 2; $NH_3$ = 17

$N_2$ = 7 ÷ 28 = 0.25 mol

$H_2$ = 1.5 ÷ 2 = 0.75 mol

$NH_3$ = 8.5 ÷ 17 = 0.5 mol

0.25 ÷ 0.25 = $1N_2$

0.75 ÷ 0.25 = $3H_2$

0.5 ÷ 0.25 = $2NH_3$

$N_2 + 3H_2 \rightarrow 2NH_3$

Divide all the values by the lowest value. If the values derived are not whole numbers, multiply all the values by the same amount to get whole numbers.

When writing balanced equations, you don't need to put a number before the formula if there is one mole of the substance.

## Exam-style practice — Grade 8

**1** 15.9 g of copper(II) oxide (CuO) was reduced by 0.4 g of hydrogen to produce 12.7 g copper and 3.6 g of water. Write the balanced equation for the reaction. **[4 marks]**

**2** **(a)** A student reacted 13 g of zinc with 14.6 g of hydrogen chloride gas, producing 27.2 g of zinc chloride and 0.4 g hydrogen gas. Give the balanced equation for the reaction. **[4 marks]**

**(b)** Describe what the numbers in front of the chemical formulae represent. **[1 mark]**

# Chemical bonds

You need to be able to apply knowledge about the types of chemical bonds to the physical and chemical properties of substances.

## 5 Types of bonding

You need to know about three types of chemical bond: ionic, covalent and metallic (page 133).

Chemical bonding occurs because atoms need a full outer shell of electrons to become stable.

Atoms can join together by **transferring** electrons (page 105) or by **sharing** electrons (page 114).

## 5 Structure

Structural analyses of atoms and compounds show that atoms can be arranged in a variety of ways. Depending on the types of bonding between atoms, simple molecular structures or giant structures can form.

Scientists have engineered new materials with useful properties using their understanding of structure and bonding.

## 10 Comparing types of bonding

| **Type of bonding** | ionic bonding | covalent bonding | metallic bonding |
|---|---|---|---|
| **Occurs between** | metals and non-metals | non-metallic elements and compounds of non-metals | metallic elements and alloys |
| **Diagram** | 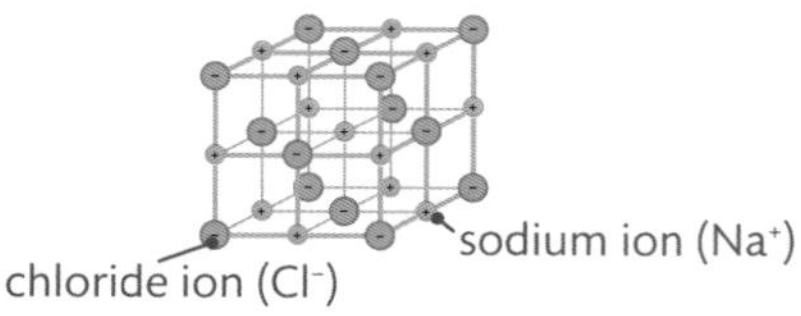  | 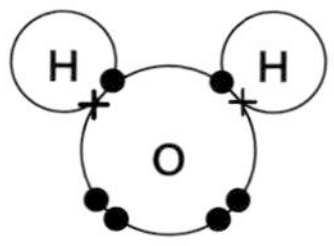  | 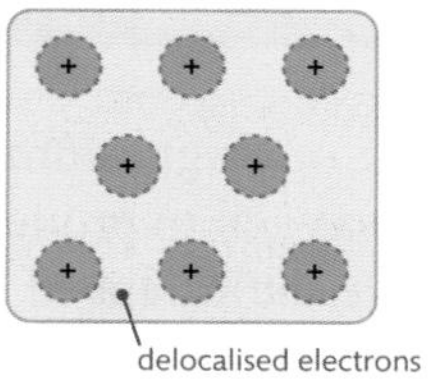  |
| **How the bonds form** | Oppositely charged ions are attracted by electrostatic attraction. | Atoms share a pair of electrons. | Positive ions are surrounded by delocalised electrons. |
| **Examples** | NaCl and MgO | $CO_2$ and $H_2O$ | Cu and Al |

## 10 Worked example — Grades 5–8

**1** Explain which type of bonding occurs in each of the following substances. **[3 marks]**

**(a)** sodium chloride

Ionic bonding because sodium is a metal and chlorine is a non-metal.

**(b)** magnesium metal

Metallic bonding because there are only metal atoms present.

**(c)** hydrogen gas

Covalent bonding because hydrogen is a non-metal.

Delocalised electrons are electrons that are free to move. The negatively charged electrons are attracted to the positively charged metal ions by electrostatic attraction.

**2** Explain each type of bonding with reference to the electrons involved and electrostatic forces. **[6 marks]**

Ionic bonding involves the transfer of electrons from one atom to another. This causes the ions to have opposite charges and so are electrostatically attracted to each other.

Covalent bonding involves the sharing of a pair of electrons to form a covalent bond. The positively charged nuclei of the bonded atoms are electrostatically attracted to the bonding pair of electrons.

Metallic bonding is formed by the electrostatic attraction between the positive metal ions and the delocalised electrons (from the outer shell of the metal atoms).

## 5 Exam-style practice — Grade 6

**(a)** Explain the term 'delocalised'. **[1 mark]**

**(b)** Name the type of bonding that involves delocalised electrons. **[1 mark]**

# Ionic bonding

You need to know how to describe ionic bonding and represent it using dot and cross diagrams.

## 5 Ionic bonding

Ionic bonding occurs in compounds formed from positive and negative ions. Metal atoms lose electrons to form positively charged ions, such as $Na^+$. Non-metal atoms gain electrons to form negatively charged ions, such as $Cl^-$.

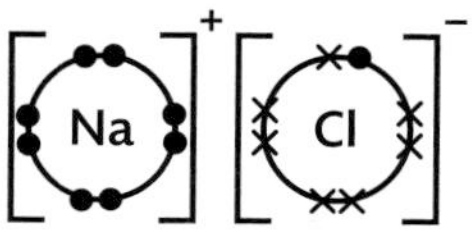


**Figure 1** Sodium loses an electron to become a positive ion and chlorine gains an electron to become a negative ion.

Sometimes, only the bonding electrons in the outer shell are displayed in dot and cross diagrams.

The ions that form the metals in Groups 1 and 2 and the non-metals in Groups 6 and 7 have the electronic structure of a Group 0 element.

## 10 Worked example — Grade 6

**Figure 3** The electronic structures of sodium and fluorine.

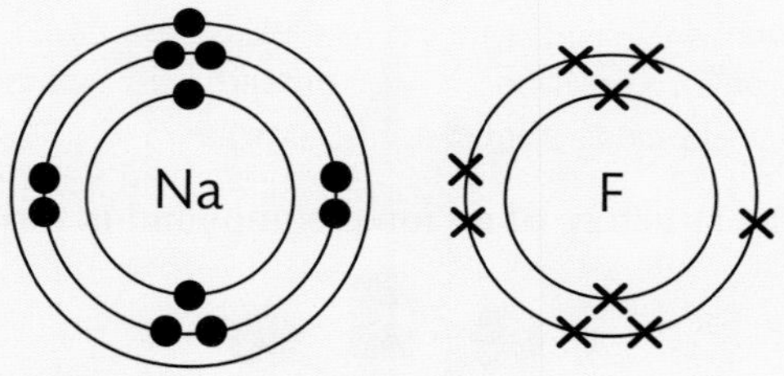


Look at **Figure 3.**

**(a)** Describe how fluorine atoms and sodium atoms form sodium fluoride. **[2 marks]**

Sodium atoms lose one electron to form ions with a $1^+$ charge. Fluorine atoms gain one electron to form ions with a $1^-$ charge.

**(b)** Draw each of the ions formed during the reaction. Give the charge on each of the ions formed. **[3 marks]**

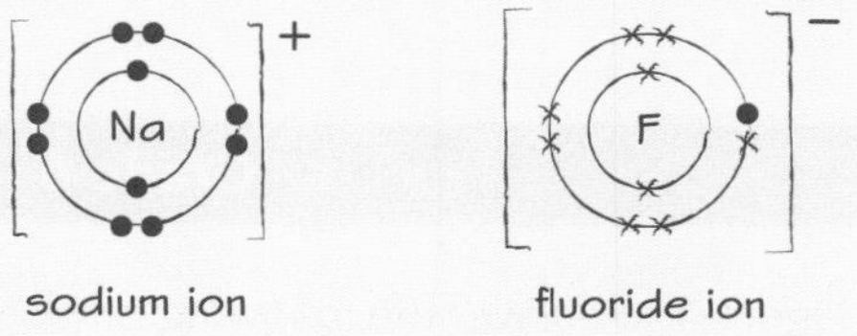


Sodium is in Group 1 so it has one electron in its outer shell. When sodium reacts, it needs to lose this outer electron to have a full outer shell. When sodium loses its negatively charged electron, the sodium ion becomes positively charged.

## 2 Electron transfer

Ionic bonds are formed by the transfer of electrons from metal atoms to non-metal atoms, so both gain a stable arrangement of electrons. Electron transfer is represented by dot and cross diagrams.

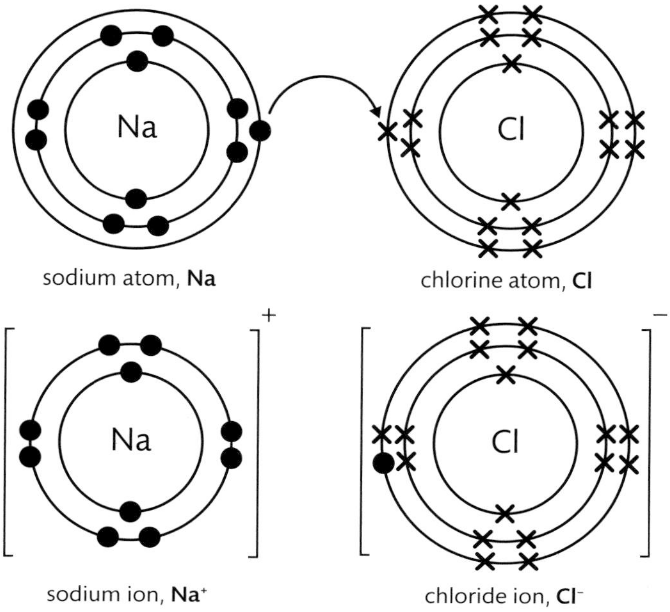


**Figure 2** The dot and cross diagrams show the formation of sodium chloride, an ionic compound. Go to page 107 to revise ionic compounds.

## 2 Exam focus

In the exam, you could be asked to draw dot and cross diagrams for ionic compounds formed between metals in Groups 1 and 2 and non-metals in Groups 6 and 7. Make sure you know the charge on the ions formed.

| Group | Charge of ion formed |
|---|---|
| 1 | 1+ |
| 2 | 2+ |
| 6 | 2– |
| 7 | 1– |

Fluorine is in Group 7 so it needs to gain one electron to have a full outer shell. Because fluorine gains an electron the fluoride ion is negatively charged.

## 5 Exam-style practice — Grade 6

Draw each of the ions formed during the reaction between magnesium and fluorine. Give the charge on each of the ions formed. **[3 marks]**

# Ionic compounds

You need to be able to identify ionic compounds and work out the empirical formula from different types of diagrams.

## 5 Giant ionic structures

Ionic compounds are comprised of many ions, which are held together by strong electrostatic forces of attraction. Ionic compounds form giant structures called **lattices**. The **electrostatic forces of attraction** between the ions are strong due to the attraction between the oppositely charged ions.

Ionic lattices are three-dimensional structures. The forces of attraction act in all directions throughout the lattice. Ionic compounds can be represented by:

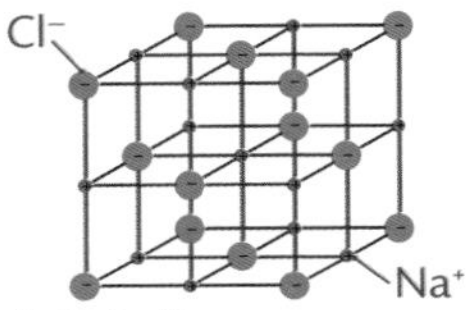


**Figure 1** A ball and stick diagram

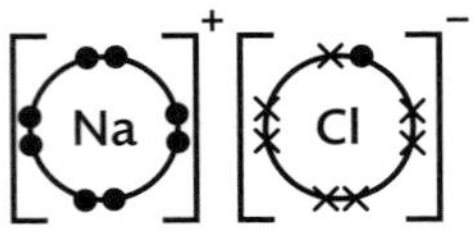


**Figure 2** A dot and cross diagram

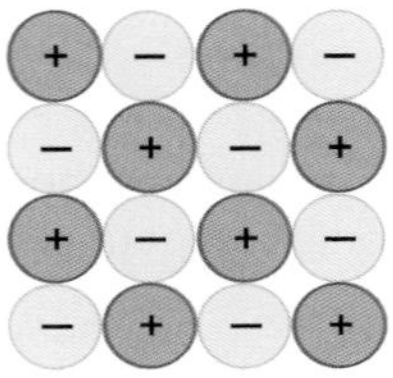

**Figure 3** Two-dimensional diagram

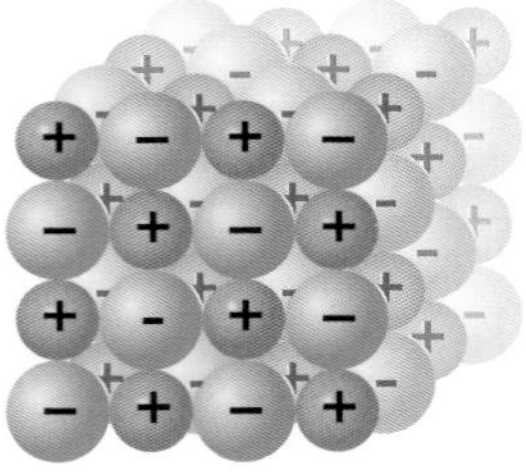

**Figure 4** A three-dimensional diagram

The empirical formula is the simplest whole number molar ratio of each ion in an ionic compound.

## 10 Worked example — Grade 7

**1** Give the limitations of each of the following models for representing ionic compounds.

**(a)** Ball and stick diagram **[2 marks]**

Ball and stick diagrams show a three-dimensional representation of the ions and indicate the bonds between the ions. However, as the models are not to scale, the size of the ions is incorrect.

**(b)** Dot and cross diagram **[2 marks]**

Dot and cross diagrams only give a two-dimensional representation of the ions in a single ionic bond. It is not possible to see the actual arrangement of the ions.

**(c)** Two-dimensional diagram **[2 marks]**

Two-dimensional diagrams don't show the electronic structure of the ions or the arrangement of giant structures.

**(d)** Three-dimensional diagram **[2 marks]**

Three-dimensional diagrams show the size of the ions and give a more realistic idea of the position of the ions; however, they do not show the bonds or the internal structure.

**2** The structure of an ionic compound is shown.

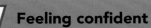

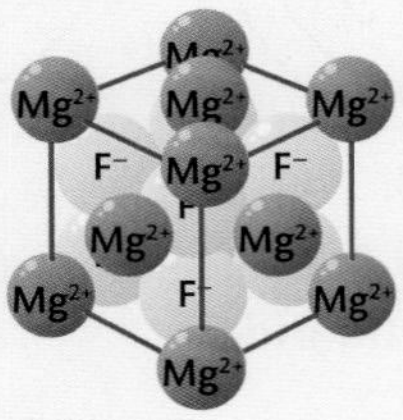


**(a)** Name the compound. **[1 mark]**

Magnesium fluoride

**(b)** State whether the empirical formula is $MgF_2$, $Mg_2F$ or MgF. **[1 mark]**

$MgF_2$

## 10 Exam-style practice — Grade 6

**1** Complete the sentence using words from the box. **[2 marks]**

| forces | electrostatic | ions | ionic | covalent |
|---|---|---|---|---|

Sodium chloride forms a giant ............ lattice, with strong ............ forces of attraction.

**2** Use **Figure 1** to answer the following questions.

**(a)** State the type of bonding shown. **[1 mark]**

**(b)** Give the empirical formula for the compound. **[1 mark]**

**(c)** Give **one** limitation and **one** advantage to using this type of model. **[2 marks]**

# Properties of ionic compounds

You can use the structure and type of bonding in an ionic compound to determine its properties.

## 5 Properties of ionic compounds

Go to page 105 to revise ionic bonding and the structure of ionic compounds.

| | |
|---|---|
| **Structure** | giant lattices |
| **Melting point** | generally high |
| **Boiling point** | generally high |
| **Electrical conductivity** | excellent conductors when molten or aqueous |
| **Solubility in water** | generally soluble |

Ionic compounds have high melting and boiling points because a large amount of energy is required to break the strong electrostatic forces that hold the oppositely charged ions together in all directions within the giant lattice structure.

Go to page 77 for more about state changes.

Ionic compounds can conduct electricity when melted (molten) or dissolved in water (aqueous) because the ions are free to move, allowing charge to flow.

## 10 Worked example — Grade 7

**Figure 1** The structure of sodium chloride

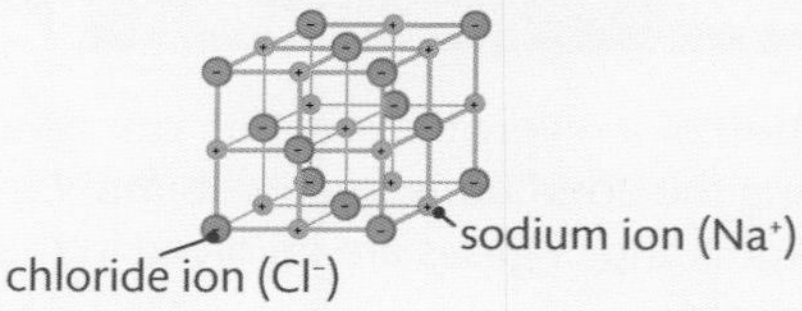


**1** Explain why sodium chloride cannot conduct electricity when solid. **[2 marks]**

*To conduct electricity, ions need to be free to allow the charge to flow. When solid, sodium ions and chloride ions are in fixed positions, held by strong ionic bonds, and so are unable to conduct electricity.*

**2** Explain why sodium chloride melts when heated strongly. **[2 marks]**

*When heated, the ions gain enough energy to overcome the forces of attraction and move apart.*

**3** Explain why sodium chloride has a high melting point (801 °C). **[2 marks]**

*Sodium chloride is made of oppositely charged ions, which are held together by strong electrostatic forces of attraction in all directions that require a large amount of energy to overcome.*

## 2 Exam focus

In your exam, you will only need to know about the structure of sodium chloride. However, you may be asked to apply your knowledge about this structure to explain the properties of other ionic compounds.

## 10 Exam-style practice — Grade 7

**1** Chlorine reacts with sodium to produce sodium chloride (NaCl).

**(a)** Give a balanced symbol equation for the reaction. **[2 marks]**

**(b)** Use a dot and cross diagram to show the bonding in sodium chloride. **[2 marks]**

**2** Magnesium oxide has a similar structure to sodium chloride. Use your understanding of ionic compounds to answer the following questions about magnesium oxide.

**(a)** Describe the structure of magnesium oxide. You may use a diagram. **[2 marks]**

**(b)** Give a reason that explains why magnesium oxide can conduct electricity when molten. **[1 mark]**

**(c)** Give a reason that explains why magnesium oxide has a high melting point. **[2 marks]**

# Reversible reactions

Many reactions, such as burning fuel, are irreversible – they go to completion and cannot be reversed easily. Some chemical reactions are reversible – the products of the reaction can react to form the original reactants.

## 5 Reversible reaction equations

A **reversible reaction** is indicated by a split arrow ($\rightleftharpoons$). This symbol means that the reaction can proceed in either direction.

A reversible reaction can be shown as:

$A + B \rightleftharpoons C + D$

In a closed system, equilibrium will be reached. **Equilibrium** occurs when the rate of the forward reaction is equal to the rate of the reverse reaction. Go to page 110 to revise equilbrium.

An **irreversible reaction** is shown by

$A + B \rightarrow C + D$

The products, C and D, do not react to form the reactants, A and B.

**Anhydrous** means without water.

## 2 A reversible reaction

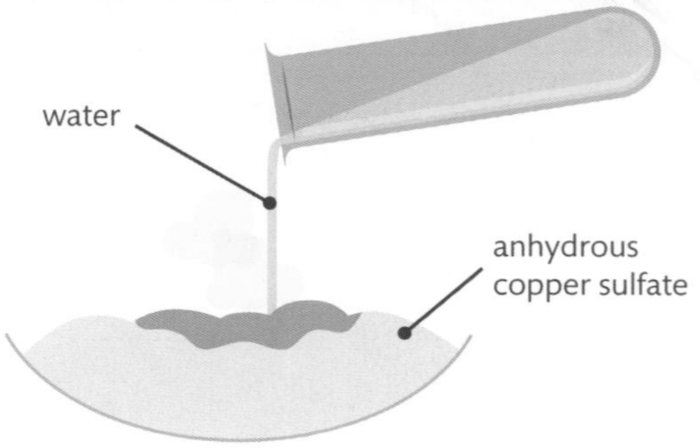


**Figure 1** When water is added to white anhydrous copper sulfate, blue hydrated copper sulfate forms. When hydrated copper sulfate is heated, it loses water and anhydrous copper sulfate forms.

The reaction between anhydrous copper sulfate and water is reversible.

hydrated copper sulfate $\rightleftharpoons$ anhydrous copper sulfate + water

## 10 Worked example — Grade 6

**1** Complete the word equation below, producing sulfur trioxide, to show that the reaction is reversible. **[1 mark]**

sulfur dioxide + oxygen $\rightleftharpoons$ *sulfur trioxide*

**2** Why is equilibrium only reached in a closed system? **[2 marks]**

*In an open system gaseous products can escape. If the system is closed, the gaseous products remain and can react to form the reactants.*

**3** The thermal decomposition of ammonium chloride, into ammonia and hydrogen chloride, is reversible. Write a word equation to show the reaction. **[2 marks]**

*ammonium chloride $\rightleftharpoons$ ammonia + hydrogen chloride*

The marks are awarded for correctly using the information from the question to write the word equation **and** for correctly showing the reaction is reversible.

**4** When water is added to a sample of blue anhydrous cobalt chloride, pink hydrated cobalt chloride forms.

**(a)** Write a word equation to show the reaction which took place. **[1 mark]**

*anhydrous cobalt chloride + water $\rightleftharpoons$ hydrated cobalt chloride*

**(b)** Explain how you could prove that this reaction is reversible. **[2 marks]**

*Heat the hydrated cobalt chloride to drive off the water. The cobalt chloride will change colour back to blue showing that the reaction has reversed.*

## 5 Direction

The direction of a reversible reaction can be altered by changing the conditions, such as temperature, concentration and, if gases are involved in the reaction, pressure.

Some reactions involve a colour change or a change of state. For example, when solid white ammonium chloride is heated, it forms two colourless gases. When these gases are cooled, solid white ammonium chloride reforms.

## 10 Exam-style practice — Grade 6

**1** The reaction between hydrogen and nitrogen is reversible. Define reversible. **[2 marks]**

**2** When hydrated copper sulfate is heated it changes colour from blue to white, producing anhydrous copper sulfate. When water is added, hydrated copper sulfate is reformed.

**(a)** Explain the observation that proves this reaction is reversible. **[1 mark]**

**(b)** Write a word equation to show the reaction taking place. **[2 marks]**

# Energy changes in reversible reactions

In a reversible reaction, the amount of energy released in one direction is equal to the amount of energy absorbed in the opposite direction.

## 5 Energy changes in reversible reactions

In a reversible reaction, energy needs to be supplied to drive the reaction in one direction. This is an **endothermic** reaction. When the reaction occurs in the opposite direction, energy will be released, usually as thermal energy. This is an **exothermic** reaction. The amount of energy released in one direction is equal to the amount of energy absorbed in the opposite direction. Go to page 145 for more about endothermic and exothermic reactions.

For example, when copper sulfate is dehydrated, energy must be supplied because it is an endothermic reaction. Energy is supplied in the form of thermal energy to drive out the water. When water is added to anhydrous copper sulfate, the reaction is exothermic and the water can be seen to bubble and spit due to the thermal energy being released.

hydrated copper sulfate $\rightleftharpoons$ anhydrous copper sulfate + water

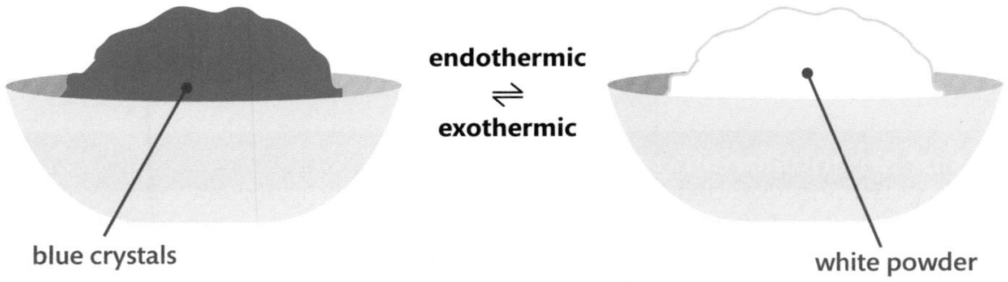


## 10 Worked example — Grade 7

The following word equation shows the reaction between anhydrous cobalt chloride paper and water, producing hydrated cobalt chloride:

anhydrous cobalt chloride + water $\rightleftharpoons$ hydrated cobalt chloride

**(a)** Describe what sort of reaction the word equation shows.

**[1 mark]**

*Reversible reaction*

**(b)** When a student adds water to the anhydrous cobalt chloride, a reaction takes place. What does the student observe?

**[2 marks]**

*The blue cobalt chloride turns pink.*

**(c)** The student repeats the reaction. During the reaction, the student measures the temperature with a thermometer. Describe how the temperature changes during the reaction. Explain why this happens.

**[2 marks]**

*The temperature increases as the water is added. This is because the reaction is an exothermic reaction in the forward direction.*

## 2 Working scientifically

The energy changes can be seen in the reversible reaction of copper sulfate. To dehydrate the copper sulfate, energy must be supplied: it is an endothermic reaction. It is heated to drive off the water.

If water is added to anhydrous copper sulfate, the reaction is exothermic and the water can be seen to bubble and spit due to the thermal energy being released.

Remember to state the appearance of the reactant at the start as well as how it appears after the reaction has taken place.

## 10 Exam-style practice — Grade 5

1. Explain why in an endothermic reaction the temperature of the surroundings decreases.

**[2 marks]**

2. Calcium carbonate is converted to calcium oxide by thermal decomposition. State if this is an exothermic or endothermic reaction. Explain your answer.

**[2 marks]**

3. If a reaction produces 256 kJ/mol of energy in the forward reaction, determine how much energy will be needed for the reverse reaction to occur.

**[1 mark]**

# Equilibrium and changing conditions

You need to understand equilibrium reactions and know about the conditions that affect them.

## 10 Reaching equilbiurm

Equilibrium is reached in a reversible reaction when the forward reaction occurs at exactly the **same rate** as the reverse reaction. For equilibrium to be achieved the reaction must take place in sealed apparatus (**closed system**).

1. At the start of the reaction there is no product.
2. As the reaction starts it proceeds in the forward direction (to the right). The moles of reactant are being used up and the moles of product are formed.
3. The reaction moves in the reverse direction (to the left), favouring the production of the reactants.
4. The reaction reaches equilibrium when the rate of the forward reaction is equal to the rate of the reverse reaction.

The amount of reactants and products at any one time are not equal but their concentrations are balanced and the proportions of each reactant and product remain constant. There is usually more of one than the other.

- If the concentration of the reactants is greater than the products, the position of the equilibrium is on the left.
- If the concentration of the products is greater than the reactants, the position of the equilibrium is on the right.

## 5 Changing conditions of an equilibrium reaction

When the conditions of a reversible reaction are altered, the position of equilibrium moves to counteract the change. This is known as **Le Chatelier's Principle**. Changing the pressure, concentration or temperature of a reaction will affect how much product or reactant is made. Go to pages 111–113 for more about how changing these conditions affects equilibrium.

Some industrial processes involve changing the conditions of an equilibrium reaction in order to maximise the yield of a product.

Product yield can be increased by:

- adding more reactants, which favours the forward reaction
- removing the products as they are produced, which favours the forward reaction
- changing the temperature and concentration or pressure (in gases) to favour the forward reaction.

## 5 Worked example — Grade 6

Ammonia and hydrogen chloride react in a reversible reaction.

ammonia + hydrogen chloride ⇌ ammonium chloride

The reaction is exothermic in the forward direction.

Use Le Chatelier's Principle to predict the effect of increasing the temperature on the amount of ammonium chloride produced. **[3 marks]**

*Increasing the temperature decreases the amount of ammonium chloride. Equilibrium will move in the endothermic direction; less ammonium chloride is produced.*

## 5 Exam-style practice — Grade 5

The contact process is a reversible reaction. It is used to make sulfur trioxide, which is used to manufacture sulfuric acid. The equation for the reaction is given below:

$2SO_2(g) + O_2(g) \rightleftharpoons 2SO_3(g)$

**(a)** Give **two** conditions that could be changed to affect the yield of sulfur trioxide. **[2 marks]**

**(b)** The forward reaction is exothermic. Explain what is meant by exothermic. **[1 mark]**

**(c)** Give a reason that explains why removing sulfur trioxide gas, as it is produced, will cause the yield to increase. **[1 mark]**

# Concentration and equilibrium

In a reversible reaction at equilibrium, if you change the concentration of a reactant or product, the system will oppose the change until equilibrium is restored. You need to know how changes in concentration will affect the position of the equilibrium and the concentrations of the reactants and products.

## 5 Changing concentration

If the concentration of the reactants or products is altered, the system is no longer at equilibrium. According to Le Chatelier's Principle, the concentrations of the reactants and products will change until equilibrium is re-established.

The table shows how changing the concentration of the components in the equation below effects the position of equilibrium.

$A + B \rightleftharpoons C + D$

| Change | Shifts the equilibrium |
|---|---|
| increase in the concentration of a reactant (A or B) | right |
| decrease in the concentration of a product (C or D) | right |
| decrease in the concentration of a reactant (A or B) | left |
| increase in the concentration of a products (C or D) | left |

Go to page 110 for more about Le Chatelier.

Shifting the equilibrium right means that more reactants will react, and so more products will be formed, until equilibrium is reached again.

## 10 Worked example — Grades 6–8

**1** Ammonia is manufactured from nitrogen and hydrogen in the Haber process, as shown in the equation below.

$N_2(g) + 3H_2(g) \rightleftharpoons 2NH_3(g)$

**(a)** How does the equation show that the it is a reversible reaction? **[1 mark]**

The arrow shows that the reaction can go in both directions.

**(b)** What would happen if the concentration of the reactants was increased? **[2 marks]**

Increasing the concentration of the reactants would shift equilibrium to the right, so more product would be formed.

**(c)** During the reaction the equilibrium of the system was found to lie to the left.

How does the concentration of the reactants compare to the concentration of the products? **[1 mark]**

The concentration of the reactants is higher than the concentration of the products.

**2** Methanol ($CH_3OH$) can be manufactured by reacting carbon monoxide and hydrogen together. The reaction is reversible. Write a balanced symbol equation to show this reaction. Explain how altering concentrations can cause the yield of methanol to be increased, relate your answer to Le Chatelier's principle. **[5 marks]**

$CO + 2H_2 \rightleftharpoons CH_3OH$

To increase the yield of methanol, the concentration of CO and $H_2$ need to be increased.

This will drive the position of equilibrium to the right hand side as the system will oppose the change and try to reduce the concentration of reactants by making more of the product.

If equilibrium lies to the left, the reverse reaction is favoured so the concentration of reactants will be higher than the products.

The yield is the amount of product obtained in the chemical reaction.

## 5 Exam-style practice — Grade 6

Hydrogen is produced industrially from reacting methane ($CH_4$) with water, as shown in the equation below.

$CH_4(g) + H_2O(g) \rightleftharpoons CO(g) + 3H_2(g)$

**(a)** Use Le Chatelier's Principle to predict how the yield of hydrogen would be affected by increasing the concentration of methane in the reaction. Give a reason for your answer. **[2 marks]**

**(b)** Describe what is meant by equilibrium. **[2 marks]**

Made a start | Feeling confident | Exam ready

# Temperature and equilibrium

In a reversible reaction at equilibrium, if you change the temperature, the system will oppose the change until equilibrium is restored. You need to know how changes in temperature will affect the position of the equilibrium in endothermic and exothermic reactions.

## 5 Changing temperature

If a reversible reaction is exothermic (gives out thermal energy) in one direction, it will be endothermic (takes in thermal energy) in the opposite direction. The amount of energy given out is always equal to the amount of energy taken in.

The system will oppose an increase in temperature by taking in thermal energy, favouring the endothermic reaction. The amount of products at equilibrium will increase in the endothermic reaction and decrease in the exothermic reaction.

The system will oppose a decrease in temperature by giving out thermal energy, favouring the exothermic reaction. The amount of products at equilibrium will increase in the exothermic reaction and decrease in the endothermic reaction.

## 10 Worked example — Grades 6–8

**1** Ammonia is manufactured from nitrogen and hydrogen. The reaction is exothermic in the forward direction.

How can the temperature be altered to give maximum yield of ammonia? **[2 marks]**

*The forward reaction is exothermic, so reducing the temperature will favour this reaction as the equilibrium will oppose the change by giving out more thermal energy.*

Exothermic reactions release thermal energy. Excess thermal energy needs to be removed to continue the reaction in the same direction, otherwise the endothermic reaction will be favoured.

**2** Ammonia and hydrochloric acid are colourless gases; ammonium chloride is a white solid.

A student reacts ammonia with hydrochloric acid in the reaction shown below.

ammonia + hydrogen chloride $\rightleftharpoons$ ammonium chloride

The reaction is exothermic in the forward direction. How could the student confirm the reverse reaction is endothermic? **[2 marks]**

*The student could heat the products. If the amount of white solid product is reduced, the backward reaction is endothermic.*

Thermal energy must be applied to ensure a reversible reaction proceeds in the endothermic direction.

**3** The reaction of $NO_2$ to $N_2O_4$ is reversible.

$2NO_2$ (brown gas) $\rightleftharpoons$ $N_2O_4$ (colourless gas)

In a closed system, the reaction reaches equilibrium, producing a pale brown mixture of $NO_2$ and $N_2O_4$. When the temperature of the reaction is increased, the mixture becomes darker. Explain this observation, relating your answer to the energy change. **[3 marks]**

*When the temperature is increased, the mixture becomes darker which means there must be more $NO_2$ in the reaction vessel as $NO_2$ is a brown gas. This suggests that the forward reaction is exothermic as increasing the temperature has driven the reaction to the left.*

## 5 Controlling yield

For industrial processes, such as the **Haber process** and the **Contact process**, it is important to maximise the yield of the product. Using Le Chatelier's Principle, scientists can ensure the optimum yield of product by changing the conditions of the reaction. Scientists have to consider how changing different factors, such as temperature and pressure will interact. They also must consider factors, such as cost and energy efficiency, when designing the **optimum conditions** for an industrial process.

## 1 Exam focus

In the exam you will be told if the forward reaction is exothermic or endothermic. Remember, the reverse reaction is always opposite to the forward reaction, so if the forward reaction is exothermic the reverse reaction will be endothermic.

## 5 Exam-style practice — Grade 5

Hydrogen is made by the reaction given below.

Use your knowledge of exothermic and endothermic reactions to answer these questions.

$CH_4(g) + H_2O(g) \rightleftharpoons 3H_2(g) + CO(g)$

**(a)** Explain why a high temperature is used. **[2 marks]**

**(b)** State what type of reaction the forward reaction is. **[1 mark]**

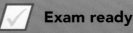

# Pressure and equilibrium

In a reversible reaction at equilibrium, if you change the pressure, the system will oppose the change until equilibrium is restored. You need to know how changes in pressure will affect the position of the equilibrium in reactions involving gases.

## 5 Changing pressure

If a reversible reaction involves a gas, changing the pressure will affect the position of the equilibrium.

If there are different numbers of gaseous molecules on either side of the equation, increasing the pressure will cause the equilibrium to move to the side with fewer molecules. If there are the same number of gaseous molecules on either side of the equation, changing the pressure will not change the position of equilibrium.

$$H_2(g) + I_2(g) \rightleftharpoons 2HI(g)$$

2 moles   2 moles

Pressure will not affect equilibrium.

$$2SO_2(g) + O_2(g) \rightleftharpoons 2SO_3(g)$$

3 moles   2 moles

Increasing the pressure will drive equilibrium to the right.

## 10 Worked example — Grades 6–7

**1** Ammonia is manufactured from nitrogen and hydrogen, as shown in the reaction below.

$N_2(g) + 3H_2(g) \rightleftharpoons 2NH_3(g)$

The equation shows that 1 mole of nitrogen reacts with 3 moles of hydrogen, giving a total of 4 moles on the left side of the reaction.

There are 2 moles of ammonia on the right.

**(a)** Deduce how many moles of reactant and how many moles of product there are in the equation above. **[1 mark]**

There are 4 moles of reactants and 2 moles of product.

The rate at which equilibrium is achieved will speed up if pressure is increased, as there will be more frequent collisions. Go to page 121 for more about rates of reaction.

**(b)** Explain how increasing the pressure will affect the amount of ammonia produced. **[2 marks]**

When pressure is increased, the system will oppose the pressure by reducing the number of moles present.

More ammonia will be produced because the system moves the position of equilibrium to the side with fewer molecules in order to reduce the pressure.

**2** The following reaction can be used to produce ethanol industrially for use as a solvent or as a fuel.

$C_2H_4 + H_2O \rightleftharpoons CH_3CH_2OH$

Give **one** advantage and one disadvantage of increasing the pressure of this reaction. **[2 marks]**

Another disadvantage is the safety issues linked to the high pressure system used.

Advantage: increasing pressure drives the reaction to the right so more ethanol is produced.

Disadvantage: increasing pressure is costly as a vessel that can withstand the pressure must be built.

## 5 Exam-style practice — Grade 7

**(a)** Which of the following equilibria are affected by a change in pressure? Tick **two** boxes. **[2 marks]**

**A** $CH_4(g) + H_2O(g) \rightleftharpoons CO(g) + 3H_2(g)$ ☐

**B** $H_2(g) + CO_2(g) \rightleftharpoons H_2O(g) + CO(g)$ ☐

**C** $CO(g) + 2H_2(g) \rightleftharpoons CH_3OH(g)$ ☐

**(b)** Of the reactions given above, which one favours the reverse direction if the pressure is increased? Give a reason for your answer. **[1 mark]**

**(c)** Use Le Chatelier's Principle to predict how decreasing the pressure in equation C will affect the yield of methanol ($CH_3OH$) produced. **[1 mark]**

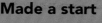

# Covalent bonding

You need to be able to identify and draw covalent bonds for small molecules, polymers and giant covalent structures.

## ⑤ Forming covalent bonds

A covalent bond is a strong bond, which forms between atoms that share a pair of electrons. Covalent bonds are found in small molecules (page 115), polymers (page 156) and giant covalent structures (page 116).

Covalent bonds form between non-metal atoms, which combine together by sharing outer shell electrons. The shared pair of electrons holds the two atoms together. When atoms bond together in this way, they are called a molecule.

Go to page 104 to revise the advantages and disadvantages of the different types of diagrams.

Only the electrons in the outermost shell can be shared.

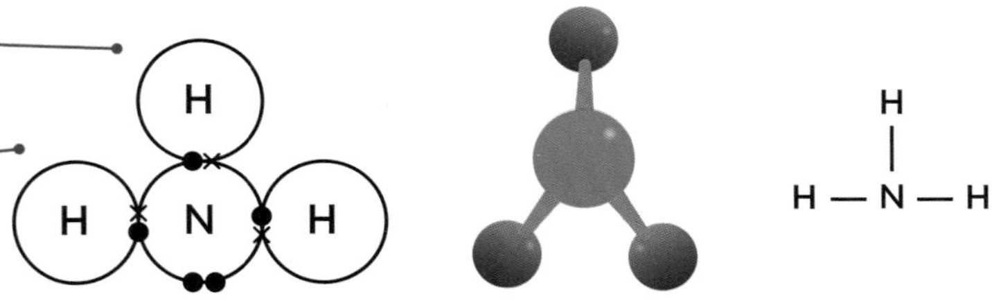

**Figure 1** The covalent bonding in ammonia can be displayed in different ways.

## ⑤ Worked example　　Grade 6

Using a dot and cross diagram, show the bonding in methane, $CH_4$. **[4 marks]**

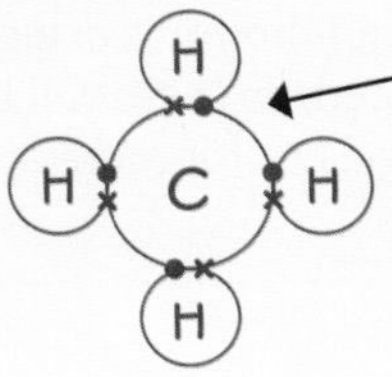

A hydrogen atom has one electron in its outer shell. Carbon has four electrons in its outer shell.

The bond must clearly show a **shared pair** of electrons, one being a dot and one being a cross.

The covalent compound must show each atom correctly bonded with a full outer shell.

Look at **Figure 3** and count how many shared pairs of electrons there are.

Alternatively, look at the periodic table. Nitrogen is in Group 5 so it is three electrons short of a full outer shell.

## ① Exam focus

In the exam, you will need to be able to recognise small molecules, polymers or giant structures from diagrams showing their bonding.

## ② Exam checklist

For the exam, you need to know how to do the following:

- ☑ Draw dot and cross diagrams for $H_2$, $Cl_2$, $O_2$, $N_2$, HCl, $H_2O$, $NH_3$ and $CH_4$.
- ☑ Show a single covalent bond as a line between two atoms.
- ☑ Describe the limitations of dot and cross, ball and stick, 2D and 3D models to represent covalent molecules and giant structures.
- ☑ Deduce the molecular formula of a substance from a given diagram.

## ⑩ Exam-style practice　　Grade 7

**1** Each of the lines in **Figure 2** represents a covalent bond. Describe a covalent bond. **[2 marks]**

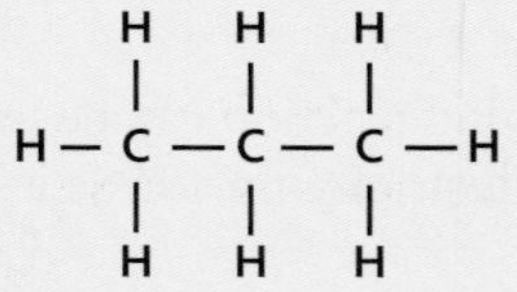

**Figure 2** Propane

**2** Look at **Figure 3**. Determine how many bonds there are between the atoms. **[1 mark]**

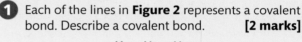

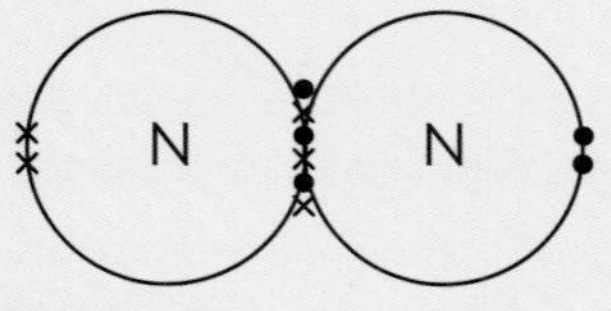

**Figure 3** A molecule of $N_2$

**3** Draw a dot and cross diagram to show the bonding in chlorine, $Cl_2$. **[2 marks]**

# Properties of small molecules

Small molecules, such as carbon dioxide and water, consist of two or three atoms bonded together. You need to use your knowledge of forces and bonding to predict the properties of small molecules.

## 5 Structure of small molecules

Small molecules, sometimes referred to as simple covalent molecules, have strong covalent bonds **within** the molecule. Go to page 114 to revise covalent bonds.

Small molecules have weak intermolecular forces **between** the molecules. The intermolecular forces increase with the size of the molecules, so larger molecules have more intermolecular forces.

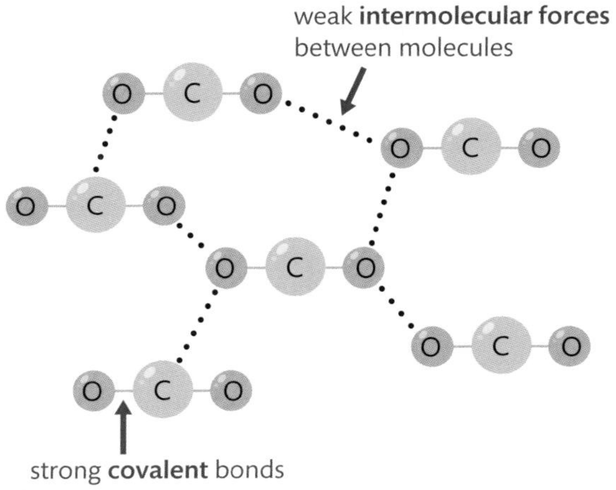


**Figure 1** Carbon dioxide is a simple covalent molecule.

## 5 Properties of small molecules

Small molecules are usually liquids or gases at room temperature. This is because they have relatively low melting and boiling points due to the weak intermolecular forces between the molecules. Larger molecules have higher melting and boiling points because there are more intermolecular forces to overcome.

Small molecules do not conduct electricity because there are no charged particles or free electrons to carry an electrical current.

## 10 Worked example — Grade 7

**1** The boiling point of chlorine, $Cl_2$, is relatively low (−34 °C). Explain this fact, relating your answer to both intermolecular forces and covalent bonds. **[3 marks]**

*Only the intermolecular forces between the $Cl_2$ molecules need to be overcome to boil chlorine, not the strong covalent bonds between the atoms.*

*Intermolecular forces are very weak, so only a small amount of energy is needed to overcome them.*

**2** **Figure 2** shows the molecular structures of two alkane molecules.

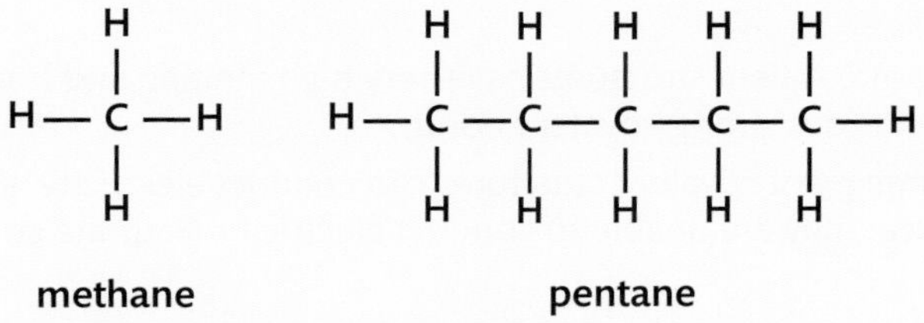


**Figure 2** Molecular structures of methane and pentane

Using ideas about intermolecular forces, explain which alkane has the higher boiling point. **[2 marks]**

*Intermolecular forces increase with the size of molecules. As pentane is a larger molecule it will have a higher boiling point.*

The covalent bonds are not broken when a substance melts or boils; only the intermolecular forces are.

## 5 Exam-style practice — Grade 6

**1** Choose **two** properties of small molecules. Tick **two** boxes. **[2 marks]**

- **A** high melting points ☐
- **B** do not conduct electricity ☐
- **C** low melting points ☐
- **D** conduct electricity ☐

**2** What must happen for a liquid containing small molecules to boil? Explain your answer in terms of forces. **[2 marks]**

Made a start | Feeling confident | Exam ready

# Giant covalent structures

You need to be able to recognise a giant covalent structure from a diagram that shows its structure and bonding.

## 5 Three types of giant covalent structures

Giant covalent structures are covalently bonded solids that contain many atoms. The atoms are usually arranged in lattices. Examples of giant covalent structures include graphite, diamond and silicon dioxide.

Each carbon atom in graphite forms three covalent bonds. Each carbon atom in diamond forms four covalent bonds. Silicon dioxide has a similar structure to diamond, but it contains silicon and oxygen atoms instead of carbon.

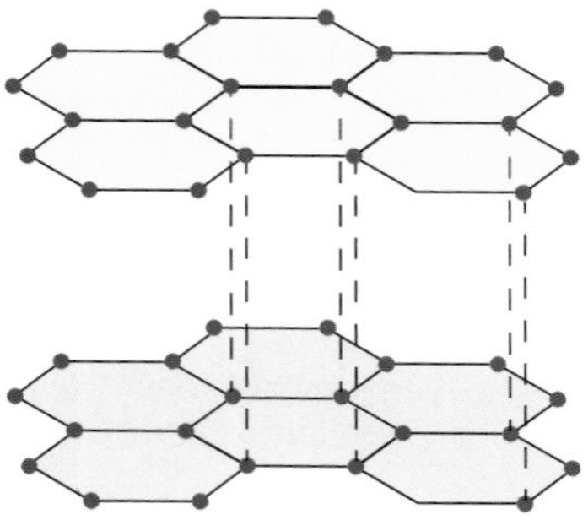

**Figure 1** Graphite (page 118)

**Figure 2** Diamond (page 117)

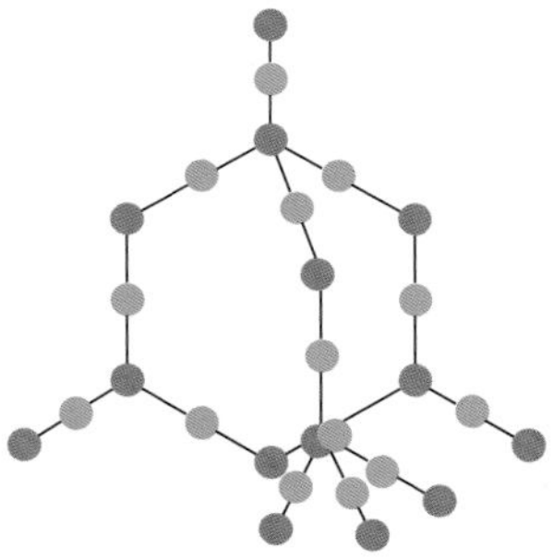

**Figure 3** Silicon dioxide (silica)

Giant covalent structures have very high melting and boiling points because a lot of energy is required to break the numerous strong covalent bonds.

Some giant covalent structures can conduct electricity and others cannot. As there are no charged particles in diamond or silica, they are unable to conduct electricity. Graphite contains charged particles so can conduct electricity.

## 5 Worked example — Grade 5

**Figures 1** and **2** show the structures of two forms of carbon. Use **Figures 1** and **2** and your knowledge of structure and bonding to explain why:

**(a)** graphite is very soft **[2 marks]**

*The layers of graphite can break off easily as they are not bonded together.*

Graphite is soft as the layers can slide. This is because they are only held together by weak forces of attraction.

**(b)** diamond is very hard. **[2 marks]**

*The atoms in diamond are bonded together in a three-dimensional structure, so the structure is harder to break.*

All the carbon atoms in diamond are held together by strong covalent bonds, which require a large amount of energy to break.

### Exam focus

Make sure you look at any diagrams, images or photos provided in the exam. If you're unsure of the answer to the question, a diagram can help.

## 10 Exam-style practice — Grades 5–7

1. State the number of bonds each carbon atom forms in graphite. **[1 mark]**
2. State the number of bonds each carbon atom forms in diamond. **[1 mark]**
3. Name the type of bonding that occurs in diamond and graphite. **[1 mark]**
4. **Figure 3** shows the structure of silicon dioxide, $SiO_2$.
   Suggest the type of lattice structure in solid $SiO_2$ and explain why the melting point of $SiO_2$ is high in terms of bonding and structure. **[3 marks]**

# Diamond

Diamond is a rare and expensive form of carbon. You need to know about its many useful properties, including high melting point and hardness.

## 5 Structure of diamond

The unique structure and properties of carbon make it suitable for many different uses.

Diamond is a giant covalently bonded lattice of carbon atoms.

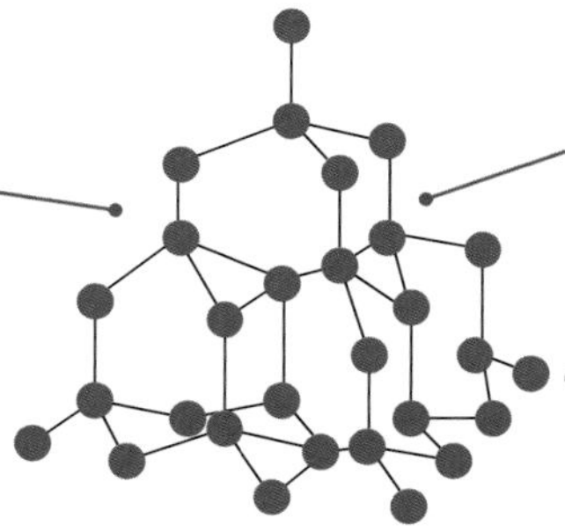

Each carbon atom is bonded to four other carbon atoms. They form the shape of a tetrahedron.

There are strong covalent bonds between each of the atoms in all different directions.

**Figure 1** Molecular structure of diamond

## 5 Properties and uses of diamond

The properties of diamond, such as high melting point, are related to its giant covalent structure. A lot of energy is required to overcome the strong covalent bonds between the carbon atoms in diamond.

| | |
|---|---|
| **State at room temperature** | solid |
| **Appearance at room temperature** | transparent |
| **Hardness** | very hard |
| **Melting and boiling points** | very high |
| **Electrical conductivity** | does not conduct |

The unique structure and properties of diamond make it suitable for many different uses.

- **Cutting tools** – diamond is one of the hardest naturally occurring substances. It can be used to cut a wide range of materials. Its high melting point prevents the diamond tools from melting under the heat generated during the cutting process.
- **Jewellery** – diamond is shiny. It reflects a high percentage of the light that strikes its surface back into the eye.
- **Engraving stone** – diamonds will not break or even scratch against the surfaces of other tough stones. They can be used to engrave hard materials, such as granite and quartz.

## 5 Worked example — Grade 7

Explain how the structure of giant covalent compounds contribute to their characteristic properties. Using diamond as an example, your answer must refer to the melting point and lack of electrical conductivity. **[6 marks]**

There are strong covalent bonds between carbon atoms in diamond. Each carbon atom forms four bonds and all of the bonds must be broken to melt diamond. A large amount of energy is required to break the large number of strong covalent bonds. Therefore diamond has a very high melting point.

Diamond cannot conduct electricity as all of the outer electrons are involved in covalent bonding, meaning there are no charged particles free to move.

## 1 Exam focus

In the exam, you need to be able to explain the properties of diamond in terms of its structure and bonding.

## 10 Exam-style practice — Grade 7

1 **(a)** Diamond has a very high melting point. Explain why. **[2 marks]**

**(b)** Diamond does not conduct electricity. Explain why. **[2 marks]**

2 Drill bits, used for cutting through rock, often have diamonds on the end.

Explain why diamond is used to make cutting tools. **[5 marks]**

# Graphite

Graphite is another form of carbon. It is a non-metal but can conduct electricity due to its structure. You need to know about the structure and properties of graphite and how they relate to its many uses.

## 5 Structure of graphite

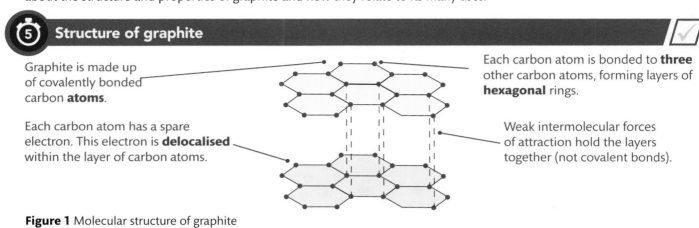

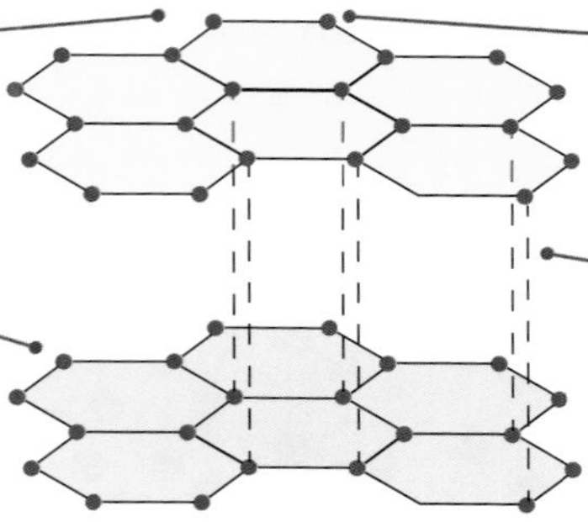

Graphite is made up of covalently bonded carbon **atoms**.
Each carbon atom has a spare electron. This electron is **delocalised** within the layer of carbon atoms.
Each carbon atom is bonded to **three** other carbon atoms, forming layers of **hexagonal** rings.
Weak intermolecular forces of attraction hold the layers together (not covalent bonds).


**Figure 1** Molecular structure of graphite

## 5 Properties and uses of graphite

Like diamond, graphite is made up of many strong covalent bonds, which require a lot of energy to be broken. This means that graphite has high melting and boiling points.

| | |
|---|---|
| **State at room temperature** | solid |
| **Appearance at room temperature** | black |
| **Hardness** | soft |
| **Melting and boiling points** | very high |
| **Electrical conductivity** | good conductor |

Graphite is a good conductor because its delocalised electrons enable it to conduct electricity. It is also a good conductor of thermal energy.

The unique structure and properties of graphite make it suitable for many different uses.

- **Pencil lead** – the forces between the layers are weak, so the layers easily slide onto paper, leaving a black mark.
- **Lubricant** – graphite is slippery, which makes it a perfect dry lubricant for machine parts and metal locks.
- **Electrodes for electrolysis (and batteries)** – graphite has a high melting point and conducts electricity, making it a suitable electrode.

## 5 Worked example — Grade 6

Use your knowledge and understanding of the structure of graphite to explain why graphite can be used:

**(a)** as an electrical conductor **[2 marks]**

*Graphite is a good conductor of electricity as there are delocalised electrons free to move within its structure.*

**(b)** as the 'lead' in a pencil. **[3 marks]**

*Graphite is made of layers of carbon atoms, which are held together by weak forces of attraction. The layers can easily slide over each other. When moved over a piece of paper, a layer can be rubbed off, marking the paper.*

## 10 Exam-style practice — Grade 5

**(a)** Give **two** properties that make graphite suitable electrodes in electrolysis. **[2 marks]**

**(b)** Complete the following statement:

Each carbon atom in graphite is joined to three other carbon atoms by ________ bonds. **[1 mark]**

**(c)** Why is graphite slippery and soft? Tick **one** box. **[1 mark]**

**A** It is made of layers. ☐

**B** It is an ionic compound. ☐

**C** It is made of small molecules. ☐

**(d)** Graphite is slippery. Name **two** uses for graphite, related to this property. **[2 marks]**

# Graphene and fullerenes

Graphene and fullerenes are carbon structures based on covalently bonded rings of carbon atoms. You need to know about the structure and properties of graphene and fullerenes and how they relate to their uses.

## 5 Graphene

### Structure and properties

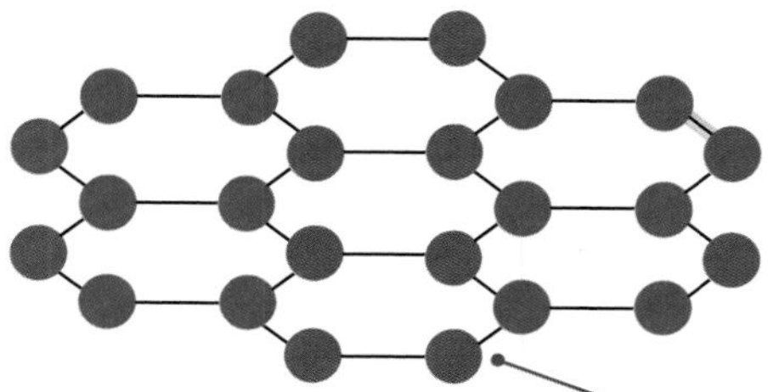


**Figure 1** Graphene

Graphene is a single layer of graphite formed from carbon atoms, each bonded to three other carbon atoms in a hexagonal ring arrangement. It is a two-dimensional compound. This arrangement gives graphene the following properties:

- good conductor of electricity
- strong
- durable
- lightweight
- flexible
- transparent, as only one atom thick.

### Uses of graphene

Potential uses of graphene include: display screens, electric circuits, solar cells. It can also be used in medical, chemical and industrial processes. Graphene is a relatively recent discovery and scientists are learning more about its uses each day.

## 5 Fullerenes

### Structure and properties

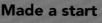

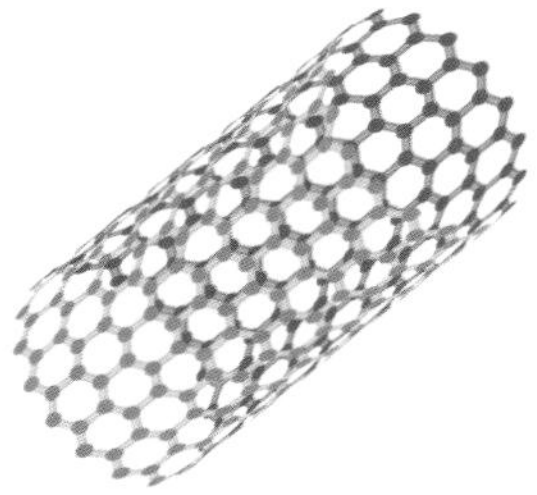

**Figure 2** Fullerene

Fullerenes are hollow cages or tubes made of carbon atoms. Cylindrical fullerenes (**carbon nanotubes**) form tubes based on hexagonal rings of carbon. Fullerenes may also form rings with five or seven carbon atoms. Fullerenes have the following properties:

- good conductor of electricity
- strong
- high tensile strength
- high length to diameter ratio
- high melting and boiling points.

### Uses of fullerenes

Fullerenes may be used for transporting drugs within the body because of their hollow structure.

The first fullerene to be discovered was **Buckminsterfullerene**, a sphere containing 60 carbons.

Fullerenes are useful for nanotechnology, electronics and in drug delivery systems for fighting cancers. Tube fullerenes (nanotubes) are used for reinforcing structures, for example tennis racket frames, as they are very light but very strong.

## 10 Worked example — Grade 6

Carbon nanotubes are cylindrical fullerenes. Explain the properties of carbon nanotubes. Answer in terms of structure and bonding. **[6 marks]**

Split the question into sections to help you to answer it; discuss the structure and the bonding of the nanotubes, relating their properties to these features.

Use scientific terminology to show your understanding.

Nanotubes consist of hexagonal rings of carbon atoms. To achieve this arrangement each carbon must bond covalently with three other carbon atoms. This also gives fullerenes a high melting point and high tensile strength.

This structure also allows carbon nanotubes to conduct electricity, as there are delocalised electrons within the structure. Delocalised electrons can move throughout the structure.

## 5 Exam-style practice — Grade 5

1. Name the element common to diamond, graphite, fullerenes and graphene. **[1 mark]**
2. Give **two** similarities and **one** difference between the structure of carbon nanotubes and graphite. **[3 marks]**

# Calculating rate of reaction

You need to be able to find the rate of a reaction using formulae or by drawing a tangent to a graph.

## Determining a value

The rate of reaction measures how much product is made per second in a particular reaction. It can be calculated using formulae or by drawing tangents to graphs.

The rate of a reaction can be found by measuring the mass of a solid, or volume of a gas, produced over a fixed period of time, during a reaction. Alternatively, it may be found by measuring the quantity of the reactant used over time.

Depending on whether the product or the reactant is being measured, either of the following formulae can be used:

$$\text{mean rate of reaction} = \frac{\text{quantity of reactant used}}{\text{time}}$$

$$\text{mean rate of reaction} = \frac{\text{quantity of product formed}}{\text{time}}$$

If mass is measured (in grams) during the reaction, the unit for rate is g/s.

If volume is measured during the reaction, the unit for rate is $cm^3/s$.

If quantity of reactants is given in moles, the unit for rate is mol/s.

Time is always measured in seconds.

## Worked example — Grade 7

A student investigates the reaction between zinc powder and hydrochloric acid. Hydrogen and a solution of zinc chloride are produced.

Consider the reaction being described; it is sometimes worth writing out an equation to see what reaction is taking place.

**(a)** Describe apparatus suitable for measuring the rate of reaction. **[2 marks]**

A gas syringe could be used to collect the hydrogen gas released.

**(b)** The table shows the results of the experiment. Calculate the mean rate of the reaction using the data in the table. **[2 marks]**

| Results | | | | | | | |
|---|---|---|---|---|---|---|---|
| **Time in s** | 0 | 10 | 20 | 30 | 40 | 50 | 60 |
| **Volume of gas in $cm^3$** | 0 | 20 | 40 | 58 | 72 | 80 | 80 |

$$\text{mean rate} = \frac{\text{volume of gas}}{\text{time}} = \frac{80}{50} = 1.6\ cm^3/s$$

The rate of reaction changes throughout the course of a reaction. It is usually quickest at the start and it slows down as the reactants are used up. The results show that the reaction had finished by 50 seconds as no more gas was produced.

**(c)** The student plots the results on a graph. Calculate the rate of the reaction at 30 s.

The rate of reaction is the difference in the *y* values divided by the difference in the *x* values. The steeper the slope, the quicker the rate of reaction.

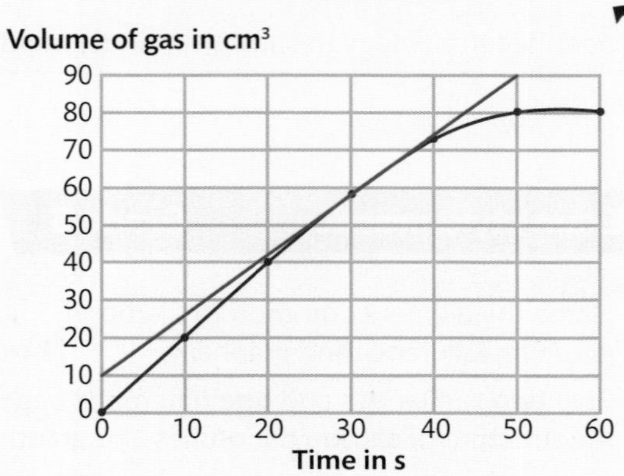


$$\frac{58 - 10}{30 - 0} = 1.6\ cm^3/s$$

## Exam-style practice — Grade 6

Look at **Figure 1**.

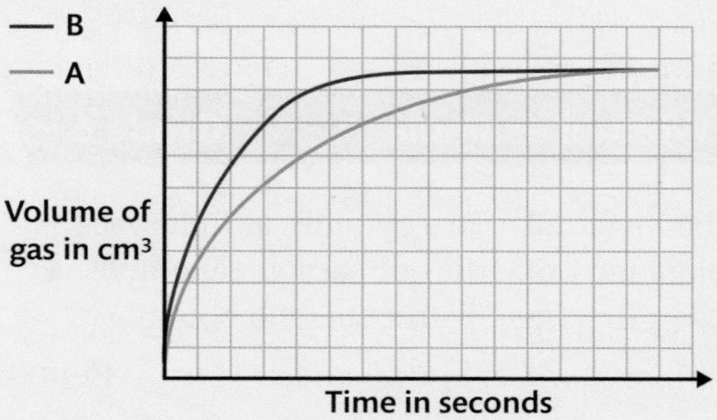


**Figure 1** A graph showing rate of reaction

**(a)** The student calculated the rate of reaction for the plotted line A. Determine the units needed. **[1 mark]**

**(b)** The reaction reaches completion after two minutes, producing 120 $cm^3$ of gas. Calculate the mean rate of reaction. **[2 marks]**

**(c)** Line B shows the same reaction, but with a catalyst. Describe how the catalyst has affected the rate of the reaction. **[2 marks]**

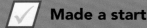

# Factors affecting rate of reaction

Chemical reactions can occur at different rates. You need to know about five main factors that can affect the rate of a reaction.

## 5 Measuring the rate

Depending on the type of reaction taking place, the rate of reaction can be measured by:

- collecting the gas given off during a reaction (with a gas syringe or upturned measuring cylinder)
- mass change (with a balance)
- colour change (disappearing cross).

## 2 Working scientifically

You need to know how to manipulate the conditions of an experiment to alter the reaction rate. Variables can affect the rate of a reaction. You can control variables to ensure that a reaction occurs efficiently within a reasonable timeframe.

## 5 Factors affecting rate of reaction

**Factors affecting rates of reactions**

**Pressure of reacting gases**
Increasing pressure gives a higher rate of reaction: gas particles are more likely to collide as they are being squashed into a smaller volume, so the rate of collision increases.

**Surface area of solid reactants**
A larger surface area on a solid gives a higher rate of reaction. Reactions take place on the surface of a solid, so a greater surface area to volume ratio means that there is a greater rate of collision.

**Concentration of reactants in solution**
The higher the concentration the higher the rate of reaction; there are more particles present in the reaction mixture, so a greater rate of collision.

**Temperature**
The higher the temperature the higher the rate of reaction; particles gain kinetic energy and so move faster, increasing the rate of collision.

**Catalysts**
Using catalysts increases the rate of a reaction. They provide an alternative pathway which requires lower activation energy.

## 5 Worked example — Grade 6

A student is investigating the rate of the reaction between sodium thiosulfate and hydrochloric acid.

**(a)** Describe how increasing the temperature would affect the rate of a reaction. **[3 marks]**

*Increasing the temperature increases the amount of kinetic energy particles have, which leads to more frequent collisions between particles, increasing the rate of reaction.*

**(b)** Describe how increasing the concentration of hydrochloric acid would speed up the reaction rate. **[3 marks]**

*Reactions occur when particles collide. Increasing the concentration means there are more particles in the same volume of acid, so there are more collisions per second, increasing the rate of reaction.*

## 10 Exam-style practice — Grade 6

A student investigates the reaction between marble chips and hydrochloric acid.

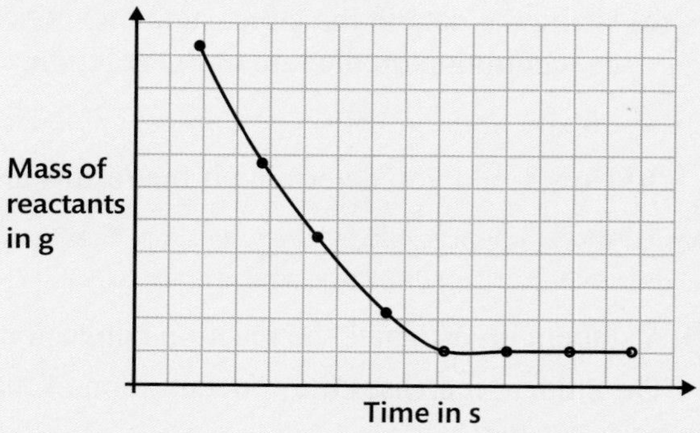


**Figure 1** A graph showing rate of reaction

**(a)** Using **Figure 1**, describe how the student knew that the reaction was complete. **[1 mark]**

**(b)** Sketch the curve to show the results if the experiment was repeated at a higher temperature. **[2 marks]**

**(c)** Suggest **two** ways of increasing the rate of the reaction other than changing the temperature. **[2 marks]**

# Rate of reaction

You need to know how to investigate the way changes in concentration affect the rates of reactions. This includes measuring the volume of a gas produced and the change in colour.

## 2 Apparatus

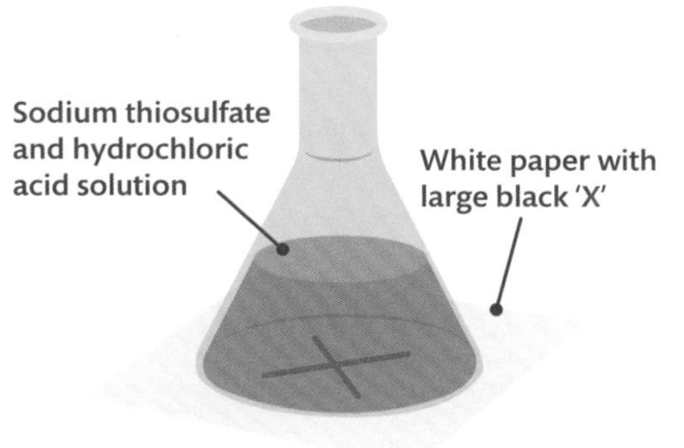


## 1 Working scientifically

Make sure you use a fume cupboard to avoid breathing in any sulfur dioxide fumes when carrying out this experiment.

## 10 Method

1. Prepare the sodium thiosulfate solution in a conical flask. Use a measuring cylinder to add water.
2. Place the conical flask on top of the printed black cross.
3. Use a measuring cylinder to measure the dilute hydrochloric acid.
4. Pour this acid into a conical flask. At the same time, swirl the flask gently and start the stop clock.
5. Look down through the top of the flask. Stop the clock when you can no longer see the cross. Record the time in seconds.
6. For reliability, repeat this process three times for each concentration of sodium thiosulfate. Calculate the mean time taken for each concentration.

Increased concentration means there are more acid particles present so more chance of successful collisions. As a result, the rate of the reaction would increase as the concentration increases.

## 10 Worked example — Grade 7

**1** The table shows the effect of changing concentration of sodium thiosulfate on the rate of reaction.

| Concentration of sodium thiosulfate in g/dm$^3$ | Time taken for cross to disappear in s | | | |
|---|---|---|---|---|
| | 1 | 2 | 3 | Mean |
| 3.95 | 202 | 206 | 206 | 205 |
| 7.91 | 127 | 125 | 128 | 127 |
| 11.86 | 76 | 72 | 74 | 74 |

(a) Using the data in the table, state **one** conclusion the student could make about the effect of concentration on the rate of the reaction. **[2 marks]**

Increasing the concentration of sodium thiosulfate caused the rate of reaction to increase.

(b) How could you determine if the results are reproducible? **[3 marks]**

Compare the results with other groups that have used the same variables. The results are reproducible if the pattern of the results is the same.

**2** A student investigates the reaction between magnesium and hydrochloric acid.
The student increases the concentration of the hydrochloric acid. Give **three** variables that must be controlled. **[3 marks]**

The temperature of the acid, the surface area of the magnesium and the volume of acid

## 5 Exam-style practice — Grade 7

**(a)** Give a hypothesis for the rate of reaction between hydrochloric acid and sodium thiosulfate. Think about the effect of the concentration on the time taken for the cross to disappear. **[2 marks]**

**(b)** Give the independent variable, dependent variable and control variables you would use in this investigation. **[3 marks]**

# Testing for gases

When chemical reactions take place, quite often a gas is released. It is important to know which gas is being produced during a reaction.

## 10 Identifying gases

You are expected to know how to test for the following gases.

**Hydrogen**
A lit splint will make a squeaky pop noise when held near to a test tube of hydrogen gas.

**Oxygen**
A glowing splint will relight if it comes into contact with a test tube of oxygen.

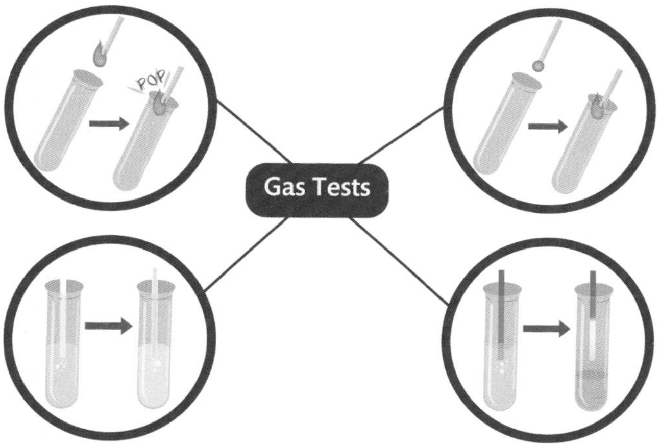


**Carbon dioxide**
Limewater (also known as aqueous calcium hydroxide) will turn cloudy if carbon dioxide is passed through it.

**Chlorine**
Damp litmus paper will become bleached and turn white if held in a test tube of chlorine gas.

## 10 Worked example — Grade 5

**1** A student carries out an experiment in which oxygen gas is produced. The student collects a sample of the gas in a test tube.
Describe how to test the gas to show that it is oxygen. **[2 marks]**

*Test: Place a glowing splint at the opening of the test tube.*
*Result: The splint will relight.*

**2** The products of the combustion of ethanol are collected and tested. One of the products is bubbled through calcium hydroxide solution and the solution immediately turns cloudy. Identify the gas being tested. **[1 mark]**

*Carbon dioxide*

**Exam focus**
Remember to answer these questions fully. For example, just stating the splint will relight will only earn half the total marks. You must show that you know how to carry out the test as well as giving the result of the test.

**3** A student tested an unknown sample of gas to identify it. The results are shown in the table.

| Test | Observation |
|---|---|
| bubbled through limewater | limewater stayed colourless |
| lit splint placed into sample of gas | flame extinguished |
| damp litmus held in sample of gas | colour of litmus bleached |
| glowing splint placed into sample of gas | flame extinguished |

Identify the gas present in the unknown sample. Explain each of the observations in your answer. **[4 marks]**

*The limewater didn't turn cloudy so it's not carbon dioxide*
*There was no squeaky pop with the lit splint so it's not hydrogen.*
*It didn't relight a glowing splint so it's not oxygen.*
*It did bleach litmus paper so it must be chlorine gas.*

## 5 Exam-style practice — Grade 5

Draw one line from each gas to its positive test result. **[4 marks]**

| | | | |
|---|---|---|---|
| chlorine | hydrogen | oxygen | carbon dioxide |
| squeaky pop | limewater turns cloudy | bleaches litmus paper | relights a glowing splint |

# The reactivity series

Metals can be arranged in order of their reactivity. You need to understand how the reactivity of metals with water or dilute acids is related to the tendency of the metal to form its positive ion and be able to deduce an order of reactivity of metals based on experimental results.

## 10 Reactivity of metals

When metals react, they lose their outer shell electrons to form positive ions. The more readily a metal loses its outer electrons to form a positive ion, the more reactive it is.

The reactivity series places metals in order from the most reactive to the least reactive metal. Hydrogen and carbon are often included in the reactivity series, although they aren't metals. This is because when hydrogen reacts it loses an electron in the same way that metals do. Carbon is used to extract metals from their ores based on their reactivity – the reactivity of carbon needs to be known to predict these reactions (see page 135).

A more reactive metal will displace a less reactive metal from a compound of the less reactive metal.

The reactivity of metals can be compared using their reactions with water and dilute acids.

### Reacting metals with acids and water

The alkali metals, potassium, sodium and lithium, all react vigorously with cold water (see page 93). Calcium and magnesium have less vigorous reactions with water. Less reactive metals, such as zinc and iron, are further down the reactivity series because they need dilute acids to react. The reactivity of these reactions can be compared by seeing how vigorously the hydrogen gas is released. The more vigorous the reaction, the more reactive the metal.

metal + acid → salt + hydrogen

metal + water → metal hydroxide + hydrogen

## 10 Worked example — Grade 7

A student investigates the reactivity of four different metals with acids. The table shows the observations.

| | Cu | Mg | Zn | Ag |
|---|---|---|---|---|
| $CuSO_4$ | no reaction | **colour change** | **colour change** | no reaction |
| $Ag_2SO_4$ | **colour change** | **colour change** | **colour change** | no reaction |
| $ZnSO_4$ | no reaction | **colour change** | no reaction | no reaction |
| $MgSO_4$ | no reaction | no reaction | no reaction | no reaction |

When given the results of reactivity experiments, you should be able to deduce the most reactive to the least reactive metals by either how many reactions they took part in or how vigorous their reactions were.

**(a)** Use the results shown in the table to place zinc, copper and magnesium in order of reactivity. **[1 mark]**

magnesium (most reactive) zinc copper (least reactive)

**(b)** What do the results suggest about the reactivity of silver? **[1 mark]**

It is the least reactive of the four metals tested.

**(c)** Give a balanced symbol equation for the reaction between copper sulfate and magnesium. **[2 marks]**

$CuSO_4 + Mg \rightarrow MgSO_4 + Cu$

## 10 Exam-style practice — Grade 8

**1** **Figure 1** shows four metals reacting with dilute hydrochloric acid.
The four metals used are magnesium, iron, copper and calcium.
Use your knowledge of reactivity to identify metals A, B, C and D. **[2 marks]**

**2** Explain how a metal's reactivity is determined by the tendency of the metal to form a positive ion. **[2 marks]**

**3** Write a balanced equation, with state symbols, for the reaction between calcium and water, producing calcium hydroxide ($Ca(OH)_2$). **[2 marks]**

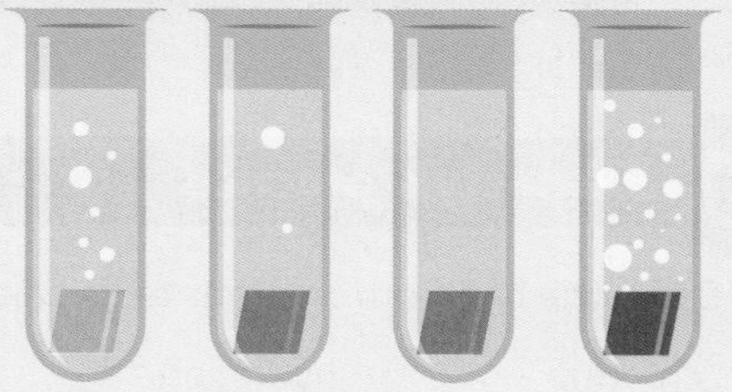


**Figure 1** Four unknown metals react with hydrochloric acid

# Limiting reactants

You need to be able to explain the effect of limiting a reactant on the amount of products.

**⑤ Chemical reactions** ☑

All reactions will eventually stop (except reactions at equilibrium). This is usually because one of the reactants is used up. This reactant is known as the limiting reactant.

The other reactant (or reactants) are said to be in excess, as there will still be some of their particles left in the reaction mixture after the limiting reactant has been used up.

## Amount of limiting reactant

When the amount of reactant is doubled, the amount of product will double.

Total product formed

The amount of product formed is directly proportional to the amount of limiting reactant used.

Amount of limiting reactant used

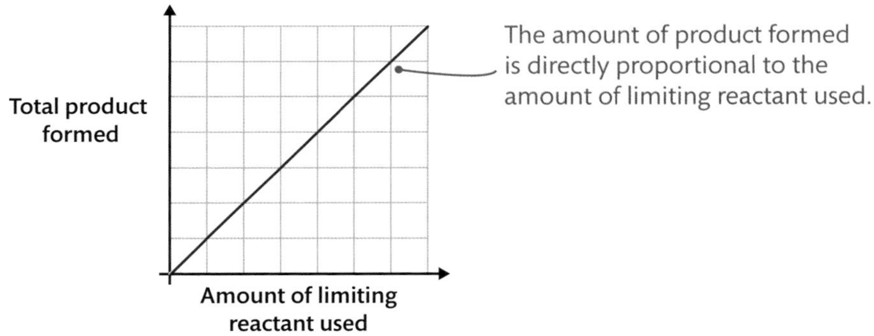

**Figure 1** A graph showing the total product formed in relation to the amount of limiting reactant used.

**⑤ Worked example**  **Grade 9** ☑

First, write a balanced equation for the reaction.

Calculate the mass of iron(III) chloride ($FeCl_3$) formed when 34.5 g of iron reacts with chlorine.

**[5 marks]**

Then work out the relative formula mass ($M_r$) for the limiting reactant and the product you are interested in.

$$2Fe(s) + 3Cl_2(g) \rightarrow 2FeCl_3(s)$$

$2Fe: 2 \times 56 = 112$

$2FeCl_3: 2 \times 162.5 = 325$

Work out the ratio of the $M_r$ of product/$M_r$ of reactant (always put the one you are finding out about on top).

$$moles = \frac{mass}{molar\ mass} = \frac{325}{112} = 2.9$$

This ratio is equal to the ratio of X (unknown mass of product)/mass of reactant.

$$\frac{X}{34.5} = 2.9$$

$$X = 34.5 \times 2.9 = 100\,g$$

Finally, rearrange this equation to find X – the mass of product formed.

**⑩ Exam-style practice**  **Grade 8** ☑

**1** A student carries out a reaction between magnesium and hydrochloric acid. She collects the gas produced. **Figure 2** shows the apparatus the student uses to collect and measure the volume of the hydrogen gas.

**(a)** Name the apparatus labelled **T**.  **[1 mark]**

After two minutes, no more gas is produced. The student adds some more hydrochloric acid and the reaction starts to produce more gas.

**(b)** Hydrochloric acid was the limiting factor in this reaction. Justify this statement.  **[1 mark]**

**2** Calculate the mass of calcium carbonate needed to produce 56 g of calcium oxide during thermal decomposition.  **[5 marks]**

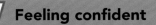

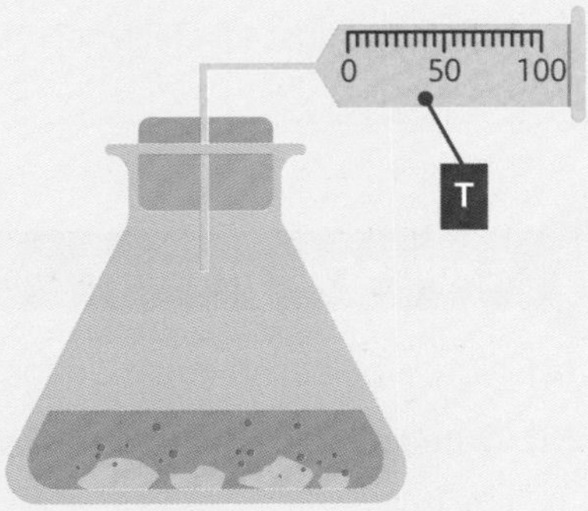

**Figure 2** Magnesium reacting with hydrochloric acid

# Oxidation and reduction

You need to be able to identify which substances are oxidised and reduced in a given reaction, symbol equation or half equation.

## 10 Redox reactions

Oxidation and reduction reactions occur when the outer shell electrons are lost or gained during a reaction.

Redox reactions involve the transfer of electrons:

- Oxidation is the **loss** of electrons.
- Reduction is the **gain** of electrons.

Many metals react with the oxygen in the air. They oxidise, losing electrons and forming **metal oxides** (see page 134).

Displacement reactions are examples of redox reactions; they involve simultaneous oxidation and reduction of the reacting species.

iron chloride + zinc → zinc chloride + iron

$FeCl_2 + Zn \rightarrow ZnCl_2 + Fe$

Zinc is more reactive than iron, so pushes it out of its compound, forming zinc chloride.

The zinc metal is oxidised, forming a zinc ion.

The iron ion is reduced; it gains two electrons.

## 5 Worked example — Grade 8

**1** Ionic equations can be used to represent redox reactions.

A redox reaction takes place when aqueous chlorine is added to potassium iodide solution.

The equation for this reaction is:

$Cl_2(aq) + 2KI(aq) \rightarrow I_2(aq) + 2KCl(aq)$

**(a)** Identify which species has been oxidised during the reaction. **[1 mark]**

The iodine is oxidised.

**(b)** Give the ionic equation for the reaction of chlorine with potassium iodide. **[2 marks]**

$2I^- + Cl_2 \rightarrow I_2 + 2Cl^-$

In this reaction, the **chlorine** has gained an electron. It has been **reduced** from Cl to $Cl^-$.

The **iodine** has lost an electron. It has been **oxidised** from $I^-$ to I.

**2** **(a)** Which of the following reactions are redox reactions? Tick **two** boxes. **[2 marks]**

**A** $CuO + H_2 \rightarrow Cu + H_2O$ ☐

**B** $HCl + NaOH \rightarrow NaCl + H_2O$ ☐

**C** $MgO + 2HCl \rightarrow MgCl_2 + H_2O$ ☐

**D** $H_2 + F_2 \rightarrow 2HF$ ☐

**(b)** Give the species that are reduced in the redox reactions in part **(a)**. **[2 marks]**

A – copper is reduced from $Cu^{2+}$ to Cu

D – fluorine is reduced from F to $F^-$

When writing an ionic equation, you don't need to include the spectator ions. In this reaction, the potassium is a spectator ion and so is not included in the ionic equation.

## 5 Exam-style practice — Grade 8

**(a)** Write a balanced equation for the reaction between copper oxide and magnesium. **[2 marks]**

**(b)** Write an ionic equation to show the oxidation of magnesium in this reaction. **[2 marks]**

# Reactions of acids with metals

When acids and some metals react, a salt and hydrogen gas are produced. You need to know the reactions of acids with metals in terms of oxidation and reduction.

## 5 Redox reactions

Acids react with some metals to produce salts and hydrogen. The following reaction takes place between a metal and an acid:

metal + acid → salt + hydrogen

Acid and metal reactions are classed as **redox reactions**; they involve a transfer of electrons:

$$Zn(s) + 2HCl(aq) \rightarrow ZnCl_2(aq) + H_2(g)$$

The chloride ion ($Cl^-$) is a spectator ion (it exists in the same form on both sides of the reaction).

The metal is oxidised (as metals lose electrons when they react).

The hydrogen ions ($H^+$) are reduced (gain electrons).

Go to page 144 to revise the process of reacting a metal and an acid to produce a salt.

When reacting acids with metals, hydrochloric acid makes chlorides and sulfuric acid makes sulfates.

## 5 Worked example — Grade 8

**1** Deduce, for the following equations, which species are oxidised.

**(a)** $Mg + H_2SO_4 \rightarrow MgSO_4 + H_2$ **[1 mark]**

Mg is oxidised

> Remember, in this type of equation metals will always be oxidised. Mg is a Group 2 metal and so will lose two electrons.

**(b)** $2HCl + 2Fe \rightarrow 2FeCl_2 + H_2$ **[1 mark]**

Fe is oxidised

> Iron is oxidised to iron(II).

**(c)** $Zn + H_2SO_4 \rightarrow ZnSO_4 + H_2$ **[1 mark]**

Zn is oxidised

> The same rules apply as in equation (b).

**2** Explain why the equations in question 1 are redox reactions. **[2 marks]**

The metals are oxidised and lose electrons, while the hydrogen gains electrons and is reduced. The transfer of electrons makes these reactions redox reactions.

> Remember OILRIG:
> **o**xidation
> **i**s
> **l**oss
> **r**eduction
> **i**s
> **g**ain.

## 2 Exam focus

You will be expected to identify which species are oxidised and which are reduced for the reactions of magnesium, zinc and iron with either hydrochloric or sulfuric acid.

See page 126 for further information on redox reactions.

## 5 Exam-style practice — Grade 7

**1** Give the balanced symbol equation, with state symbols, for the reaction between magnesium and hydrochloric acid. **[2 marks]**

**2** State what is meant by the term 'reduction'. **[1 mark]**

# Electrolysis

You need to understand the process of electrolysis and be able to write half equations for the reactions occurring at the electrodes.

## ⑤ The process ☑

Electrolysis is a process that uses electricity to break down a compound into simpler substances. Ionic compounds cannot conduct when solid; however, when molten or in solution the ions are free to move, allowing the substance to conduct electricity.

Electrolysis causes the charged ions to move towards oppositely charged electrodes.

The ions are discharged at the electrodes, producing elements.

The reactions at the electrodes can be represented by half equations.

Go to page 132 for more about half equations.

## ⑤ Key words ☑

- ☑ **Electrolysis** – using electricity to decompose a compound
- ☑ **Electrolyte** – the liquid or solution used in electrolysis, conducts electricity
- ☑ **Electrode** – a solid electrical conductor, usually metal or carbon
- ☑ **Anode** – the positively charged electrode (remember **A**node **A**dd +)
- ☑ **Cathode** – the negatively charged electrode

The command word 'explain' means you should state the electrode **and** give a reason for your answer.

## ⑩ Worked example   Grade 6 ☑

Look at **Figure 1**.

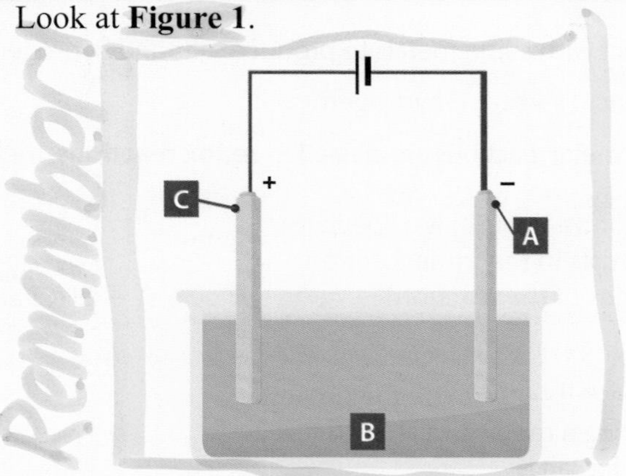

**Figure 1** An electrolysis cell

**(a)** Identify A, B and C using the words below.

**[3 marks]**

**electrolyte**   **cathode**   **anode**   **cell**

A: cathode

B: electrolyte

C: anode

**(b)** Why are electrodes normally made from inert substances?   **[1 mark]**

Electrodes are normally made from inert materials so that they don't react with the electrolyte.

**(c)** Which electrode are metals attracted to? Explain your answer.   **[2 marks]**

Metal ions are positively charged and the cathode is negatively charged. Metals are attracted to the cathode as opposite charges attract.

## ② Working scientifically 🧪 ☑

Electrolysis is used to extract reactive metals from their ore if they cannot be extracted by reduction with carbon.

Electrolysis can also be used in making jewellery. Lower value metals are electroplated with precious metals to increase their value.

Electroplating can also be used to protect a metal from corrosion, for example, tin plating on steel food cans.

## ⑤ Exam-style practice   Grade 6 ☑

❶ Draw lines to link the terms to the correct definitions.   **[4 marks]**

electrolyte          electrode with positive charge

electrode            electrode with a negative charge

anode                solid, electrical conductor

cathode              liquid used for electrolysis

❷ Metals form positive ions. Identify the electrode the ions will travel to.   **[1 mark]**

# Electrolysis of molten ionic compounds

You need to know how molten ionic compounds separate during electrolysis and be able to state the reactions that occur at each electrode.

## Reactions at electrodes

Ionic compounds consist of positive metal ions and negative non-metal ions. These ions can move when the compound is in a molten state. This allows a current to flow when electricity is passed through the molten compound.

The positive metal ions will always travel to the negatively charged cathode, where they gain electrons (reduce) to form the metal element.

At the anode, the non-metal ions will lose electrons (oxidise) forming the non-metal element.

## Half equations

During electrolysis, metal ions will always be reduced and non-metals will be oxidised. This is an example of a redox reaction. Go to page 126 for more about redox reactions.

Half equations can be used to show the reactions of the ions at the electrodes (see page 132). For example, the half equations for the electrolysis of silver chloride (AgCl) are:

- Cathode: $Ag^+ + e^- \rightarrow Ag$ (reduction)
- Anode: $Cl^- \rightarrow Cl + e^-$ (oxidation)

## Worked example — Grade 8

**(a)** Why must sodium chloride be molten or in solution for electrolysis? **[1 mark]**

The ions can only move when molten or in solution.

**(b)** Describe what happens at the positive electrode during the electrolysis of sodium chloride. **[3 marks]**

The chloride ions lose one electron each to form chlorine (gas).

**(c)** Write the half equation for the reaction at the negative electrode for molten sodium chloride. **[1 mark]**

$Na^+ + e^- \rightarrow Na$

Ionic compounds must be molten or in solution to have free ions. If the compound is dissolved in an aqueous solution, different products may form at the electrodes (page 130).

The negative non-metal ion is attracted to the positive electrode; here it becomes **oxidised** (loses electrons).

The half equation shows the reaction taking place at the cathode. Positive metal ions are attracted to the cathode where they are **reduced** (gain electrons) to form the metal element.

## Exam focus

You could be asked to draw a labelled diagram of electrolysis in the exam. Go to page 128 to see what you should include in the diagram.

## Exam-style practice — Grade 8

**1** Magnesium is produced by the electrolysis of molten magnesium chloride.

**(a)** Draw a diagram of the apparatus that you could use for the electrolysis of magnesium chloride. **[4 marks]**

**(b)** Balance the half equations, to show the reactions that will take place at each electrode. **[2 marks]**

$Mg^{2+}$ + ___ → Mg

$2Cl^- \rightarrow Cl_2$ + ___

**(c)** Explain what happens at the cathode. **[2 marks]**

**2** For each of the following ionic compounds, predict the product at the anode and at the cathode. **[4 marks]**

**(a)** lead bromide

**(b)** zinc iodide

**(c)** magnesium oxide

**(d)** lithium chloride

Made a start | Feeling confident | Exam ready

# Electrolysis of aqueous solutions

You need to be able to describe what happens to aqueous solutions during electrolysis (where an ionic substance is dissolved in water).

## 5 Ions

When an electrical current is passed through an aqueous solution of ionic compounds, the water molecules break down so $H^+$ and $OH^-$ ions are produced along with the solute ions. The ion that is discharged from each electrode is dependent upon the relative reactivity of the elements involved in the reactions.

At the anode: oxygen is produced, unless the solution contains a halide ion ($Cl^-$, $Br^-$, $I^-$) in which case the halogen is produced ($Cl_2$, $Br_2$, $I_2$).

At the cathode: hydrogen is produced, unless the metal in the solution is less reactive than hydrogen (lower position in the reactivity series, such as copper or platinum).

## 5 Working scientifically

If a gas is produced during the electrolysis of an aqueous solution, you will see bubbles forming at the electrodes. The gases can be collected and tested for identification (see page 123).

- Chlorine bleaches damp litmus paper.
- Hydrogen causes a squeaky pop with a lit splint.
- Oxygen relights a glowing splint.

## 10 Worked example — Grade 7

**Figure 1** Method for the electrolysis of brine

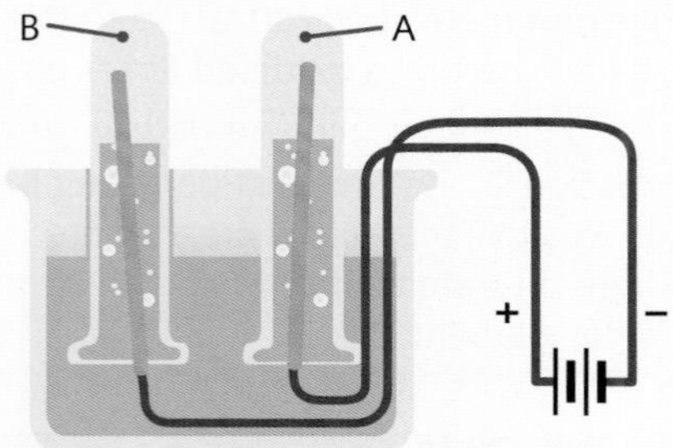


Brine is a concentrated solution of salt (sodium chloride) in water. The ions present are $Na^+$, $H^+$, $OH^-$ and $Cl^-$.

**Exam focus**
If you are asked to draw the apparatus for electrolysis, make sure you include a power source as shown here.

Look at **Figure 1.**

**(a)** Name gases A and B. **[2 marks]**

A: chlorine

B: hydrogen

As sodium is more reactive than hydrogen, hydrogen will be discharged at the cathode.

Chlorine is a halogen and so will be discharged at the anode.

**(b)** After the reaction has taken place what substance is found in the solution in the beaker? **[1 mark]**

Sodium hydroxide

As hydrogen and chlorine have been discharged at the electrodes, $Na^+$ and $OH^-$ are left in the solution, forming NaOH.

**(c)** Give the half equation for the reaction at the cathode. **[2 marks]**

$2H^+ + 2e^- \rightarrow H_2$

Remember to balance the number of charges with the correct number of electrons.

Go to page 132 to revise half equations.

## 10 Exam-style practice — Grade 7

Electrolysis can be used to show that aqueous sodium chloride contains ions.

**(a)** Explain what happens when an electrical current passes through the solution. **[4 marks]**

**(b)** Give the half equation for the reaction that takes place at the anode. **[2 marks]**

# Electrolysis of copper(II) chloride

You need to know what happens when aqueous solutions are electrolysed using inert electrodes. This page covers the electrolysis of copper(II) chloride.

## 2 Apparatus

- 50 cm$^3$ copper(II) chloride solution
- 100 cm$^3$ beaker
- Petri dish lid
- two carbon rod electrodes
- two crocodile/4 mm plug leads
- low-voltage power supply
- blue litmus paper
- tweezers

Another suitable answer is platinum.

## 5 Electrolysis of copper(II) chloride

1. Pour copper(II) chloride solution into the beaker to about 50 cm$^3$.
2. Add the Petri dish lid and insert carbon rods through the holes. **The rods must not touch each other**. Attach crocodile leads to the rods. Connect the rods to the **DC (red and black)** terminals of a low-voltage power supply.
3. Switch on the power supply (4 V).
4. Look at both electrodes. Is there bubbling at neither, one or both of the electrodes?
5. Use tweezers to hold a piece of blue litmus paper in the solution next to the positive electrode.
6. Record your observations. Repeat with other solutions.

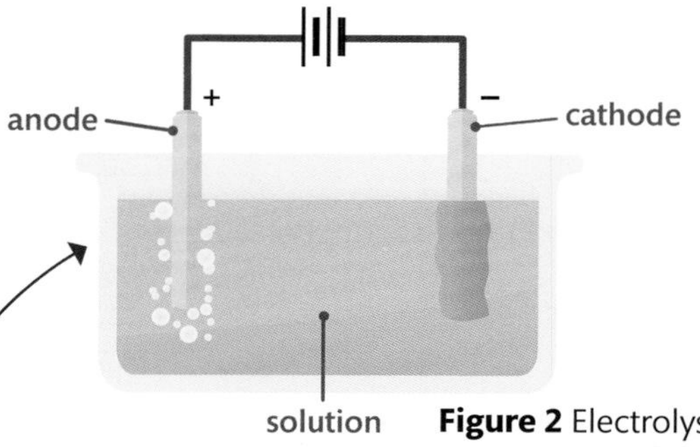


**Figure 2** Electrolysis apparatus

The products of electrolysis are reactive, so it is important to use inert (unreactive) materials for the electrodes.

## 10 Worked example — Grade 8

**Figure 1** Apparatus for the electrolysis of copper(II) sulfate solution

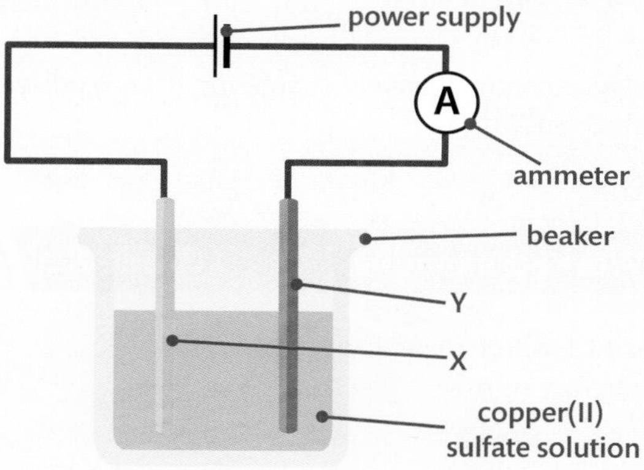


**(a)** Give the name of the electrodes X and Y. **[1 mark]**

X is the anode; Y is the cathode.

**(b)** Suggest an element that can be used for the electrodes. **[1 mark]**

Carbon (graphite)

**(c)** Name the products at each electrode. **[2 marks]**

Copper metal at the cathode and oxygen gas at the anode.

**(d)** Explain why the copper ions travel to the negative electrode. **[2 marks]**

Copper ions have a positive charge so they are attracted to the negative charge at the cathode.

**(e)** The student repeated the experiment using copper chloride as the electrolyte. Suggest the gas produced at the anode and how it could be tested to prove its identity. **[2 marks]**

Chlorine gas would be produced, which would bleach blue litmus paper.

If a gas is produced at the anode and it does **not** bleach blue litmus paper, it will be oxygen. If a gas is produced at the cathode, it will be hydrogen.

## 10 Exam-style practice — Grade 7

**(a)** Name the products of the reaction when sodium chloride solution is electrolysed. **[2 marks]**

**(b)** Explain which product is formed at the positive electrode and which product is formed at the negative electrode. **[2 marks]**

# Half equations

You need to be able to represent the reactions occuring at each electrode during electrolysis using half equations.

## Ionic equations

$Mg^{2+} + 2I^- \longrightarrow MgI_2$

The ionic equation above can be represented by two half equations, showing the reactions at each electrode.

At the cathode: the positively charged ion ($Mg^{2+}$) is reduced; it gains electrons:

$Mg^{2+} + 2e^- \longrightarrow Mg$

At the anode: the negatively charge ion ($I^-$) is oxidised; it loses electrons:

$2I^- \longrightarrow I_2 + 2e^-$

## Balancing half equations

You should follow these steps to balance half equations:

1. Write the formulae of the reactant (or reactants) and the product (or products).
2. Balance the number of ions on either side of the arrow.
3. Work out the number of charges and then balance with electrons so that both sides of the equation have the same overall charge.

## Worked example — Grade 8

**Figure 1** Electrolysis of magnesium sulfate

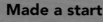

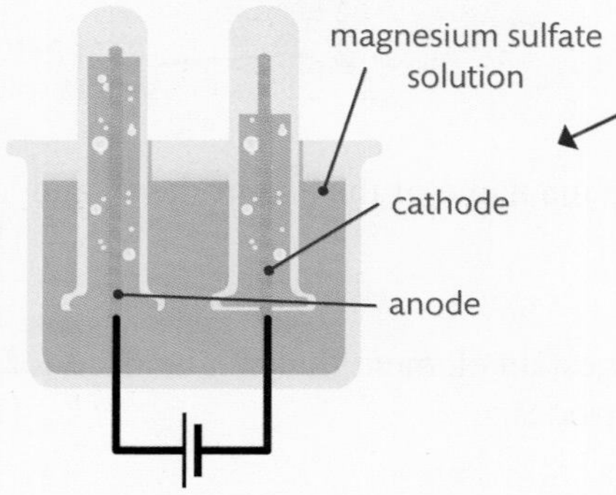


A solution of dilute magnesium sulfate is electrolysed as shown in **Figure 1**.

Oxygen gas is discharged at the anode.

**(a)** Explain why oxygen is produced at the anode. **[1 mark]**

*Hydroxide ions discharge, forming oxygen and water.*

**(b)** Give the half equation for the reaction at the anode. **[2 marks]**

*$4OH^- \longrightarrow 2H_2O + O_2 + 4e^-$*

**(c)** Name the substance released at the cathode. **[1 mark]**

*Hydrogen gas*

**(d)** Give the half equation for the reaction at the cathode. **[2 marks]**

*$2H^+ + 2e^- \longrightarrow H_2$*

**Exam focus**

Make sure you look at diagrams carefully in the exam. Look at any labels or keys, and pay attention to any details that may be important, e.g. gas bubbles.

Negative ions are attracted to the anode, so $SO_4^-$ ions and $OH^-$ ions accumulate at the anode. Oxygen gas will always be discharged at the anode, unless a halide is present. $OH^-$ ions give up their electrons more readily than $SO_4^-$ ions, so the sulfate ions are left in solution.

Hydroxide ions will react to produce oxygen gas and water: $4OH^- - 4e^- \longrightarrow 2H_2O + O_2$ (or as shown in the worked example). Learn this equation.

Magnesium is **more reactive** than hydrogen so hydrogen gas will be **discharged** at the cathode.

Hydrogen ions are reduced to form molecules of hydrogen gas.

Go to page 131 for more about the electrodes used in electrolysis.

## Exam-style practice — Grade 7

1. Molten copper chloride ($CuCl_2$) is electrolysed. Give the half equation for the reaction at each electrode. **[2 marks]**
2. Suggest why inert electrodes must be used when a molten substance is electrolysed. **[1 mark]**

# Metallic bonding

Metals have very strong bonds due to the presence of free electrons. You need to be able to recall the structure and arrangement of metal particles.

## 5 Structure of metals

Most metals (excluding the transition metals) have between one and three electrons in their outer shell. These electrons are said to be 'delocalised', which means they are not in fixed positions but instead are free to move throughout the metal structure.

As the electrons can move, they are shared within the structure, giving rise to strong metallic bonds.

The metallic bonds are formed from the strong attraction between positively charged nuclei and the negatively charged electrons.

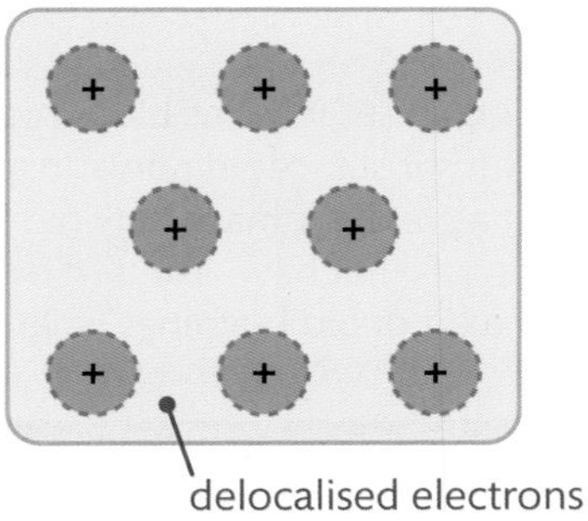


**Figure 1** The arrangement of metal ions and electrons in metallic bonding

**Figure 2** Metals, such as copper, are used to make saucepans because of their high strength and thermal conductivity.

## 10 Worked example — Grade 7

**1** Describe the structure of a metal. **[3 marks]**

*Metals consist of giant structures of metal atoms arranged in a regular pattern, with delocalised electrons.*

**2** Draw a diagram to show the arrangement of particles in a metal. Label the diagram. **[3 marks]**

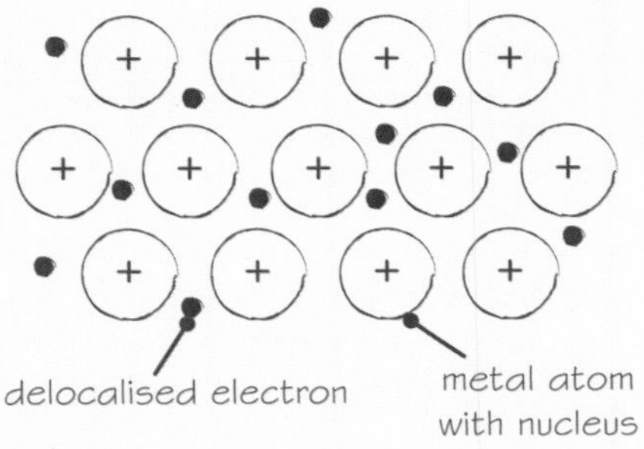


**3** Explain the term 'delocalised electron'. Which electrons, in a metal atom, become delocalised? **[2 marks]**

*Delocalised electrons are not fixed to one atom, they are free to move. Only the electrons in the outer shell of a metal atom are delocalised.*

**Exam focus**
Make sure you use key scientific terminology, such as delocalised electrons, in your answer.

Show the regular arrangement of the metal atoms as positively charged particles surrounded by negative electrons.

## 5 Exam-style practice — Grade 6

**1** Which of these statements best describes metallic bonding? Tick **one** box. **[1 mark]**

- **A** transfer of electrons ☐
- **B** sharing electrons ☐
- **C** attraction of positive nuclei and electrons ☐
- **D** atoms form hexagonal rings ☐

**2** Explain why metal particles are shown as positively charged in metallic bonding. **[2 marks]**

**3** How does a metallic bond form? **[2 marks]**

# Metal oxides

You need to be able to state the properties of metal oxides and give equations for their formation.

## 2 Formation of metal oxides

Metal oxides are formed when a metal reacts with oxygen.

metal + oxygen → metal oxide

Metal oxides are examples of a giant ionic lattice structure. They are usually solid at room temperature. They generally have high melting and boiling points.

## 5 Naming metal oxides

When metals react to form oxides, they gain oxygen so they are **oxidised**.

- copper + oxygen → copper oxide
- calcium + oxygen → calcium oxide
- Iron(III) oxide - iron is in +3 oxidation state.
- lead + oxygen → lead oxide

When copper oxidises it forms black copper oxide. This reacts with substances in rain and atmospheric gases to form a green patina. Many old buildings have copper roofs that have oxidised over time, which is why a lot of old buildings have green roofs.

## 5 Worked example — Grade 6

A student investigates magnesium oxide, a metal oxide.

**(a)** What type of bonding is present in the magnesium oxide? **[1 mark]**

ionic bonding

**(b)** The student finds that the substance **X**:

- does not conduct electricity when solid
- does conduct electricity when dissolved in water.

Explain why solid **X** does **not** conduct electricity but a solution of **X** does conduct electricity. **[2 marks]**

When solid, ions are not free to move but they can move when dissolved in a solution.

**(c)** Use the equation below to prove that the formation of a metal oxide is a redox reaction. **[2 marks]**

$2Mg + O_2 \rightarrow 2MgO$

Atoms and molecules are neutral, so at the start of the reaction:

Mg = 0

$O_2 = 0$

When the reaction takes place:

Mg loses 2 electrons as it is in Group 2, forming $Mg^{2+}$.

The magnesium has been oxidised (loss of electrons).

O gains 2 electrons as it is in Group 6, forming $O^{2-}$.

The oxygen has been reduced (gain of electrons).

Magnesium has lost electrons and oxygen has gained electrons. The reaction is a redox reaction.

## 5 Exam-style practice — Grade 6

**(a)** Write a word equation to identify the product formed in the reaction of iron and oxygen. **[1 mark]**

**(b)** Give the name of this type of reaction. **[1 mark]**

**(c)** Give the name of the substance that is reduced in this reaction. **[1 mark]**

# Extraction of metals and reduction

You need to know how carbon is used to extract metals from their ore. Ores are naturally occurring rocks that contain a sufficient amount of metal or metal compounds.

## 5 Extracting metals

The method used to extract metals from their ore depends on their reactivity. Metals that are less reactive than carbon can be extracted from their oxides by reduction with carbon.

For example: iron oxide + carbon → iron + carbon dioxide.

The extraction process removes the oxygen from the metal oxide. This means the metal is reduced. At the same time, the carbon is oxidised to form carbon dioxide.

Metals extracted by reduction with carbon include zinc, iron, tin, lead and copper.

Unreactive metals, such as gold, are found in the ground in metal form, so chemical separation is unnecessary. However, chemical reactions may be needed to remove other elements that could contaminate the gold.

Some metals, such as aluminium, are so reactive that their oxides cannot be reduced by carbon. Go to page 136 for more about extracting these types of metals.

Metals such as zinc, iron and copper are present in ores as their oxides.

## 10 Worked example — Grades 5–6

**1** Iron can be extracted from its oxide.

**(a)** What name is given to this type of process? **[1 mark]**

Reduction

The iron loses the oxygen it is combined with and is **reduced**.

**(b)** Explain how oxygen can be removed from iron oxide to make iron. **[2 marks]**

Heat the iron oxide with carbon to reduce the iron and remove the oxygen.

It may seem obvious that the iron oxide is heated but you need to always state the conditions used in a reaction. Although carbon is given in the answer, any element that is more reactive than iron could be used to extract it from its oxide.

**(c)** Explain why this process cannot be used to extract aluminium from its oxide. **[2 marks]**

Aluminium is above carbon in the reactivity series so carbon cannot remove oxygen from aluminium oxide.

Only metals below carbon in the reactivity series can be extracted from their oxides using this process. As aluminium is further up the reactivity series than carbon, a different process is required.

**2** The following equation is an example of a reduction reaction used to extract a metal from its ore.

$2CuO + C \rightarrow 2Cu + CO_2$

**(a)** Write the word equation for the reaction taking place. **[1 mark]**

copper oxide + carbon → copper + carbon dioxide

**(b)** Explain why this reduction reaction can take place. **[1 mark]**

Because copper is less reactive than carbon

## 10 Exam-style practice — Grade 7

**1** Lead oxide reacts with carbon to form the products lead and carbon dioxide.

**(a)** Write a word equation to show the reduction of lead oxide using carbon. **[1 mark]**

**(b)** Give the name of the type of reaction that occurs between carbon and oxygen during the reaction. **[1 mark]**

**(c)** Explain, in terms of electrons, how the lead in lead oxide (PbO) is reduced. **[3 marks]**

**2** Calcium cannot be reduced from calcium oxide using carbon. Explain why. **[2 marks]**

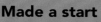

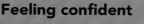

# Electrolysis to extract metals

You need to know how reactive metals can be extracted from their compound using electrolysis.

## 5 Reactive metals

Metals that are more reactive than carbon cannot be extracted by reduction, so electrolysis is used instead.

The electrolysis of metals involves large amounts of energy as the metal compound must be in a molten state. Energy is also needed to produce the necessary electrical current.

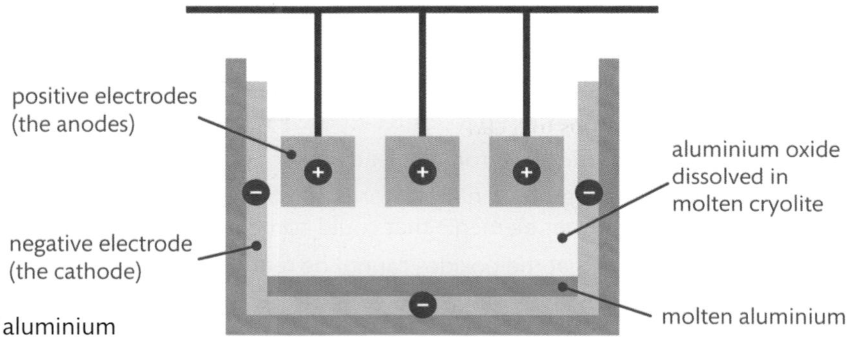


**Figure 1** Electrolysis of aluminium

## 10 Worked example — Grade 7

**(a)** The electrolyte for electrolysis of aluminium is a molten mixture of aluminium oxide dissolved in cryolite. Explain why. **[2 marks]**

Cryolite melts at a lower temperature than aluminium oxide, so less energy is needed to form the electrolyte.

**(b)** What substance is used for the electrodes in the electrolysis of aluminium? **[1 mark]**

Graphite (a form of carbon)

**(c)** Oxygen is produced at the anode. Why does the positive electrode need replacing regularly? **[2 marks]**

The oxygen produced reacts with the carbon electrode to produce carbon dioxide. This results in the electrode gradually wearing away.

**(d)** Complete the half equation to show the reaction at the positive electrode. **[2 marks]**

$2O^{2-} \rightarrow O_2 + 4e^-$

**(e)** Why does aluminium form at the negative electrode? **[3 marks]**

Aluminium ions are positive, therefore they are attracted to the negative electrode (the cathode) where they gain electrons and are reduced.

## 10 Exam-style practice — Grade 6

**1** **Figure 2** shows how magnesium can be produced from magnesium chloride using electrolysis.
Explain why large amounts of energy are used in the extraction process. **[2 marks]**

**2** The melting point of aluminium oxide is over 2000 °C. Name the substance used to produce an electrolyte at a lower temperature. **[1 mark]**

**3** Depending on their reactivity, metals can be extracted from their ores either by reduction with carbon or electrolysis. Reduction involves heating the ore to a very high temperature in a furnace with carbon. This reaction produces an impure sample of the metal and carbon dioxide.
Electrolysis requires a metal to be molten. Electricity is passed through the electrolysis cell to separate the metal from its impurities.
Evaluate the use of each of the processes. **[4 marks]**

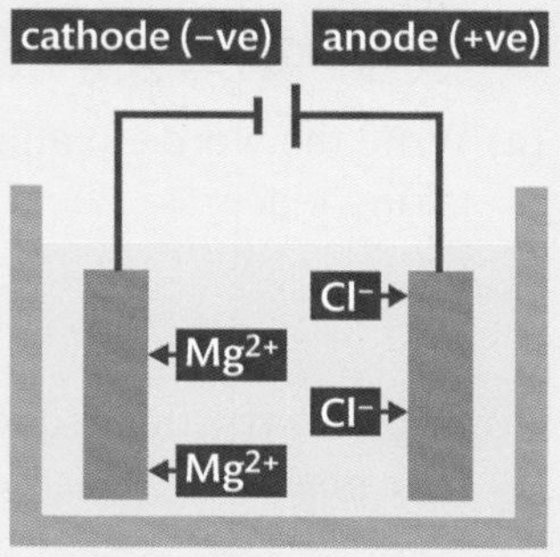


**Figure 2** Extracting magnesium using electrolysis

# Alternative methods of extracting metals

Earth's resources of metal ores, such as copper ores, are limited. You need to know about the new methods that are being developed to extract metals from other sources.

## 10 Bioleaching and phytoming

Traditional methods of metal extraction involve mining and digging. This produces vast amounts of waste rock that needs to be removed from the mining sites.

**Bioleaching** and **phytomining** are newer methods that can be used to extract metals, such as copper, from low-grade ores (ores that contain only a small percentage of copper).

The metal can then be obtained from the ore using scrap metal displacement or electrolysis.

### Bioleaching

1. Bacteria feed on low-grade ore.
2. Biological and chemical processes are used to produce a leachate (a solution of copper ions).
3. Scrap iron displacement or electrolysis can be used to extract the copper from the leachate.

### Phytomining

1. Plants are grown in copper-rich soils.
2. When the plants have absorbed the copper ions, they are harvested.
3. The plants are burned to produce an ash containing copper compounds.
4. Sulfuric acid is added to leach the copper ions (dissolve them).
5. Scrap iron displacement or electrolysis can be used to extract the copper.

## 5 Worked example — Grade 6

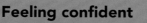

**Figure 1** Open cast mine

1. Copper metal can be removed from Earth's crust by open-cast mining. Suggest **two** environmental problems that are caused by the mining of copper ore. **[1 mark]**

   *It produces large amounts of waste rock and dust pollution.*

2. Explain why scrap metal displacement is used to extract copper. **[2 marks]**

   *Scrap metal displacement is used as it is a cheaper method than electrolysis. Scrap iron displaces copper as iron is more reactive than copper.*

3. Describe how bioleaching is used to obtain copper compounds. **[2 marks]**

   *Bacteria feed on low-grade copper compounds. Biological and chemical processes produce a leachate, which contains copper compounds.*

## 15 Exam-style practice — Grade 7

1. Give **two** reasons why copper is now extracted from low grade ores. **[2 marks]**
2. Phytomining is used near mines to extract copper from soil that contains small concentrations of copper compounds. Describe how phytomining is used to obtain copper compounds. **[3 marks]**
3. Draw a circle around the correct answer to complete the sentence.

   Using bacteria to extract metal is called ____________________. **[1 mark]**

   Biodiversity     Bioleaching     Biosynthesis
4. Copper is a very useful metal. It can be extracted by mining and reduction with carbon or by phytomining.

   The process of mining for copper involves mining for copper ore, crushing the rocks and separating the ore from the crushed rock. The ore is then processed before smelting with carbon in a furnace at around 1200 °C.

   Phytomining usually takes place where copper ore has been mined, as there may be areas of land that contain very low percentages of copper compounds. One way to extract the copper is to grow specific plants on the land. The plants absorb copper compounds through their roots. The plants are then burned to produce an ash containing copper compounds. The ash is then reacted with sulfuric acid to extract the copper.

   Evaluate each of these processes. Include the economic and environmental effect of each method in your answer. **[6 marks]**

# Properties of metals and alloys

You need to know how the properties of metals are linked to their bonding and structure.

## 5 Properties of metals

Metals form giant structures in which electrons in the outer shells of the metal atoms are free to move. This gives them the following properties. Go to page 133 to revise the structure of metals.

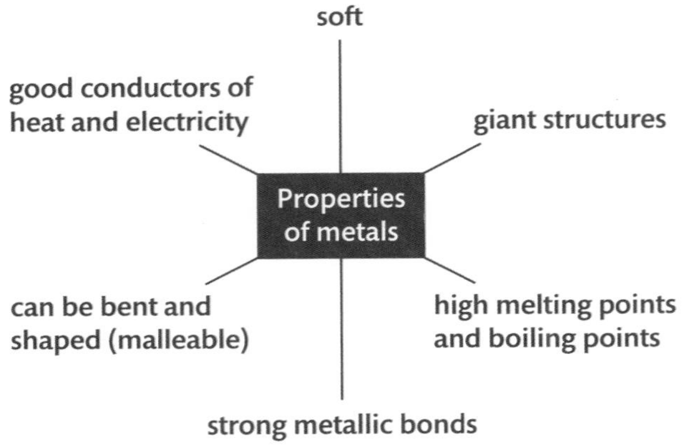


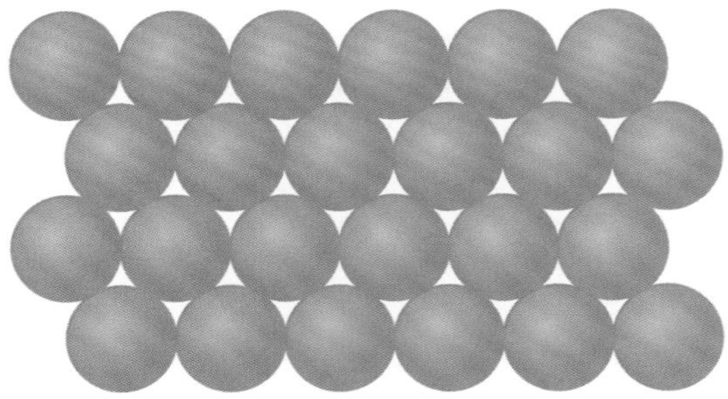

**Figure 1** The atoms in a metal are arranged in layers; this allows metals to be bent and shaped.

## 5 Properties of alloys

An alloy is a mixture of two or more metals. Different metals are mixed together to form a material with specific properties, such as high strength.

The strength of an alloy is based on its structure. Each metal in the alloy has a different sized atom. The different sizes of the atoms distort the structure of the layers and so prevent the layers sliding over each other when a force is applied.

**Figure 2** Alloys are harder than metals because they have different elements mixed in with the metal.

## 5 Worked example — Grade 6

**(a)** Describe how the structure of an alloy is different from the structure of a pure metal. **[2 marks]**

*An alloy is a mixture of a metal with one or more other elements. The atoms of each element are all different sizes, so the layers in the alloy are distorted.*

**(b)** How does the structure of an alloy make it harder than a pure metal? **[2 marks]**

*The layers in alloys are distorted by the different sizes of atoms. The layers cannot slide over each other when a force is applied.*

### Exam focus

Sometimes it is easier to answer this type of question with diagrams, so long as they are correctly labelled.

Be careful with use of language – alloys are **mixtures** not **compounds**.

Metals are malleable because their atoms are in layers which can slide easily over each other; this makes them easy to bend and shape. This is not the case for the distorted layers in alloys.

## 5 Exam-style practice — Grade 6

**(a)** Explain why metals have high melting and boiling points. **[2 marks]**

**(b)** Suggest why gold is not used for jewellery, but a gold alloy is. **[1 mark]**

# Metals as conductors

You need to be able to explain the electrical and thermal conductivity of metals.

## 5 Electrons and conductivity

Metals are good conductors of both heat and electricity because they have delocalised electrons within their metallic structure.

The more electrons available in the outer shell, the more efficient a conductor the metal is. This is because there are more electrons available to carry:

- electrical charge
- thermal energy.

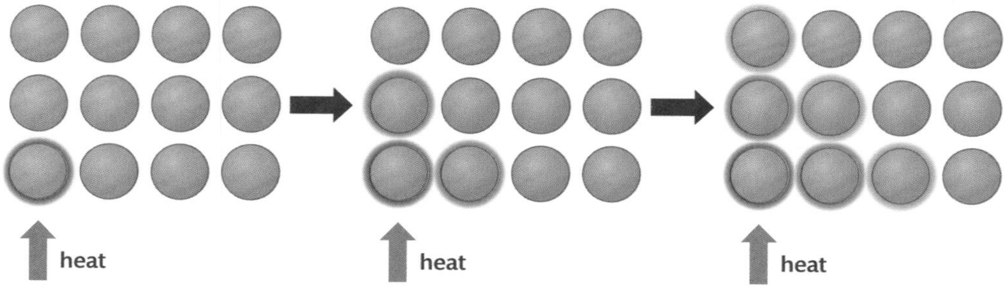


**Figure 1** Ion conductivity – when heat is applied to one part of a metal, the metal ions vibrate more vigorously, transferring thermal energy as they collide into neighbouring particles.

## 10 Worked example — Grade 6

**1** Iron is a metal. Explain why iron is a good electrical conductor. **[2 marks]**

*The electrons in the outer shell are delocalised, so they are free to move.*

> Remember, it is only the electrons in the outer energy level (or highest energy level) that are free to move throughout the metallic structure.

**2** Explain how heat is transferred along a copper rod. **[3 marks]**

> Although thermal energy, and electrical charge, are transferred by metal ions, it is the presence of free electrons within a metal that enables them to be such efficient conductors.

*Delocalised electrons gain energy and move quickly through the metal. When the electrons collide with other electrons, or metal atoms, thermal energy is transferred.*

**3** Explain why aluminium, a Group 3 metal, is a better conductor than sodium, a Group 1 metal. **[2 marks]**

> Go to page 138 for more about the properties of metals.

*Aluminium has more electrons in its outer shell, so more free electrons are available to conduct heat and electricity.*

> Think about how the electron structure of elements changes in different groups in the periodic table.

## 10 Exam-style practice — Grade 6

1. Give the term used to describe materials that allow energy transfer to take place within the material. **[1 mark]**
2. Give a reason that explains why metals are better thermal conductors than non-metals. **[1 mark]**
3. Describe how thermal energy is transferred through a metal. **[3 marks]**

# The pH scale and neutralisation

You need to know how to use the pH scale to measure how acidic or alkaline a solution is.

## 10 Acids, bases and alkalis

### Acids

An acid is a substance that produces hydrogen ($H^+$) ions when dissolved in water.

Acids have a pH of less than 7.

The lower the pH number, the stronger the acid.

### Bases and alkalis

Bases react with acids and neutralise them to make a salt and water. They are usually metal oxides or metal hydroxides.

Alkalis are bases that are dissolved in water. Copper oxide is a base but not an alkali, whereas sodium hydroxide is an alkali and a base because it dissolves in water.

An alkali is a substance that produces hydroxide ($OH^-$) ions when dissolved in water.

Aqueous solutions of alkalis have a pH greater than 7.

The higher the pH number, the stronger the alkali.

### Neutralisation reactions

A solution with pH 7 is neutral. When acids and alkalis react, a neutralisation reaction occurs.

The hydrogen ions react with the hydroxide ions to produce water:

$H^+(aq) + OH^-(aq) \rightarrow H_2O(l)$

Indicators, such as universal indicator, are used to measure the approximate pH of a solution. Universal indicator changes colour to show the pH of a substance. pH can also be measured using a pH probe.

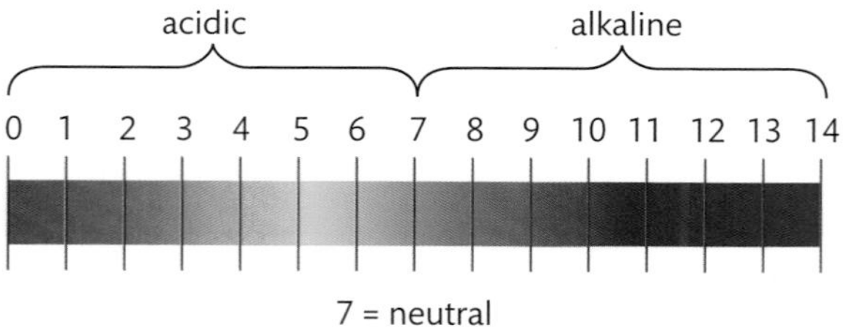


**Figure 1** The pH scale

## 1 Maths skills

Divide by 1000 to convert from $cm^3$ to $dm^3$.

## 5 Working scientifically

If there is the same concentration (e.g. 3.65 g/dm³) of a strong acid, such as HCl, and a strong alkali, such as NaOH, that react in a 1:1 ratio, then it takes the same volume of NaOH to neutralise a particular volume of HCl (e.g. 25 cm³).

$NaOH + HCl \rightarrow NaCl + H_2O$

1 : 1

mass = volume ($dm^3$) × concentration ($g/dm^3$)

= (25 ÷ 1000) × 3.65

= 0.09125 grams of HCl

volume of NaOH = grams ÷ concentration

= 0.09125 ÷ 3.65

= 0.025 $dm^3$

= 25 $cm^3$

## 5 Worked example — Grade 5

Vinegar has a pH of about 2.5.

**(a)** What is pH a measure of? **[1 mark]**

How acidic or alkaline a substance is

**(b)** From the pH value of vinegar, what type of substance is vinegar? Explain your answer. **[2 marks]**

Its pH is lower than 7 so vinegar is an acid.

**(c)** What ion is responsible for the pH at 2.5? **[1 mark]**

$H^+$

## 5 Exam-style practice — Grade 6

1. Write a word equation for the neutralisation reaction between hydrochloric acid and sodium hydroxide. **[1 mark]**
2. An unknown solution is tested using universal indicator. The indicator changes to a deep blue colour.
   **(a)** Identify the type of solution being tested. **[1 mark]**
   **(b)** Name the type of ions present in the solution tested. **[1 mark]**
3. Suggest how you could prove that a solution has a neutral pH. **[1 mark]**

# Strong and weak acids

You need to know what is meant by a strong or weak acid and how the strength of an acid is measured.

## 5 Acid strength

Ionisation occurs when acid particles dissociate, releasing hydrogen ions. The strength of an acid depends on the degree of ionisation that occurs when the acid is in aqueous solution.

A strong acid is more easily able to lose a hydrogen ion and will completely ionise in aqueous solution. The concentration of $H^+$ released in the solution is a measure of the strength of an acid. Strong acids include:

- sulfuric acid
- nitric acid
- hydrochloric acid.

A weak acid will only partially ionise in aqueous solution. Weak acids include:

- citric acid
- ethanoic acid
- carbonic acid.

Go to page 140 for more about acids.

## 5 Working scientifically

You can show the ionisation of an acid in solution with the equation:

$HA \rightarrow H^+ + A^-$

The higher the hydrogen ion concentration of a solution, the stronger the acid (as more of the acid particles dissociate to release $H^+$ in the solution).

For every 1 unit decrease on the pH scale, the hydrogen ion concentration of the solution increases by a factor of 10.

| pH | 0 | 1 | 2 | 3 | 4 | 5 | 6 | 7 | 8 | 9 | 10 | 11 | 12 | 13 | 14 |
|---|---|---|---|---|---|---|---|---|---|---|---|---|---|---|---|
| $[H^+]$ | 1 | $10^{-1}$ | $10^{-2}$ | $10^{-3}$ | $10^{-4}$ | $10^{-5}$ | $10^{-6}$ | $10^{-7}$ | $10^{-8}$ | $10^{-9}$ | $10^{-10}$ | $10^{-11}$ | $10^{-12}$ | $10^{-13}$ | $10^{-14}$ |

So pH 7 $(1 \times 10^{-7}) = 0.0000001\ g/dm^3$

pH 6 $(1 \times 10^{-6}) = 0.000001\ g/dm^3$.

## 2 Strength vs. concentration

The strength of an acid refers to the degree of ionisation. The opposite of strong is weak.

The concentration of an acid refers to the number of moles of acid in a given volume of acid solution (usually 1 $dm^3$). The more moles of an acid in solution, the more concentrated the acid. The opposite of concentrated is dilute.

An acid can be concentrated and weak at the same time.

## 10 Worked example — Grades 6–7

**1** **(a)** What ions are produced when hydrochloric acid is in solution? **[2 marks]**

$H^+$ and $Cl^-$

**(b)** How do the ions produced show that it is an acidic solution? **[1 mark]**

Hydrogen ions ($H^+$) are produced.

**2** What observations are made if universal indicator is used to compare the strength of citric acid with hydrochloric acid, if both acids are the same concentration? **[2 marks]**

Sulfuric acid is the stronger acid so the indicator would be a deeper red.

**3** **(a)** What does the pH scale measure? **[1 mark]**

How strong or weak an acid or an alkali is

**(b)** Explain the difference between a strong acid and a weak acid. **[2 marks]**

The stronger an acid is the more dissociation takes place. This means that the acid can more readily lose a hydrogen ion ($H^+$).

You could also answer this in terms of ionisation – pH is a measure of the degree of ionisation which occurs to an acid in aqueous solution.

## 5 Exam-style practice — Grade 6

**1** Describe what is meant by a strong acid. **[2 marks]**

**2** Give **two** examples of strong acids. **[1 mark]**

**3** **(a)** Write the ionic equation for the neutralisation reaction between sodium hydroxide and nitric acid ($HNO_3$). **[2 marks]**

**(b)** Name the ion responsible for the strength of an acid. **[1 mark]**

**(c)** Suggest how the concentration of these ions affects the pH of a solution. **[1 mark]**

# Salt production

You need to know how salts are formed and the conventions used for naming them.

## Forming salts

Salts are produced by the reaction between an acid and an alkali. When an acid is neutralised by an alkali, such as a soluble metal hydroxide, or by a base, the products are always a salt and water.

acid + metal oxide → salt + water

acid + metal hydroxide → salt + water

If a metal carbonate is neutralised, then carbon dioxide is also produced.

acid + metal carbonate → salt + water + carbon dioxide

These are redox reactions. The metal ions lose electrons (oxidation) and the $H^+$ ions gain electrons (reduction).

Go to page 126 for more about redox reactions.

## Naming salts

A salt has a name with two parts; the first part is just the name of the metal reacting.

For example, if the base is magnesium hydroxide, the first name of the salt is magnesium.

The second part comes from the type of acid reacting:

| Acid reacting | Second part of salt name |
|---|---|
| sulfuric | sulfate |
| nitric | nitrate |
| hydrochloric | chloride |

So, magnesium hydroxide and sulfuric acid would produce a salt called magnesium sulfate (and water).

If magnesium carbonate reacted with nitric acid, then magnesium nitrate would be produced (with water and carbon dioxide).

## Worked example — Grade 6

**(a)** Calcium oxide is added to hydrochloric acid; a neutralisation reaction occurs. Give a word equation for the reaction. **[1 mark]**

*calcium oxide + hydrochloric acid → calcium chloride + water*

**(b)** Give the balanced symbol equation for the reaction. **[2 marks]**

$CaO + 2HCl \rightarrow CaCl_2 + H_2O$

1. Identify the metal reacting. It is calcium.
2. Work out the salt name ending from the acid. The acid is hydrochloric acid, so the second part of the name of the salt is chloride.
3. Name the salt. It is calcium chloride.
4. Complete the equation.

When you are constructing the formula of a compound, remember the charges on each of the ions must balance. Ca is in Group 2 so has a charge of +2; Cl is in Group 7 so has a charge of −1. In order for the charges to balance, there needs to be two chloride ions with one calcium ion.

## Working scientifically

When producing a balanced symbol equation, you will need to work out the formula of the salt produced. The overall charge on a compound of the salt is 0, so any charges must be balanced.

### Charges on common ions

| Ion | Charge |
|---|---|
| carbonate | $CO_3^{2-}$ |
| sulfate | $SO_4^{2-}$ |
| nitrate | $NO_3^-$ |
| chloride | $Cl^-$ |

## Exam-style practice — Grade 7

1. Name the salt produced in the reaction between potassium hydroxide and nitric acid. **[1 mark]**
2. Give the name of the type of reaction that produces a salt. **[1 mark]**
3. Name the acid reactant used to produce the salt copper chloride. **[1 mark]**
4. Give the ionic equation for the production of the salt zinc sulfate ($ZnSO_4$). **[2 marks]**
5. Give the formula for each of the following salts.
   **(a)** lithium sulfate **[1 mark]**
   **(b)** magnesium chloride **[1 mark]**
   **(c)** calcium nitrate **[2 marks]**

# Soluble salts

You need to be able to describe the preparation of a soluble salt.

## 5 Making a soluble salt

A soluble salt can be produced by reacting an acid with solid insoluble substances, such as metals, metal oxides, hydroxides or carbonates.

1. Add solid, e.g. metal oxide, to the acid until no more reaction takes place.

↓

2. Filter to remove excess solid.

↓

3. Heat gently, then leave to crystallise into a solid salt. Soluble salts can be dissolved in water.

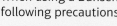

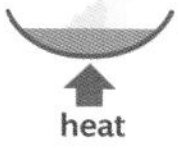


**Working scientifically**
When using a Bunsen burner you should take the following precautions:
- Wear eye protection.
- Stand at a reasonable distance away from the flame.
- Place the Bunsen burner on a heat-resistant mat.

Remember, the solid is added in excess to the acid until the reaction is complete, as the excess solid can then be filtered to remove it.

## 5 Different types of reactants

Some metals are too reactive, or not reactive enough, to produce soluble salts. This is why metal oxides, hydroxides or carbonates are used.
- Sodium chloride – sodium is too reactive, so sodium hydroxide or sodium carbonate is used instead.
- Copper chloride – copper does not react with dilute hydrochloric acid so copper oxide or copper carbonate is used instead.

Crystallisation is a separation technique used to separate solids from liquids by evaporating some of the solvent. See page 80 for more information on separation techniques.

## 5 Worked example — Grade 7

1. A student reacts sodium carbonate with dilute sulfuric acid.
How could the student ensure that all of the acid has completely reacted? **[2 marks]**

*Keep adding sodium carbonate until the fizzing stops.*

2. Name the process used to produce a sample of solid salt from a solution of soluble salt. **[1 mark]**

*Crystallisation*

## 10 Exam-style practice — Grade 6

1. When producing a soluble salt by reacting an acid with an insoluble base, suggest how you would remove the excess solid. **[1 mark]**
2. Identify the reactants used to safely produce sodium sulfate. Tick **one** box. **[1 mark]**
   **A** sodium hydroxide and hydrochloric acid ☐
   **B** sodium and sulfuric acid ☐
   **C** sodium hydroxide and sulfuric acid ☐
3. Name the soluble salt produced when copper oxide reacts with nitric acid. **[1 mark]**
4. State what is meant by the term 'soluble'. **[1 mark]**

# Making salts

You need to know how to prepare a sample of a pure, dry soluble salt from an insoluble oxide or carbonate.

## Making a salt

1. Pour 200 cm$^3$ sulfuric acid into a beaker and warm.
2. Stir in copper(II) oxide powder until no more reacts. The liquid will turn blue.

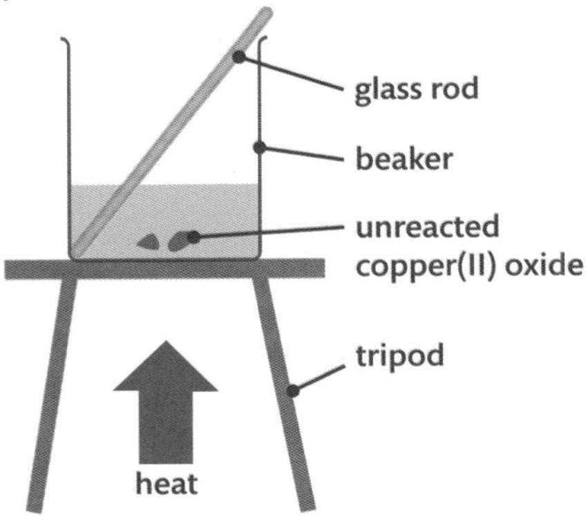


**Figure 1** Adding copper(II) oxide to sulfuric acid

3. Allow the apparatus to cool.
4. Set up funnel and filter paper apparatus.
5. Filter the solution.

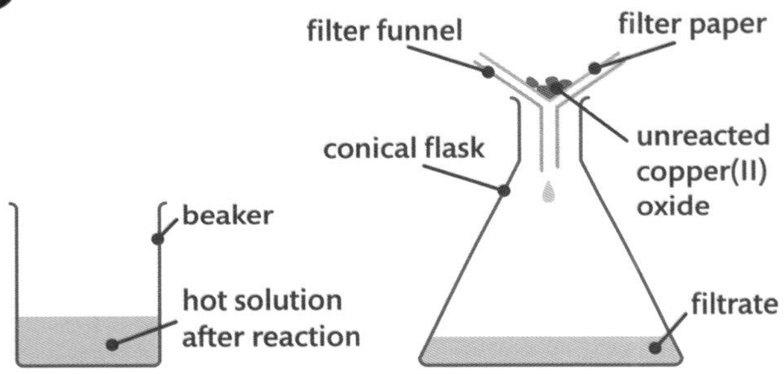


**Figure 2** Filtration

6. Collect the filtrate in a conical flask.
7. Gently heat the filtrate, so that it evaporates and crystals begin to form.
8. Pour the filtrate into an evaporating dish and leave to crystallise for 24 hours.
9. Remove crystals from evaporating dish, put onto filter paper and pat dry. The crystals can then be weighed if required.

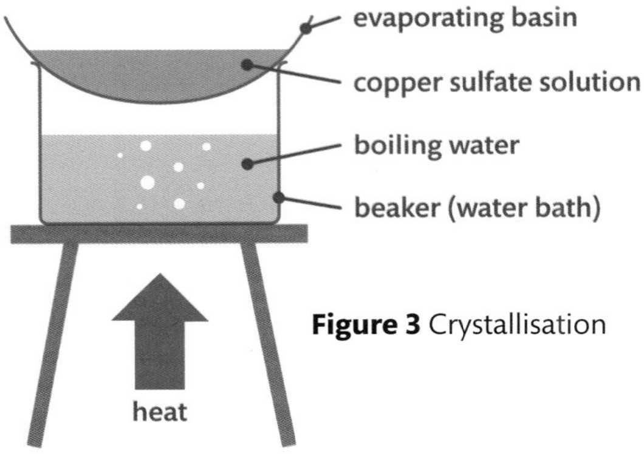


**Figure 3** Crystallisation

## Worked example — Grade 7

1. A salt can be made by reacting an acid and an alkali. Name this type of reaction. **[1 mark]**

Neutralisation

2. (a) Write a balanced symbol equation for the reaction between sulfuric acid and copper(II) oxide. **[1 mark]**

$H_2SO_4 + CuO \rightarrow CuSO_4 + H_2O$

(b) Explain why the following steps are important in the production of the salt copper sulfate. **[4 marks]**

Warming the acid: speeds up the reaction

Adding excess copper oxide: ensures all the acid reacts

The mixture is filtered: collects any excess copper oxide

The filtrate is heated to begin evaporation: encourages the formation of crystals

(c) Explain how the observations for a reaction with sulfuric acid and copper carbonate would differ from the reaction between copper oxide and sulfuric acid. **[2 marks]**

The reaction with copper carbonate would bubble because carbon dioxide gas is being produced. The reaction with copper oxide would not bubble.

State the observation and explain why it is occurring.

## Exam-style practice — Grade 6

1. Sort the following statements into the correct order, to describe how to prepare a salt. **[5 marks]**

**A** Leave to cool so more crystals will form. ☐

**B** Heat the solution until it has evaporated and crystals start to form. ☐

**C** Warm dilute sulfuric acid and add excess zinc hydroxide. ☐

**D** Dry the crystals obtained. ☐

**E** Filter the solution. ☐

2. Name the salt produced in Question 1. **[1 mark]**

# Exothermic and endothermic reactions

You need to know the difference between endothermic and exothermic reactions and be able to identify the type of reaction when given details about temperature changes.

## 5 Classifying reactions

During a reaction, energy is transferred from the reactants to the surroundings, or from the surroundings to the reactants. **Exothermic** reactions **release** energy (usually as thermal energy) to the surroundings. The temperature of the surroundings **increases**. Examples include: oxidation, metal displacement, neutralisation and combustion.

**Endothermic** reactions **take in** energy from the surroundings. The temperature of the surroundings **decreases**. Examples include: thermal decomposition, photosynthesis, electrolysis and citric acid reacting with sodium hydrogencarbonate.

## 10 Worked example — Grade 6

**1** A student investigates the energy change in the reaction between sodium carbonate and ethanoic acid by measuring the temperature at the start and end of the reaction.

Starting temperature: 46 °C    Final temperature: 25 °C

What type of reaction took place? Explain your answer. **[2 marks]**

*An endothermic reaction – this is evident because the temperature decreased.*

**2** Exothermic and endothermic reactions can be used for everyday purposes.

**(a)** Which type of reaction do hand warmers and self-heating cans use? **[1 mark]**

*Exothermic*

**(b)** Which type of reaction do headache cooling pads and sports injury packs use? **[1 mark]**

*Endothermic*

**3** A student measured the energy change that took place in three different chemical reactions. The student wants to identify which reaction would be best used for the production of hand warmers. The table shows the results and costs. Evaluate the use of each reaction and decide which is the most suitable. **[4 marks]**

| Reaction | Temperature change in °C | Cost in £ |
|---|---|---|
| A | +6 | 3.50 |
| B | –3 | 2.00 |
| C | +17 | 25.00 |

*A – releases thermal energy and is relatively inexpensive*

*B – takes in thermal energy so not useful*

*C – releases a lot of thermal energy but very expensive*

*A is best used for hand warmers because the reaction releases thermal energy and is comparatively cheap.*

## 5 Exam-style practice — Grade 5

**1** A student reacts two substances and measures the energy levels of the reactants and the products during the reaction. The products have less energy than the reactants. Give the name of this type of reaction. **[1 mark]**

**2** Thermal decomposition is an example of an endothermic reaction. Describe how the temperature of the reaction mixture will change during the reaction. **[1 mark]**

Made a start | Feeling confident | Exam ready

# Temperature changes

You need to know how to investigate variables that affect temperature changes in reacting solutions, e.g. acid with metals or carbonates, neutralisation reactions and displacement of metals.

## ② Apparatus

- ☑ 2 mol/dm³ dilute hydrochloric acid
- ☑ 2 mol/dm³ sodium hydroxide solution
- ☑ expanded polystyrene cup and lid
- ☑ 250 cm³ beaker
- ☑ measuring cylinder
- ☑ thermometer

## ⑤ Maths skills

You may need to plot a graph of your results.

You will need to draw a line of best fit. This is a line that is produced to show the trend or correlation in the points plotted on a graph. The line should be drawn so that the points the line does not pass through are evenly distributed either side of the line.

## ② Working scientifically

**Control variables** are the things you need to keep the same during the experiment, to ensure it is a fair test. In this reaction, the concentration and volume of sulfuric acid must be kept the same.

## ⑩ Method

**1** Using a measuring cylinder add 20 cm³ dilute hydrochloric acid into a polystyrene cup.

**2** Stand the cup inside a beaker. This will make it more stable and will insulate it.

**3** Use a thermometer to measure the temperature of the acid. Record the temperature.

**4** Measure 10 cm³ of sodium hydroxide.

**5** Pour the sodium hydroxide into the cup. Loosely fit the lid and gently stir the solution with the thermometer through the hole. When the reading on the thermometer remains constant record the temperature in your table.

**6** Repeat steps **4** and **5** two more times, adding 5 cm³ more of sodium hydroxide solution each time.

**7** Repeat this experiment two more times and record the findings.

| Total volume of NaOH added in cm³ | Increase in temperature in °C | | | |
|---|---|---|---|---|
| | 1 | 2 | 3 | Mean |
| 10 | 8 | 6 | 5 | 6.3 |
| 15 | 17 | 19 | 19 | 18.3 |
| 20 | 24 | 25 | 26 | 25.0 |

## ⑤ Worked example <span style="float:right">Grade 6 </span>

A student uses the apparatus in **Figure 1** to measure the temperature change when sulfuric acid reacts with calcium carbonate.

**(a)** Describe how the apparatus can be altered to reduce heat loss to the surroundings. **[2 marks]**

Use a polystyrene cup instead of the beaker and loosely place a lid on top of the cup.

**(b)** When observing the reaction, how would the student know if it is exothermic? **[2 marks]**

The reading on the thermometer would increase.

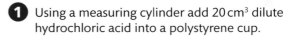

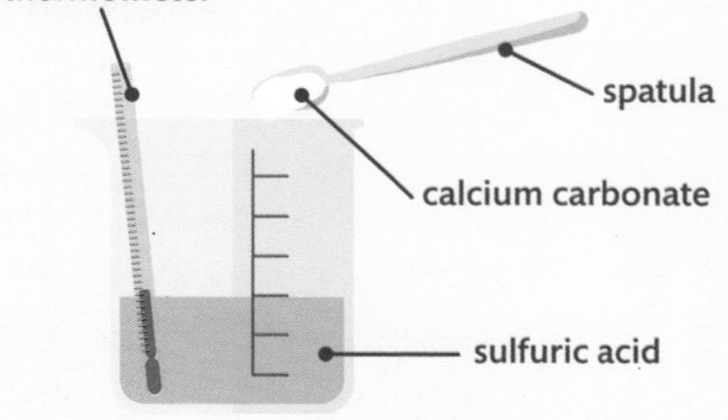

**Figure 1** Adding calcium carbonate to sulfuric acid

## ⑤ Exam-style practice <span style="float:right">Grade 6 </span>

A student measures the temperature change when water is added to anhydrous cobalt chloride and hydrated cobalt chloride is formed. Calculate the mean temperature change and identify the type of reaction that took place. **[3 marks]**

| | Trial 1 | Trial 2 | Trial 3 | Mean |
|---|---|---|---|---|
| Temperature change in °C | −6 | −8 | −5 | |

# Collision theory and activation energy

You need to know how factors such as temperature, concentration, surface area and pressure (of gases) can be altered to affect the rate of a reaction, using collision theory.

## 5 Collision theory

For a reaction to happen reacting particles must **collide** with **enough energy** to react.

**Activation energy** is the minimum amount of energy required for a reaction to take place.

### Factors affecting rate of reaction

The rate of reaction is directly proportional to the frequency of collisions. This means that increasing factors that make collisions more frequent will increase the rate of reaction.

- Increasing the **temperature** gives the reacting particles more energy, so they are more likely to collide.
- Increasing the **concentration** results in more particles in the reaction mixture, so there is a higher chance of collisions.
- Increasing the **pressure** causes the gas particles to become more restricted, so they are more likely to collide.
- Increasing the **surface area** of solid reactants results in increased frequency of collisions.

Go to page 121 for more about factors that affect rate of reaction.

## 10 Worked example — Grade 7

A student investigates the volume of gas produced in the reaction between magnesium ribbon and hydrochloric acid. **Figure 1** shows the student's results.

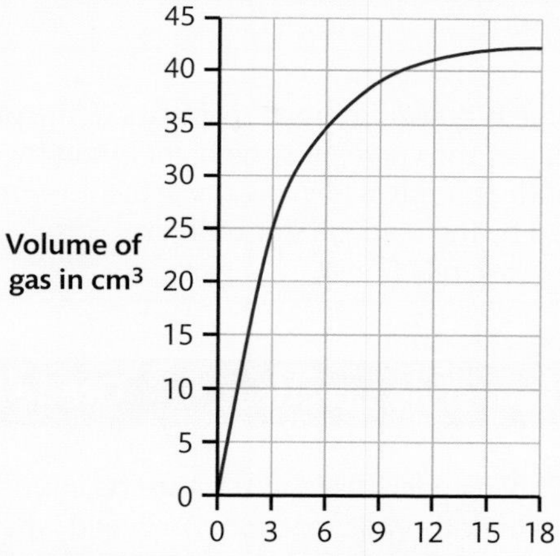


**Figure 1** Student's results

The student then repeats the experiment using a more concentrated solution of hydrochloric acid with the same mass of magnesium.

**(a)** Describe and explain how changing the concentration of hydrochloric acid affects the line on the graph. **[4 marks]**

If the concentration of the acid is increased, the rate of reaction will be faster, as there will be more chance of successful collisions occurring. Therefore, the line will be steeper at the start of the reaction. As there is the same number of magnesium particles in the reaction mixture, the reaction will still produce the same volume of gas, so the curve should plateau at the same volume.

**(b)** The student repeats the experiment using powdered magnesium, rather than magnesium ribbon. Explain why the rate of reaction will increase with powdered magnesium. **[2 marks]**

Magnesium powder has a larger surface area than magnesium ribbon. This will facilitate more collisions between the acid and magnesium.

## 5 Exam-style practice — Grade 7

1. A student investigated the reaction between zinc powder and sulfuric acid.
   Explain what will happen if the temperature of the reaction mixture is increased. **[3 marks]**
2. The reaction to produce ammonia is given below.
   $3H_2 + N_2 \rightarrow 2NH_3$
   Explain, in terms of rate of reaction, why increasing the pressure increases the amount of ammonia produced. **[2 marks]**

# Reaction profiles

You need to know how reaction profiles, also known as energy level diagrams, are used to compare the energy of reactants and products to determine the type of reaction taking place.

## 5 A reaction profile

A reaction profile provides information on:

- the energy of the reactants
- the energy of the products
- the amount of activation energy needed for the reaction
- whether the reaction is exothermic or endothermic.

Go to page 145 for more information about endothermic and exothermic reactions.

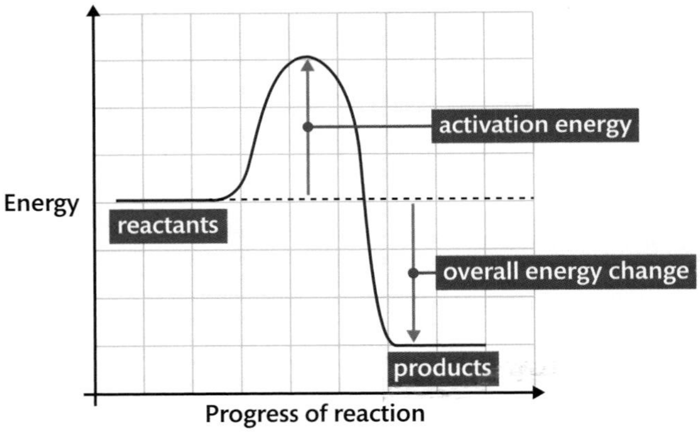


**Figure 1** A reaction profile for an exothermic reaction

## 10 Worked example Grade 8

The reaction between ammonium chloride and water is endothermic. Draw an energy level diagram to show the reaction. Include the following labels on the diagram:

- activation energy
- energy change. **[4 marks]**

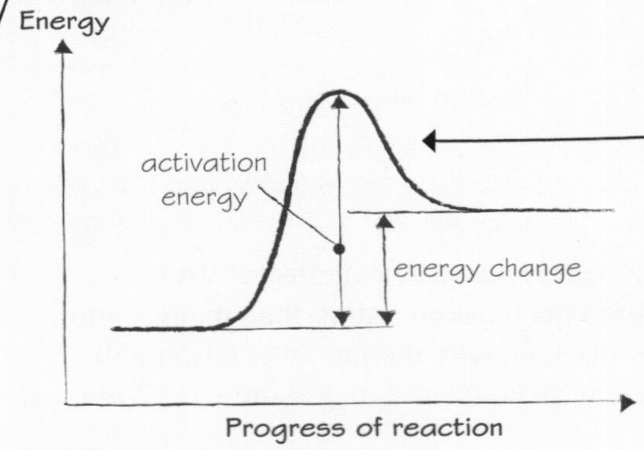


The reaction is endothermic, which means that the products will have more energy than the reactants because energy is being absorbed from the surroundings.

The activation energy is demonstrated by the increase in energy from the energy level of the reactants to the peak of the curve (for both exothermic and endothermic reactions).

The curve is drawn from the reactants to the products. The peak of the curve must be higher than the energy level of the products to show the activation energy required by the reaction (for both exothermic and endothermic reactions).

The energy change is the difference between the energy possessed by the products and the energy possessed by the reactants.

## 5 Exam focus

In the exam, you could be asked to do the following:

- Draw energy level diagrams for exothermic and endothermic reactions.
- Label the activation energy and the overall energy change of a reaction.
- Use energy level diagrams provided to identify the type of reaction taking place.

## 10 Exam-style practice Grade 8

1. Cooling packs used to treat sports injuries involve an endothermic reaction. Draw and label an energy level diagram for this type of reaction. **[4 marks]**

2. The diagram below shows the reaction profile for the combustion of methane.

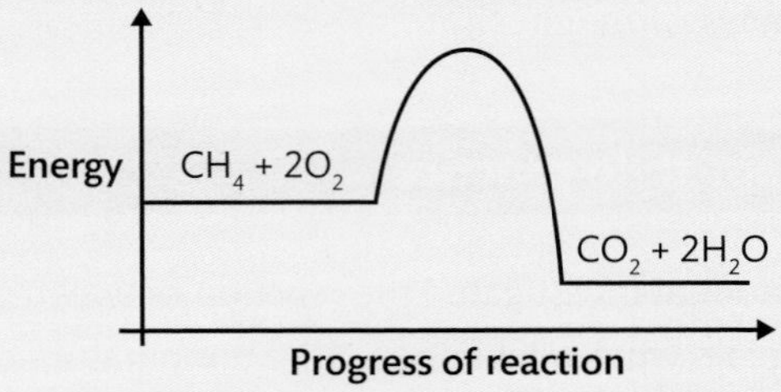


**(a)** Using the diagram, explain what type of reaction is taking place. **[2 marks]**

**(b)** Label the activation energy of the reaction on the diagram. **[1 mark]**

# Energy changes in reactions

You should be able to describe chemical reactions in terms of the breaking and making of bonds.

## 5 Bond energy

Energy is **required** to **break** bonds, so breaking is endothermic. Energy is **released** when bonds are **formed**, so bond making is exothermic. Bond energies can be used to work out if the overall reaction is exothermic or endothermic**.**

In an exothermic reaction, the energy released from forming bonds is greater than the energy needed to break bonds. Exothermic reactions always have **negative** energy values.

In an endothermic reaction, the energy released from forming bonds is less than the energy needed to break bonds. Endothermic reactions always have **positive** energy values.

## 1 Maths skills

You can calculate the overall energy change for a reaction with the following calculation.

overall energy change = energy used to break the bonds in the reactants − energy used to form the bonds in the products

Bond energy is measured in kilojoules per mole (kJ/mol).

## 10 Worked example — Grade 7

**Figure 1** shows the balanced equation for the combustion of methane using structural formulae.

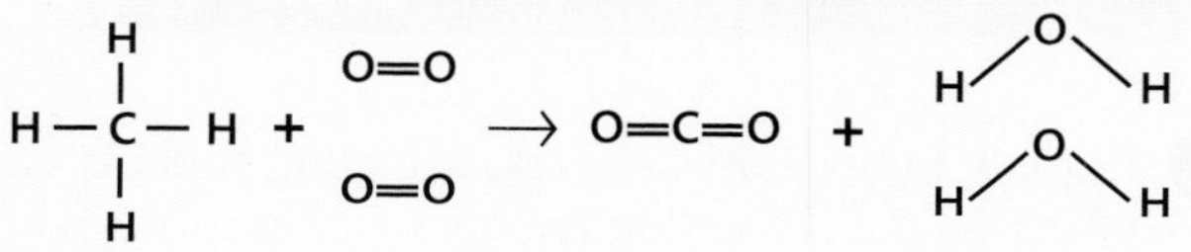

**Figure 1** Combustion of methane

The bond energies for the reactants and products are given in **Table 1**.

**Table 1**

| Bond | Bond energy in kJ/mol |
|---|---|
| C–H | 413 |
| O=O | 498 |
| C=O | 805 |
| H–H | 464 |

**(a)** Calculate the energy change for the reaction. **[3 marks]**

*energy change = bond breaking − bond making*

*bond breaking: (4 × 413) + (2 × 498) = 2648*

*bond making: (4 × 464) + (2 × 805) = 3466*

*energy change = 2648 − 3466*

*= −818 kJ/mol*

**(b)** What type of reaction has taken place? **[1 mark]**

*An exothermic reaction*

You will need to use the bond energy values provided. These values are per bond. In methane, the bond energy is 413 kJ/mol per C–H bond, so the total energy to break all four bonds in methane is 4 × 413 = 1652 kJ/mol.

## 5 Exam-style practice — Grade 7

The bond energies for the reactants and products are given in **Table 2**. **Figure 2** shows ethene reacting with fluorine.

**Table 2**

| Bond | Bond energy in kJ/mol |
|---|---|
| C-H | 413 |
| C=C | 614 |
| F-F | 155 |
| C-C | 348 |
| C-F | 485 |

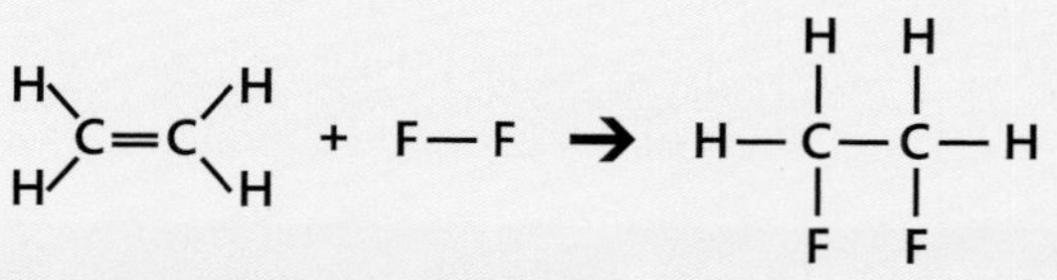

**Figure 2** Reaction of ethene and fluorine

**(a)** Use the bond energy values to calculate the energy change for the reaction. **[3 marks]**

**(b)** Name the type of reaction taking place. **[1 mark]**

# Catalysts

You need to know what a catalyst is and how it affects the rate of a chemical reaction.

## 5 Reaction pathways

A **catalyst** is a substance that can change the rate of a chemical reaction but is not used up during the reaction. Catalysts increase the rate of reaction by providing a different pathway for the reaction. The pathway provided has a lower activation energy. Different catalysts are needed for different reactions. For example, enzymes are biological catalysts.

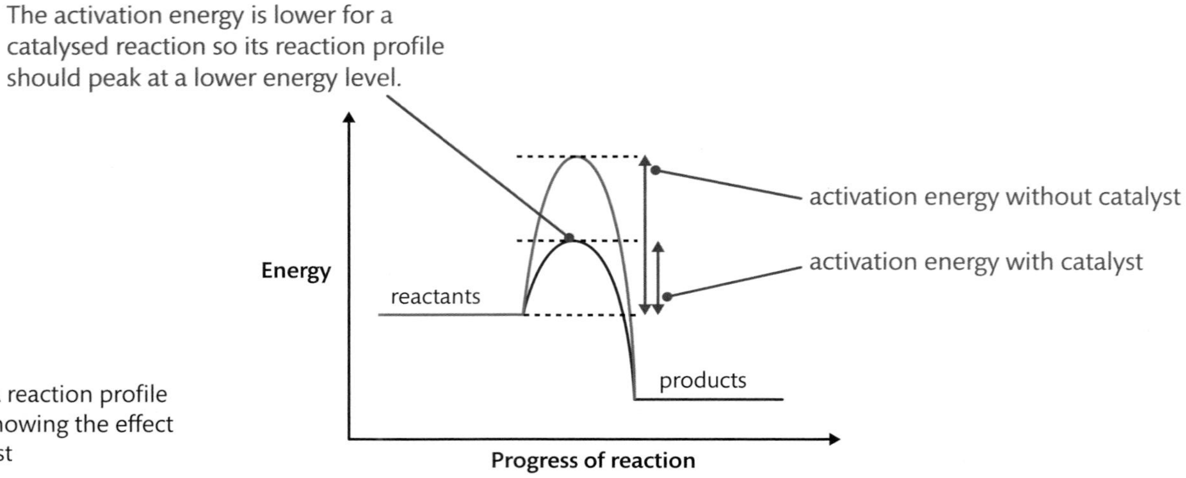


**Figure 1** A reaction profile diagram showing the effect of a catalyst

## 10 Worked example — Grade 6

**1** Hydrogen peroxide decomposes **slowly** to produce water and oxygen.

$2H_2O_2 \rightarrow 2H_2O + O_2$

Using **Figure 2**, draw and label the reaction profile for the reaction with a catalyst added. **[2 marks]**

**Figure 2** Reaction profile for the decomposition of hydrogen peroxide

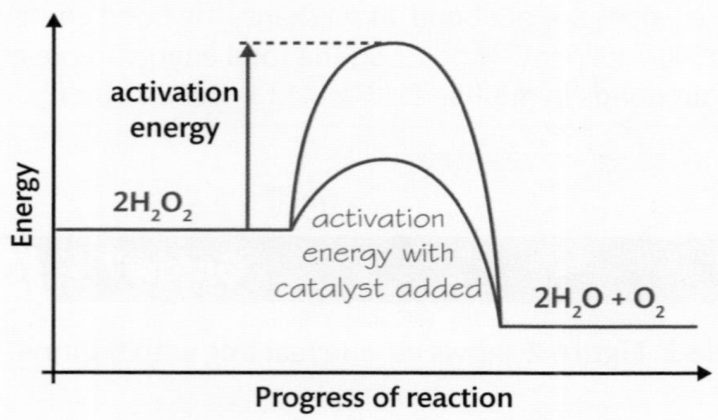


**2** Explain how catalysts work, referring to their effect on the activation energy of a reaction. **[2 marks]**

A catalyst provides an alternative pathway for the reaction, which requires less energy. This makes more of the collisions successful, therefore increasing the rate of reaction.

**3** Name the catalyst in the reaction below.

hydrogen + nitrogen $\xrightarrow{\text{iron}}$ ammonia **[1 mark]**

iron

You can identify a catalyst in a reaction in a few different ways:

- if something is written above the arrow, it is a catalyst
- if a substance is the same on both sides of the reaction, i.e. it's not part of the reaction
- if you are told a reaction speeds up, but the same reaction occurs, when a substance is added.

## 10 Exam-style practice — Grade 6

**1** Draw an energy level profile for an endothermic reaction.

**(a)** Label the activation energy on the diagram. **[1 mark]**

**(b)** Label the activation energy for the catalysed reaction. **[2 marks]**

**2** Name the catalysts used in biological systems. **[1 mark]**

# Crude oil, hydrocarbons and alkanes

Organic chemistry is the study of the structure, properties and reactions of the large variety of compounds that contain carbon. The main sources of these organic compounds are living or once-living organisms. You need to know the general formula for alkanes, as well as the names of the first four.

## 5 Crude oil

Crude oil is a mixture of a very large number of compounds. It formed millions of years ago from the remains of biomass (mainly plankton) buried in mud. Crude oil can be found in rocks and trapped under the seabed of oceans.

Crude oil is a finite resource; current supplies are estimated to run out in around 55 years with continued use.

Most of the compounds in crude oil are hydrocarbons – compounds only consisting of hydrogen and carbon. Most of these hydrocarbons belong to a homologous series called the alkanes.

## 10 Alkanes

Alkanes share the general formula $C_nH_{2n+2}$ where *n* is equal to the number of carbon atoms in the compound. Alkanes are saturated; this means they have no double bonds between carbon atoms.

To name the first four alkanes, remember the mnemonic: **M**ary **E**ats **P**eanut **B**utter.

| Name | Displayed formula | Molecular formula |
|---|---|---|
| methane | 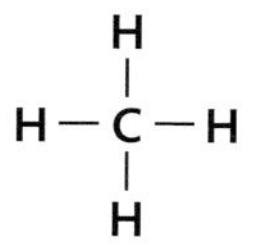 | $CH_4$ |
| ethane | 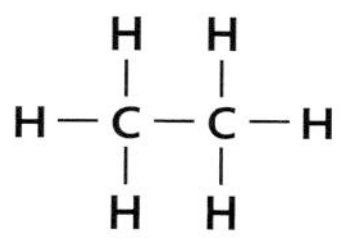 | $C_2H_6$ |
| propane | 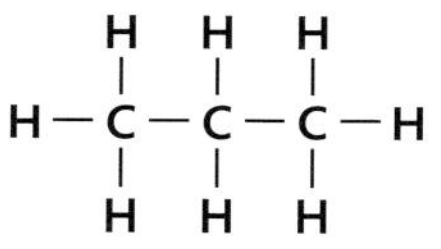 | $C_3H_8$ |
| butane | 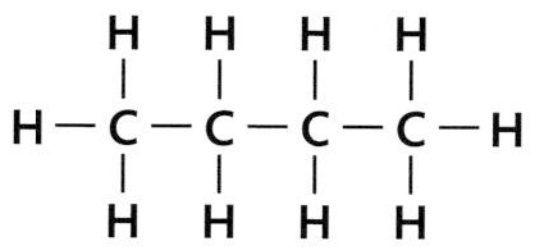 | $C_4H_{10}$ |

The size of a hydrocarbon is dependent on the number of carbon atoms, so the smallest hydrocarbon will have only one carbon atom.

Each carbon atom needs to make four covalent bonds to be stable.

## 5 Worked example — Grade 6

1. Give the molecular formula for an alkane with eight carbons. **[2 marks]**

$C_8H_{18}$

Using the general formula $C_nH_{2n+2}$
if C = 8 then H = (8 × 2) + 2 = 16 + 2 = 18
The formula can also be applied to question 2 to work out the number of hydrogen atoms drawn.

2. Pentane has five carbons. Draw the displayed formula for pentane. **[2 marks]**

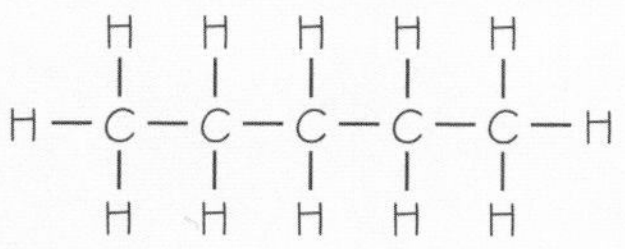

3. What is meant by the term **hydrocarbon**? **[2 marks]**

A compound that contains only hydrogen and carbon

## 5 Exam-style practice — Grade 6

1. Crude oil is a finite resource. Describe what is meant by **finite**. **[1 mark]**
2. Explain why alkanes are said to be saturated. **[1 mark]**
3. Use the general formula for alkanes to prove that the molecular formula of hexane is $C_6H_{14}$. **[1 mark]**

# Fractional distillation

You need to know how fractional distillation is used to separate mixtures of several liquids, such as crude oil.

## 10 Fractions

Crude oil is a mixture of substances, which can be separated into fractions. Each fraction contains hydrocarbon molecules with a similar number of carbon atoms.

The fractions are then processed to produce fuels such as petrol, diesel oil, kerosene, heavy fuel oil and liquefied petroleum gases (LPG).

The fractions are also processed to be used as the raw materials for the petrochemical industry to produce an array of products, such as lubricants, solvents, detergents and polymers.

The fractionating column has a **temperature gradient**. The temperature is controlled so that the hottest part of the column is actually at the bottom, not the top as you might expect.

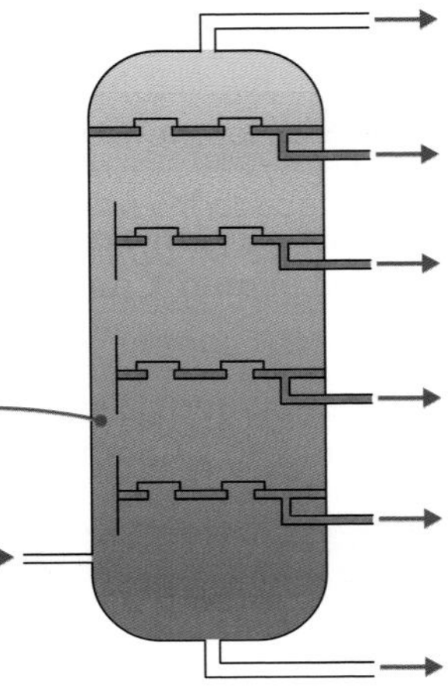


**Figure 1** The fractional distillation column used to separate crude oil.

## 10 Worked example — Grade 7

**1** Complete the sentence. **[1 mark]**

Crude oil can be separated into fractions because the fractions have different boiling points.

**2** Crude oil is a mixture of hydrocarbons. Explain how fractional distillation is used to separate crude oil into useful fractions. **[4 marks]**

Crude oil is heated to evaporate the hydrocarbons. The column is cooler at the top and hotter at the bottom. The gaseous fractions travel up the column until they reach their boiling point, where they condense and can be collected.

**3** Explain the term hydrocarbon. **[1 mark]**

A hydrocarbon is a compound of hydrogen and carbon only.

**4** How are the molecules in a fraction similar to each other? **[1 mark]**

They all contain a similar number of carbon atoms.

**5** Give **one** use for the diesel produced during fractional distillation. **[1 mark]**

Diesel can be used in engines (of cars, buses, tractors etc).

It may not seem significant but without the word 'only' this definition is not complete.

## 10 Exam-style practice — Grade 7

**1** Heavy fuel oil has many uses. It is separated from crude oil by fractional distillation.

Using **Figure 1** to help you, describe the steps involved in the fractional distillation of crude oil. **[4 marks]**

**2** **Figure 2** shows a laboratory experiment used to separate crude oil.

Describe what processes are taking place at X and Z. **[2 marks]**

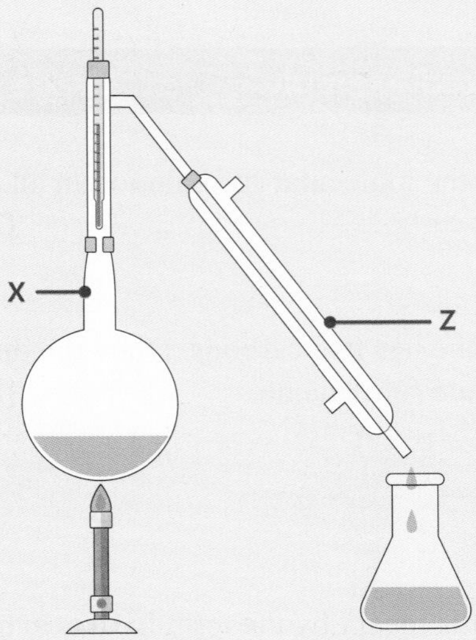


**Figure 2** Laboratory scale fractional distillation



Made a start / Feeling confident / Exam ready

# Properties of hydrocarbons

You need to know how the size of hydrocarbon molecules affects their properties.

## Properties of hydrocarbons

As the hydrocarbon chain increases in length, hydrocarbons become less flammable, more viscous and their boiling points increase.

When a hydrocarbon burns in plenty of oxygen, **complete combustion** takes place. The hydrocarbon fuel is oxidised. This process releases thermal energy.

When complete combustion of hydrocarbon fuel occurs, the same products are always produced.

hydrocarbon fuel + oxygen → carbon dioxide + water

## Worked example — Grade 7

1. Petrol is a fuel produced from crude oil. Petrol can be used to produce energy through combustion.

   Write a word equation to show the complete combustion of petrol. **[2 marks]**

   petrol + oxygen → water + carbon dioxide

2. The properties of methane, $CH_4$, and decane, $C_{10}H_{22}$, were compared. Complete the sentences to show how the properties of methane and decane differ. **[3 marks]**

   Methane is more flammable than decane.

   Decane is more viscous than methane.

   Methane has a lower boiling point than decane.

3. Write a balanced equation for the **complete combustion** of methane, $CH_4$. **[2 marks]**

   $CH_4 + 2O_2 \rightarrow CO_2 + 2H_2O$

The term **complete combustion** means there is enough oxygen available for the fuel to completely react.

The type of hydrocarbon given is not important. If complete combustion of a hydrocarbon is taking place, the products will always be **water** and **carbon dioxide**.

You need to consider the length of the hydrocarbon chain to determine how the properties will change from one hydrocarbon to another. Decane is longer than methane.

Write the formulae for each of the reactants and products first, then balance the number of each type of atom on either side of the arrow.

## Working scientifically

You need to know that there are a vast array of natural carbon compounds, including alcohols, esters which are used as solvents and perfumes, and carboxylic acids, such as vinegar. There are also synthetic carbon compounds, including plastics, such as polystyrene, nylon and PTFE used in non-stick saucepans.

## Key terms

- **Viscous** describes the thickness of a liquid: the more viscous a liquid, the thicker and less runny it is (like treacle).
- **Flammable** is used to describe materials that will catch fire more easily.

### Exam focus

When balancing an equation in the exam, check your answer. There should be the same number of atoms of each element on both sides of the equation.

## Exam-style practice — Grade 7

1. Name the products of the complete combustion of a hydrocarbon. **[1 mark]**
2. Balance the following equation for the complete combustion of ethane. **[1 mark]**

   $\_\_ C_2H_6 + \_\_ O_2 \rightarrow \_\_ CO_2 + \_\_ H_2O$

3. Describe how the viscosity of hydrocarbons changes with increasing molecular size. **[1 mark]**
4. Give a reason that explains why combustion is classified as an oxidation reaction. **[1 mark]**

Made a start | Feeling confident | Exam ready

# Cracking and alkenes

You need to understand how hydrocarbons can be cracked to produce smaller more useful alkane and alkene molecules.

## 10 Cracking

Cracking is a method used to break down longer hydrocarbons into shorter, more useful ones.

Cracking produces shorter alkane molecules and alkenes. Shorter alkane molecules and alkenes are in much higher demand than long hydrocarbons. Shorter alkanes can be used to produce fuels, such as petrol. Alkenes can be used to make polymers, such as poly(ethene), the plastic used in carrier bags, which is formed from ethene.

### Catalytic cracking

A catalyst, such as aluminium oxide ($Al_2O_3$) or porous pottery (broken up), is used to crack long hydrocarbons. The hydrocarbon is vaporised and then passed over the hot catalyst; this breaks the hydrocarbon chain into at least two shorter hydrocarbon chains.

### Steam cracking

The hydrocarbon is vaporised, steam is added and the mixture is heated to about 800 °C.

## 1 Alkenes

Alkenes are unsaturated hydrocarbons – they have a double bond between two carbon atoms, shown as C=C. Alkenes share the general formula $C_nH_{2n}$.

The total number of C and H atoms in the products should equal the total number of C and H in the hydrocarbon (on the left) being cracked. So, there should be a total of 12 C and 26 H either side of the arrow.

## 2 Bromine test

Bromine water can be used to identify alkenes and distinguish them from alkanes.

**Alkanes** are relatively unreactive and do not decolourise bromine water. The bromine water stays orange.

**Alkenes** are reactive and decolourise bromine water. The bromine water becomes colourless.

## 5 Worked example — Grade 7

**1** Hydrocarbons can be cracked to produce shorter hydrocarbons. Complete the equation to show the cracking of dodecane ($C_{12}H_{26}$). **[1 mark]**

$$C_{12}H_{26} \rightarrow C_5H_{12} + C_4H_8 + C_3H_6$$

**2** **Figure 1** shows how cracking can be performed in the laboratory.

**(a)** Why is aluminium oxide used? **[1 mark]**

To speed up the reaction (it is a catalyst).

**(b)** Why is cracking classed as a thermal decomposition reaction? **[2 marks]**

It uses thermal energy to break something down.

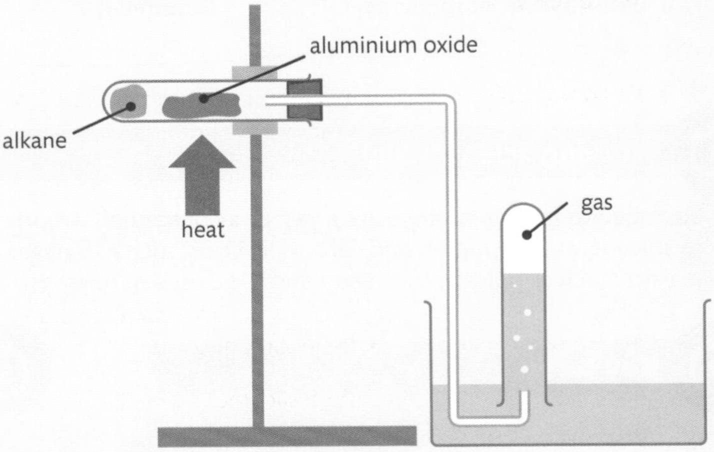


**Figure 1** Apparatus for cracking alkanes

## 5 Exam-style practice — Grade 7

**1** Explain why cracking is used in the oil industry. **[3 marks]**

**2** Complete the equation below to show the products of cracking. **[1 mark]**

$C_{28}H_{58} \rightarrow C_{20}H_{40} +$ ________

# Atmospheric pollutants

You need to know how pollutants are produced and what affects they may have.

## 5 Pollutants

Many fuels, such as coal, contain some sulfur, as well as carbon and/or hydrogen.

When fuels are burned, gases are produced. Carbon dioxide, carbon monoxide, sulfur dioxide and oxides of nitrogen can all be produced when fuels burn. These gases are all pollutants. Water vapour may also be produced.

Carbon particles (soot) and unburnt hydrocarbons form solid particulates that may be released into the atmosphere, causing further pollution.

Go to page 163 to revise the carbon footprint.

## 5 Incomplete combustion

When a fuel burns with a limited supply of oxygen **incomplete combustion** occurs.

The chemical reaction that takes place when oxygen supplies are limited is as follows:

fuel + oxygen → carbon monoxide + carbon (soot) + water

## 10 Effects of atmospheric pollutants

**Effects of atmospheric pollutants**

**Oxides of nitrogen, $NO_x$**
- heat in car engines and burning fuels cause nitrogen from the air to react with oxygen from the air
- cause respiratory problems in humans and can lead to acid rain

**Particulates**
- small solid particles released into the atmosphere
- cause global dimming as they block the light from the Sun
- may also cause health issues, such as cancer, in humans

**Sulfur dioxide, $SO_2$**
- produced when sulfur from fuels is burned
- reacts with water vapour to produce acid rain
- can cause respiratory problems in humans

**Carbon dioxide, $CO_2$**
- produced when a fuel burns
- contributes to the greenhouse effect (global warming)

**Carbon monoxide, CO**
- a poisonous gas
- not easily detected as it is colourless and odourless

## 5 Worked example — Grade 7

1 Write the word equation for the reaction when methane burns in a plentiful supply of oxygen. **[2 marks]**

methane + oxygen → carbon dioxide + water

2 What are the products when a hydrocarbon fuel burns in a limited supply of oxygen? **[3 marks]**

Carbon monoxide, soot and water

## 10 Exam-style practice — Grade 7

1 When a fuel burns, it produces atmospheric pollutants that can cause environmental issues. Draw a straight line to link the pollutant to its corresponding environmental issue. **[4 marks]**

| | |
|---|---|
| carbon dioxide | global dimming |
| sulfur dioxide | toxic gas |
| solid particulates | acid rain |
| carbon monoxide | global warming |

2 Give **one** environmental problem if sulfur dioxide gas was released into the atmosphere. **[1 mark]**

3 Describe how each of the following is produced by burning fuels.

**(a)** carbon monoxide and soot **[2 marks]**

**(b)** sulfur dioxide **[2 marks]**

**(c)** oxides of nitrogen **[2 marks]**

Made a start | Feeling confident | Exam ready

# Polymers

You need to be able to identify polymers and describe their structure and bonding.

## 10 Polymers

Polymers are very large molecules. The atoms in a polymer molecule are joined together by strong covalent bonds in long chains. There are variable numbers of atoms in the chains of a particular polymer. One example of a polymer is poly(ethene).

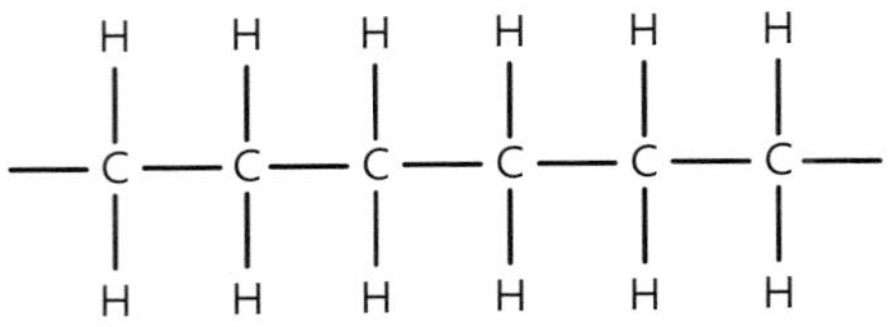

**Figure 1** Part of a poly(ethene) molecule

Go to page 114 for more about covalent bonds.

The intermolecular forces between polymer molecules are strong compared to the intermolecular forces between small molecules, so polymers melt at higher temperatures. Polymers are solids at room temperature.

### Repeat units

Polymer molecules consist of lots of identical, repeat units in a chain.

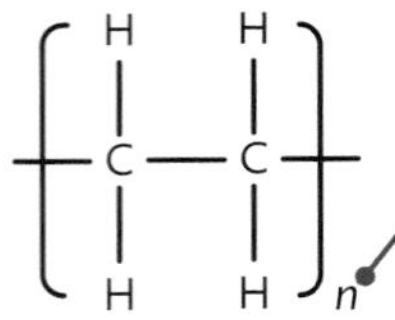

The value of 'n' varies

**Figure 2** The repeat unit of poly(ethene)

The word poly means 'many' so poly(ethene) is made from many ethene molecules joined together.

Go to page 154 for more about the formation of polymers from alkenes.

A repeat unit will always include two of the carbon atoms joined together in the chain and any other atoms attached to the carbons (that are not part of the carbon chain).

## 10 Worked example — Grade 7

**Figure 3** The structure of the polymer poly(propene)

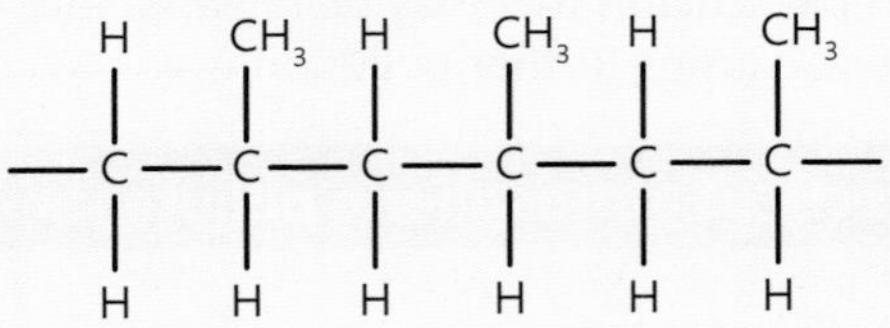

1. Use **Figure 3** to draw one repeat unit of poly(propene). **[2 marks]**

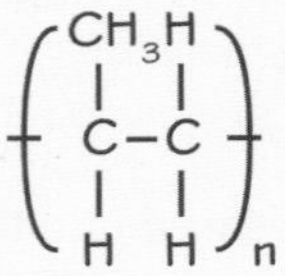

2. Polymers are usually solids and not liquids at room temperature. Suggest why. **[1 mark]**

Because they have relatively strong intermolecular forces between the molecules

**Figure 4** The structure of poly(butene)

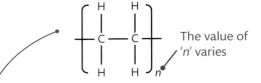

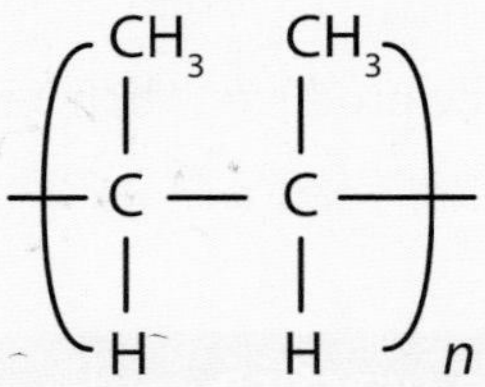

3. Explain how you can tell that **Figure 4** is a polymer. **[3 marks]**

The structure is a repeat unit of a polymer. It contains a chain of carbon atoms linked with a single bond, and a bond at each end of the repeat unit. It repeats $n$ times, indicating that it is part of a polymer.

## 5 Exam-style practice — Grade 7

1. Draw the repeat unit of poly(ethene). **[2 marks]**
2. Give the definition of the term 'polymer'. **[1 mark]**
3. State what type of bond joins the atoms together in a polymer molecule. **[1 mark]**

# Gases in the atmosphere

You need to know the proportions of the most abundant gases in the atmosphere today.

## 5 Earth's atmosphere

The composition of Earth's atmosphere has stayed mostly the same for the past 200 million years, but the exact proportions of each gas varies constantly. Scientists can use software to measure the effects humans are having on the atmosphere to develop solutions to reduce the impact.

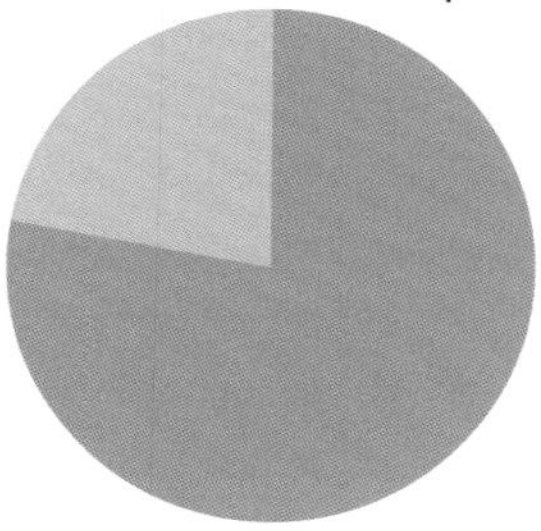


**Figure 1** The proportions of gases in the atmosphere today

### Maths skills

To convert from a percentage to a fraction you must divide the percentage of oxygen by the total percentage of the atmosphere: $20 \div 100 = \frac{1}{5}$.

## 10 Worked example — Grade 7

The table shows the approximate proportions of gases in the atmosphere today.

| Gas | Percentage composition |
|---|---|
| nitrogen | 80 |
| oxygen | 20 |
| other gases | $< 1$ |

**(a)** Using the data in the table, approximately what fraction of gas in Earth's atmosphere is oxygen? **[1 mark]**

$\frac{1}{5}$

**(b)** Using the grid below, draw a graph to represent the data in the table. **[3 marks]**

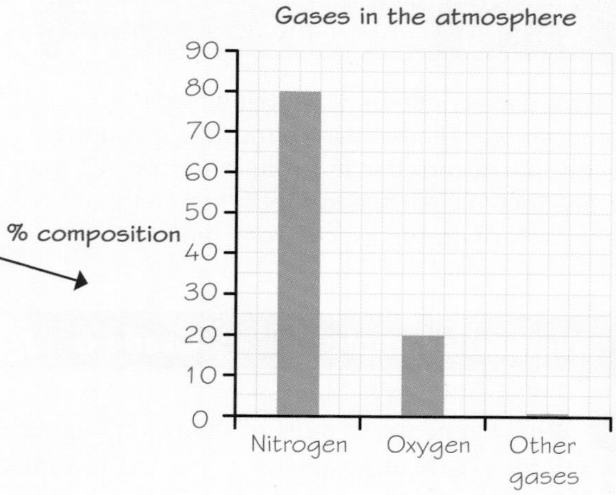


## 2 Maths skills

You are expected to be able to convert data provided as percentages, ratios and fractions. For example, the ratio of nitrogen to oxygen in the atmosphere is:

| | | | |
|---|---|---|---|
| | 80 | : | 20 |
| divide by 20 | 4 | : | 1 |

Ratios are a comparison of values. They are shown in their simplest form. This is done by dividing both values by the same factor.

### Exam focus

You will need to draw graphs in the exam.

- Choose a sensible scale to work with.
- Ensure the graph covers more than half of the grid provided.
- Label the axes to identify what they are showing and give units if applicable.

## 5 Exam-style practice — Grade 5

1. Give the proportion of Earth's atmosphere that is nitrogen gas. **[1 mark]**
2. Show that the fraction of oxygen in the atmosphere is approximately one fifth. **[1 mark]**

# Earth's early atmosphere

You need to know how Earth's atmosphere has developed over time.

## 15 Evolution of Earth's atmosphere

Scientists believe that Earth formed about 4.6 billion years ago. To begin with, Earth was a ball of molten rock. Many scientists believe that Earth's early atmosphere was formed from the gases given out by volcanoes.

Although Earth was a volatile place with a lot of volcanic activity, significant changes occurred within its first billion years that changed the make-up of the atmosphere, allowing life to begin and thrive.

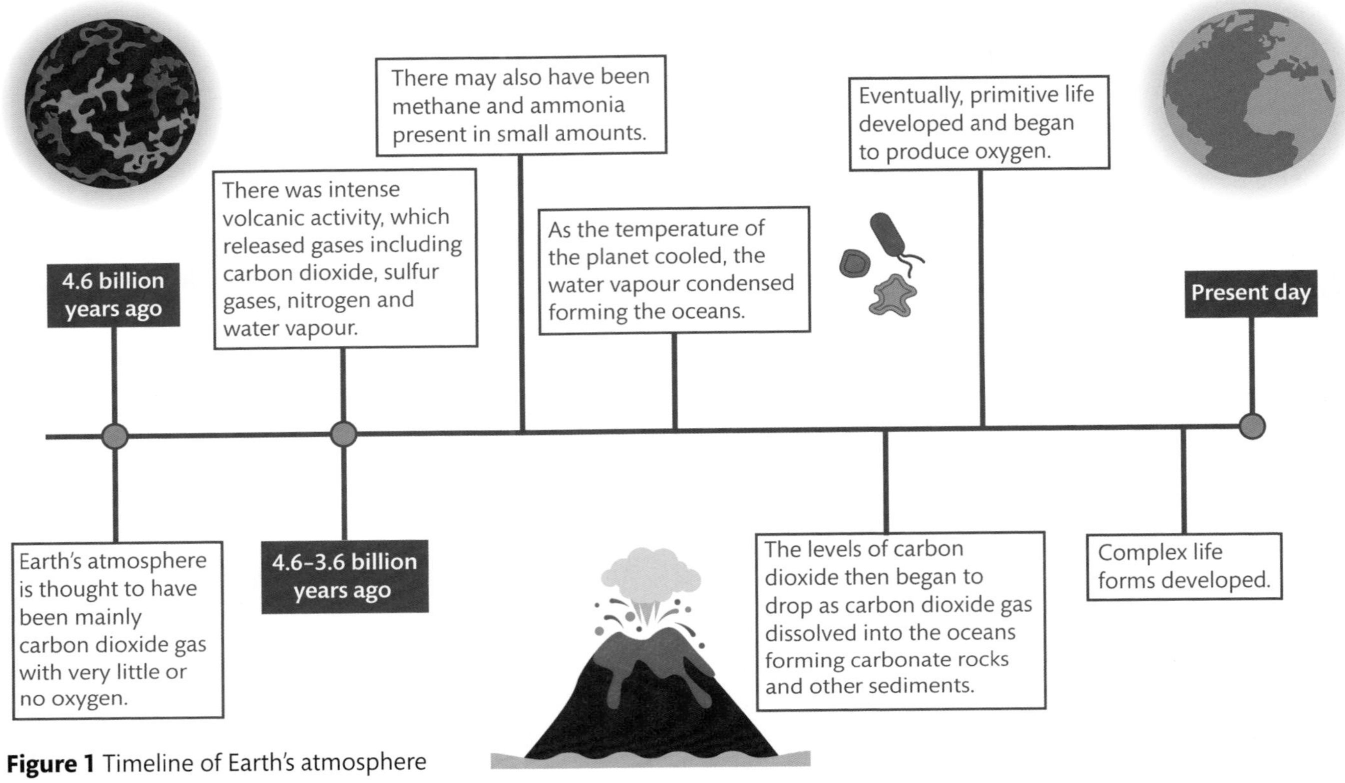

4.6 billion years ago
Earth's atmosphere is thought to have been mainly carbon dioxide gas with very little or no oxygen.
There was intense volcanic activity, which released gases including carbon dioxide, sulfur gases, nitrogen and water vapour.
4.6–3.6 billion years ago
There may also have been methane and ammonia present in small amounts.
As the temperature of the planet cooled, the water vapour condensed forming the oceans.
The levels of carbon dioxide then began to drop as carbon dioxide gas dissolved into the oceans forming carbonate rocks and other sediments.
Eventually, primitive life developed and began to produce oxygen.
Complex life forms developed.
Present day


**Figure 1** Timeline of Earth's atmosphere

## 2 Working scientifically

There are many different theories about the composition of Earth's early atmosphere and the events that occurred in its evolution. However, there is very limited evidence to support these theories because Earth formed such a long time ago.

## 5 Worked example — Grade 6

1. What happened to most of the water vapour in Earth's early atmosphere? **[2 marks]**

   *The water vapour condensed and formed the oceans.*

2. What activity is thought to have contributed to the high levels of carbon dioxide? **[1 mark]**

   *Volcanic activity*

## 5 Exam-style practice — Grade 7

The current atmospheres of Mars and Venus are very similar to Earth's early atmosphere.

The approximate proportions of the gases in the atmosphere of Mars are given below.

| Gas | Percentage composition |
|---|---|
| carbon dioxide | 95 |
| nitrogen | X |
| oxygen | 0.5 |
| argon | 1 |

**(a)** Give the approximate value of X. **[1 mark]**

**(b)** Suggest why there is only a small percentage of oxygen on Mars. **[2 marks]**

**(c)** The percentage of argon in Earth's atmosphere has remained the same since its formation. Suggest why the percentage of argon on Mars is unlikely to change as the atmosphere changes. **[1 mark]**

# Oxygen and carbon dioxide levels

Earth's early atmosphere is thought to have been mainly carbon dioxide with little or no oxygen. You need to know how the oxygen and carbon dioxide levels have changed over time.

## 5 Increasing $O_2$ levels

Over billions of years, numerous events have caused dramatic changes to the carbon dioxide and oxygen levels on Earth. About 2.7 billion years ago, cyanobacteria, also known as blue-green algae, started to produce oxygen, increasing the levels present in the atmosphere.

Over the next billion years, plants evolved, causing the levels of oxygen to increase further (to about 20 per cent). This increase in oxygen enabled animals to evolve.

The process by which plants and algae produce oxygen is called **photosynthesis**. It can be represented by the following equation:

$$\text{carbon dioxide} + \text{water} \xrightarrow{\text{light}} \text{glucose} + \text{oxygen}$$

$$6CO_2 + 6H_2O \longrightarrow C_6H_{12}O_6 + 6O_2$$

## 5 Decreasing $CO_2$ levels

Algae and plants gradually reduced the levels of carbon dioxide by photosynthesis.

Atmospheric carbon dioxide levels further decreased as a result of the following processes:

- the production of sedimentary rocks, such as calcium carbonate
- the formation of shells in marine life
- the production of fossil fuels, such as crude oil, from the remains of dead plants and animals
- dissolving in the oceans.

When plants and animals die, the carbon inside them became trapped. Under specific conditions of temperature and pressure their remains become fossil fuels.

## 10 Worked example — Grade 8

**1** (a) Describe **four** processes that caused atmospheric levels of carbon dioxide to change from around 95% to around 0.04%. **[3 marks]**

$CO_2$ was absorbed by plants and algae for photosynthesis. It was also used to form sedimentary rocks, fossil fuels and the shells of marine life.

(b) Work out the ratio of carbon dioxide in Earth's early atmosphere to carbon dioxide in Earth's current atmosphere. **[2 marks]**

early : current

2375 : 1

**2** (a) Name the process carried out by plants and algae that increases the levels of oxygen in the atmosphere. **[1 mark]**

Photosynthesis

(b) Give the balanced symbol equation for this process. **[2 marks]**

$6CO_2 + 6H_2O \rightarrow C_6H_{12}O_6 + 6O_2$

The equation for photosynthesis is the reverse of the equation for respiration. Remember there are six of each of the compounds reacting (except glucose).

### Exam focus

If you know the chemical formula of a substance, you can write it in your answer to save time.

### Maths skills

To work out the ratio of the gas levels divide both values by the lowest value.

$95 \div 0.04 = 2375$

$0.04 \div 0.04 = 1$

## 10 Exam-style practice — Grade 7

**1** State the approximate percentage of Earth's atmosphere today that is oxygen. **[1 mark]**

**2** Explain why the formation of limestone ($CaCO_3$) caused a decrease in carbon dioxide levels in the atmosphere. **[2 marks]**

**3** Explain how carbon dioxide from the atmosphere can be trapped in fossil fuels. **[3 marks]**

# Greenhouse gases

You need to know about the effects greenhouse gases have on the temperature of the Earth.

## Production of greenhouse gases

Greenhouse gases in the atmosphere, such as carbon dioxide, water vapour and methane, maintain the temperature of Earth by trapping solar energy from the Sun. Theories suggest that greenhouse gases were originally produced by volcanic activity as Earth formed. Today, greenhouse gases are mainly produced by burning fossil fuels, such as coal, oil and gas.

### Trapping solar energy

Greenhouse gases trap solar energy from the Sun in Earth's atmosphere, keeping it warm enough to support life.

Solar energy from the Sun reaches us as infrared (IR) radiation, visible and ultraviolet (UV) radiation. UV radiation has a short wavelength and can travel through the greenhouse gases to the surface of Earth.

Some of the solar energy is absorbed by rocks and Earth's crust, causing the planet to warm up.

Some of the solar energy is reflected away from Earth's surface. The energy is reflected as IR radiation. Some of the IR radiation is absorbed by the greenhouse gases in the atmosphere and re-emitted back towards Earth. This heats up the surface of the planet, including the oceans.

Go to page 161 to revise how human activity is increasing the amount of greenhouse gases in Earth's atmosphere.

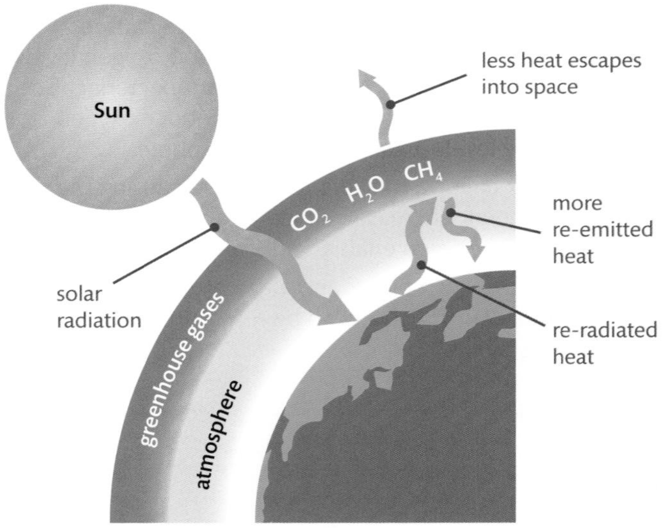


**Figure 1** Trapping solar energy

## Worked example — Grade 8

**1** What is a greenhouse gas? **[2 marks]**

It is a gas that traps solar energy in the atmosphere, thus maintaining the temperature of Earth's surface.

**2** Water vapour is a greenhouse gas found in Earth's atmosphere. Explain how the greenhouse effect increases the amount of water vapour in the atmosphere. **[2 marks]**

Water vapour traps the radiation that is being reflected from Earth's surface, causing Earth to warm up. As Earth warms up more water will evaporate, which will result in the formation of more water vapour.

**3** The greenhouse gases methane, water vapour and carbon dioxide are all produced by natural and artificial processes. For each gas, suggest a natural source and an artificial source. **[6 marks]**

Methane: Natural source – produced when organic material such as plants rot
Artificial source – rotting of waste in landfill and agriculture, e.g. cattle and rice fields

Water vapour: Natural source – evaporation from water bodies, e.g. lakes and rivers
Artificial source – burning fossil fuels

Carbon dioxide: Natural source – respiration of plants and animals, forest fires
Artificial source – combustion of fossil fuels

## Exam-style practice — Grade 8

1. Name **three** greenhouse gases. **[1 mark]**
2. Explain how the wavelength of the Sun's radiation contributes to maintaining temperatures on Earth. **[4 marks]**
3. Describe how greenhouse gases were produced in Earth's early atmosphere. **[1 mark]**

# Human contribution to greenhouse gases

You need to know how some human activities increase the amount of greenhouse gases in the atmosphere.

## 5 Greenhouse gases

Carbon dioxide levels are increasing as a result of:
- increasing combustion of fossil fuels
- increasing population
- increasing waste and landfill
- deforestation.

Methane levels are increasing due to:
- increasing production and use of fossil fuels
- increasing livestock farming
- increasing waste and landfill
- use of biomass and biofuels.

## 5 Working scientifically

Many scientists believe that human activity is causing global temperatures to rise and that it is likely to result in global climate change. This idea is based on peer-reviewed evidence.

Peer review is a process where scientists evaluate the reliability of other scientists' investigations and results in order to help validate the research.

Go to page 159 for more about carbon dioxide levels.

## 5 Worked example — Grade 8

1. Explain why many scientists are concerned with the use of fossil fuels in cars. **[2 marks]**

Fossil fuels release carbon dioxide, which contributes to global warming.

2. Over the past 250 years, carbon dioxide levels in the atmosphere have increased from 0.03% to 0.04%. Is this change likely to cause environmental issues? **[2 marks]**

Yes, increasing levels of carbon dioxide will contribute to global climate change.

Questions that ask for your opinion do not necessarily have a correct answer. You must back up your response with relevant evidence.

This question has two possible responses. Another possible answer is:

No, the level has only increased by 0.01%. This is a negligible amount compared with the level of carbon dioxide in Earth's early atmosphere.

3. Explain why scientists cannot produce accurate models for future global climate change. **[1 mark]**

There are many different variables involved so only simplified models can be produced.

It is very difficult to model global climate change because it is such a complex system. There is an abundance of simplified models, which together with speculation, can lead to biased reporting within the media.

## 2 Exam focus

Make sure you can recall at least two human activities that are increasing the level of carbon dioxide in the atmosphere, and two that are increasing the level of methane.

## 10 Exam-style practice — Grade 7

1. Give **two** human activities that are causing carbon dioxide levels to increase. **[2 marks]**
2. Explain why peer review is an important step in the development of theories. **[1 mark]**
3. Explain why many scientists are concerned about the increasing levels of greenhouse gases. **[1 mark]**
4. Explain why it is important that scientists' results are made available to a wide audience. **[2 marks]**

# Global climate change

You need to be able to describe the effects of climate change on Earth and the environment.

## 5 Impacts of climate change

The impacts of climate change can be observed across the globe. If climate change continues at its current rate, scientists predict that these impacts will continue to intensify.

**Global warming** is the overall warming of the planet, based on average temperature over the entire surface.

**Climate change** refers to changes in regional climate characteristics, including temperature, humidity, rainfall and wind.

The effects of global climate change can already be observed across the world:

- Natural habitats are changing, making them inhospitable for some plants and animals.
- Unpredictable weather patterns are making it increasingly difficult for farmers to grow crops.
- Flooding and other extreme weather events destroy buildings and cause deaths.

### Agriculture

Crop yields are expected to decrease for all major world crops. Agricultural land on the edge of deserts will become unusable, through the process of desertification. Crops could be wiped out in low-lying areas that suffer from flooding. With fewer crops available on the world market, prices are likely to increase. The growing season in some areas will increase. This would be a benefit to places such as the UK as more crops could be grown.

### Sea level increases

Coastal land is at risk, especially land on deltas. Sea defences are under more stress. Low-lying land is threatened so the lives of 80 million people across the globe will be threatened.

### Water and ice

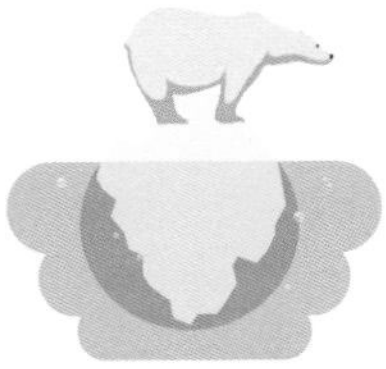

Sudden shifts of landmass, such as avalanches and rockfalls, can occur as glaciers melt. Habitats will be destroyed or flooded, which may displace or destroy entire species. Communities that use the melt water from glaciers may see this supply decrease, increasing the number of water stressed areas. This is especially the case in Asia. Less fresh water will be available in coastal areas as it will mix with sea water. Economically, areas that rely on winter tourism may suffer from a lack of snow.

### Population

People will migrate from areas suffering drought. Any that remain will be in danger of dying from starvation and lack of water.
17 million people in Bangladesh alone will be threatened by flooding. As the world population increases, more people will be living in cities located on the coast. More people will be affected by coastal flooding as a result.

## 10 Worked example — Grade 6

Evidence suggests that global climate change is melting the polar ice caps, changing precipitation patterns, causing more intense heat waves and droughts, and increasing the intensity of storms.

Describe the problems caused by these environmental issues. **[5 marks]**

*Melting of the polar ice caps is causing sea levels to rise, increasing flooding and eroding rocks and beaches. Rising temperatures cause more water to evaporate, which will lead to an increased amount of rain and snow. This may also lead to flooding. In some areas, there may be too little rainfall leading to drought and starvation. Heat waves also will lead to droughts. This will result in countries not having enough water to sustain the growth of crops for food, which in the long term could lead to starvation. Increased storm intensity is leading to millions of pounds worth of damage, which can have significant effects on a country's economy.*

## 5 Working scientifically

You need to know how scientists collect data that gives them an insight into the composition of Earth's atmosphere in the past. When ice forms it traps bubbles of air. This sample of the atmosphere can then be tested to measure the concentration of greenhouse gases and evaluate how they have changed over time, providing evidence about climate change.

## 5 Exam-style practice — Grade 5

1. Name **two** impacts of climate change. **[2 marks]**
2. Suggest how a change in the amount of rainfall could have a negative impact on the population. **[2 marks]**
3. Give the major cause of climate change. **[1 mark]**

# The carbon footprint

You need to know what the carbon footprint is and how it can be reduced.

## 5 What is the carbon footprint?

Whenever you use electricity, carbon dioxide is released into the atmosphere. Carbon dioxide and other greenhouse gases contribute to the carbon footprint.

The **carbon footprint** is the total amount of greenhouse gases emitted in a full life cycle by:

- a person
- a country
- a company
- a product, such as a kettle
- a service, such as street lighting
- an event, such as a concert.

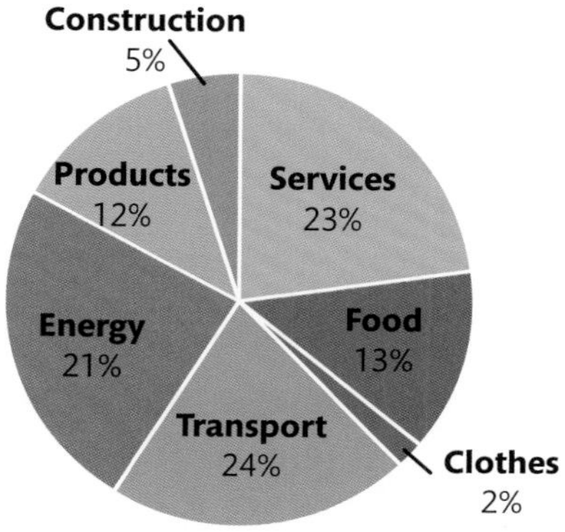


**Figure 1** Sources of carbon emissions in the UK

## 10 Reducing the footprint

Individuals, countries and industrial companies, such as steel producers, can reduce their carbon footprints by making a variety of different changes which reduce carbon dioxide and methane emissions.

### Individuals and companies

- **Recycle and reuse** – processing waste and decomposing waste releases methane.
- **Use energy efficient appliances** – the more energy efficient the appliance, the lower its carbon footprint.
- **Switch things off** – leaving lights on and appliances on standby uses electricity.
- **Buy local produce** – travelling to shops far away or buying food that has been transported from other countries increases the carbon footprint.
- **Share cars, catch a bus or walk** – motor vehicle emissions significantly increase the carbon footprint. Some companies encourage employees to reduce their carbon footprint with the Cycle to Work scheme.

### Countries

- **Use renewable energy** – renewable energy sources, such as solar and wind, don't produce carbon dioxide.
- **Use nuclear fuel** – nuclear fuel does not release greenhouse gases and can be used as replacement for fossil fuels.
- **Use carbon neutral fuels** – biofuels and biodiesel are classed as carbon neutral as the carbon dioxide they release, when burned, is equivalent to the carbon dioxide they absorb during photosynthesis.
- **Carbon capture and storage** – carbon dioxide can be pumped underground into porous rocks.
- **Tax high greenhouse gas emitters** – to encourage a reduction in car usage and transportation.

**Exam focus**

In your exam you could be asked to give reasons why actions to reduce our carbon footprint may be limited. Make sure you think about both individuals and countries in your answer.

If a product is carbon neutral, it gives off no net carbon dioxide in its life cycle. This means that it has no carbon footprint.

## 5 Worked example — Grade 7

Explain why it is difficult to reduce carbon emissions. **[3 marks]**

*It is expensive to convert industries from fossil fuels to alternative energies. Not all countries agree to reduce their carbon emissions and individuals don't want to change their lifestyles.*

## 5 Exam-style practice — Grade 5

1. Give **two** ways individuals can reduce their carbon footprint. **[2 marks]**
2. Give **two** ways industrial companies can reduce their carbon footprint. **[2 marks]**

# Earth's resources

You need to know how Earth's resources provide humans with everything they need to survive and flourish – shelter, warmth, transportation and sustenance.

## 5 Natural resources

Earth's natural resources can provide many useful materials, such as:

- crops for food
- cotton and wool for clothing
- coal, oil and gas for fuels
- trees for construction, paper and many other uses.

**Figure 1** Logging is the process in which trees are cut down to harvest wood for a variety of industries and uses.

Metals and minerals are found in Earth's crust. They play a vital role in the demands of modern day life.

### Sustainable development

**Sustainable development** involves managing Earth's natural resources to meet today's needs whilst protecting the needs of future generations and the environment. It includes replanting trees and crops, as well as preserving reserves of metal ores by recycling and reusing.

## 5 Finite resources

Some of Earth's natural resources are **renewable**. These are resources which will always naturally be available, such as solar or wind, or can be replaced within a short enough period of time that the resource will not run out, e.g. wood.

**Figure 2** Cotton is a natural fibre grown on a plant.

Unfortunately, many of the most useful resources, such as fossil fuels and metals, are **finite**. A finite resource is a resource that will run out (non-renewable), for example:

- Fossil fuels have a high energy value but they cannot be remade once they have been used.
- There is a limited supply of copper metal.
- There is a limited supply of uranium, used for nuclear power.
- Groundwater, any water that lies in aquifers beneath the land surface, is considered non-renewable as it is used faster than it can be replenished.

## 10 Worked example — Grade 7

1. Crude oil is a natural resource. Explain how industrial processes can be used to provide new and improved products from crude oil. **[4 marks]**

Fractional distillation can be used to separate crude oil into more useful fractions such as petrol, which is in high demand for use in transport.

The process of cracking can be used to produce alkenes, which can be processed to produce polymers; these are a much more useful alternative to wood and metal for storage containers. Polymers can also be used as synthetic rubber as they have a wider range of uses than natural rubber.

2. Suggest how agriculture has been adapted to help to sustain an increased population. **[2 marks]**

Agriculture has been adapted to become more efficient, so more food can be produced. These methods of agriculture include the use of pesticides, fertilisers, crop rotation, genetic modification and hydroponics. They allow more food to be produced from the same area of land.

## 10 Exam-style practice — Grade 6

1. Scientists are developing processes and new products to support sustainable development. Explain the term **sustainable development**. **[2 marks]**
2. Give **one** advantage and **one** disadvantage of using fossils fuels as an energy source. **[2 marks]**
3. Explain the difference between 'finite' and 'renewable' when applied to resources. **[2 marks]**

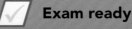

# Potable water

You need to know how potable water (drinking water) is produced.

## 15 Pure water and potable water

**Pure water** only contains water molecules. **Potable**, or drinking, water is not pure as it still contains dissolved substances (at safe levels), such as minerals. The origin of the term 'potable' is the Latin word *potare* which means to drink.

### Producing potable water

For water to be suitable for human consumption, it must be treated to remove microbes. The concentration of dissolved salts must be low enough to not cause harm.

The processes used to produce potable water depend on the water source and the local conditions. If supplies of fresh water are limited, desalination of salt water may be required. Desalination processes are expensive because they require large amounts of energy.

| Type of water | Source | Treatment processes |
|---|---|---|
| fresh water | rainwater, which collects underground (the most common source of potable water in the UK) or in lakes and rivers | **Filtration**<br>The rain water is filtered through layers of gravel, then sand, to remove any solid waste.<br>Smaller particles can be coagulated using chemical substances in **sedimentation**. They can then be filtered out.<br>**Sterilisation**<br>The final stage of water treatment is to use chlorine, ozone or ultraviolet light to kill any microbes present in the sample of water. |
| salt water | from the oceans | **Distillation**<br>The salt water is heated until it evaporates, leaving the salt behind. The water is then condensed to give a sample of fresh water. Go to page 80 for more information on distillation.<br>**Reverse osmosis**<br>This process involves passing water through a membrane, under pressure, to remove any ions, molecules, sediment and microbes. |

Go to page 166 for more about this method of purifying water.

## 5 Worked example — Grade 6

1. There are **two** main steps involved in the treatment of rainwater to produce potable water. Name and explain the role of each step. **[2 marks]**

Filtration removes solid particles. This is followed by sterilisation, which removes microbes.

2. Distillation of salt water is expensive due to the high amounts of energy required. State why energy is needed for distillation. **[1 mark]**

The water must be heated until it evaporates.

3. How can waste water be treated to produce potable water? **[2 marks]**

It can be filtered to remove any solid particles, then treated with chlorine, ultraviolet light or reverse osmosis to remove microbes.

## 10 Exam-style practice — Grade 7

1. Name **two** methods that can be used to produce potable water from salt water. **[2 marks]**
2. Name **one** substance that can be used to sterilise rainwater. **[1 mark]**
3. Give a reason why unprocessed sea water is not used as drinking water. **[1 mark]**
4. Name the main source of potable water in the UK. **[2 marks]**
5. Suggest **three** sources of water that can be used to produce potable water. **[3 marks]**

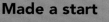

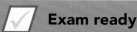

Page 165 LINKS

# Purifying water

You will be expected to analyse and purify water samples from different sources, testing for pH and dissolved solids as well as performing a distillation.

## Apparatus

- universal indicator
- test tubes and rack
- Bunsen burner
- 10 $cm^3$ measuring cylinder
- tripod
- gauze
- heatproof mat
- 250 $cm^3$ beaker
- watch glass
- tongs
- clamp stand
- 250 $cm^3$ conical flask
- delivery tube with bung
- ice

## Method

1. Using universal indicator and a pH chart, test the pH of the water samples and record the results in a table.
2. Weigh a dry watch glass. Record its mass in the table.
3. Pour a measured volume of sea water into the watch glass and place it above a beaker acting as a water bath.
4. Allow all the water to evaporate from the watch glass. The dissolved solids will remain on the watch glass.
5. Remove the watch glass with tongs and allow to cool. Dry the bottom of the watch glass.
6. Reweigh the watch glass and record the new mass.
7. Wash the watch glass, then repeat steps 2–6 for the other water samples.

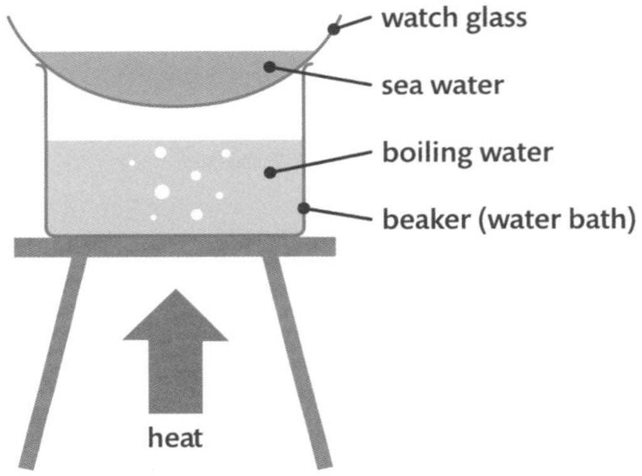


**Figure 2** Apparatus for purifying water

## Worked example — Grade 8

**Figure 1** Distillation

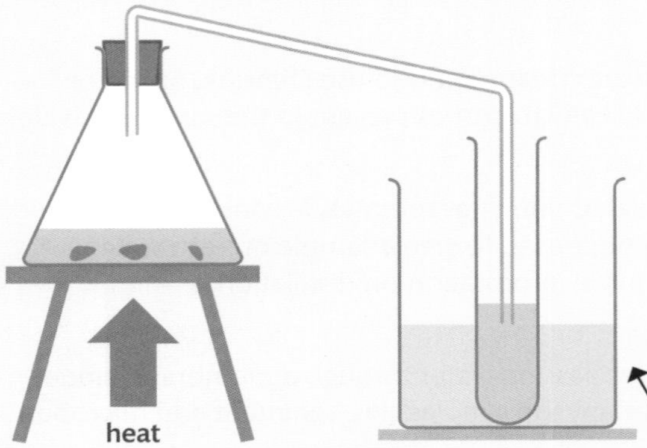


**Figure 1** shows how water can be separated from substances dissolved in it.

**(a)** Describe how simple distillation is used to purify sea water. **[4 marks]**

Heat the sea water until it starts to boil and evaporate. Reduce the heat so that the water boils gently; distilled water will condense and collect in the cooled test tube. Collect a small sample of water, then stop heating.

**(b)** Describe one way of testing if a sample of water is pure. **[2 marks]**

The pH would be 7 and there would be no solids left after the sample had evaporated. The boiling point of the sample would be exactly 100 °C.

### Working scientifically

When carrying out this experiment, the conical flask must be held firmly in place on the tripod and gauze using the clamp stand. A mixture of ice and water is put into the beaker surrounding the test tube to encourage the sample to condense.

One way to check the purity of a water sample is to use indicator paper or a pH meter to check the pH. The pH should be 7, as this is neutral. The sample can then be tested for dissolved solids by evaporating a sample in a watch glass. The mass of the watch glass should remain constant if the sample is pure.

## Exam-style practice — Grade 6

1. Name a process used to purify water. **[1 mark]**
2. Suggest how you could test a sample of water for dissolved solids in the home. **[2 marks]**
3. Give the boiling point of pure water. **[1 mark]**

# Waste water treatment

You need to know that waste water can be potentially harmful to our environment and how it can be treated to ensure it is safe.

## 5 Treating waste water

Vast volumes of waste water are produced by industries and individuals everyday. Individuals produce waste water when washing clothes and dishes, bathing and showering, and when flushing the toilet.

This waste water must be treated to remove any harmful substances before it can be released back into the environment.

- Human sewage and agricultural waste contain organic matter and microbes.
- Industrial waste water contains dangerous substances and organic matter. Processed waste water can be used for the irrigation of crops.

### Effects of untreated waste water

- Eutrophication, caused by pesticides and fertilisers, results in excessive plant growth in rivers and lakes. This harms aquatic life.
- Beaches, rivers and groundwater become polluted.
- Pollutants kill fish and other aquatic organisms.
- Substances enter the food chain and cause harm to humans.

## 5 Sewage treatment

Sewage treatment is the process of removing contaminants from waste water. There are four stages in the treatment of sewage.

1. Screening and grit removal involves taking out any rubbish, grit and other large objects that may block or damage the sewage treatment plant.
2. Sediment or settlement tanks are large tanks that allow the solid sediment to settle out as sludge. **Effluent**, such as grease and oils, is skimmed off the surface.
3. Microbes feed on organic matter found in the effluent, converting it into carbon dioxide, water and energy. The tanks are aerated to increase the digestive action of the microbes.
4. The sludge is placed in oxygen-free tanks, called digesters, where it is heated to stimulate the growth of anaerobic bacteria. The bacteria then consume organic material in the sludge, releasing water, carbon dioxide and methane gas.

Methane, produced by the anaerobic digestion of sludge, can be used as an energy source to generate electricity.

## 10 Worked example — Grade 7

Give the products of aerobic treatment of effluent. State which environmental issue they contribute to.

**[2 marks]**

*Carbon dioxide and water vapour. Carbon dioxide and water vapour are greenhouse gases which contribute to global warming when produced in excess.*

### Exam focus

You need to be able to describe the methods of obtaining potable water from waste, ground and salt water. Go to page 165 for more about potable (drinking) water.

Go to page 160 for more about greenhouse gases.

## 10 Exam-style practice — Grade 7

1. Name **two** sources of waste water in the home. **[2 marks]**
2. Waste water from agriculture contains pesticides and fertilisers. Suggest **two** reasons why this is potentially harmful to the environment. **[2 marks]**
3. Describe what is meant by anaerobic digestion. **[1 mark]**

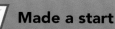

# Life cycle assessment

You need to know how a life cycle assessment (LCA) is used to assess the environmental impact of a product, from the raw material extraction to the disposal of the product.

## 5 Stages of an LCA

An LCA studies the environmental impact at several stages in the life of a product, including:

- extraction and processing of the raw material
- manufacture and packaging
- use during its lifetime
- disposal by incineration, landfill or recycling.

Waste, as well as the final product, will need to be disposed of.

During each stage, energy is used, pollution is produced and waste is created.

### What are LCAs used for?

LCAs are used to compare products that have the same use or function but that are made from different materials, for example, paper cups and drinking glasses. In each case, the stages listed above need to be evaluated to identify which product will have the least environmental impact.

## 10 Worked example — Grade 8

The table shows the energy used and waste created during the production of four different types of carrier bag. The figures shown are per 1000 carrier bags produced.

The data given illustrates the environmental impact of the production of the different bags. It doesn't indicate the environmental impact of people reusing the bags.

| Bag type | Electricity used in kWh | Waste in g |
|---|---|---|
| conventional high-density polyethylene (HDPE) | 6.15 | 418.4 |
| starch-polyester blend (biopolymer) | 17.24 | 94.8 |
| poly(propene) (PP) | 87.75 | 5850.0 |
| cotton | 11.00 | 1800.0 |

1 Which **two** types of bag are made from renewable resources? **[2 marks]**

*The cotton bag and the starch-polyester bag as it is made from a biopolymer.*

2 Evaluate the environmental impact of producing the four carrier bags. Explain your answer using the data provided. **[4 marks]**

*The starch-polyester bags produce the least waste, only 98.4 g but they use nearly three times as much electricity in their production when compared with the HDPE bag.*

*The HDPE bags use the least amount of electricity, just over 6 kWh, but produce four times the waste of the biopolymer bags.*

*The poly(propene) bags would have the greatest environmental impact as they produce the most waste, nearly 6 kg, and use the most electricity, 87.75 kWh. The cotton bags have the second lowest electrical usage. However, the production of cotton bags produces the second to largest amount of waste.*

## 2 Working scientifically

You need to understand that LCAs cannot be classed as an objective process.

It is straightforward to quantify the use of water, energy and production of waste. However, it is more difficult to give numerical values to the effect of pollutants. This can lead to LCAs being biased to misrepresent products for advertising.

## 10 Exam-style practice — Grade 8

1 Design an LCA to compare a plastic shopping bag with a paper shopping bag. **[6 marks]**

2 Explain how pollution may be produced during the life cycle of a plastic bag. **[3 marks]**

# Reducing the use of resources

Using resources more efficiently by **reusing, recycling** and **reducing** them is vital because it leads to less waste, minimises damage to the environment and is more cost effective. You need to know how resources can be preserved using these methods.

## Reusing and recycling

Reusing a resource creates no waste or pollution, for example refilling a drinks bottle or reusing a plastic bag.

Recycling reduces waste; however, energy is required to transform something into a new product, so pollution will still be created. The amount of energy required for recycling depends on the material and the final product. The levels of energy consumed and pollution produced by recycling are usually less than when the same product is made from raw materials.

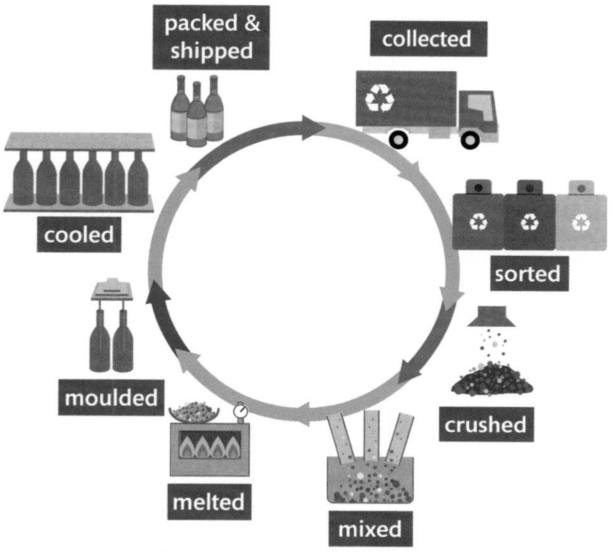


**Figure 1** Glass bottles can be reused or crushed and melted to make different glass products.

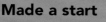

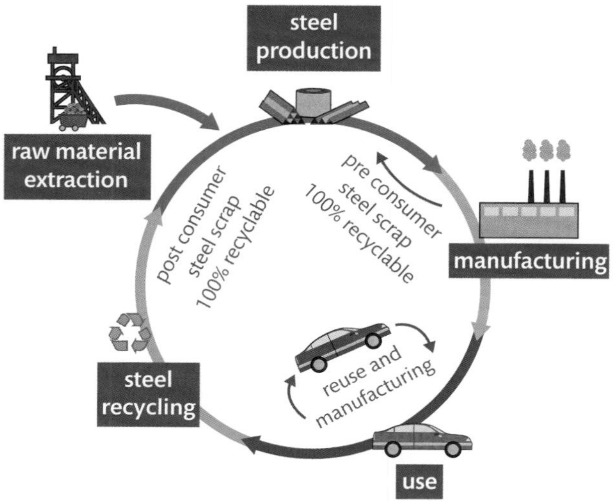


**Figure 2** Metals can be melted, recast or reformed into new products. Scrap steel can be added to iron from the blast furnace to reduce the amount of iron that needs to be extracted.

## Worked example — Grade 6

**1** The UK government sets targets for companies to recycle materials.

Give **four** reasons why the government would want to encourage recycling of metals.

**[4 marks]**

1. To save resources/ores
2. To use less energy compared with manufacturing from raw materials
3. So that smaller volumes of greenhouse gases are produced (reducing carbon footprint)
4. To avoid using up landfill

Governments and companies measure the amount of resources being used in footprints, e.g. the carbon footprint. This enables them to set targets to manage use of these resources.

**2** Building materials, such as clay, glass and metal, are produced from limited raw materials. Much of the energy for the processes also comes from limited resources. Extracting these raw materials by quarrying and mining has significant environmental impacts.

Evaluate ways in which the level of raw materials being used can be reduced. **[4 marks]**

The materials used for buildings are in limited supply, so these valuable resources could be saved by recycling or reusing them. The processes of recycling and reusing are usually better for the environment than the extraction processes, as less energy is required, so less fossil fuels are burned. This also means there would be less pollution released. Quarrying damages the landscape and creates dust and noise pollution. Waste materials are sent to landfill if not recycled or reused.

## Exam-style practice — Grade 6

**1** It is estimated that two billion tonnes of iron ore are extracted every year. Suggest why it is a good idea to recycle iron. **[2 marks]**

**2** Describe how recycling produces pollution and explain the environmental impact of the pollution. **[4 marks]**

# Scalar and vector quantities

You need to know the difference between a scalar quantity and a vector quantity.

## 2 Definitions

**Scalars** are quantities that have only a **magnitude** (a size).

**Vectors** are quantities with both a magnitude and a direction.

You can add scalar quantities like numerical values. When adding vectors, you need to consider the direction.

## 2 Vector quantities

- velocity (m/s)
- displacement (m)
- acceleration ($m/s^2$)
- force (N)
- weight (N)
- momentum (kg m/s)
- gravitational field strength (N/kg)

## 2 Scalar quantities

- distance (m)
- speed (m/s)
- charge (C)
- density ($kg/m^3$)
- efficiency
- energy (all types) (J)
- frequency (Hz)
- mass (kg)
- power (W)
- pressure (Pa)
- temperature (°C)
- time (s)
- wavelength (m)
- volume ($m^3$)
- area ($m^2$)

Efficiency does not have a unit. It is usually given as a decimal or percentage.

## 10 Adding vectors

Vector quantities can be represented by arrows. The length of the arrow represents the magnitude. The direction of the arrow represents the direction of the vector quantity.

If two vectors act in a straight line they can be added (same direction) or subtracted (opposite direction).

Vectors that are at right angles can also be added to find the resultant vector. Draw the arrows end to end to make a right-angled triangle. The resultant vector is the hypotenuse of the triangle and can be found using a scale drawing.

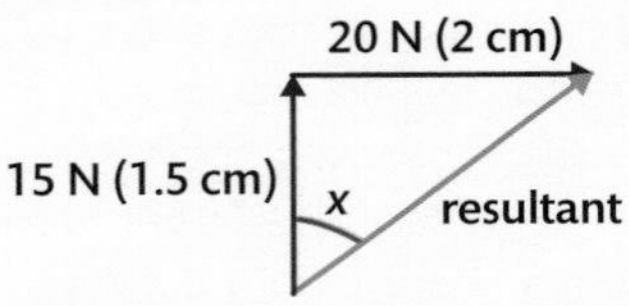


**Figure 1** A scale drawing showing the resultant vector

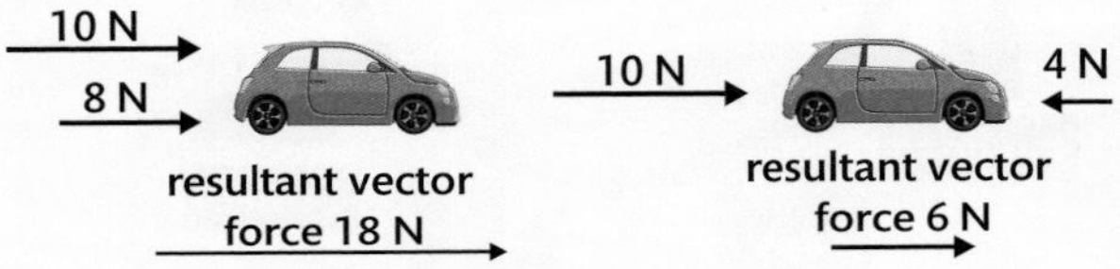


**Figure 2** Finding the resultant vector

Choose a suitable scale, such as 10 N = 1 cm. Draw the diagram to scale (use a protractor or set square, or use squared paper to make sure the right angle is exactly 90°).

Measure the length of the resultant vector. This should be 2.5 cm at this scale.

Convert this to the correct unit. $2.5 \times 10 = 25$ N

Use a protractor to measure the angle $x$. This is 53° when drawn to scale. You can also use Pythagoras' theorem to calculate resultant vectors. See page 171.

## 2 Worked example — Grade 5

Write down **one** similarity and **one** difference between speed and velocity. **[2 marks]**

Similarity: they both measure how fast something is moving.

Difference: only velocity gives its direction.

## 5 Exam-style practice — Grade 5

1. When there is no wind blowing, a plane travels at 65 m/s. The plane enters an area where the wind is blowing at 12 m/s due north. The output of the engines remains the same. Calculate the plane's velocity if it:

   **(a)** flies due north. **[1 mark]**

   **(b)** flies due south. **[1 mark]**

2. A bird flies north at 12 m/s. The wind blows it east at 9 m/s. Use a scale drawing to find the resultant velocity. **[3 marks]**

# Distance and displacement

Distance and displacement mean different things in Physics. You need to understand the difference between them.

## 5 Distance and displacement

**Distance** is how far an object has travelled. Distance only has a magnitude. It is a scalar quantity (page 170).

**Displacement** is the distance travelled in a straight line, in a particular direction. Displacement has direction as well as magnitude, so it is a vector quantity (page 170). The displacement at the end of a journey is usually less than the total distance travelled because of turns or bends in the journey.

The distance is how far you walk.

The magnitude of the displacement is a lot less than the distance. You walk for 110 metres, but end up only 50 metres from where you started.

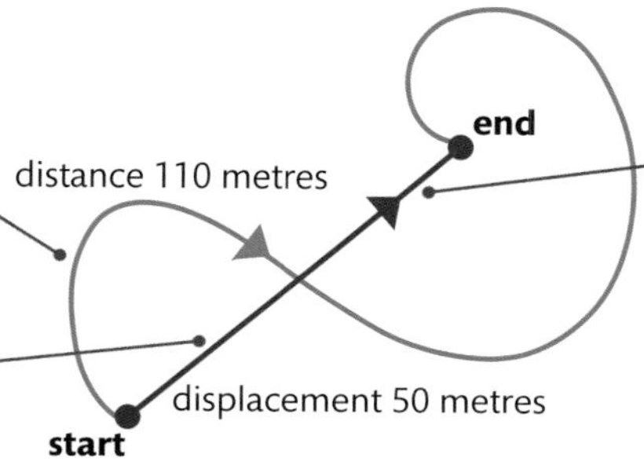


The arrow shows the direction of the displacement.

Directions can be given as compass bearings or simple descriptions like 'to the right' or 'up'.

**Figure 1** Going for a walk

## 5 Worked example — Grade 5

Mahad walks from home to the shop, then to school. The diagram shows the route he takes. Give Mahad's final displacement from his starting position. **[3 marks]**

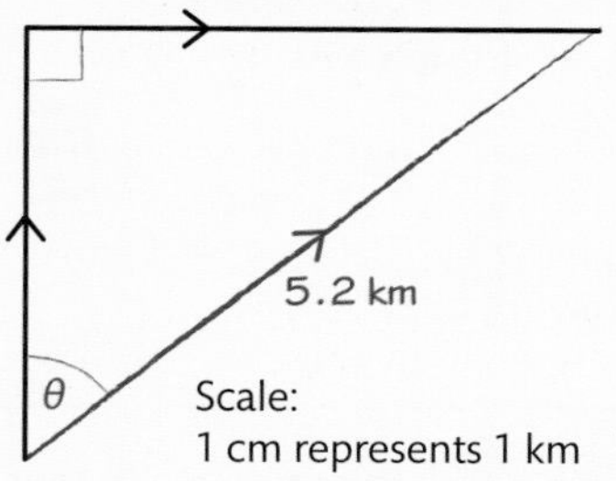


5.2 cm = 5.2 km

bearing = 050°

**Exam focus**

You need to give a length and a distance. Make sure you apply the scale to your measurement.

Use a ruler to draw a diagonal line from the start point to the finish point. Measure this and apply the scale. You also need to measure the angle from the vertical to the diagonal.

Bearings should be written as a three figure number, giving the angle going clockwise from north.

## 10 Exam-style practice — Grade 5

For each of the journeys given below, find:

- the total distance travelled
- the displacement.

**(a)** travel 200 km north, 200 km east and 200 km south **[2 marks]**

**(b)** go up 180 m in a lift, then walk 50 m along the corridor **[2 marks]**

**Exam focus**

You need to use the equation for the circumference of a circle. Check your formulae sheet on page 244.

**(c)** run 350 m to the shops, then the same distance back to your home **[2 marks]**

**(d)** run once around a circle with a diameter of 10 m. **[2 marks]**

# Speed and velocity

You need to know the difference between speed and velocity. Speed is how fast an object is moving. Speed only has magnitude so is a scalar quantity. Velocity is the speed of an object in a particular direction. Velocity has magnitude and direction so is a vector quantity.

## 5 Speed

**Speed** is a measure of the distance an object has moved in a specific amount of time.

distance travelled (m) = speed (m/s) × time (s)  $s = v \times t$

As most moving objects do not have a constant speed, this equation gives the average speed over a time.

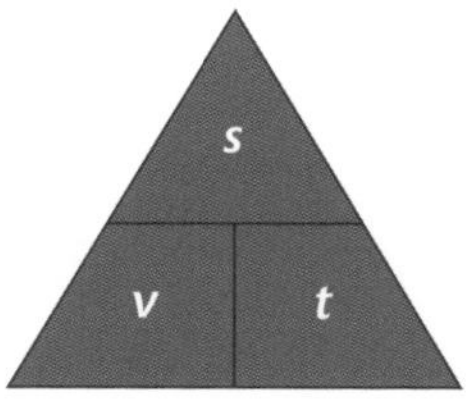


**Figure 1** You can use this formula triangle to help you to rearrange the equation and calculate an unknown value.

You need to know typical examples of everyday speeds.

| **Activity** | walking | running | cycling | cars on a motorway | sound waves |
|---|---|---|---|---|---|
| **Approximate speed in m/s** | 1.5 | 3 | 6 | 15–30 | 330 |

The speed of sound can vary.

## 5 Velocity

**Velocity** is speed in a particular direction.

Unlike speed, velocity has a direction. This can be shown as:

- a word, such as 'north' or 'left'
- a positive (+) or negative (−)
- an arrow.

Even at constant speed, the velocity changes if an object changes direction. A car driving around a roundabout at 20 km/h will have constant speed but its velocity changes as it changes direction. If the car drives in one full circle, the displacement is zero, which means the car's average velocity will be zero but the average speed will be 20 km/h.

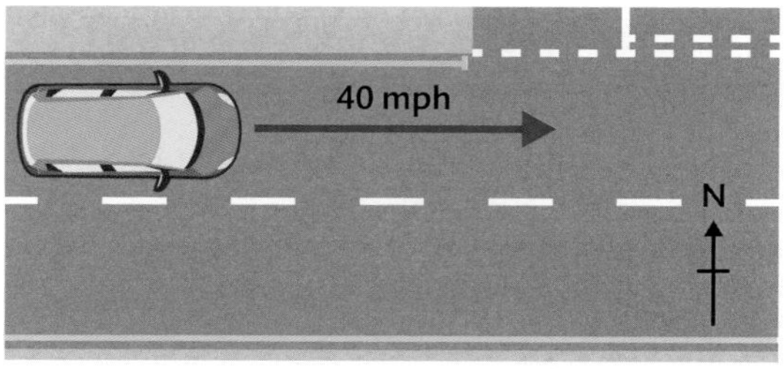


**Figure 2** A car has a velocity of 40 mph east

### Maths skills

Convert km to m by multiplying by 1000;
hours to minutes by multiplying by 60;
minutes to seconds by multiplying by 60.

## 10 Worked example — Grade 6

Train A travels in a straight line due east and covers 4.5 km in 2 minutes.

**(a)** Calculate its average speed. **[2 marks]**

$v = \frac{s}{t} = \frac{4500}{120} = 37.5\text{ m/s}$

**(b)** Write down its velocity. **[1 mark]**

37.5 m/s east

Train B travels at twice the speed of train A.

**(c)** Calculate the distance travelled by train B in 4 minutes. **[2 marks]**

Train B speed = 37.5 × 2 = 75 m/s

$v \times t = s$

75 × 240 = 18 000 m = 18 km

Write down the equation and check the units as you put the numbers in.

The questions give a compass direction (due east), so you should include a direction in your answer.

Make sure your answer is realistic. At this speed, train B would travel 270 km in an hour.

## 10 Exam-style practice — Grade 7

**1** A runner travels 22 km at an average speed of 3 m/s. Calculate the time he takes. Give your answer in minutes. **[2 marks]**

**2** The table shows the distances travelled in certain amounts of time by four cars. Which car has the fastest average speed? **[5 marks]**

| **Car** | A | B | C | D |
|---|---|---|---|---|
| **Distance** | 600 m | 200 km | 20 m | 3000 km |
| **Time** | 24 s | 1.5 hours | 0.5 s | 1 day |

# Distance–time relationships

Distance–time graphs show the distance an object travels over a period of time. You need to be able to interpret these types of graph to work out the speed of an object moving in a straight line.

## 5 Distance–time graphs

A **distance–time graph** shows how far an object moves over time.

The gradient of a distance–time graph represents the speed of an object.

- When the line on the graph becomes steeper, the gradient increases. This means the object is **accelerating**.
- When the line on the graph becomes less steep, the gradient decreases. This means the object is **decelerating**.
- When the line on the graph is horizontal, it has a gradient of zero. This means the object is **stationary**.

## 10 Worked example — Grade 7

**1** Look at **Figure 1**.

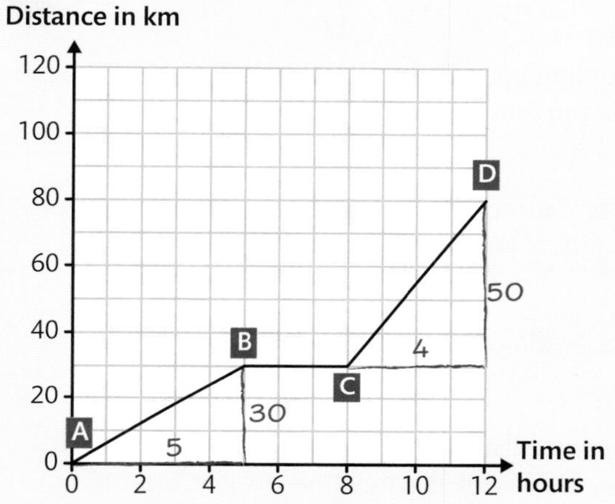


**Figure 1** The journey of a horse rider

Describe the journey in as much detail as possible. **[4 marks]**

A–B the horse travels 30 km in 5 hours

The speed (gradient) = 30 ÷ 5 = 6 km/h

B–C the horse is stationary for 3 hours

C–D the horse moves a further 50 km in 4 hours

Its speed is 50 ÷ 4 = 12.5 km/h

> When asked to describe a graph in detail, you should describe the different sections of the graph, giving the times for each section, the distance travelled and the speed.

**2** Look at **Figure 2**.

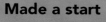

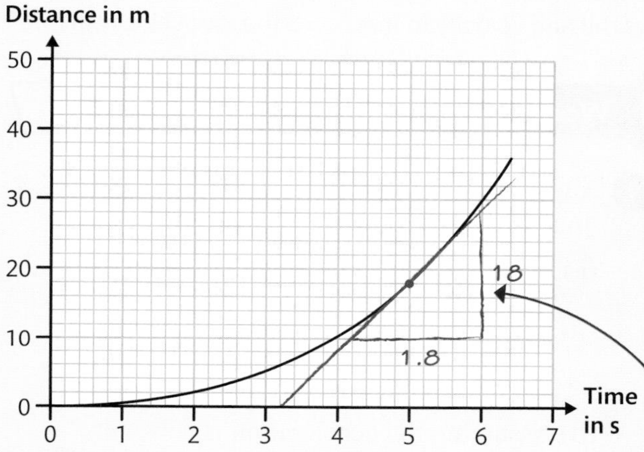


**Figure 2** The journey of a cyclist

**(a)** Describe the motion of the cyclist. **[1 mark]**

The cyclist is accelerating.

**(b)** Estimate the speed at 5 s. **[4 marks]**

18 ÷ 1.8 = 10 m/s

> **Maths skills**
> Draw a tangent to the curve at the time where you want to know the speed.

## 10 Exam-style practice — Grade 7

**1** Look at **Figure 2**. Without performing any calculations, explain how the graph shows that the cyclist is accelerating. **[2 marks]**

**2** A new Mars exploration vehicle is tested in the lab for the first time. For the first 8 seconds it moves 4 metres then stops for 2 seconds. It then moves at full speed covering a further 12 metres in the next 6 seconds. Draw a distance-time graph to show this motion. **[3 marks]**

# Uniform acceleration

Acceleration is the measure of how quickly an object's velocity changes. Acceleration is a vector quantity. **Uniform** means the acceleration is constant. You need to know how to calculate acceleration for the exam.

## 5 Calculating acceleration

The **average acceleration** of an object can be worked out using this equation:

$$\text{acceleration (m/s}^2) = \frac{\text{change in velocity (m/s)}}{\text{time taken (s)}}$$

$$a = \frac{\Delta v}{t}$$

For uniform acceleration:

$$v^2 - u^2 = 2as$$

*s* is the distance

*v* is the end velocity in m/s

*u* is the start velocity in m/s

## 2 Acceleration examples

You need to know some typical accelerations and the forces needed to achieve them.

| Action | Acceleration ($m/s^2$) | Force needed (N) |
|---|---|---|
| Train pulling off | 0.5 | 50 000 |
| Person | 1 | 70 |
| Car | 1–5 | 1000–5000 |
| Object in free fall | 9.8 | equal to the weight of the object |

**Exam focus**

This equation appears on your formula sheet. You need to be able to rearrange it.

## 10 Worked example — Grades 6–8

**1** A train travelling at 50 m/s must slow down to 20 m/s before it reaches a bend.

*Write s, u, v, a and t in the margin and make a note of what numbers you know as you read the question.*

**(a)** It takes 90 s to slow down. Find the acceleration of the train. **[2 marks]**

*It is decelerating, so the answer will be negative.*

$$a = \frac{\Delta v}{t} = \frac{20 - 50}{90} = -0.33\ \text{m/s}^2$$

*Ensure you get the start and end velocities the right way around. This gives a negative answer, indicating deceleration.*

**(b)** Assuming the deceleration is constant, calculate the distance it takes the train to slow down to 20 m/s. **[3 marks]**

$$s = \frac{v^2 - u^2}{2a} = \frac{20^2 - 50^2}{2 \times (-0.33)} = 3182\ \text{m}$$

**2** A ball is dropped and hits the floor at 6 m/s. Calculate how long it takes to fall. **[2 marks]**

$$t = \frac{\Delta v}{a} = \frac{6 - 0}{9.8} = 0.61\ \text{s}$$

**3** Each lorry in **Figure 1** is accelerating at a constant rate of $-2\ \text{m/s}^2$. The initial velocity of each lorry is shown. Calculate the velocity of each lorry after 5 seconds. **[2 marks]**

*Negative acceleration can cause an object to speed up if the object is moving in the negative direction. Calculate the end velocity first. Then add it to the initial velocity.*

**Figure 1** Three lorries accelerating at a constant rate

$\Delta v = a \times t$

$= -2 \times 5 = -10\ \text{m/s}$

A: $20 + -10 = 10\ \text{m/s}$

B: $0 + -10 = -10\ \text{m/s}$

C: $-20 + -10 = -30\ \text{m/s}$

## 10 Exam-style practice — Grade 8

**1** An apple falls from a branch onto the ground. The time taken for the apple to fall is 1.5 s. Calculate the speed of the apple when it hits the ground. ($g = 9.8\ \text{m/s}^2$) **[2 marks]**

**2** **(a)** A jet lands at 65 m/s and has a constant acceleration of $-5\ \text{m/s}^2$. Calculate how long it takes to stop. **[2 marks]**

**(b)** Calculate the minimum length of runway needed for the jet in part **(a)**. **[2 marks]**

**3** Explain why an object moving in a circle is accelerating even though its speed does not change. **[2 marks]**

**4** Describe how the speed of an object travelling at 40 m/s is changing if its acceleration is:

**(a)** $2\ \text{m/s}^2$ **[1 mark]**

**(b)** $-2\ \text{m/s}^2$ **[1 mark]**

# Velocity–time graphs

Velocity–time graphs show how the velocity of an object changes over time. You need to know how to calculate acceleration from the gradient of a velocity–time graph and distance travelled from the area under the velocity–time graph.

## 5 Distance and acceleration

- The acceleration for a given section is equal to the gradient of the line. If the line is straight, the acceleration is constant.
- The distance travelled is the area under the line.

acceleration = gradient
$= 7 \div 30$
$= 0.23\ m/s^2$

acceleration = gradient
$= 2 \div 20$
$= 0.1\ m/s^2$

distance between 0 and 20 seconds
= area under line
$= \frac{1}{2} \times 20 \times 2 = 20$ m

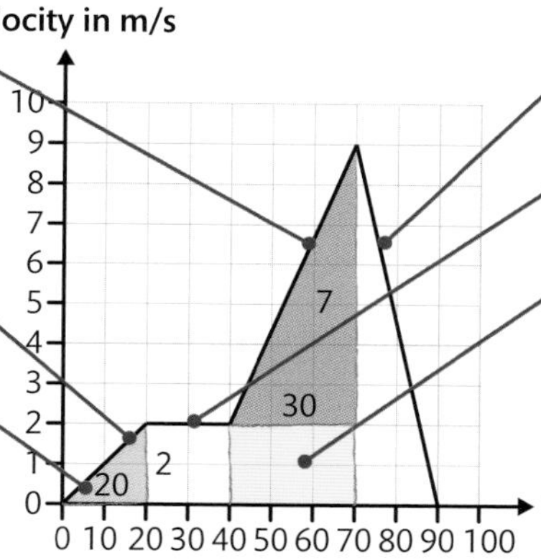


Here, gradient is negative, giving a deceleration.

A horizontal line (gradient = 0) indicates a constant speed.

The distance covered between 40 and 70 seconds is the sum of the area of the rectangle and the triangle.
$= \frac{1}{2} \times 30 \times 7 + 30 \times 2 = 165$ m

**Figure 1** A velocity–time graph

## 10 Curved velocity–time graphs

### Distance

You can estimate the area under the graph by counting squares and working out what distance is represented by one square.

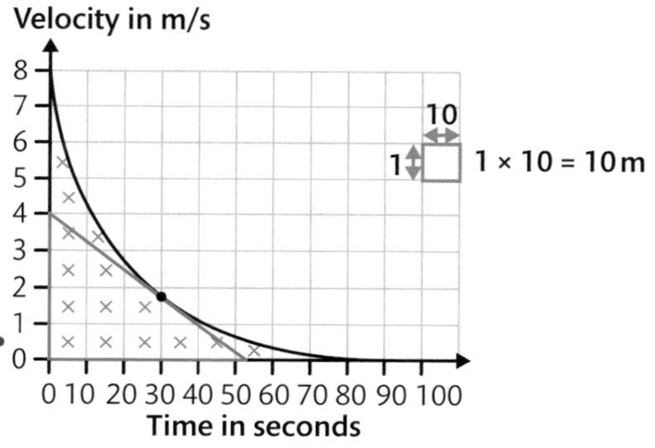


**Figure 2** A velocity–time graph

The 'area' of each square is 1 m/s × 10 s. Every square represents 10 m of distance. There are 15 squares. 15 × 10 m = 150 m distance travelled.

The distance travelled is the area under the curve. Work out the area of one square and multiply this by the number of squares below the line. Don't count any squares that are less than half covered.

### Acceleration

For a curved line the acceleration is always changing because the gradient is always changing. To find the acceleration at a point, draw a tangent line at that point and calculate its gradient. The blue triangle on the graph lets you calculate that the acceleration is $(0 - 4) \div 50 = -0.08\ m/s^2$.

## 5 Worked example — Grade 8

The diagram shows the velocity–time graphs for the motion of three different objects

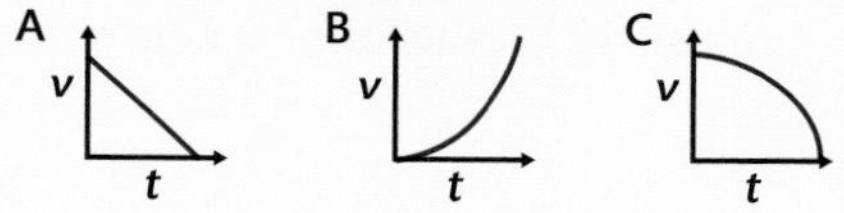


Describe the motion of each object. **[3 marks]**

*A is decelerating at a constant rate (or accelerating at a constant negative rate).*

*B is increasing in velocity with non-uniform acceleration.*

*C is decelerating at a non-uniform rate.*

## 10 Exam-style practice — Grade 8

The graph shows the velocity of a golf cart over 45 seconds.

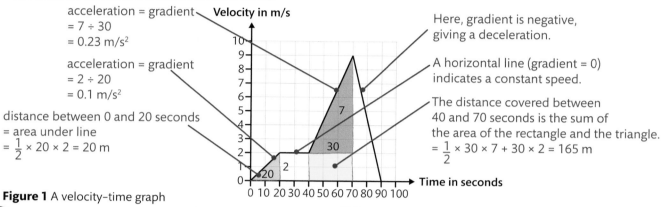

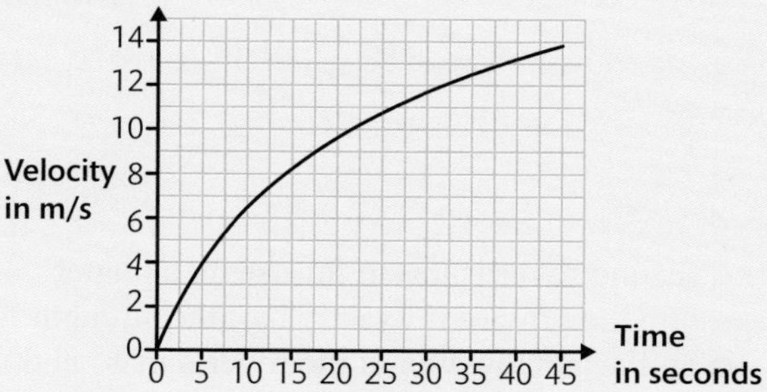


**(a)** Describe the motion of the golf cart without any calculations. **[2 marks]**

**(b)** Calculate the acceleration of the golf cart at 10 s and at 35 s. **[4 marks]**

# Gravity

You need to know the relationship between gravity, weight and mass.

## Mass, weight and gravity

The weight of an object is dependent on its mass and the strength of gravity. The weight of an object may change but its mass remains constant.

### Mass (*m*)
- the amount of matter in an object
- measured in kilograms, kg

### Weight (*W*)
- the force of gravity acting on a mass; the force acts downwards, towards the centre of the planet
- measured in newtons, N
- measured using a calibrated spring-balance (newtonmeter)

### Gravitational field strength (*g*)
- the strength of gravity at any one point
- measured in N/kg or $m/s^2$
- also called acceleration due to gravity (they are the same thing)

You need to know the equation:
weight (N) = mass (kg) × gravitational field strength (N/kg)

$W = mg$

## Centre of mass

The weight of all the parts of an object act in the same way as a single force acting from a point called the **centre of mass**.

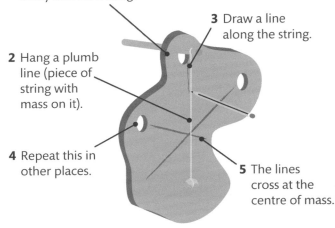

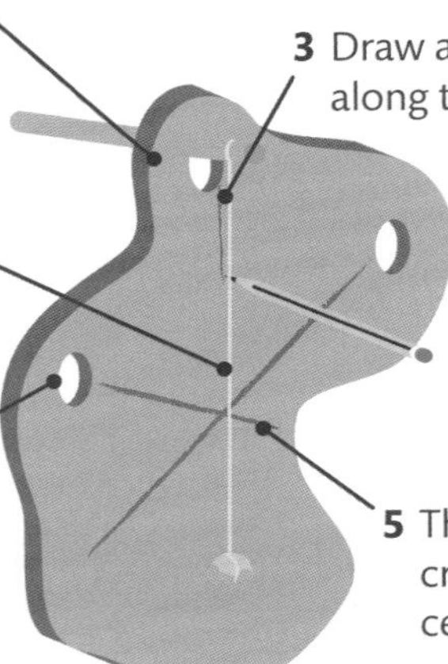

1 Suspend the shape freely and let it hang.
2 Hang a plumb line (piece of string with mass on it).
3 Draw a line along the string.
4 Repeat this in other places.
5 The lines cross at the centre of mass.

**Figure 1** Finding the centre of mass of an irregular shape

## Worked example — Grade 7

A Mars rover weighs 670 N on Earth.
Gravitational field strength = 9.8 N/kg

**(a)** Find the mass of the rover. **[2 marks]**

$m = \frac{W}{g}$

$\frac{670}{9.8} = 68.4 \text{ kg}$

**(b)** On Mars, g = 3.7 N/kg.
Find the mass and, hence, the weight of the rover on Mars. **[2 marks]**

Mass does not change so on Mars it is still 68.4 kg.

$W = mg$

$68.4 \times 3.7 = 253 \text{ N}$

**(c)** A second rover is tested for use on a planet where the gravity is exactly half the strength it is on Earth. How would the rover's mass and weight on this new planet compare to when it is on Earth? **[2 marks]**

Its mass would be the same on the new planet, but its weight would be half what it is on Earth.

## Weight and mass

Weight and mass are directly proportional.

weight $\propto$ mass

If one object has twice the mass of another, it will also have twice the weight for the same gravitational field strength. Mass is constant. Weight depends on the gravitational field strength at the point where the object is.

## Exam-style practice — Grade 7

1. State where the centre of mass would be on a ring donut. **[2 marks]**
2. Suggest how to measure the weight of an object. **[1 mark]**
3. State what direction the weight of an object is in. **[1 mark]**
4. Dave says that an astronaut on the Moon will have difficulty walking because of the lack of atmosphere. Part of his statement is true. Give a more correct version and explain your statement. **[3 marks]**

# Newton's laws of motion

Newton's three laws of motion explain how forces affect the motion of objects. You need to consider resultant forces when using Newton's laws. There is more about calculating resultant forces on page 180.

## 5 Newton's First Law

If all the forces acting on an object are balanced (the resultant force = 0), the object will remain at a constant velocity or at rest.

### What does it mean?

This means that once an object is moving, it keeps moving at the same velocity as long as no overall (resultant) force acts upon it.

To make the object speed up, slow down, or change direction, you need to apply a resultant force.

If an object has no resultant force then all the forces are balanced. It will continue to move with constant velocity, or remain stationary.

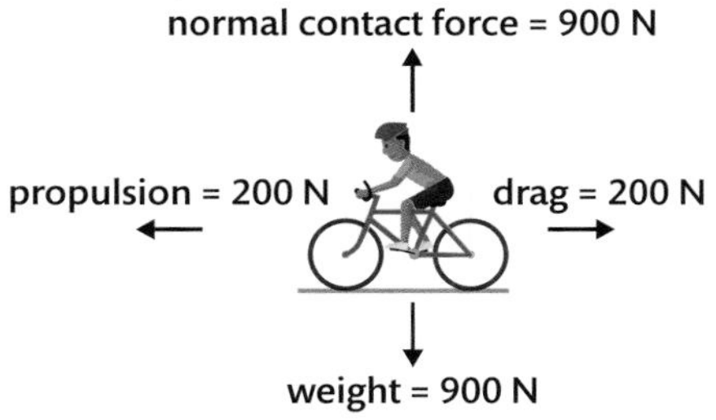


**Figure 1** Balanced forces acting on a cyclist

The vertical and horizontal forces add up to zero. We cannot say all the forces are equal, we say they are balanced or in equilibrium.

The cyclist will continue at a constant speed because the resistive force (drag) balances the driving force (propulsion). If the cyclist stops pedalling, the forces become unbalanced and the cyclist slows down.

Most moving objects that are not being moved by another force will eventually stop because of the force of friction.

## 5 Newton's Third Law

When two objects interact they exert an equal and opposite force on each other.

### What does it mean?

When one object applies a force to another, it experiences the same force itself but in the opposite direction. Note that the two forces:

- are the same size
- act in exactly opposite directions
- act on different objects, so they do not cancel out.

A bat hits a ball with a force of 200 N. The ball exerts a force of 200 N on the bat in the opposite direction.

The force has a greater effect on the ball's speed because the ball has a smaller mass.

## 5 Newton's Second Law

If the forces acting on an object are unbalanced, the object's acceleration will be:

- in the direction of the resultant force
- directly proportional to the resultant force.

The acceleration is inversely proportionate to the mass of the object: acceleration $\propto \frac{1}{\text{mass}}$

### What does it mean?

An unbalanced force makes an object accelerate. It might speed up, slow down or change direction.

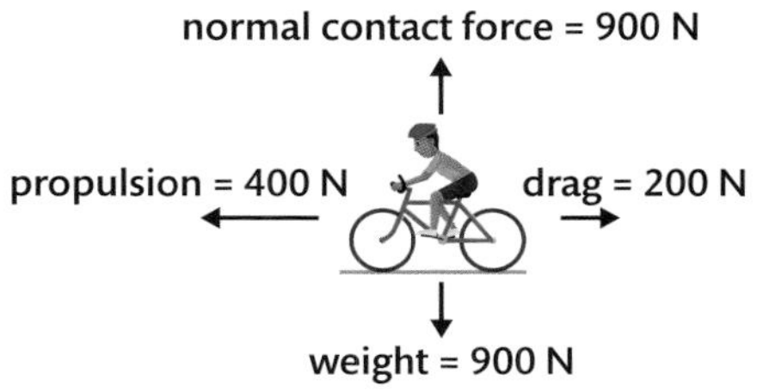


**Figure 2** Unbalanced forces acting on a cyclist. There is a resultant force in the forwards direction so the cyclist will accelerate.

If you double the resultant force, the acceleration will also double. If the mass being accelerated doubles then the acceleration will halve for the same force.

If something is slowing down and stopping, it is decelerating. This means there must be a resultant force acting in the opposite direction to its motion.

## 2 Worked example — Grade 7

Explain why a vehicle has a lower acceleration when it is heavily loaded than when it is empty. **[2 marks]**

*Acceleration is inversely proportional to an object's mass. So for the same force, if its mass increases, its acceleration will decrease by the same amount (so if the mass doubled, the acceleration would halve).*

## 10 Exam-style practice — Grade 7

1. Why is it necessary to keep a foot on the accelerator to keep a car moving at uniform speed? **[2 marks]**
2. A student pushes on a desk with a force of 30 N.
   **(a)** Give the force the student experiences as a result. **[1 mark]**
   **(b)** Explain, in terms of forces, how the desk could remain in equilibrium. **[2 marks]**

# Newton's second law

Newton's second law shows the relationship between force, mass and acceleration.

## F = ma

Newton's second law tells you how much force you need to accelerate a mass.

force (N) = mass (kg) × acceleration (m/s$^2$)

The force that causes the acceleration must be the resultant (overall) force.

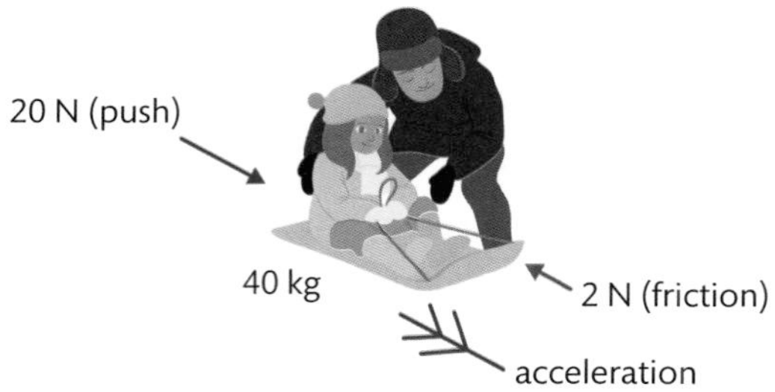


**Figure 1** The sledge and passenger have a combined mass of 40 kg. The resultant force is 18 N. (20 N forwards force − 2 N frictional force)

$$a = \frac{F}{m} = 18 \div 40 = 0.45 \text{ m/s}^2$$

## Worked example — Grade 6

A firework has an initial mass of 400 g. It is launched vertically upwards with a thrust of 45 N.

**(a)** Calculate its initial acceleration. **[2 marks]**

Resultant upwards force, $F$ = thrust − weight:

$45 - (0.4 \times 9.8) = 41.08$

$a = F \div m$

$= 41.08 \div 0.4 = 102.7$ m/s$^2$

**(b)** What would your answer be if the thrust was twice as large? **[1 mark]**

$F_2 = F_1 + 45 = 86.08$

$86.08 \div 0.4 = 215.2$ m/s$^2$

**(c)** As the firework burns, its mass decreases. What effect would this have on its acceleration? **[2 marks]**

$a \propto \frac{1}{m}$ so as mass decreases, acceleration increases.

**(d)** Other than losing mass, explain how the acceleration is affected in the seconds after the firework has launched. **[2 marks]**

Air resistance would lower the resultant force. $F \propto a$ so acceleration would also decrease.

Drag and friction act in the opposite direction to the way the object is moving. Drag increases with speed.

## Inertial mass

An object will tend to remain at rest or carry on with uniform motion. This is called **inertia**. Inertial mass is a measure of how difficult it is to accelerate an object, or how hard it is to stop it moving once it has started. It is defined as the ratio of force over acceleration.

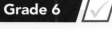

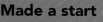

**Figure 2** The trolley with the larger inertial mass requires a greater force to stop or change its direction once it has started moving.

All masses need to be in kilograms not grams.
$400 \div 1000 = 0.4$ kg

**Maths skills**
The thrust has increased by 45 N, but the resultant force has not doubled. Use the new resultant force to calculate the new acceleration. You don't need to write down the formula again.

Consider the proportionality between mass and acceleration:

$$a = \frac{F}{m} \text{ so } a \propto \frac{1}{m}$$

**Exam focus**
Be specific when talking about how something changes. Explain which quantity decreases and which increases.

## Exam-style practice — Grade 6

**(a)** A scooter accelerates at 1.67 m/s$^2$. The forward force is 300 N and there is 50 N of drag. Calculate the total mass of the scooter and its rider. **[3 marks]**

**(b)** Carrying a passenger and luggage doubles the scooter's mass. Calculate its acceleration if the forces remain the same. **[2 marks]**

# Forces

A force is a push or pull that acts on an object due to its interactions with another object. You need to know about forces that require contact to exert the force and forces that can act at a distance (non-contact).

## Contact forces

- friction
- normal contact force
- air resistance
- water resistance
- push
- tension
- drag
- lift
- upthrust
- pull

## Free body diagrams

**Free body diagrams** show a simplified version of the forces acting on the centre of mass of an object, usually just shown as a dot. The forces can be labelled with their name or the magnitude of the force.

Remember, forces are vectors so the direction of the arrow shows the direction of the force and the length of the arrow shows the magnitude. Larger forces have longer arrows.

**Figure 1** Forces on an aeroplane

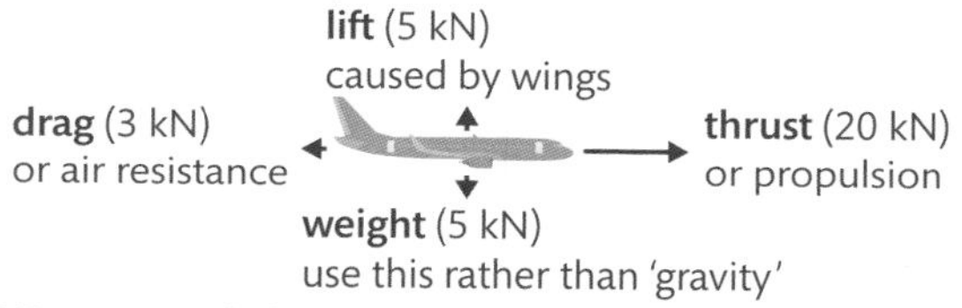


**Figure 2** Forces on a ball rolling down a slope

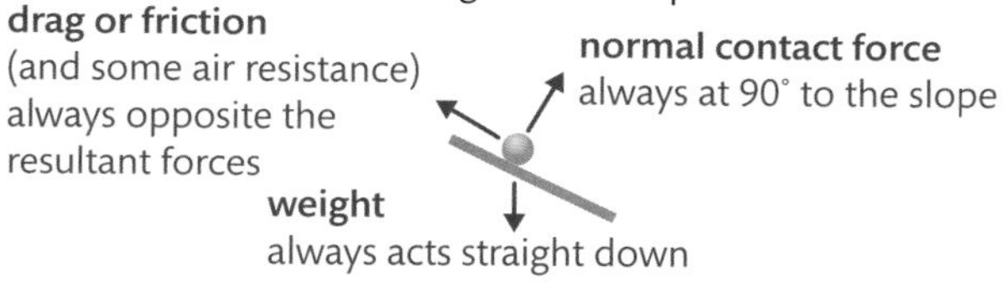


The aeroplane has four forces acting on it. You can draw these forces as a free body diagram. Draw a dot to represent the aeroplane, then draw an arrow from the dot in the direction of each force. You should draw the arrows to scale. The thrust arrow should be four times as long as the weight arrow.

You can then rearrange the arrows to find out whether there is a resultant force. Draw the dot and any one arrow first, then draw the next arrow from where the first ends. Continue until you have drawn all four arrows end to end.

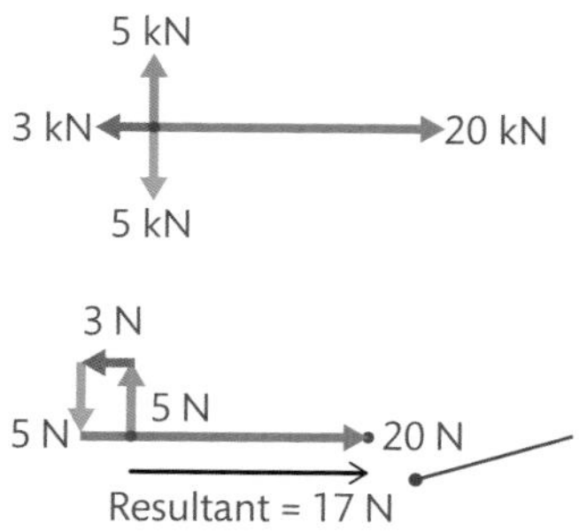


The vector diagram does not go back to where it started. The distance between where it started and ended is the resultant force. Measure the line and use the scale to find the resultant force.

## Non-contact forces

- gravitational force (weight)
- electrostatic force
- magnetic force

## Exam focus

When talking about forces, use 'weight' or 'gravitational force' instead of 'gravity'.

When drawing a force diagram, make sure the arrows point in exactly the right direction. The weight arrow should always point straight down, never at an angle. Check the direction an object is moving in before drawing a drag force.

## Worked example — Grade 6

**(a)** Draw and label a free body diagram to show the forces acting on a magnet stuck to a fridge. **[2 marks]**

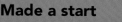

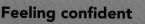

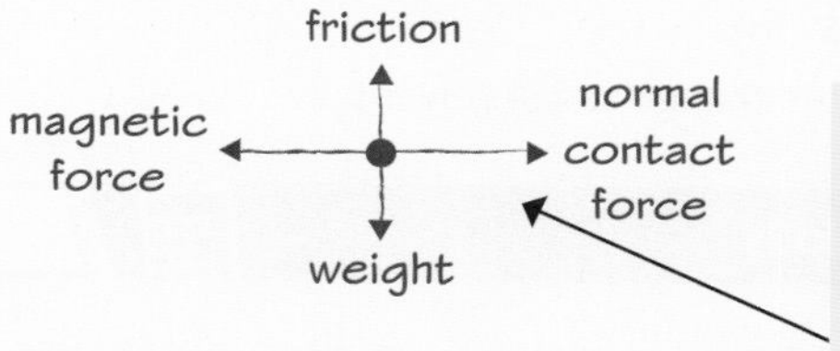


The magnet is stationary, so opposite forces are balanced.

**(b)** Describe the features of your diagram that show that the magnet is stationary. **[2 marks]**

The arrows acting in opposite directions to each other are equal in length, so the forces are balanced.

## Exam-style practice — Grade 6

1. A maglev train uses magnets to float above the track. Draw a free body diagram to show the forces acting on the train if it is travelling at a constant velocity and a constant height. **[2 marks]**
2. If Amy is statically charged, her hair stands on end. Give the name of the force that is making her hair repel. **[1 mark]**
3. A student suggests that air resistance is a non-contact force. Explain why the student is incorrect. **[1 mark]**

# Resultant forces

If multiple forces are acting on an object, they can be represented as one **resultant force**, which has the same effect as all the original forces acting together. You should be able to find the resultant force of a given object.

## (10) Forces on a skydiver

As a skydiver falls, their weight stays constant, but the drag will increase with speed. This changes the resultant force and the acceleration.

skydiver mass = 75 kg

individual forces ↓   resultant force ↓

drag = 0 N

$F = 735$ N

$a = \dfrac{F}{m}$

$\quad = \dfrac{735 \text{ N}}{75 \text{ kg}}$

$\quad = 9.8 \text{ m/s}^2$

weight = 735 N

drag = 400 N

$F = 735 - 400 = 335$ N

$a = \dfrac{F}{m}$

$\quad = \dfrac{335 \text{ N}}{75 \text{ kg}}$

$\quad = 4.5 \text{ m/s}^2$

weight = 735 N

drag = 735 N

$F = 335$ N

$a = \dfrac{F}{m}$

$\quad = 0 \text{ m/s}^2$

weight = 735 N

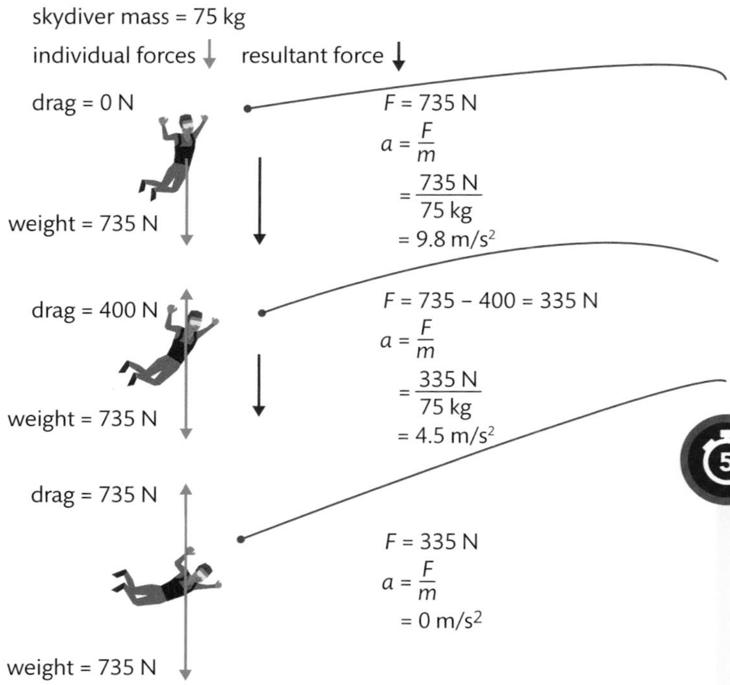

**Figure 1** The forces change as a skydiver falls.

As the skydiver jumps, they are not yet moving. They have no air resistance (drag). The resultant force is just the weight, so they accelerate at 9.8 m/s². This is the acceleration due to gravity.

As speed increases, drag increases. This cancels part of the weight. The resultant force, which causes the acceleration, is a lot smaller. The skydiver is still increasing in speed, but at a reduced acceleration.

When weight and drag are equal, the resultant force and the acceleration are zero. The skydiver has reached maximum speed. This is called terminal velocity.

## (5) Worked example          Grade 8

**Figure 3** shows two forces acting on a plane: thrust of 600 N and wind of 400 N.

thrust = 600 N

resultant

wind = 400 N

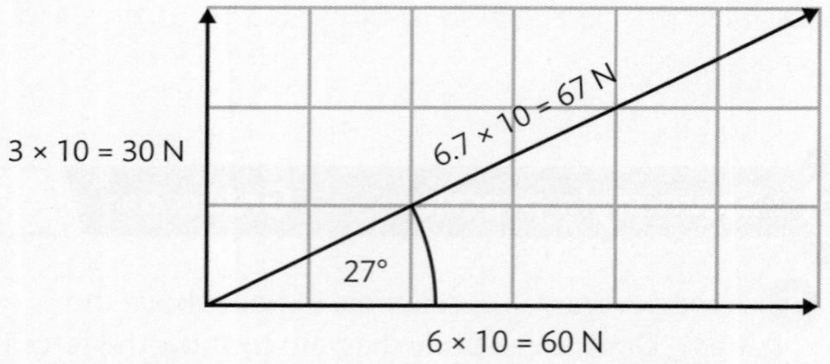

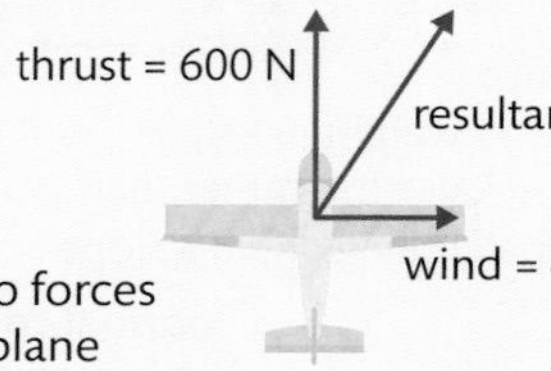

**Figure 3** Two forces acting on a plane

Draw a scale diagram to find the resultant force of these two forces.          **[4 marks]**

Scale: 1 cm = 200 N

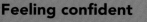

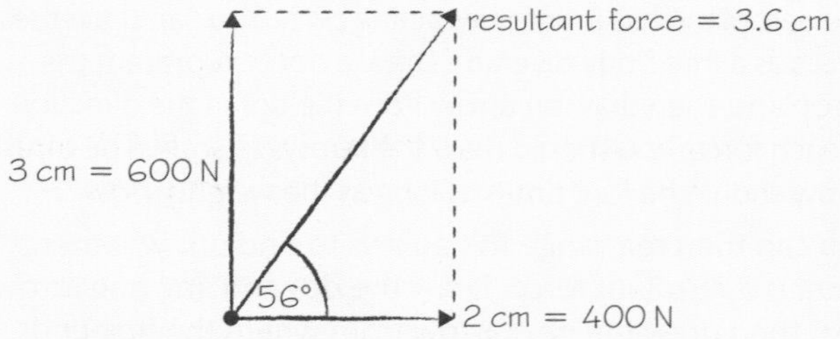

resultant force = 3.6 cm

3 cm = 600 N

56°

2 cm = 400 N

Resultant force = 3.6 × 200 = 720 N

Angle = 34° to the right of the aeroplane's heading

## (5) Maths skills

When you have a force at an angle it can be resolved into two forces at right angles to each other, one horizontal and one vertical. These two forces have the same effect as the original force, but can be more useful when solving problems.

3 × 10 = 30 N

6.7 × 10 = 67 N

27°

6 × 10 = 60 N

**Figure 2** A diagonal force can be resolved into vertical and horizontal forces using a diagram.

Draw the arrow at the correct angle using an appropriate scale (such as 1 cm = 10 N so 67 N = 6.7 cm).

This line is the diagonal of a rectangle. Draw in the sides of the rectangle and measure their lengths.

A force of 67 N at 27° has the same effect as a horizontal force of 60 N and a vertical force of 30 N.

## (10) Exam-style practice          Grade 8

**1** A car is travelling at a constant speed. Explain what the resultant force on it is.          **[2 marks]**

**2** A car of mass 1200 kg is accelerating at 1.4 m/s². The drag force is 800 N. Calculate the force from the engine.          **[2 marks]**

# Investigating acceleration

You need to know how to investigate the effect of force and mass on acceleration.

## 5 Two experiments

### Experiment 1

1. Increase the force on the trolley (**Figure 1**) by moving masses from the trolley to the hanging masses.
2. The interrupt card passes through the light gate. A data logger calculates the acceleration.

The masses accelerate as well as the trolley, so this keeps the total mass the same.

### Experiment 2

1. Increase the mass of the trolley by fixing masses to it.
2. Measure the acceleration. Keep the force (hanging mass) the same.

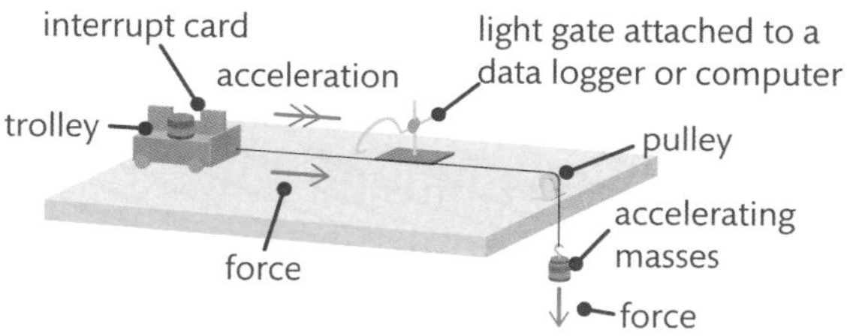


**Figure 1** Apparatus for measuring acceleration

## 10 Worked example — Grade 8

**(a)** Give the expected findings of Experiment 1. **[2 marks]**

Increasing the force on the trolley would increase its acceleration. Force and acceleration are proportional.

**(b)** State **one** other force acting on the trolley. Explain what could be done to minimise its impact on your results. **[2 marks]**

Friction – lift the ramp so the trolley runs slightly downhill to counteract friction.

**(c)** A graph is plotted using the results from Experiment 1. **[3 marks]**

**(i)** What would be plotted on each axis?

Force on the $x$-axis and acceleration on the $y$-axis

**(ii)** What is the significance of the gradient?

The gradient gives $\frac{1}{\text{mass of trolley}}$.

**(d)** For Experiment 2, give **one** variable you would need to control and explain why. **[2 marks]**

The force used to accelerate the trolley would need to be the same. If a different force was used when the trolley mass was increased, you would not be able to tell what caused the change in acceleration.

## 2 Interrupt card

The two sections of card break the light beam for a period of time. The data logger calculates the speed for each side:

$$\text{speed} = \frac{\text{card length}}{\text{time}}$$

It also measures the time between interruptions:

$$\text{acceleration} = \frac{\text{difference in speeds}}{\text{time between interruptions}}$$

They are proportional (written $F \propto a$) because if you double the force, the acceleration doubles.

Doing the experiment on an air track would be ideal, but there will still be friction in the pulley. Drag is another force that acts on the trolley. You could make the trolley more streamlined to minimise its effects.

### Maths skills

The gradient is acceleration ÷ force. Rearrange the equation $F = ma$, to give $\frac{a}{F} = \frac{1}{m}$. This is the gradient.

If you reverse the axes (plot force on the $y$-axis) the gradient would be the trolley mass.

## 10 Exam-style practice — Grade 8

1. In Experiment 1, explain how you would find the magnitude of the force accelerating the trolley and what the size of this force depends on. **[3 marks]**
2. A student says it does not matter where the light gate is placed as long as the trolley is accelerating when it passes through. While the student is correct, explain why the light gate should not be moved during the experiment. **[3 marks]**
3. Describe in detail the relationship between the mass of the trolley and its acceleration, and the force acting on the trolley and its acceleration. **[3 marks]**

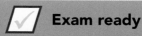

# Forces and elasticity

Forces can cause objects to change shape permanently or temporarily, by bending, stretching or compressing them. You need to know the effects of forces on elastic objects like springs.

## 2 Types of deformation

**Deformation** is the term used to describe an object changing shape. Deformation can be elastic or inelastic:

- **elastic deformation** – an object changes shape when a force is applied but returns to its original shape when the force is removed.
- **inelastic deformation** – an object changes shape when a force is applied but does not return to its original shape when the force is removed.

The amount an object changes shape is the **extension** or **compression**. To cause an object to compress, stretch or bend, you usually need two forces working against each other. If you try to squash a rubber ball, you have to push from both sides or the ball will simply move.

## 2 Hooke's Law

Hooke's Law states that the extension of an elastic object is directly proportional to the force applied to it:

force (N) = spring constant (N/m) × extension (m)

$F = ke$

- The force, $F$, is the load or weight applied to the object being deformed.
- The spring constant, $k$, is a measure of how stiff the spring or object is.
- Extension, $e$, is the amount the object changes shape.

This equation works as long as the elastic limit (the limit of proportionality) is not exceeded.

## 5 Springs

### Force against extension of a spring

An object that obeys Hooke's Law has a straight line up to the elastic limit on a force-extension graph. Beyond the elastic limit the object is being permanently deformed.

The gradient gives you the spring constant, but be careful to only use the straight line section.

### Energy in a spring

Anything that stretches, compresses or bends stores elastic potential energy.

elastic potential energy (J) = 0.5 × spring constant (N/m) × extension² (m)

$E_e = \frac{1}{2}ke^2$

When released, the stored energy usually converts into kinetic energy.

This is true up to the elastic limit. Above the elastic limit, work is being done in permanently deforming the object.

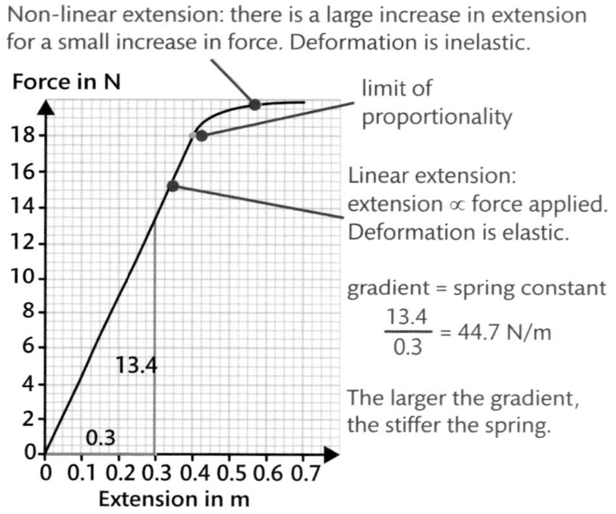

Non-linear extension: there is a large increase in extension for a small increase in force. Deformation is inelastic.
Force in N
limit of proportionality
Linear extension: extension ∝ force applied. Deformation is elastic.
gradient = spring constant
13.4 / 0.3 = 44.7 N/m
The larger the gradient, the stiffer the spring.
13.4
0.3
0 2 4 6 8 10 12 14 16 18
0 0.1 0.2 0.3 0.4 0.5 0.6 0.7
Extension in m

**Figure 1** A graph showing how the extension of a spring changes when different force is applied

## 5 Worked example — Grade 7

A force is applied to a spring so that it is deformed elastically. 18 N of weight is added to make the spring 36 cm longer.

**(a)** Calculate the spring constant of the spring. **[3 marks]**

$k = \frac{F}{e} = \frac{18}{0.36} = 50\,\text{N/m}$

**(b)** Calculate the total elastic potential energy stored in the spring. **[4 marks]**

$E_e = \frac{1}{2}ke^2$

$= 0.5 \times 50 \times 0.36^2 = 3.24\,\text{J}$

## 10 Exam-style practice — Grade 7

Look at **Figure 1**.

**(a)** Give the maximum force that the spring can take before being damaged. **[2 marks]**

**(b)** Explain how the graph shows the limit of proportionality has been reached. **[1 mark]**

**(c)** Calculate the energy stored in the spring at the limit of proportionality. **[1 mark]**

**(d)** The original length of the spring is 9 cm. Calculate its length when supporting a 10 N weight. **[2 marks]**

# Force and extension

You need to know how to investigate the relationship between force and extension with a spring.

## 5 Method ✓

clamp stand · spring · metre ruler · masses and hanger

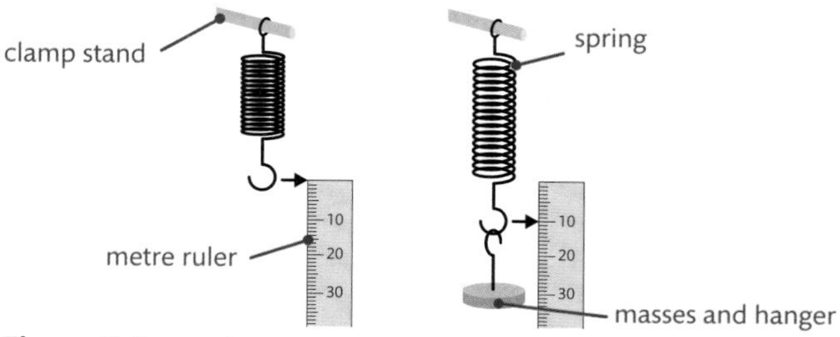

**Figure 1** Apparatus

**1** Clamp a ruler so that the zero mark is next to the end of the spring.

**2** Hang a range of masses from the spring.

**3** Record the force, which is the weight of each mass.

**4** Record the extension of the spring for each force.

**5** Plot a graph of force ($y$-axis) against extension ($x$-axis).

**6** You can then use the graph to estimate the weight of another object that is hung from the spring by measuring the extension.

### Maths skills

The force is in newtons and the extension ($e$) in m, so the gradient is N/m. The gradient is also the spring constant, calculated from $F = ke$. If the graph is plotted with the axes reversed remember that the

$$\text{spring constant} = \frac{1}{\text{gradient}}.$$

If the plotted points are not close to the line of best fit, it might mean that errors need reducing in the experiment.

## 2 Reducing errors ✓

- Measure the spring length from the same point on the spring each time.
- Make sure the spring is at eye level when measuring it.
- Repeat each extension by removing and rehanging the mass in case larger masses deform the spring inelastically.

## 5 Worked example — Grade 7 ✓

**Figure 2** A graph showing the force and extension of springs A and B

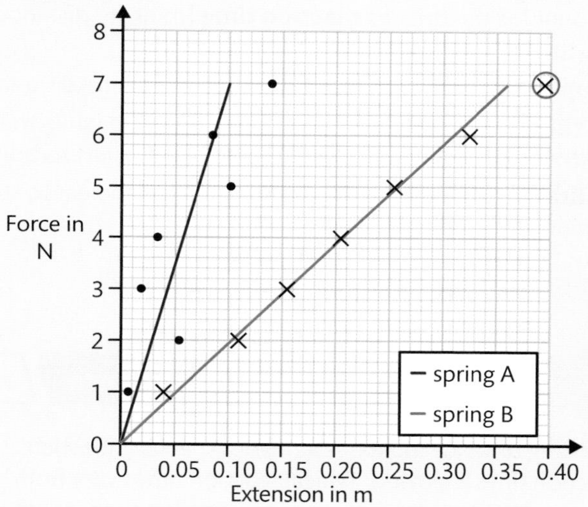

Look at **Figure 2**.

**(a)** An outlier in the results of spring B has been circled in red. Suggest why this point may not fit the pattern. **[2 marks]**

*The spring may have exceeded the elastic limit, so force is no longer proportional to extension. Therefore, the line would start to curve and the gradient decrease.*

**(b)** The gradient of the line for spring A is 70. Give the unit for the gradient. **[1 mark]**

*N/m*

**(c)** Looking at the graph, a student suggests that the spring constant calculated for spring B is more accurate than the spring constant calculated for spring A. Do you agree with this? Explain your answer. **[2 marks]**

*The points in spring B are closer to the line of best fit. This means that there is less uncertainty in its position and gradient compared to line A so you can be more confident about the value of the gradient and spring constant for spring B.*

## 10 Exam-style practice — Grade 7 ✓

Look at **Figure 2**.

**(a)** Find the spring constant of spring B. **[2 marks]**

**(b)** A student wants to determine if the outlier in spring B is part of a change in the pattern. State how this might be achieved. **[1 mark]**

**(c)** Suggest **two** possible reasons for the increased scatter in the results for spring A. Give some ways this could be reduced. **[3 marks]**

 **Made a start**  **Feeling confident**  **Exam ready**

# Stopping distance

Stopping distance refers to the distance over which a vehicle stops. It is the total of the thinking distance and the braking distance. You need to know about factors that affect the stopping distance of a vehicle.

## 15 Calculating stopping distance

To calculate the stopping distance of a car, you need to account for the driver's **reaction time** (thinking distance) and the braking distance.

stopping distance = thinking distance + braking distance

- **Thinking distance** – the distance travelled while the driver is reacting. This occurs before they start to brake.
- **Braking distance** – the distance it takes the car to stop once the brakes have been applied.

Revise the factors affecting braking on page 185.

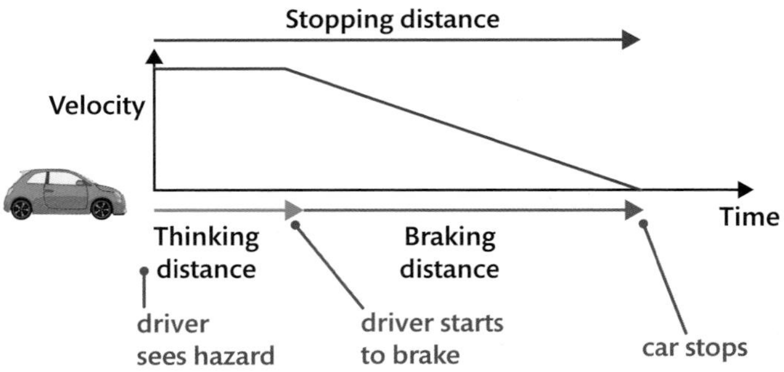


**Figure 1** A graph showing the stopping distance of a car

## 2 Factors affecting thinking distance

Thinking distance increases at higher speeds and when reaction time is slowed. Typical reaction times vary from 0.2 s to 0.9 s. Factors that can slow reaction time include:

- alcohol
- drugs/medicine
- being tired
- poor visibility, e.g. due to fog
- distraction, e.g. using a mobile phone.

## 5 Measuring reactions

### Method 1

Reaction times can be measured using a stop clock. One person presses start and the other has to hit the stop button as quickly as possible.

### Method 2

One person holds a ruler vertically while the other holds their finger and thumb at the bottom of the ruler. When the ruler is dropped they have to catch it. The slower their reactions, the more of the ruler passes through their fingers.

## 5 Worked example — Grade 9

A student's reaction time is measured using the two methods described above. Measurements are taken while the student concentrates and again while being distracted by being asked questions. Each measurement is repeated and the results are recorded in the table.

| | Time or distance 1 | Time or distance 2 |
|---|---|---|
| **Method 1 concentrating** | 0.31 s | 0.35 s |
| **Method 1 distracted** | 0.60 s | 0.64 s |
| **Method 2 concentrating** | 10 cm | 15 cm |
| **Method 2 distracted** | 24 cm | 28 cm |

Use the information in the table to describe the effect of being distracted on the student's reaction time. **[2 marks]**

*Distractions caused an increase in the reaction times in both Method 1 and Method 2. For Method 1, the reaction time almost doubled with distraction. For Method 2, the ruler travelled almost double the distance when the student was distracted.*

## 10 Exam-style practice — Grade 9

You need to use the equation that relates speed, distance and time. Go to page 172 to revise how to use this equation.

1. A driver's reaction time is 0.6 s. Calculate their thinking distance at 31 m/s (70 mph). **[1 mark]**
2. Using the table, compare and evaluate the two methods used for determining the reaction time of the student. **[3 marks]**

# Braking distance

You need to know how to calculate braking distance and the factors that affect it.

## Factors affecting braking distance

Factors such as greater speed and greater mass increase the kinetic energy, which means there is more work for the brakes to do. The car therefore travels further before it stops.

Go to page 184 to revise stopping distances.

The following factors reduce friction and brake force:

- worn brakes
- worn tyres
- adverse weather conditions such as rain or snow
- adverse road conditions such as loose road surface or wet/icy roads.

As the work done by brakes = force × distance, a smaller force means the car will travel further before it stops. Go to page 211 to revise work done.

Braking distances vary from 6 m at 20 mph (32 km/h) up to 96 m at 70 mph (112 km/h). That is why when travelling faster or in conditions that make the braking distance longer, drivers need to leave larger gaps between them and the vehicle in front. Cars decelerate in emergencies at ~ 3–5 m/s$^2$. Rapid deceleration can cause the car to skid and the driver to lose control.

### The energy of braking

Brakes use friction to do work and stop the car.

The work done is equal to the kinetic energy.

This energy is transferred to thermal energy in the brakes.

If the brakes overheat they may not function as well.

You can use the following equations for braking calculations:

work done by brakes = kinetic energy of car

force (N) × distance (m) = 0.5 × mass (kg) × velocity$^2$ (m/s)

$$Fd = \frac{1}{2}mv^2$$

This can be rearranged, for example, to find the braking force if the mass, speed and braking distance are known.

$$F = \frac{mv^2}{2d}$$

## Worked example — Grade 7

Look at **Figure 1**.

**1** **(a)** Work out the stopping distance when the car is travelling at a speed of 25 m/s. **[2 marks]**

thinking distance + braking distance = stopping distance

17 + 46 = 63 m

**(b)** The car accelerates so it is now travelling at 30 m/s. Will the stopping distance be higher or lower than that calculated in part **(a)**? Give a reason for your answer. **[2 marks]**

Higher because the thinking distance and braking distance increase with speed.

**2** A driver brakes over a long period of time while driving down a hill. Explain why this could be dangerous. **[2 marks]**

Friction causes brakes to heat up as they are used. As the brakes get hotter they apply less friction so the brakes are not as effective.

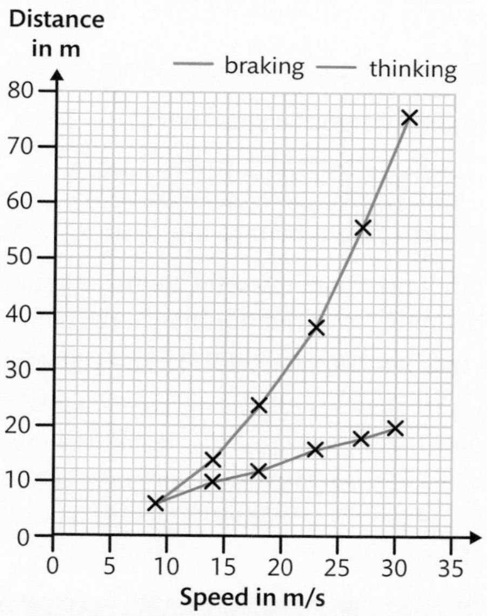


**Figure 1** A graph showing the effect of speed on stopping distance

## Exam-style practice — Grade 9

**1** A car has a mass of 1200 kg and it travelling at 25 m/s. It takes 40 m to stop. Calculate the braking force. **[2 marks]**

**2** What effect does doubling the speed have on braking and thinking distances? Explain your answer. **[2 marks]**

# Momentum

You need to know how to calculate an object's momentum from its velocity and mass.

## 5 Calculating momentum

momentum (kg m/s) = mass (kg) × velocity (m/s)

$p = mv$

The unit for momentum is kg m/s, a combination of the units for mass and velocity. Make sure you learn the unit but if you forget, use the equation to remind you.

As momentum depends on velocity, momentum is also a vector. This means it can have a negative value, to indicate a different direction.

Remember that no matter how much mass something has, if its velocity is zero then it has no momentum.

**Figure 1** This train does not go very fast, but it has a huge mass which gives it a high momentum even at low speeds.

## 10 Worked example — Grade 8

**(a)** A ferry of mass 125 000 kg is travelling at 12 m/s. Calculate its momentum. **[1 mark]**

$p = mv$

125 000 kg × 12 m/s = 1 500 000 kg m/s ($1.5 \times 10^6$ kg m/s)

Keep track of all the zeroes in long numbers, or write your answer in standard form.

**(b)** A second ferry has a higher momentum. Choose the incorrect statement from the following. Tick **one** box. **[1 mark]**

- **A** The ferry might have a higher mass. ☐
- **B** The ferry might be moving more quickly. ☐
- **C** The ferry might be stationary. ☑
- **D** The ferry might have a lower mass. ☐
- **E** The ferry might be moving more slowly. ☐

If it was stationary the momentum would be zero, so it could not possibly have more momentum.

D and E are true. An object with lower mass could still have more momentum if it moves fast enough. An object moving more slowly could have more momentum if it has a much higher mass.

**(c)** As a firework flies upwards, its mass changes as it burns fuel. Its speed doubles at the same time as its mass halves. Explain what has happened to its momentum. **[2 marks]**

It has the same momentum. Doubling the speed would double the momentum, but halving the mass would halve the momentum.

Momentum is proportional to velocity and to mass. If either double, momentum doubles.

## 10 Exam-style practice — Grade 7

1. **(a)** A horse and rider have a momentum of 5400 kg m/s. If the velocity is 12 m/s, find the mass of the horse and rider. **[2 marks]**

   **(b)** Give the horse and rider's momentum if they are travelling in the opposite direction. **[1 mark]**
2. Find the momentum of a snail with mass 22 g travelling at 1.5 cm/s. **[2 marks]**
3. A firework of mass 850 g is travelling at 20 m/s. After a few seconds, it has accelerated to 35 m/s and has burned 300 g of fuel. Calculate its change in momentum. **[3 marks]**

# Conservation of momentum

You need to know that the total momentum, $p$, is constant if there are no external forces acting on the system.

## 15 Conserving total momentum

In a closed system, the total momentum before any interaction must equal the total momentum after the interaction. This is the vector addition of momentum, not just the arithmetic sum.

When solving problems, work out the momentum of every moving object. Add them all together to get the total momentum.

### One moving object

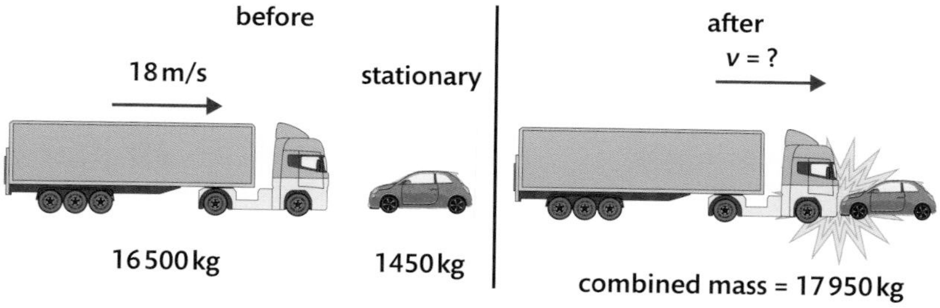


A lorry crashes into a stationary car. In the collision, the lorry and the car stick together. The momentum must be conserved. This means that the momentum of the lorry and car must be the same after the collision as the momentum of the lorry before. To have the same momentum, the velocity after the collision must be slightly lower than it was before, as the mass has increased due to the mass of the car.

### Two moving objects

When two objects travelling in opposite directions collide, the total momentum still has to be conserved. Momentum is a vector, so choose one direction to be positive and one to be negative. As a convention, objects travelling towards the left of the page have a negative velocity.

After the collision, the objects may bounce off each other or stick together. Their total momentum after the collision will be equal to their total momentum before. Positive and negative velocities indicate the direction of motion.

If the two objects had equal momentum in opposite directions, their momentum would be zero before and after the collision. They could either stick together and become stationary, or bounce off each other in opposite directions with equal momentum.

## 5 Worked example — Grade 8

A car with a mass of 3200 kg is travelling at 3 m/s. It collides with a car with a mass of 2500 kg travelling at 5 m/s in the opposite direction. After the collison, the two cars move together.

Calculate the velocity and direction of travel of the cars after the collision. **[3 marks]**

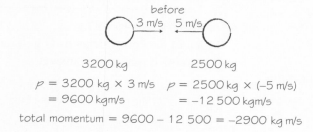

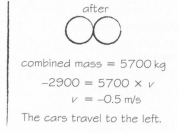

3200 kg — 2500 kg

$p = 3200 \text{ kg} \times 3 \text{ m/s} = 9600 \text{ kgm/s}$

$p = 2500 \text{ kg} \times (-5 \text{ m/s}) = -12\,500 \text{ kgm/s}$

total momentum = 9600 − 12 500 = −2900 kg m/s

combined mass = 5700 kg

$-2900 = 5700 \times v$

$v = -0.5 \text{ m/s}$

The cars travel to the left.

## 2 Explosions

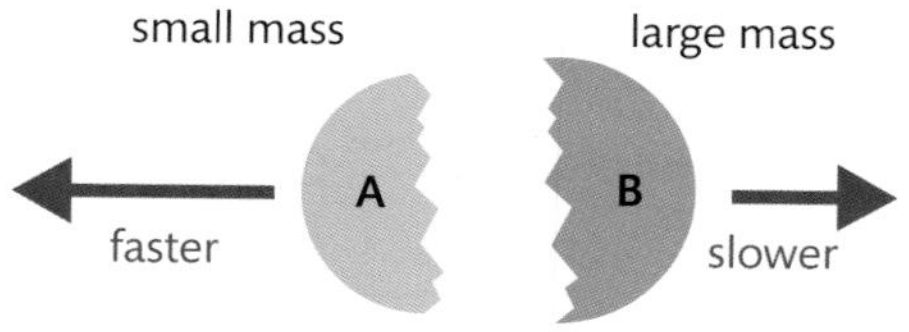


**Figure 3** A stationary object explodes

The momentum before the explosion is zero, so the momentum after the explosion must also be zero.
Momentum of A = −(momentum of B).
The larger mass (B) will have a lower velocity.

## 10 Exam-style practice — Grade 8

1. When a cannon fires a cannonball, the cannon recoils. Compare the motion of the cannon and cannonball just after it is fired and explain the differences. **[3 marks]**
2. In a rugby match, a player running at 8 m/s tackles another player who is standing still. Immediately after the tackle, the two of them move together. Explain why the velocity of the pair just after the tackle is around 4 m/s. **[3 marks]**

# Circuit diagrams

You need to be able to recognise and draw the universal symbols used to represent the components of a circuit.

## 5 Circuit symbols

Make sure you know all the symbols by name as well as their uses.

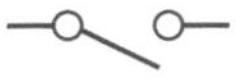
**switch (open)**
breaks a circuit

**switch (closed)**
closes a circuit

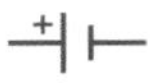

**cell**
provides energy to the circuit

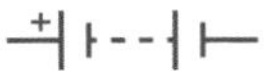

**battery**
more than one cell in series

**diode**
only lets current flow in one direction

**variable resistor**
a resistor you can change

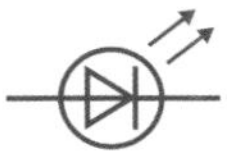
**LED (light emitting diode)**
lights up when current flows in the direction of the arrow

**thermistor**
resistance decreases as temperature increases; can be used to control temperature related devices such as thermostats in central heating systems or electronic thermometers

**fuse**
melts and breaks the circuit if the current gets too high

**resistor**
resists the flow of current

**lamp**
lights up when current flows

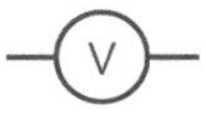

**voltmeter**
connected to a circuit in parallel, measures the potential difference

**ammeter**
connected to a circuit in series, measures the current

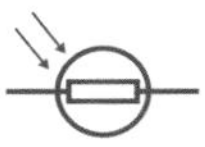
**LDR (light dependent resistor)**
resistance decreases as light intensity increases; can be used to control light sensitive devices such as street lights that come on when it's dark

## 5 Circuits

For a current to flow, there must be a complete circuit. Conventional current flows from positive to negative (even though the electrons flow the opposite way). This is particularly important when dealing with diodes and LEDs.

### Test circuits

A **test circuit** allows the current and potential difference of a component to be measured. You could replace the lamp in this circuit with any other component. Any circuit powered by a battery carries **direct current** (dc). The **resistance** of a component can be found using a test circuit and the equation:

$$\text{resistance } (\Omega) = \frac{\text{voltage (V)}}{\text{current (A)}} \qquad R = \frac{V}{I}$$

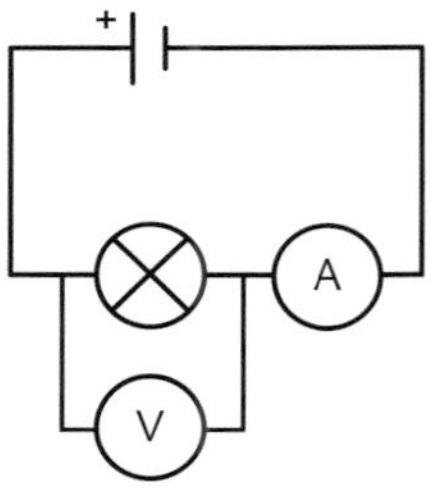

**Figure 1** A test circuit

## 5 Worked example — Grade 6

Look at **Figure 2**.

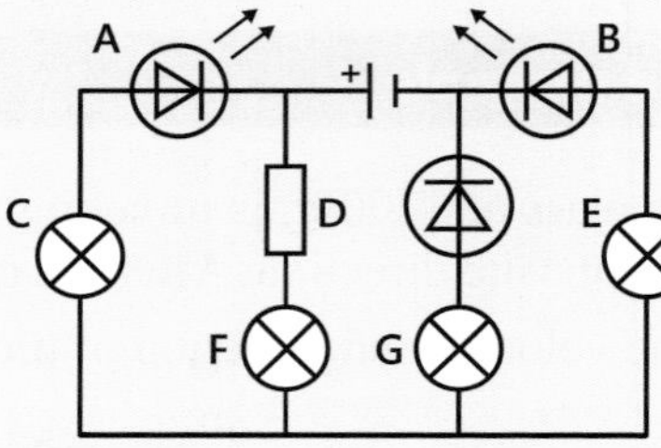

**Figure 2** A circuit diagram

Which of the components A–G will receive a flow of current? Explain your answer. **[3 marks]**

D, F, G, E and B, as the current can pass through all the LEDs and diodes in the right direction.

LED A is the wrong way around and would conduct no current so current cannot flow to lamp C.

## 15 Exam-style practice — Grade 7

1. Look at **Figure 3**. When the switch is closed, state if the bulbs A, B, C or the LED would light up. If not, explain why. **[4 marks]**
2. Draw a circuit diagram for a circuit containing a cell and
   **(a)** a bulb in parallel with an LDR **[2 marks]**
   **(b)** a resistor in series with a variable resistor. **[2 marks]**
3. Compare a variable resistor, an LDR and a thermistor. Suggest a device that might use each one. **[5 marks]**

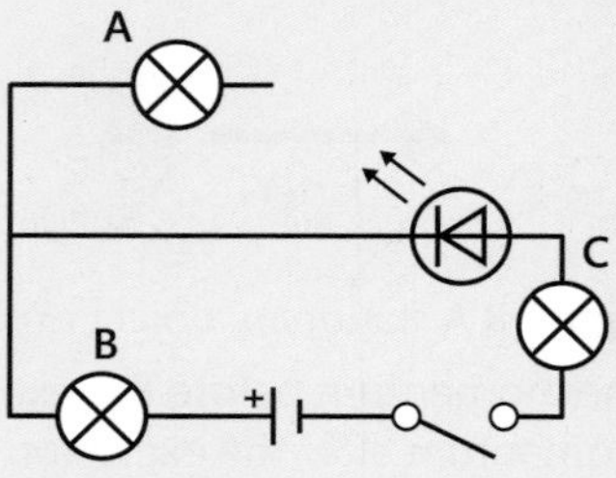

**Figure 3** A circuit diagram

# Current, resistance and potential difference

You need to understand current, resistance and potential difference to understand the basics of electrical circuits.

## Key definitions

**Current** is the flow of charge. In wires, this is carried by electrons. The greater the current, the greater the rate of flow of electrical charge.

**Potential difference (pd)**, measured in volts, is the energy transferred to or from the charge as it flows around the circuit. You will sometimes hear this referred to as *voltage*, but potential difference is the proper name.

**Resistance** opposes the flow of current. It is measured in ohms or Ω (for example, 10 Ω or 10 ohms). Resistance is caused by electrons colliding with the metal ions inside a wire.

## $V = IR$

The current in a circuit depends on the resistance and the potential difference.

potential difference (V) = current (A) × resistance (Ω)

$V = IR$

When the potential difference is increased, more energy is given to the charge, increasing the current.

If you increase the resistance, it becomes harder for charge to flow. If the pd is kept the same, the current decreases.

## Maths skills

Potential difference is proportional to current.

$V \propto I$ (for ohmic conductors where $R$ is constant)

If you double $V$ you also double $I$ for the same resistance.

Current is inversely proportional to resistance.

$$I \propto \frac{1}{R}$$

If you double the resistance you halve the current.

## Worked example — Grade 7

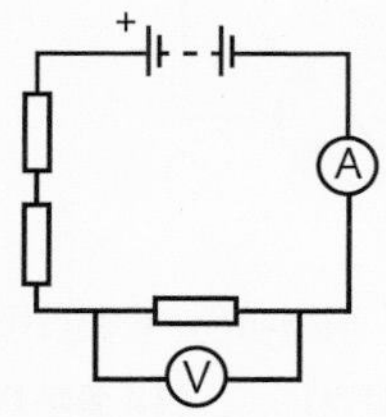


**Figure 1** A circuit diagram

Each resistor in **Figure 1** has resistance 15 Ω. The battery has a potential difference of 3 V.

**(a)** Give the reading on the voltmeter. **[1 mark]**

1 V

**(b)** Work out the reading on the ammeter. **[2 marks]**

$I = \frac{V}{R} = \frac{3}{(15+15+15)} = 0.0667\text{ A}$

**(c)** What happens to the current if the resistance in the circuit is doubled? **[1 mark]**

The current would halve. 0.0667 ÷ 2 = 0.033 A

**(d)** What happens to the current if the potential difference of the battery is doubled? **[1 mark]**

The current would double. 0.0667 × 2 = 0.13 A

You will need to understand resistances in series circuits for these questions. Go to page 193 to revise resistance. Remember, the potential difference is split across components. If they are identical they will take an equal share, so 1 V each.

You need to use the equation here, so you have to work out the total resistance first. Add the three resistors that are in series together.

## Exam-style practice — Grade 7

1. Calculate the resistance of the bulb in **Figure 2**. **[2 marks]**
2. A second identical bulb is added in series with the first. Explain whether this would change the potential difference of the battery and give the potential difference that would be measured across each bulb. **[2 marks]**
3. **(a)** The second bulb is removed and the original bulb replaced with an 80 Ω resistor. Calculate the new current. **[2 marks]**

   **(b)** The battery pd is doubled to 12 V. State how this will change the current in the circuit. **[1 mark]**

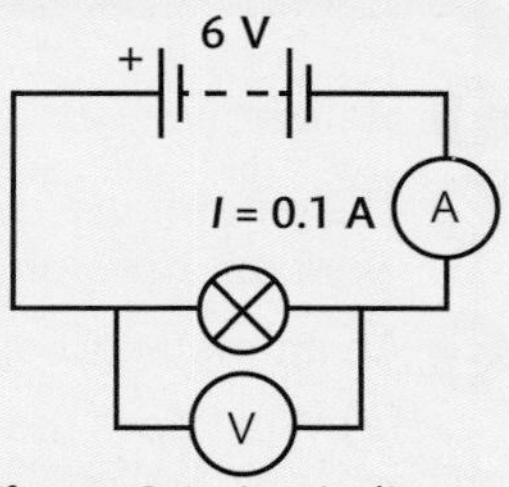


**Figure 2** A circuit diagram

Made a start | Feeling confident | Exam ready

# Electrical charge

Electrical current is a flow of charge, usually carried by electrons in wires. You need to be able to calculate charge, given the current and length of time the charge has been flowing.

## 5 Charge and current

The size of the electrical current ($I$) is the rate of flow of the electrical charge ($Q$). Charge is measured in coulombs (C) and current is measured in amps (A), which is the coulombs of charge per second.

The equation to work these quantities out is

$Q = I \times t$

An ammeter can be used to measure the current over a period of time, and this equation can be used to work out the electrical charge.

Using the charge and the potential difference in a circuit, you can use the equation $E = QV$ to find out how much energy is transferred. This can then be used to work out the work done or the power of an electrical circuit.

## 2 Calculations

**Charge flow**

charge flow (C) = current (A) × time (s)

$Q = It$

**Energy**

energy transferred (J) = charge flow (C) × potential difference (V)

$E = QV$

You can also calculate the energy if you know the power.

Go to page 197 to revise this.

## 1 Exam focus

The equations on this page won't be on your exam sheet, so you need to be able to remember them. Make sure you know how to rearrange the equations as well.

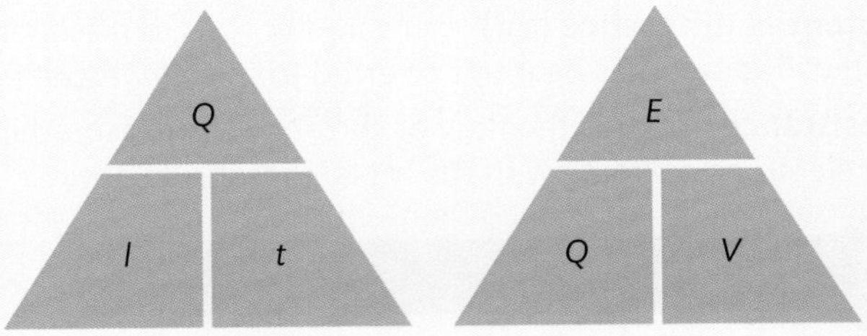


## 5 Worked example — Grade 6

**Figure 1** shows two bulbs in series.

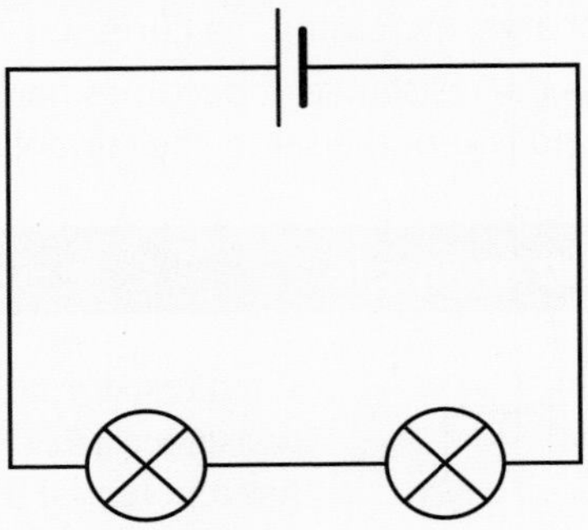

**Figure 1** A circuit diagram

**(a)** A current of 0.6 A flows for 5 minutes. Calculate the amount of charge transferred. **[2 marks]**

$Q = It = 0.6 \times 300 = 180\,\text{C}$

> Make sure the 5 minutes is converted to 300 s before you use the equation.

**(b)** How much charge will pass through each bulb in this time? **[1 mark]**

180 C

> Remember that the current is the same in all places in a series circuit. This also means that the amount of charge flowing through each bulb is the same.

**(c)** Calculate the current if 30 C of charge flows in 20 s. **[1 mark]**

$I = \frac{Q}{t} = \frac{30}{20} = 1.5\,\text{A}$

## 10 Exam-style practice — Grade 6

1. State how much charge is transferred each second by a TV using 2 A. **[1 mark]**
2. The current in a car starter motor needs to be 6 A to start the car. If it needs to transfer 30 C of charge, work out how long it needs to be switched on. **[2 marks]**
3. An ammeter is connected on the positive side of two bulbs connected in series. It reads 0.6 A.
   **(a)** What does the ammeter read when placed between the bulbs? **[1 mark]**
   **(b)** Calculate the charge transferred in 15 s. **[2 marks]**

# Resistance

This practical investigates the factors affecting the resistance of electrical circuits. You need to be familiar with the method and results.

## 5 Wire length and resistance

Set up a circuit with a cell, an ammeter connected in series and a voltmeter connected in parallel across a variable length of wire. Once the potential difference and current have been measured, the resistance can be calculated.

$$\text{resistance} = \frac{\text{potential difference}}{\text{current}} \qquad R = \frac{V}{I}$$

As the wire increases in length, the resistance increases proportionally.

Resistance is caused when electrons collide with metal ions. The longer a wire is, the more metal ions there are for electrons to collide with, so the greater the resistance.

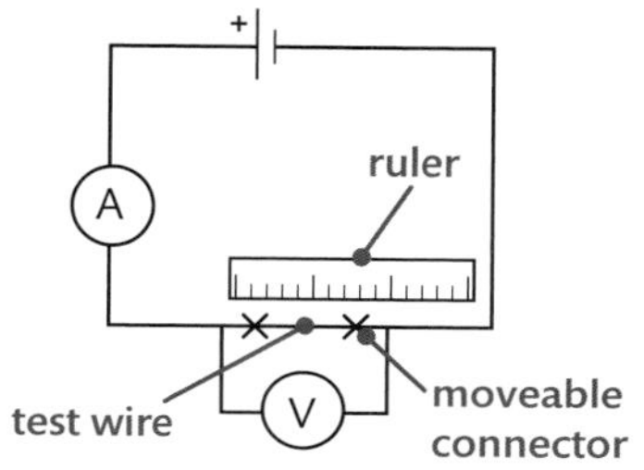


**Figure 1** The effect of wire length on resistance is investigated by measuring the current and potential difference over different lengths of wire and seeing how the resistance changes.

## 5 Resistors in series and parallel

Instead of varying the length of wire, you can insert any number of resistors in series or parallel into the circuit. You have to be able to measure the potential difference across the whole set and the total current in the circuit. The voltmeter should be connected across all the resistors, or across the power supply to get the total potential difference. The ammeter should be connected so it measures the total current from the power supply.

**Figure 2** You can find the total resistance of the combination of resistors using the equation above.

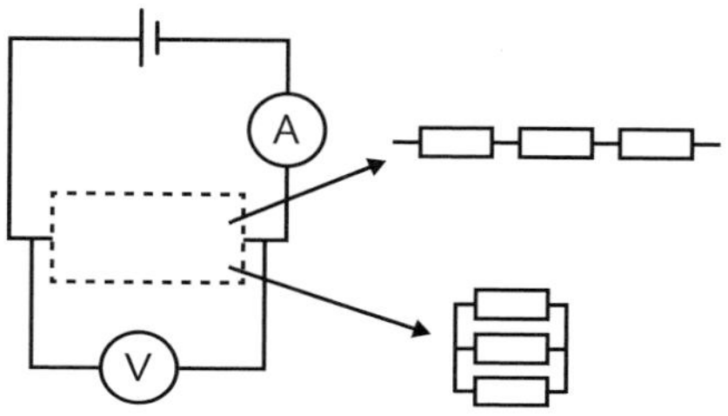


## 5 Reducing errors

- Keep the length long and the current low to limit how hot the wire will get. Resistance is increased by high temperature.
- Clean the wire with wire wool to remove any dirt or oxide that might increase the resistance in the connections.
- Taping the wire to a wooden metre rule will help keep it straight and make the length measurements more accurate.
- Switch off between tests to allow cooling.

## 5 Worked example — Grade 8

A student finds the resistance of 8 different lengths of the same wire. She plots a graph of resistance against length.

**(a)** State **two** advantages of plotting a graph to show the results. **[2 marks]**

*It is easier to identify a pattern from a graph than from a table, and it is easier to spot any results that may be errors or that do not follow the pattern.*

**(b)** Describe the graph the student should obtain, and the conclusion she should draw from this. **[2 marks]**

*The line on the graph should be a straight line through the origin, showing that resistance is directly proportional to the length of the wire.*

## 10 Exam-style practice — Grade 8

Describe how you could use a test circuit to perform an experiment to test the effect of light intensity on an LDR and of temperature on a thermistor. State what you would find in each case. **[6 marks]**

# Resistors

Some components have constant resistance. These are called ohmic conductors. The resistance of other components, such as lamps, diodes, thermistors and LDRs, changes as the current through the component changes. You need to be able to interpret an *I–V* graph to study the resistance of a component.

## 5 Ohmic conductors

### *I–V* graphs for resistors

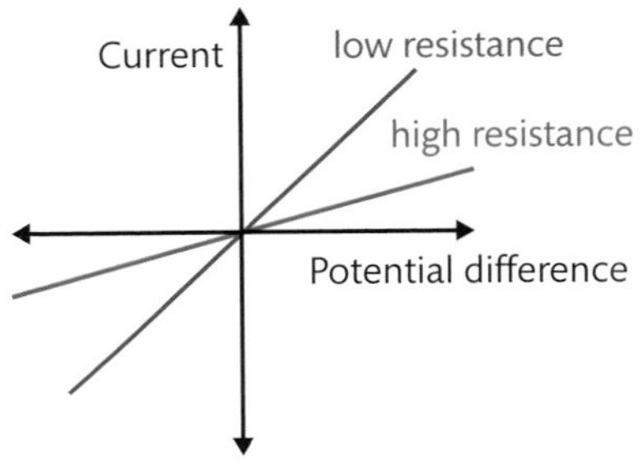


**Figure 1** An *I–V* graph

The gradient of the *I–V* graph indicates the resistance. The **higher** the gradient, the **lower** the resistance.

If the resistance is constant then the graph will be a straight line.

For ohmic conductors (at constant temperature) potential difference ∝ current, $V \propto I$.

You can calculate the resistance using

$R = \frac{V}{I}$.

Read the values for pd and current off the graph at the desired point.

**Resistance and temperature**

When temperature is increased, the metal ions in the wire vibrate with more energy. Electrons in the wire collide more often with the ions, making it harder for them to flow. This increases the resistance and reduces the current.

Ohmic conductors will only keep a constant resistance if their temperature stays constant.

The *I–V* graph for a diode is non-linear. The *I–V* graphs for ohmic conductors are linear.

## 5 Diodes

Diodes are like electrical valves. They only let current flow one way. Above a small threshold pd the gradient is very high, meaning they have virtually no resistance. If the current is reversed, the graph is flat and shows a very high resistance, so no current can flow.

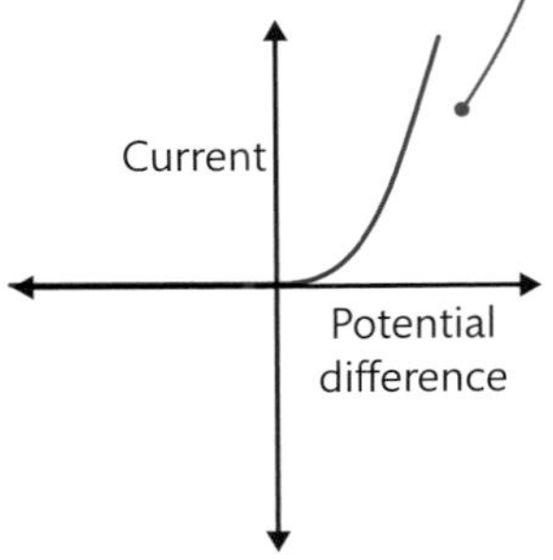


**Figure 2** An *I–V* graph for a diode

## 10 Worked example — Grades 6–8

**1** Sketch the *I–V* graph for a filament lamp and describe how the resistance changes as the pd increases. **[4 marks]**

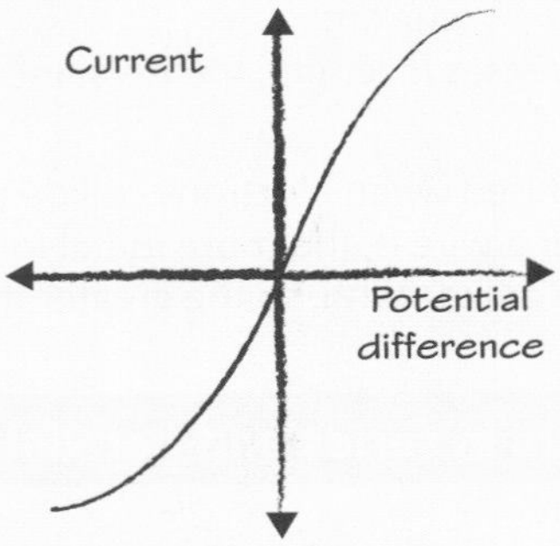


The gradient decreases as the potential difference increases or decreases from 0. As resistance is indicated by $\frac{1}{\text{gradient}}$, the resistance gets higher as pd increases.

**2** As potential difference is increased across a filament bulb, it causes an increase in current. Explain how this affects the resistance. **[5 marks]**

Any electrical current flowing through a component causes heating. The increased current at higher potential differences increases the temperature of the filament, and so increases its resistance. Higher currents cause heating in the filament, which increases the resistance.

Increasing the resistance does not make the current decrease, but it does reduce the rate at which it increases when the pd is increased.

## 10 Exam-style practice — Grade 7

**1** Sketch the shape of a graph for a wire that is allowed to heat up as potential difference increases. **[2 marks]**

**2** Describe how you can tell that pd is proportional to current for a resistor but not for a filament bulb. **[3 marks]**

# Series and parallel circuits

Electrical components can be joined either in series or in parallel. You need to know the differences between series and parallel circuits.

## 5 Series and parallel circuits

Potential difference and current behave differently in series and parallel circuits.

| | Series circuit | Parallel circuit |
|---|---|---|
| **Current** | same through all components | sum of the current through each component |
| **Potential difference (pd)** | split across components | same across each component |
| **Total resistance** | sum of all resistances (equivalent to a single resistor with the same value) | less than the smallest resistance |

## 5 Resistors

**In series**

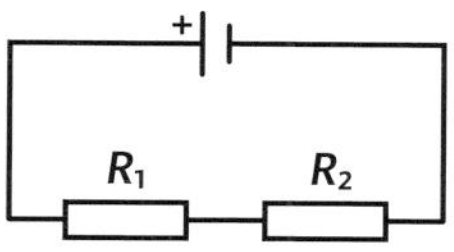


Any components connected in the same loop are in series. The resistances can be added together to give a total resistance equivalent to using just one resistor of that size. $R_{total} = R_1 + R_2$

**In parallel**

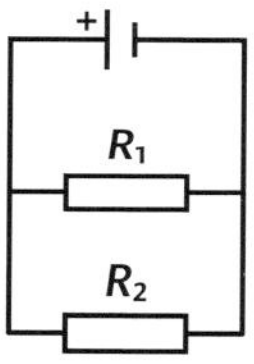


Components connected in different loops are in parallel. The total resistance of the two resistors is less than the resistance of the smallest individual resistor.

## 5 Total resistance

In series, each added component increases the resistance and decreases the current. This is because every additional component makes it more difficult for current to flow.

In parallel circuits, every new loop gives the current a new route to get around the circuit. Even though each route contains a component, it is easier overall for the current to flow, decreasing the overall resistance. The total resistance of two resistors in parallel is always less than the resistance of the smaller of the two resistors.

## 5 Worked example — Grade 7

Two identical bulbs are connected **(i)** in series and **(ii)** in parallel.

(i)

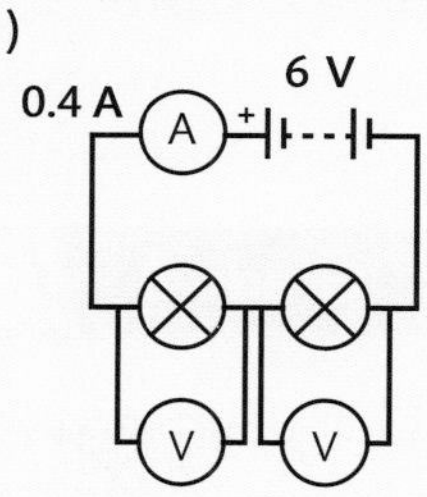


(ii)

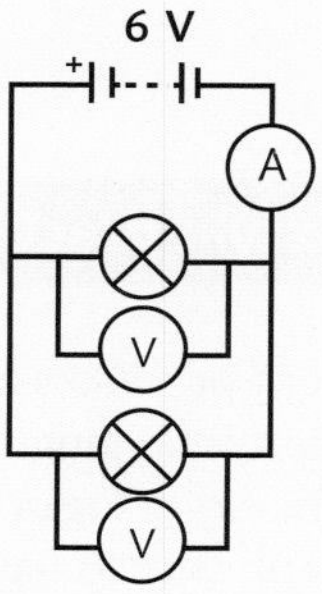


**(a)** State the reading on each voltmeter in each circuit. **[2 marks]**

(i) Each voltmeter reads 3 V. The pd splits up evenly as the bulbs are identical.

(ii) Each voltmeter reads 6 V as they get the same pd.

**(b)** What current flows through each bulb in circuit **(i)**? **[2 marks]**

0.4 A, current is the same in every component.

**(c)** Each bulb in circuit **(ii)** conducts 0.3 A of current. State the reading on the ammeter. **[1 mark]**

0.6 A, the two currents are combined.

## 10 Exam-style practice — Grade 8

1. A series circuit has two resistors, $R_1 = 12\,\Omega$ and $R_2 = 4\,\Omega$. Calculate the total resistance. **[1 mark]**
2. Two bulbs are connected in series. Describe what happens to the brightness of the bulbs when additional bulbs are added and explain why this happens. Describe what happens if they are connected in parallel. **[3 marks]**
3. A heater has five heating elements connected in parallel. One of the elements breaks. Explain what happens to the total current in the circuit of the heater. **[2 marks]**

# I–V characteristics

You need to be able to plot an I–V graph for a filament bulb, a diode and a resistor.

## 5 Plotting an I–V graph

To plot a graph for current against pd:

- Change the potential difference across the component and measure the current passing through it.
- Switch the direction by changing the pd from positive to negative. The current and potential difference will be negative numbers in this direction. Diodes do not behave the same in both directions, although most other components do.
- Plot potential difference on the *x*-axis and current on the *y*-axis.

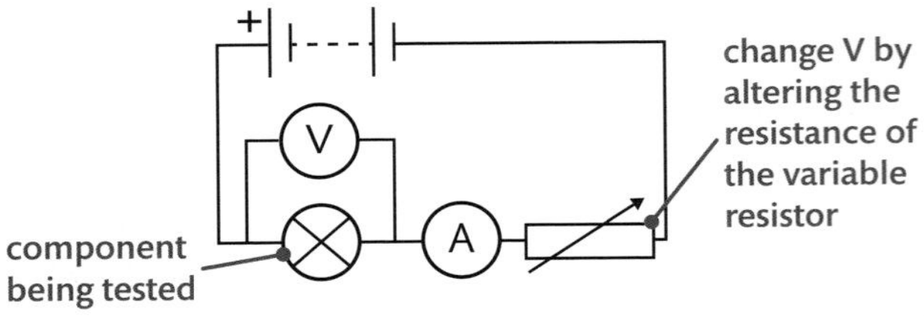


**Figure 1** This circuit is bit more complex than the circuit used to find the resistance of components as you need to be able to change the potential difference across the component.

## 2 Resistor and diode

### Resistor

Allow the resistor to cool between readings in order to keep the temperature constant.

It should give a straight line showing constant resistance.

### Diode

In one direction the resistance will be tiny, meaning a high current can flow. A high current will damage the diode. Use an extra resistor in series to keep the current low and protect the diode.

## 2 Gradient and resistance

A general straight line equation is $y = mx + c$, where:

- $m$ is the gradient
- $c$ is the $y$-intercept.

Rearrange the equation $V = IR$ to give:

$$I = \frac{1}{R} V$$
$$y = m x + c$$

The gradient is $\frac{1}{\text{resistance}}$ so resistance is $\frac{1}{\text{gradient}}$.

Even for curves, the gradient still **indicates** the resistance. Where the gradient is lower at larger potential differences, the current increases more slowly as potential difference increases, showing that the resistance increases.

## 2 Reducing errors

- If doing repeat readings, make sure the component has a chance to cool down between tests. Do this by switching the circuit off between readings.
- For wires and resistors, keep the potential difference low to reduce heating from large currents.

## 1 Exam focus

- Make sure you know what the shape of the graph would be for each component and what this tells you about the resistance.
- A constant gradient means constant resistance.
- For curves, link the change in gradient to the pd.

## 3 Worked example — Grade 8

A student produces an I–V graph for a diode. Their conclusion is 'a diode only works in one direction.' Write a better conclusion. **[3 marks]**

*In one direction the graph's gradient is very high. This shows that the resistance is very low, so high currents can flow. In the other direction, the graph's gradient is zero. This shows that the resistance is very high, so no current can flow. Therefore, the diode only lets current flow in one direction.*

## 10 Exam-style practice — Grade 8

1. A student produces an I–V graph for a length of wire, shown in **Figure 2**. The graph should have produced a straight line. Suggest what could have caused the line to be curved and give one way to improve the experiment in order to avoid this. **[4 marks]**

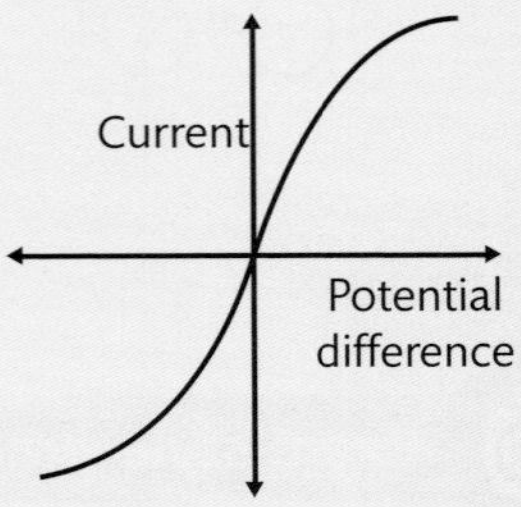


**Figure 2** An I–V graph for a diode

2. A student plots an I–V graph for a resistor. The points have a lot of scatter; this suggests random error. Suggest how the student could reduce the effect of random error. **[2 marks]**

# Mains electricity

Mains electricity is alternating current and uses three colour-coded wires.

## Alternating and direct currents

- **Alternating current (ac)** changes direction from positive to negative and back very quickly.
- **Direct current (dc)** only flows in one direction.

Mains electricity in the UK uses ac with a frequency of 50 Hz. It changes direction between +230 V and −230 V and back 50 times a second.

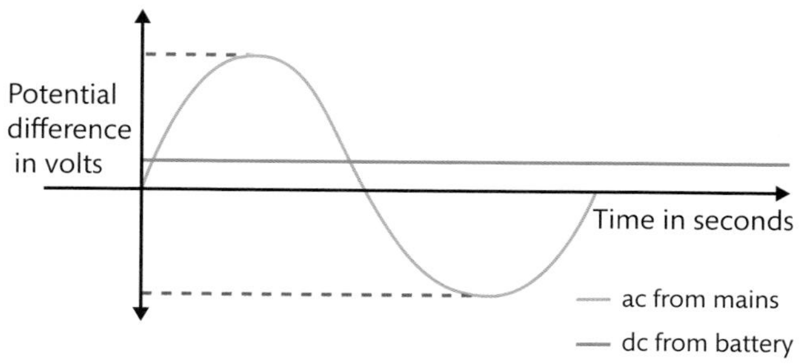


**Figure 1** Batteries provide dc while mains electricity uses ac.

## Three wires in a plug

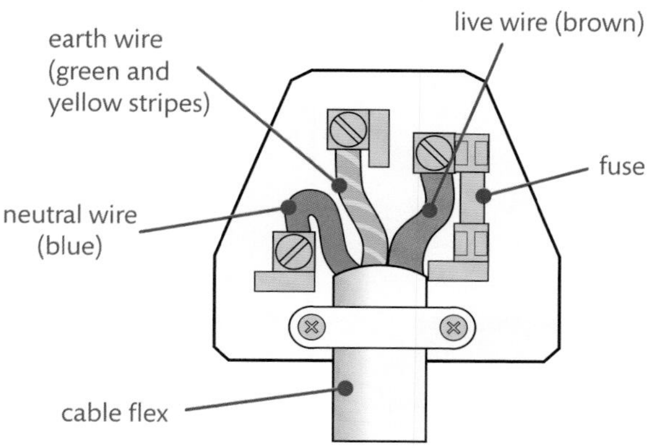


**Figure 2** Appliances are connected to the mains using a three-core cable and a plug.

The **live wire** carries the ac pd at +/−230 V.

The **neutral wire** has a pd of 0 V. It completes the circuit.

The **earth wire** is at 0 V. It only carries a current if there is a fault. It 'earths' a casing that has become live, reducing the risk of an electric shock. The earth wire is only required to earth a metal casing.

The earth wire connects the outer case to the ground. If it is live, the current flows through the earth wire rather than shocking a person who touches it.

## Electrical safety

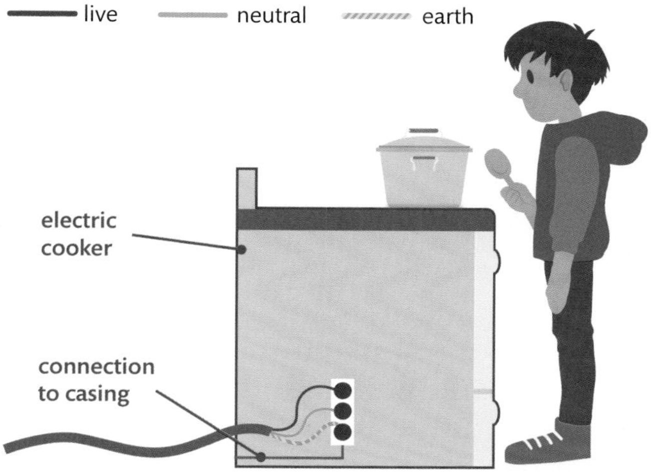


**Figure 3** Take care when handling electrical equipment.

Even if the socket switch is in the off position, touching the live wire can give you a shock. This is because you are completing a new circuit between the live wire and the ground. If the live wire touches the earth wire it causes a short circuit. In a short circuit very large currents can flow. This breaks the fuse and disconnects the appliance. It can also cause a fire.

If there is a fault, the metal outer casing might become live. If someone touches the casing, they would receive an electric shock as the current flows through them to the ground.

## Worked example — Grade 6

If a person touches a live outer casing, the current flows through an earth cable rather than the person. Explain why this happens. **[2 marks]**

*The current will flow through the wire because it has a much smaller resistance than the person. A very small current will flow through the person, but usually not enough to cause harm.*

## Exam-style practice — Grade 6

1. Explain why a plastic appliance does not need an earth wire. **[2 marks]**
2. Give **three** differences between ac and dc. **[3 marks]**
3. Potential difference in a circuit increases and decreases repeatedly from 0 V to 120 V. Explain if the current is ac or dc. **[2 marks]**

# Energy transfers in appliances

All electrical appliances transfer electrical energy into other useful forms; however, some energy is always wasted.

## 2 Energy stores

Energy cannot be created or destroyed, only transferred. All the energy going into an appliance has to go somewhere.

- Mains appliances transfer electrical energy into other **energy stores**.
- Battery-powered appliances transfer chemical energy to electrical energy, then into other energy stores.

Work is done when charge flows in a circuit.

## 5 Energy transfers

The appliances shown below transfer electrical energy into other useful types of energy. The amount of energy transferred depends on the power of the appliance and how long it is switched on for.

The useful energy outputs are in blue, and wasted energy outputs are in red.

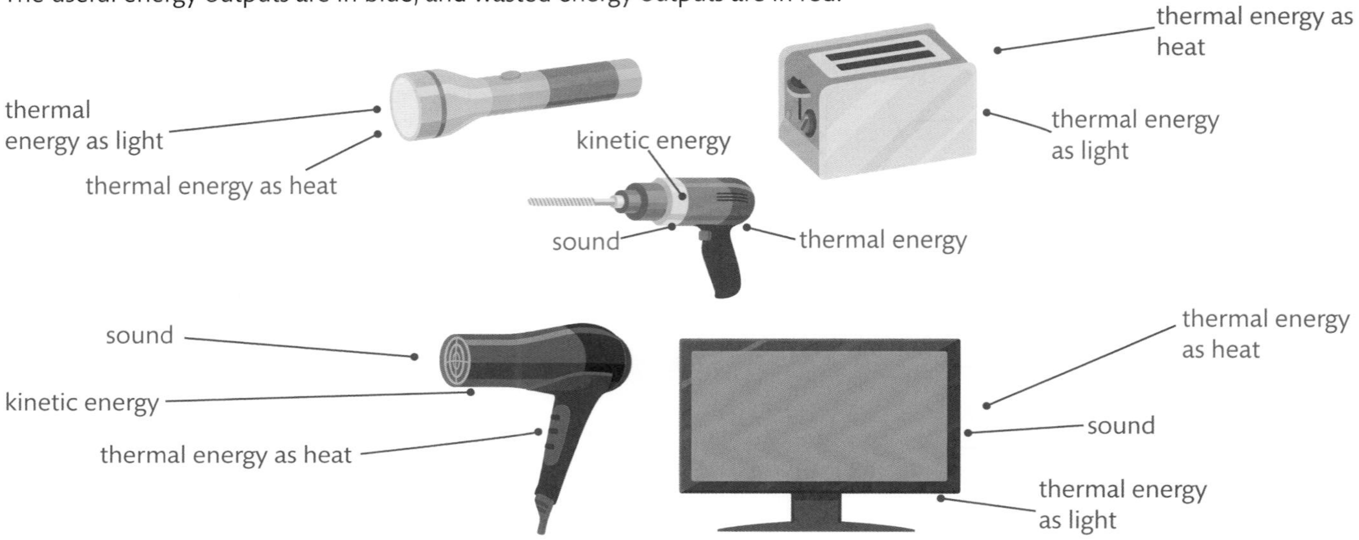


### Wasted energy

It is important to always identify all the types of energy that are transferred, whether they are useful or not. The most common forms of wasted energy are heat (often caused by friction) and sound. Some devices are meant to produce these forms of energy, in which case they are not wasted.

## 2 Worked example — Grade 5

Explain why heat is such a common form of wasted energy in devices. **[2 marks]**

*Any machine with moving parts will have some friction that converts kinetic energy into heat. Electrical appliances convert electrical energy into thermal energy in the wires.*

## 10 Exam-style practice — Grade 5

1. Give the energy transfers and state the wasted energy for:
   **(a)** a radio **[1 mark]**
   **(b)** an electric fan **[1 mark]**
   **(c)** an electric car motor **[1 mark]**
   **(d)** a mobile phone **[1 mark]**
2. If an electric room heater does not glow or make noise, the only type of energy it produces is heat. Explain why the heater may still have some wasted energy. **[2 marks]**
3. A torch uses 1000J of chemical energy and 800J is transferred as light. State how much is transferred to other forms of energy. **[1 mark]**

# Electrical power

Electricity transfers energy from a source to its components via an electrical circuit. Power is a measure of how quickly the energy is transferred. You need to be able to calculate power from several different equations.

## 2 Power

energy transferred (J) = power (W) × time (s)
$E = P \times t$

1 W = 1 J/s; 1 joule of energy is transferred per second.

Many electrical appliances have power ratings measured in kilowatts. 1 kW = 1000 W.

## 5 Electrical power equations

power (W) = potential difference (V) × current (A)

$P = VI$

power (W) = current$^2$ (A) × resistance (Ω)

$P = I^2R$

The larger the potential difference across a component, or the higher the current through it, the more power it uses.

The power of a circuit tells us how quickly it transfers energy.

## 10 Worked example — Grade 6

Two kettles boil 1 litre of water each. They are compared to see which is more efficient.

| Kettle | Power | Time to boil |
|---|---|---|
| A | 2.4 kW | 3 min 50 s |
| B | 6.0 kW | 70 s |

Note the units are kW. You may need to convert these to W.

This must be changed to seconds. 3 × 60 s = 180 s
180 s + 50 s = 230 s

**(a)** Which kettle transfers the most energy? **[2 marks]**

A: $E = Pt = 2.4 \times 230 = 552$ kJ

B: $E = Pt = 6 \times 70 = 420$ kJ

Kettle A uses most energy.

You need to work out how much energy is transferred by kettle A and by kettle B in order to make this comparison.

You can leave the power in kW if you give the answer in kJ. Read the question to check if you need to give specific units with your answer.

**(b)** How long does it take kettle B to boil 2.5 litres of water? **[2 marks]**

2.5 times longer.
2.5 × 70 = 175 s

If there is 2.5 times more water, 2.5 times more energy will be required to boil it. If the power is the same, this means it will take 2.5 times longer to boil.

**(c)** Kettle A uses mains pd (230 V). Calculate the current passing through it. **[2 marks]**

$$I = \frac{P}{V} = \frac{2400}{230} = 10.4\,A$$

**(d)** Kettle B uses 13 A of current. Find the resistance of the heating element. **[2 marks]**

$$R = \frac{P}{I^2} = \frac{6000}{13^2} = 35.5\,\Omega$$

You need to convert to standard units before putting the numbers in.

## 10 Exam-style practice — Grade 8

1. A TV uses 230 V and 5 A. Calculate its power rating. **[3 marks]**
2. A heater has power 2.2 kW and resistance 140 Ω. Calculate the current it uses. **[2 marks]**
3. A battery gives out an average current of 0.4 A and has potential difference 1.5 V.
   **(a)** Calculate its average power output. **[1 mark]**
   **(b)** The battery stores 13 kJ of energy. Calculate how long it will last. **[1 mark]**

# Types of wave

All waves are either transverse or longitudinal. You need to know the differences between these two types of wave.

## 5 Longitudinal waves

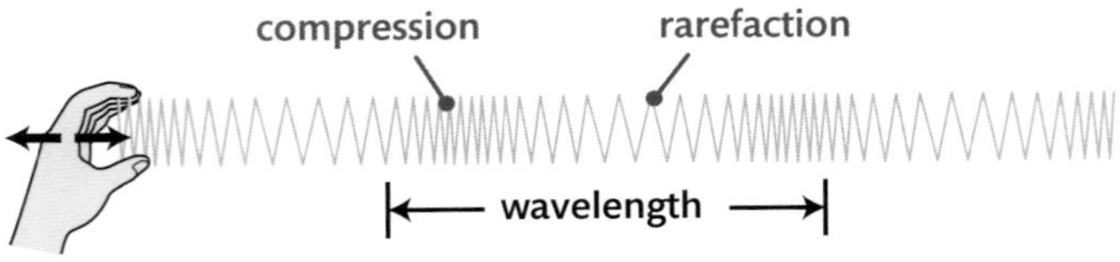


**Figure 1** Longitudinal waves

For **longitudinal waves**, the vibrations are parallel to the direction of the wave (or energy transfer).

There are no **peaks** or **troughs**. Instead, the wave has **compressions** (for sound, this means regions of high pressure) where particles are close together and **rarefactions** (regions of low pressure), where the particles are more spread out.

A **wavelength** is measured from the centre of one compression to the next. You could use rarefactions, but the centre of a compression is easier to find.

Examples:

- sound (in any medium)
- a slinky being pushed and pulled.

### Measuring the speed of sound in air

Measure the distance to a large wall that reflects sound.

Clap and ask a friend time how long it takes for the echo to be heard. The wave has travelled the distance to the wall twice so:

$$\text{wave speed (m/s)} = \frac{\text{distance to wall (m)} \times 2}{\text{time (s)}}$$

## 5 Transverse waves

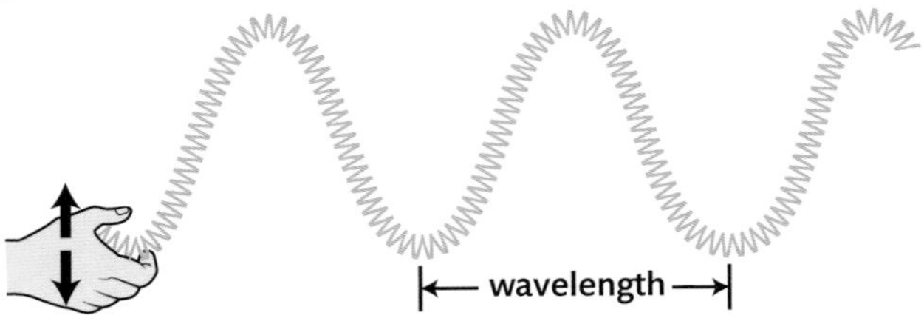


**Figure 2** Transverse waves

For **transverse waves**, the vibrations are perpendicular to the direction of the wave (or energy transfer).

Examples:

- ripples on water
- a slinky being shaken
- light (and all electromagnetic waves).

### Measuring the speed of ripples on water

Lay a ruler flat on the bottom of a ripple tank so the ripples pass over it.

Measure the time it takes for a ripple to travel the length of the ruler.

$$\text{wave speed} = \frac{\text{distance}}{\text{time}}$$

Alternatively, set the frequency of the ripples using a signal generator attached to the motor and measure the distance between the ripples.

$$\text{wave speed} = \text{frequency} \times \text{wavelength}$$

## 2 Waves transfer energy

Place a piece of paper on a slinky and create the two types of wave. Notice that the paper moves back and forth or up and down, but it does not move along the wave. This shows that waves do not transport material from one place to another. They only use vibrations in matter to transfer energy.

## 2 Worked example — Grade 8

Describe the motion of the air particles in a sound wave. **[2 marks]**

*Air particles vibrate in the direction the wave is travelling. This creates a pattern of compressions (where the particles are close together and the pressure is high) and rarefactions (where the particles are further apart and the pressure is lower).*

## 15 Exam-style practice — Grade 8

1. A student stands 200 m away from a large building. When they clap, an echo is heard. The student claps repeatedly, timing each clap with the sound of the echo. The student starts a stop clock on one clap and then times a further ten claps. Explain how this could be used to find the speed of sound. **[3 marks]**
2. A seagull floats on the ocean. As the waves pass, the seagull bobs up and down but does not move forwards. Explain what this demonstrates about ocean waves. **[2 marks]**
3. A student is trying to measure the speed of sound in air, using the method described in question 1. They stand in the playground and measure the time for the echo from the side of the sports hall. Give the most significant source of error in this experiment and suggest how it could be improved. **[2 marks]**
4. Explain why sound cannot pass through a vacuum. **[2 marks]**

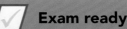

# Properties of waves

A wave transports energy through a medium using vibrations. You need to understand the properties of waves.

## 10 Parts of a wave

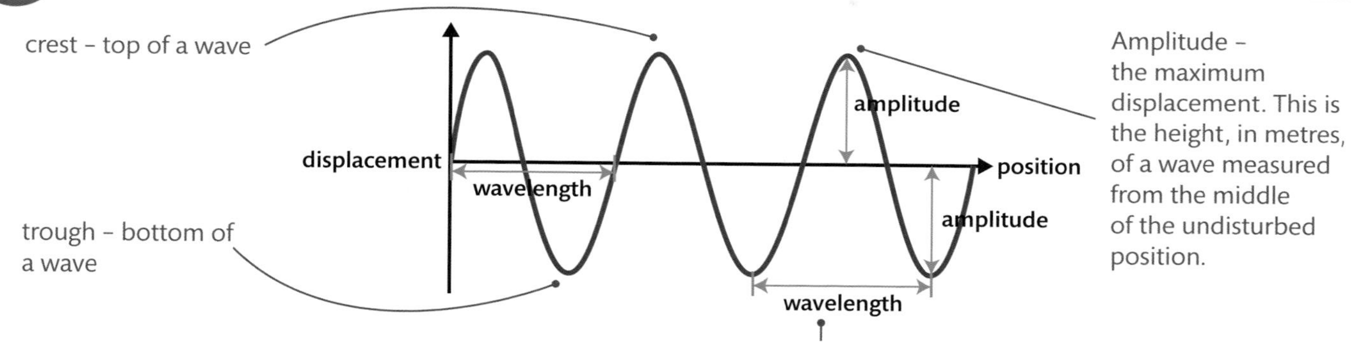


Wavelength, $\lambda$ – the length of one complete wave. It can be measured from anywhere on the wave to the next equivalent point, but crest to crest or trough to trough are the easiest to find and measure.

**Figure 1** A wave

- **Wavelength**, $\lambda$, is measured in metres, but may be given in centimetres depending on the type and size of wave.
- Time period, or just **period**, $T$, is the time to complete one full cycle or wave, measured in seconds, s.
- **Wave speed**, $v$, is the speed that energy is transferred (or the wave moves) through the medium.
- **Frequency**, $f$, is the number of waves passing a point per second, measured in hertz, Hz.

## 5 Key equations

- time period (s) $= \dfrac{1}{\text{frequency (Hz)}}$ $\qquad T = \dfrac{1}{f}$
- frequency (Hz) $= \dfrac{1}{\text{period (s)}}$ $\qquad f = \dfrac{1}{T}$
- wave speed (m/s) = frequency (Hz) × wavelength (m) $\qquad v = f\lambda$
- speed (m/s) $= \dfrac{\text{distance (m)}}{\text{time (s)}}$ $\qquad v = \dfrac{s}{t}$

## 2 Worked example — Grade 7

It takes 1.51 s for a sound to travel 500 m.
Calculate the speed of sound.

**[2 marks]**

$$\text{speed} = \frac{\text{distance}}{\text{time}}$$

$$\frac{500}{1.51} = 331\text{ m/s}$$

## 5 Displacement graphs

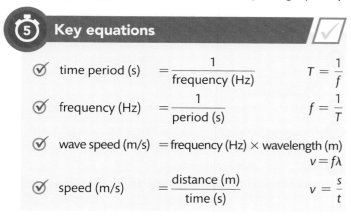

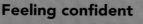

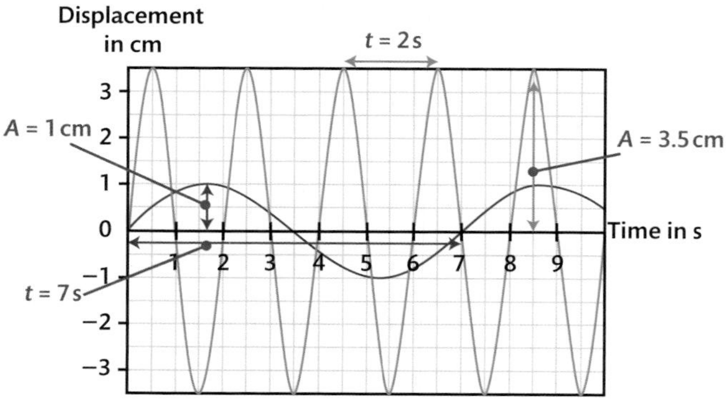


**Figure 2** A displacement graph

The **amplitude** is read off as the maximum **displacement**.

If the *x*-axis shows time, the period can be read off.

If the *x*-axis shows position, the wavelength can be read off instead of period.

## 15 Exam-style practice — Grade 7

1. The two waves in **Figure 2** both have a speed of 1.5 m/s.
   Calculate:
   **(a)** the frequency of each wave
   **(b)** the wavelength of each wave. **[4 marks]**
2. It takes 1.51 s for a sound to travel 500 m. Calculate the speed of sound. **[2 marks]**
3. The speed of sound in water is 1500 m/s. Calculate how long it will take the sound made by a fish to reach a shark that is 2 km away. **[2 marks]**
4. 20 ripples on a pond are measured to be 15 cm long in total and take 5 s to pass a point. Calculate the frequency, period and wave speed of these ripples. **[3 marks]**

# Investigating waves

These practicals investigate the speed, frequency and wavelength of waves in a ripple tank and in solids.

## 10 Speed of waves in a ripple tank

1. Time how long it takes for one wave to travel from the paddle to the edge of the ripple tank.
2. Measure the distance.
3. Calculate the wave speed.

$$\text{wave speed (m/s)} = \frac{\text{distance (m)}}{\text{time (s)}}$$

4. Time 10 rotations of the motor and divide by 10 to get the period. Calculate the frequency.

$$\text{frequency (Hz)} = \frac{1}{\text{period (s)}}$$

5. Calculate the wavelength.

$$\text{wavelength (m)} = \frac{\text{wave speed (m/s)}}{\text{frequency (Hz)}}$$

6. Alternatively, hold a ruler next to the water and try to estimate the distance from one ripple to the next.

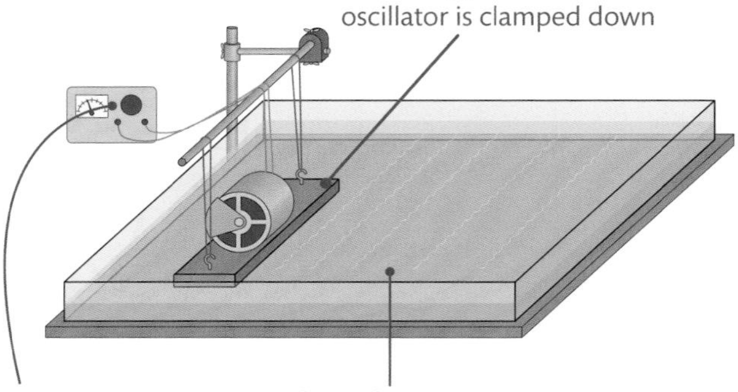

oscillating paddle – make sure the oscillator is clamped down
Keep power supplies away from the ripple tank.
A ripple tank uses an oscillating paddle to create plane (straight) waves across shallow water.

**Figure 1** Using a ripple tank to measure the speed of waves

## 10 Studying waves on a string

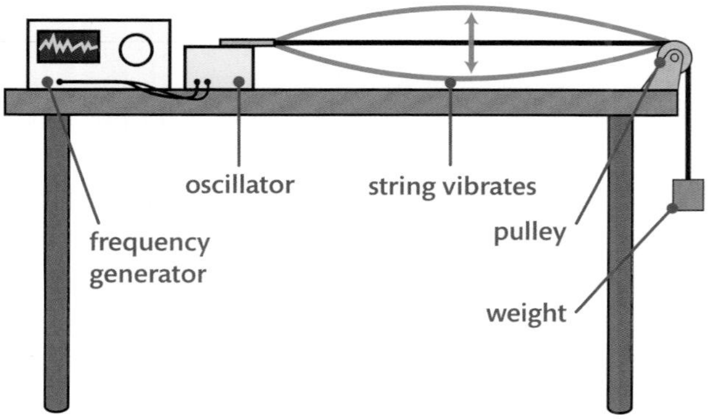


**Figure 2** Using a string to measure the speed of waves

You could use a wire instead of string.

1. Using the frequency generator attached to the oscillator, adjust the frequency until you get a wave on the string as shown.
2. Read the frequency from the frequency generator.
3. Measure the length, $L$, of the string from oscillator to pulley. This is half a wavelength, so $\lambda = 2L$.
4. Calculate wave speed using:

wave speed (m/s) = frequency (Hz) × wavelength (m)

## 2 Worked example — Grade 6

A student uses a camera to help them to carry out Step 6 in the practical described above. Explain how this will affect the accuracy of their results. **[2 marks]**

*The accuracy should improve. It is difficult to measure a distance when the object is moving. If they take a photograph of a ruler next to the waves, they will obtain a more accurate wavelength.*

## 1 Working scientifically

- Wear goggles if you use wire.
- Keep clear of hanging weights.

## 5 Exam-style practice — Grade 7

Student A uses a stopwatch to time how long the sound of a starting gun takes to cover a certain distance. Student B uses a datalogger connected to the starting gun and a microphone to measure the time. Explain which student will obtain the most accurate value. **[4 marks]**

# Types of electromagnetic waves

Waves on the electromagnetic spectrum are continuous but are grouped according to their wavelength and frequency. You need to know the properties of electromagnetic waves.

## 10 Properties of electromagnetic waves

Electromagnetic (EM) waves have properties that depend on their wavelength. All waves on the electromagnetic spectrum are transverse and transfer energy from the source to an absorber. All electromagnetic waves travel at the same velocity through a vacuum or air.

Radio waves are produced by vibrations of electrons in electrical circuits. They have low energy so are harmless.

Microwaves have slightly higher energy than radio waves. They can cause a heating effect in water.

Infrared radiation is thermal energy travelling as a wave. It is emitted from hot objects.

Visible light is seen as different colours by the human eye depending on its wavelength.

Ultraviolet (UV) light is present in sunlight. It is linked to premature ageing and skin cancer.

X-rays pass through soft tissue but are absorbed by denser bones.

Gamma rays are produced by changes to the nucleus of an atom.

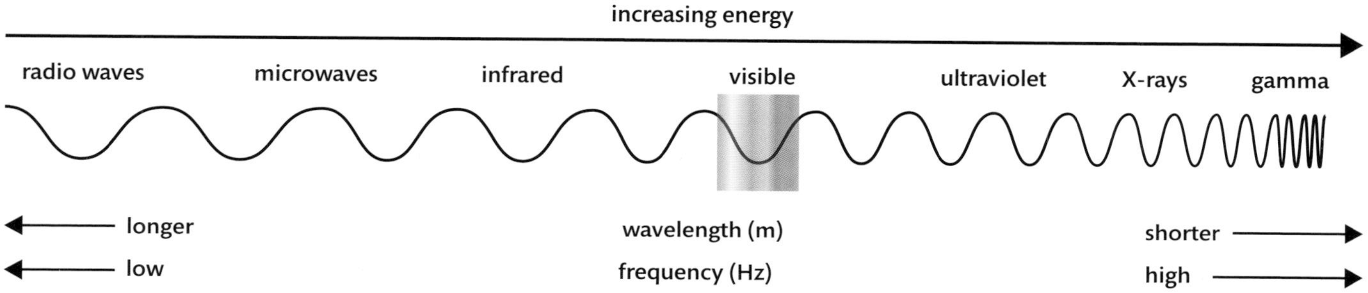


**Figure 1** Electromagnetic waves

The harmful effects of radiation depend on the type of radiation and the dose. X-rays and gamma rays are ionising radiation. Ionising radiation can change genes, which can cause cancers and kill cells. Radiation dose is measured in millisieverts. 1000 millisieverts (mSv) = 1 sievert (Sv).

EM waves are often produced over a large range of frequencies by changes to atoms, such as nuclear processes or electrons moving. When EM waves are absorbed, they can cause changes, for example, they can cause electrons to move, or even be lost from, an atom. When radio waves are absorbed they can create an alternating current with the same frequency as the radio wave. They can induce oscillations in an electrical circuit.

> The speed of light is $3 \times 10^8$ m/s (300 000 000 m/s)
> You can use the wave equation $v = f\lambda$.
> wave speed (m/s) = frequency (Hz) × wavelength (m)

## 2 Worked example — Grade 8

The wavelength of visible light ranges from $4 \times 10^{-7}$ m to $7 \times 10^{-7}$ m. Calculate the frequencies of visible light. **[2 marks]**

$$f = \frac{v}{\lambda} = \frac{3 \times 10^8}{4 \times 10^{-7}} = 7.5 \times 10^{14}\ \text{Hz}$$

$$f = \frac{v}{\lambda} = \frac{3 \times 10^8}{7 \times 10^{-7}} = 4.3 \times 10^{14}\ \text{Hz}$$

## 15 Exam-style practice — Grade 8

1. Give **two** examples that show that electromagnetic waves transfer energy. **[2 marks]**
2. Give some risks posed by sunbathing. **[2 marks]**
3. Explain why hospitals use X-rays despite the risk of cell damage. **[2 marks]**
4. The maximum yearly dose for people working with radiation is 50 millisieverts (mSv). A patient having an X-ray receives a 0.1 mSv dose.
   **(a)** Calculate the maximum number of X-rays a patient would be allowed to have in one year. **[2 marks]**
   **(b)** Explain why a patient would be advised to have far fewer than this. **[1 mark]**

# Properties of electromagnetic waves

When electromagnetic waves are incident on a surface they can be reflected, refracted, absorbed or transmitted. You need to be able to predict the effect depending on the substance and the wavelength of the electromagnetic wave.

## 10 Properties of visible light

### Reflection

Visible light is made up of different wavelengths, which are split into a spectrum of seven colours: red, orange, yellow, green, blue, indigo and violet.

In **Figure 1** we see the banana as yellow because only the yellow light is reflected. All the other colours that make up white light are absorbed.

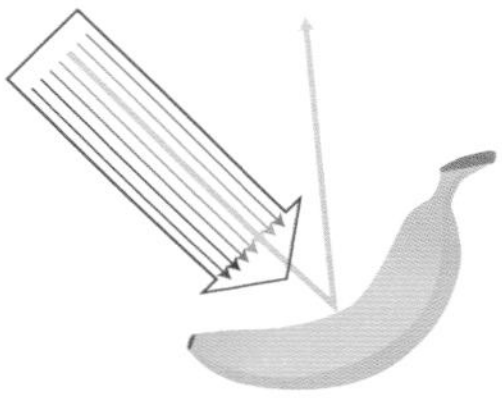

**Figure 1** A banana reflecting yellow light

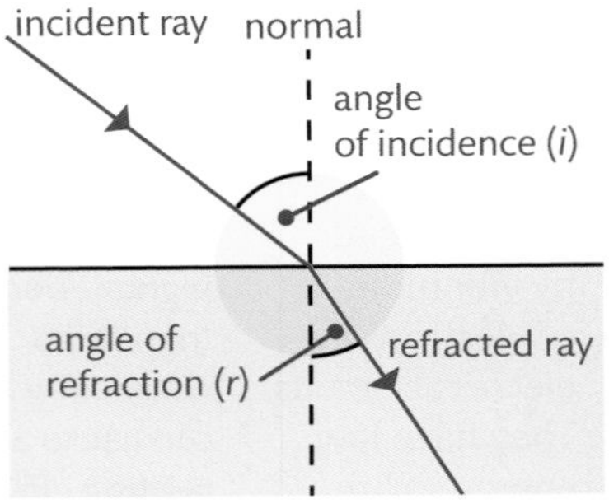


**Figure 2** Refraction

### Refraction

When light enters a substance, like water or glass, it slows down. The light can change direction and bend closer to the normal line. This is refraction. The angle of refraction will be smaller than the angle of incidence.

When leaving a substance, the waves speed up and bend away from the normal.

Refraction occurs with all types of electromagnetic waves when they change speed in a new medium. Different wavelengths will refract by different amounts.

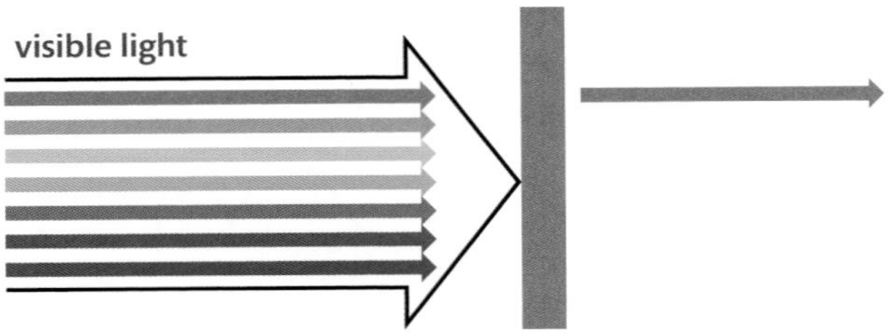


**Figure 3** The red filter only transmits red light. The other colours are absorbed.

### Transmission

If a substance is transparent, light may be transmitted and pass through it.

## 5 Wavefronts

**Wavefront** diagrams are used to represent all types of waves the way you might draw a diagram of ripples on water. When light waves hit glass, they slow down. The waves 'bunch up', making the wavelength smaller, but the frequency stays the same. When the wave hits at an angle, one side slows down first, so the wavefront bends and the wave changes direction.

The experiments you will do will most likely use only light waves, but remember that all waves in the electromagnetic spectrum will behave in this way.

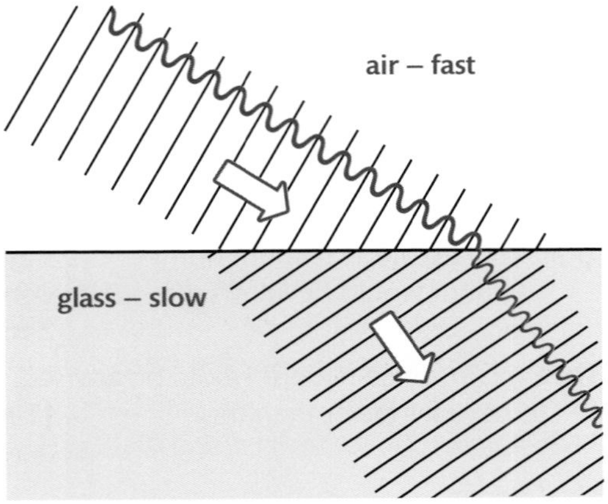


## 2 Worked example — Grade 7

Explain what happens if you shine red light at a green piece of paper. **[2 marks]**

*The paper would absorb the red light and not reflect any light, so it would look black.*

## 10 Exam-style practice — Grade 7

1. Suggest what type of energy light is transferred to when it is absorbed by a surface. **[1 mark]**
2. Explain what happens when you shine white light at:
   **(a)** transparent green glass **[1 mark]**
   **(b)** a black t-shirt **[1 mark]**
   **(c)** a white car. **[1 mark]**
3. A glass prism splits white light into a spectrum of colours. Explain why this happens and what it tells us about the speed of different colours in glass. **[3 marks]**
4. A student says that when light hits a glass block with an incident angle of 0° it does not slow down, because it does not change direction. Explain whether or not the student was correct. **[2 marks]**

# Infrared radiation

Infrared radiation (IR) is a type of electromagnetic wave emitted from hot objects. The amount of IR absorbed or radiated by a surface depends on the nature of the surface. You need to know how to investigate how the nature of a surface affects how much infrared radiation it absorbs or radiates.

## 5 Experiment 1: Absorption of infrared

1. Fill the cans with hot water and measure the start temperature of each can.
2. Measure the temperature after 5 minutes.
3. Calculate the difference.

Black, dark or matt colours absorb radiation more quickly than white, shiny or silver colours. You can prove this by showing that the temperature of the darker object increases more rapidly.

The silver (or lighter) colours reflect radiation more than absorb it, so they do not heat up as quickly.

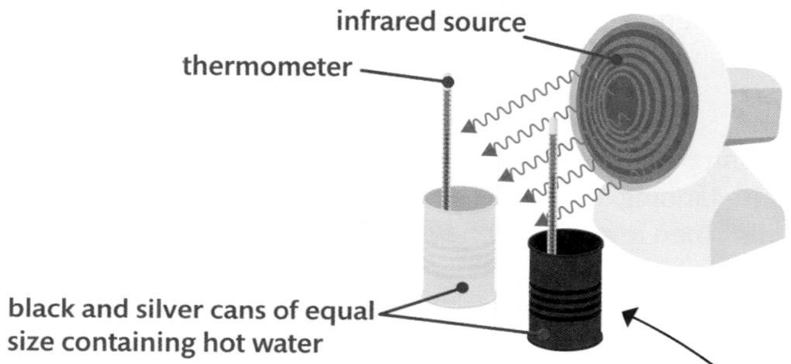


**Figure 1** Apparatus for measuring infrared absorption

### Working scientifically

Be careful when working with high temperatures. Allow equipment to cool before handling.

## 2 Worked example — Grade 6

Explain why you might choose to wear a white t-shirt rather than a black one on a hot sunny day. **[2 marks]**

*A black t-shirt would absorb infrared light and make you hot, whereas a white t-shirt would reflect more infrared and keep you cooler.*

## 5 Experiment 2: Emission of infrared

1. Use a funnel to fill the **Leslie's cube** with hot water. Once it is full do not try to move it.
2. Use the infrared detector to measure the IR being emitted from the white side of the Leslie cube.
3. Repeat step 2 with the black and silver sides.

Darker colours emit more IR radiation than light or shiny colours.

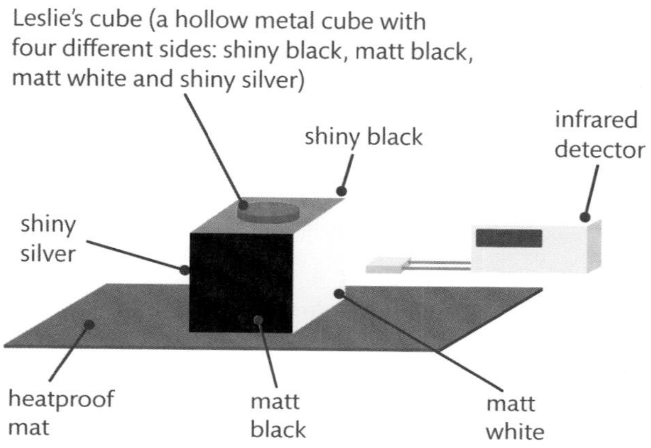


**Figure 2** Apparatus for measuring infrared emission

## 2 Reducing errors

### Experiment 1

- Each can must contain the same volume of water.
- The cans need to be an equal distance from the IR source.
- They must be heated for the same amount of time.
- They must start at the same temperature.

### Experiment 2

- Hold the detector at the same distance from each surface and at the same height on all sides.
- Minimise time delay between measurements so the water does not cool too much.

## 10 Exam-style practice — Grade 6

1. Discuss how the findings of these experiments might be useful when designing energy-efficient housing. **[3 marks]**
2. A café wants to use take away cups for hot drinks. Suggest what colour would be best to use and why. **[2 marks]**
3. A student wants to alter the second experiment by covering one side in tin foil and another in black paper. Identify **one** additional source of error with this method. **[2 marks]**
4. Suggest how you might present the results of these experiments. **[1 mark]**

# Applications of EM waves

Electromagnetic waves have many different uses. You should be able to explain why each type of electromagnetic wave is suited to its applications.

## 15 Electromagnetic wave applications

| Type of wave | Applications | How does it work? |
|---|---|---|
| radio waves | • radio and TV communications<br>• walkie-talkies. | The frequency of radio waves allows them to be transformed into electrical signals when received by aerials, and allows aerials to emit radio waves using electrical signals. |
| microwaves | • cooking<br>• satellite communication, such as mobile phones. | Microwaves are absorbed by water, so can be used to heat most food. They penetrate food up to about 1 cm, which means that they cook food faster than infrared. |
| infrared | • cooking and heating<br>• thermal imaging is used to 'see' infrared radiation. | The frequency of infrared waves means that when an object absorbs them, its temperature increases. |
| visible light | • lasers (pointers, etching and eye surgery)<br>• fibre optic cables use light to carry telecommunication signals<br>• endoscopes use fibre optics to see inside the body. | Visible light waves have a frequency that interacts with the rods and cones in the eyes, causing the retina to detect light. Fibre optic cables transmit information through internal refraction. |
| ultraviolet (UV) | • tanning<br>• invisible markings (money)<br>• strip lights. | UV can penetrate skin cells and interact with pigments to cause tanning. UV can be absorbed by some substances which then re-emit the energy as visible light, such as invisible ink. In strip lights, an electrified gas emits UV, which is absorbed by a powder that glows emitting visible light. |
| X-ray | • medical scans<br>• security scanners at aiports. | X-rays can penetrate through soft materials like skin and suitcases. They are absorbed by dense materials like bones and metal. This makes them ideal for seeing inside bodies and luggage. |
| gamma | • treatment of cancer<br>• medical tracers (body scan)<br>• sterilisation of medical equipment. | Gamma radiation is very high energy and can kill cells and bacteria easily. As it can penetrate through most materials, a weak source can be used for medical scans and large doses can target cancer cells deep within the body. |

## 1 Walkie-talkies

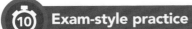

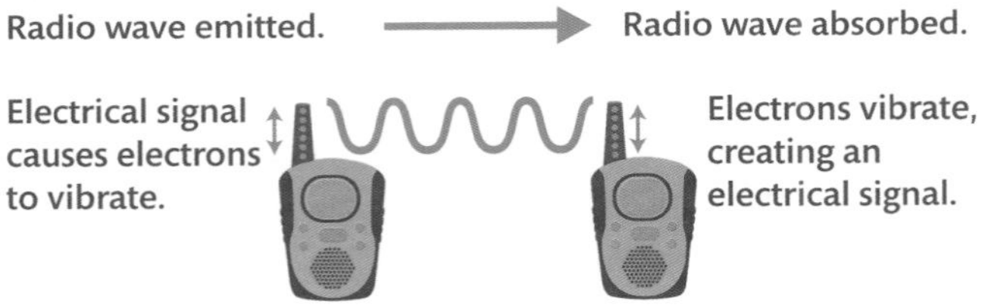
Radio wave emitted.
Radio wave absorbed.
Electrical signal causes electrons to vibrate.
Electrons vibrate, creating an electrical signal.

**Figure 1** Radio waves

## 2 Worked example — Grade 7

Suggest why the police might use a thermal imaging camera to find a person.

**[2 marks]**

*It can pick up their body heat even if it is night time or they are hidden.*

## 10 Exam-style practice — Grade 7

1. Give an example of each type of wave used for communication. **[3 marks]**
2. Give **two** other uses for invisible markings that show up under ultraviolet light. **[2 marks]**
3. Explain why any electrical equipment might cause interference with a radio. **[2 marks]**

# Magnetic fields

A magnetic field is the region around a magnet where forces are exerted on another magnet or on materials with magnetic properties. A magnet can attract or repel another magnet, but always attracts magnetic materials.

## 10 Magnetic fields and forces

Magnets do not have to touch to exert forces. Magnetism is a non-contact force. The closer the magnets, the stronger the force. The magnetism gets weaker as the magnets get further apart. Compasses point in the direction of a **magnetic field**.

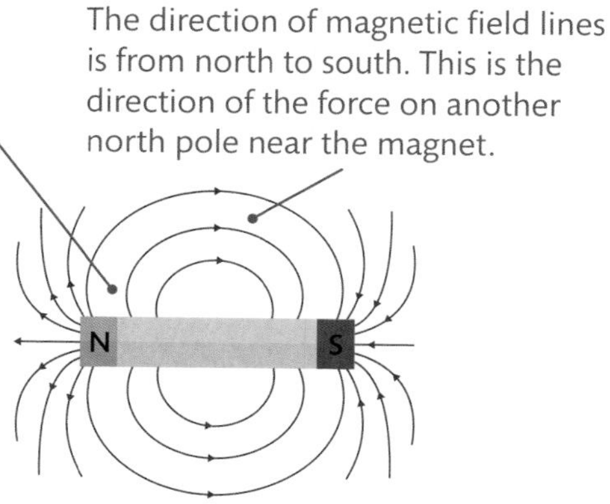

The field is strongest at the poles.
The direction of magnetic field lines is from north to south. This is the direction of the force on another north pole near the magnet.
N
S


**Figure 1** A magnetic field

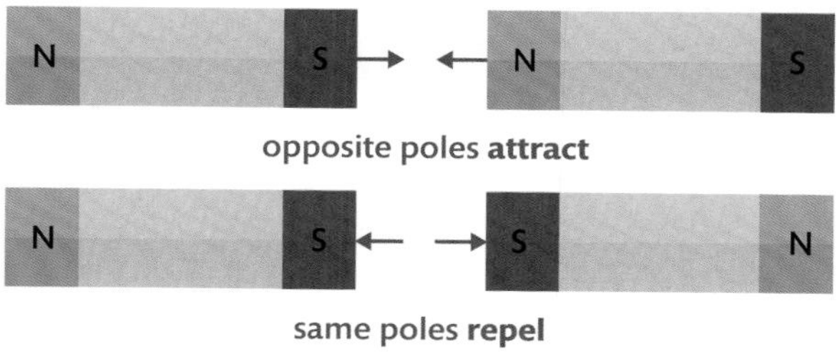


opposite poles attract

same poles repel

**Figure 2** Magnetic forces

Because compasses point in the direction of magnetic fields, they can be used as evidence of Earth's magnetic field.

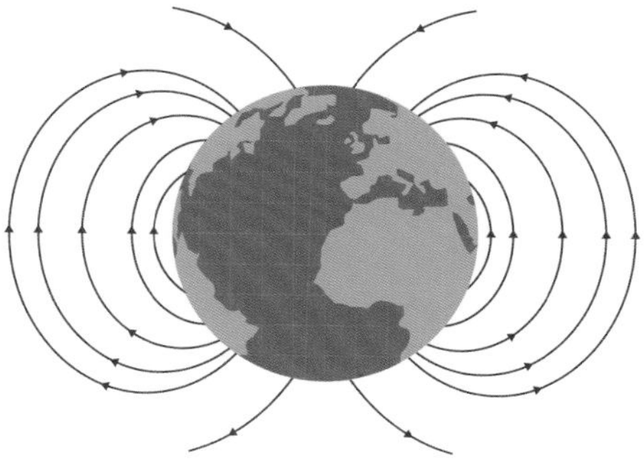

**Figure 3** Earth's magnetic field is the same shape as the field around a bar magnet. It is produced by the rotating iron core.

Permanent magnets (like bar magnets) produce their own magnetic field. They can cause objects made from magnetic materials such as cobalt, iron, nickel and steel (remember CoINS) to become **induced magnets**.

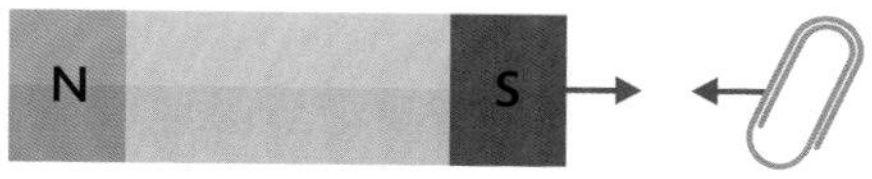


**Figure 4** Induced magnets do not stay magnetic like permanent magnets. The magnetic force is always attractive.

## 5 Mapping field lines

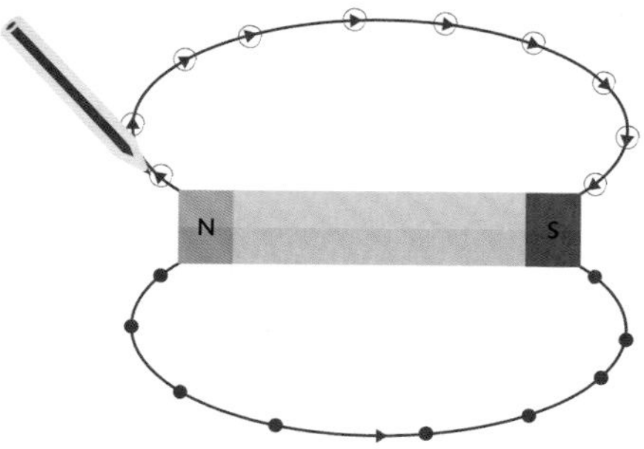


**Figure 5** Drawing field lines around a magnet

1. Place a plotting compass at the north pole of a magnet. It will point away in the direction of the field. Draw a dot where it points.
2. Move the compass so the back of the needle is on the dot and draw another dot.
3. Repeat until the compass reaches the other side of the magnet.
4. Join all the dots together. Don't forget to put an arrow showing the direction of the field, north to south. This shows the direction the compass is pointing.

## 2 Worked example — Grade 6

Describe how **Figure 1** shows that the magnetic force is stronger at the poles. **[2 marks]**

*The closer together the lines are, the stronger the field. At the poles, the lines are closer together, so the force must be stronger.*

## 10 Exam-style practice — Grade 6

1. Show how you could find the north pole of an unmarked bar magnet. **[2 marks]**
2. The north pole of a compass points up. What does this say about Earth as a magnet? **[2 marks]**
3. How could you demonstrate that the magnetic force of attraction is non-contact? **[2 marks]**
4. State the difference between a permanent magnet and an induced magnet and give an example of each. **[2 marks]**

# Electromagnetism

Electromagnets are made from coils of wire. You need to know how to use electric currents to make a magnetic field the same shape as the magnetic field around a bar magnet.

## ⑤ Electrical wires ✓

Wires carrying an electrical current generate a magnetic field. The strength of the magnetic field depends on the current through the wire and the distance from the wire.

The magnetic field around a wire is circular.

Using your right hand, if your thumb shows the direction of the current, your fingers wrap around the wire in the direction of the field.

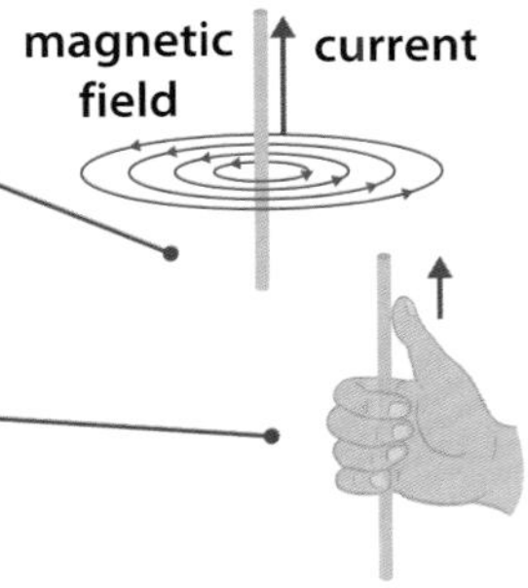

**Figure 1** A magnetic field around a wire

## ② Advantages and disadvantages ✓

- 👍 Electromagnets can be switched off.
- 👍 Their strength can be altered easily by controlling the current.
- 👎 Electromagnets use electricity, so cost money to run.
- 👎 They can get hot, as electrical energy is transferred to thermal energy.

## ⑤ Solenoids ✓

A **solenoid** is a coil of wire carrying a current that generates a magnetic field like the field around a bar magnet. When you add an iron core, the field is strengthened and the solenoid becomes an electromagnet.

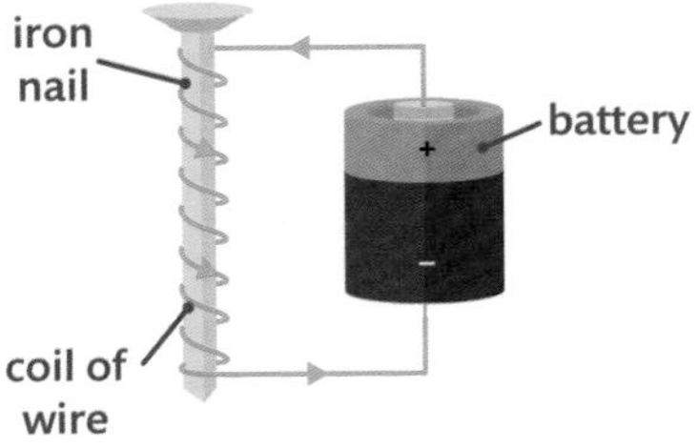

**Figure 2** You can make an electromagnet by coiling wire around an iron nail and passing an electrical current through the wire.

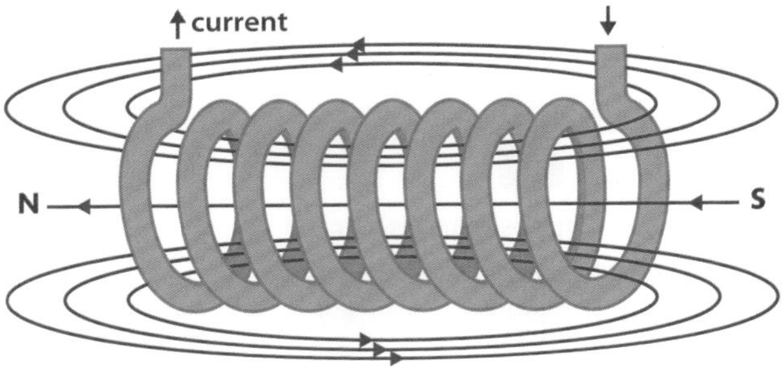

**Figure 3** Coiling the wire into a solenoid increases the strength of the magnetic field. The magnetic field inside a solenoid is strong and uniform.

## ⑤ Electromagnetic fields 🧪 ✓

You can test the strength of an electromagnet by seeing how many paperclips it picks up as you change factors like current and number of coils.

**Direction**

The current will flow positive to negative. Curl the fingers of your right hand as shown in **Figure 1**, with your fingers pointing in the direction of the current. Your thumb will point in the direction of the north pole of the magnet.

You could also use a compass which will point towards the south pole.

## ② Worked example          Grade 6 ✓

Describe how you would find the direction of the magnetic field on an electromagnet.

**[2 marks]**

Hold a compass over the magnet. The arrow will point in the direction of the magnetic field from north to south.

## ⑩ Exam-style practice          Grade 6 ✓

1. A scrapyard uses an electromagnet rather than a permanent magnet. Explain why. **[2 marks]**

2. Sketch the image of an electromagnet (**Figure 2**) including the magnetic field. **[3 marks]**

3. Suggest how you would change the direction of the magnetic field in an electromagnet. **[1 mark]**

# The motor effect

If two magnetic fields combine, a force may be exerted. For example, a wire carrying a current that is placed in a magnetic field will experience a force. The conductor will also exert a force on the magnet. This is called the motor effect.

## 5 Force on a wire

The force acting on the wire is at right angles to the magnetic field and to the direction of the current. The direction of the current refers to conventional current (from + to −), not the direction of electron travel. This force is called the **motor effect**.

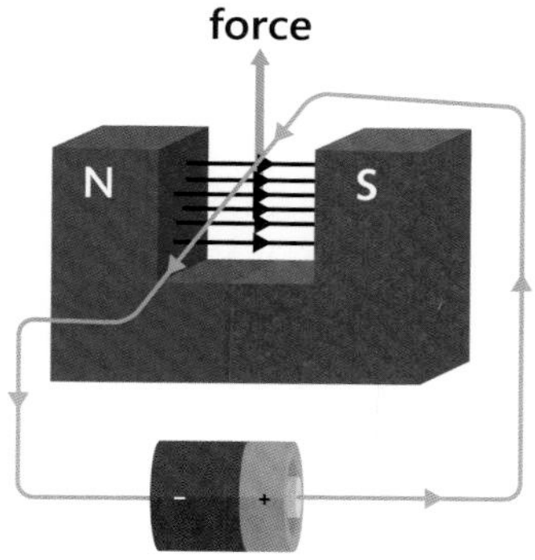


**Figure 1** The motor effect

## 2 Left-hand rule

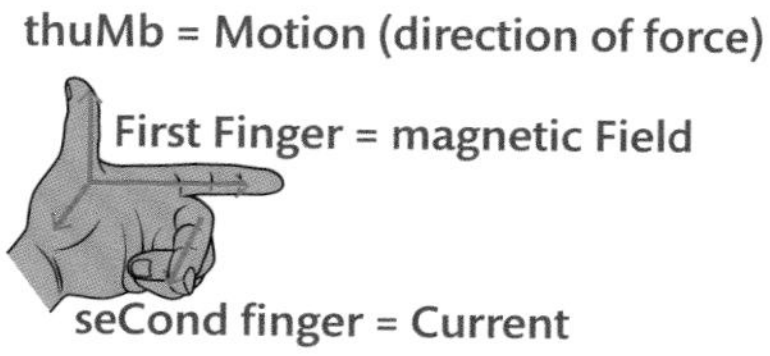


**Figure 2** Fleming's left-hand rule.

Use your left hand. Line up your fingers and thumb with two of the directions of: magnetic field, motion (force) or current. You can now work out the direction of the third.

> Only one thing has changed direction, so the force direction will switch to down. You can check this using the left-hand rule.

## 5 Magnetic flux density

The **magnetic flux density** is the strength of the magnetic field, measured in teslas (T).

You can increase the force by:

- increasing the current
- increasing the length of wire in the magnetic field (in an electric motor this is done by making it into a coil)
- increasing the magnetic flux density by using stronger magnets.

The size of the force can be found using the equation:

force (N) = magnetic flux density (T) × current (A) × length (m)

$F = B\,I\,l$

> You are given this equation in the exam but you need to be able to rearrange it.

## 5 Worked example — Grade 8

**1** The current in **Figure 1** is reversed. What is the direction of the force on the wire? **[1 mark]**

Down

**2** What magnetic flux density would be needed to make a 10 cm length of wire carrying 0.2 A experience a force of 0.0025 N? **[1 mark]**

$$\text{magnetic flux density} = \frac{\text{force}}{\text{current} \times \text{length}} = \frac{0.0025}{0.2 \times 0.1} = 0.125\,\text{T}$$

> Most lengths of wire will be small, and might be measured in cm. Make sure you convert them to metres.

## 10 Exam-style practice — Grade 8

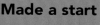

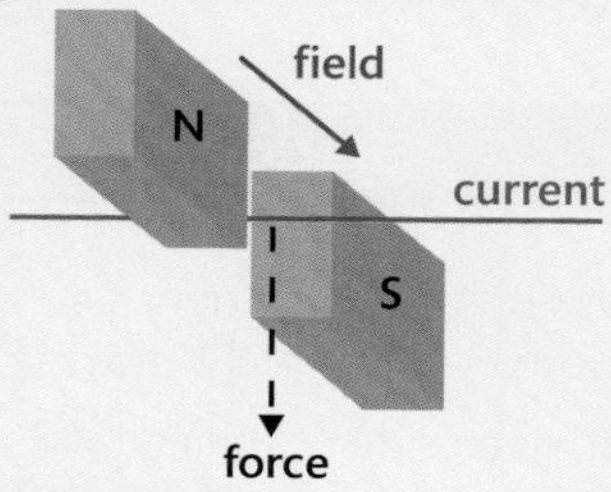


**Figure 3**

1. Give the direction that the current is flowing in **Figure 3**. **[1 mark]**
2. The current changes direction and the north and south poles are swapped. Describe what happens to the direction of the force. **[2 marks]**
3. The flux density in **Figure 3** is 0.1 T and the current 3 A. Calculate the force on 5 cm of wire. **[3 marks]**
4. Give **three** ways that the size of the force could be increased. **[3 marks]**

Made a start | Feeling confident | Exam ready

# Electric motors

Electric motors use the motor effect, transferring electrical energy to kinetic energy.

## Motor effect

Passing a current through a coil of wire in a magnetic field causes it to rotate. This is how motors work.

You can apply **Fleming's left-hand rule** to one side of the coil. This will help you to find which way the force will make it move: up or down.

The other side of the coil will move in the opposite direction as the current is flowing the other way.

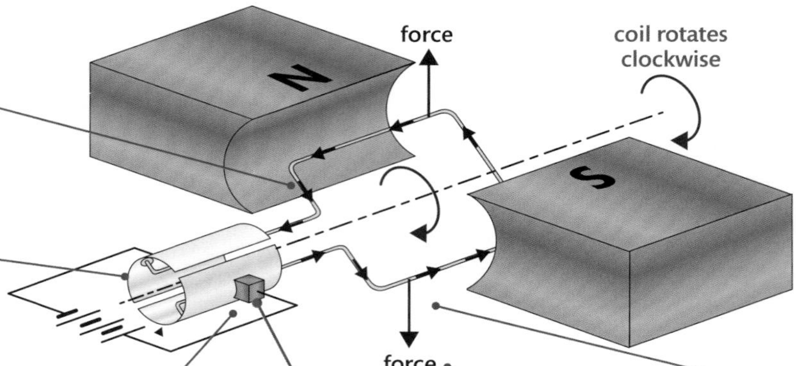


The coil contains a wire wrapped around in many turns.

The split ring commutator allows the current to change direction every half turn. This changes the direction of the force and allows the coil to keep spinning.

Carbon brushes keep electrical contact while still allowing the coil to rotate.

When the current flows, the motor effect causes the coil to experience a force.

The force on one side of the coil changes direction every half turn, but the current in that side of the coil changes at the same time. The combined effect of these two changes keeps the coil spinning in the same direction.

**Figure 1** An electric motor

## Worked example — Grade 8

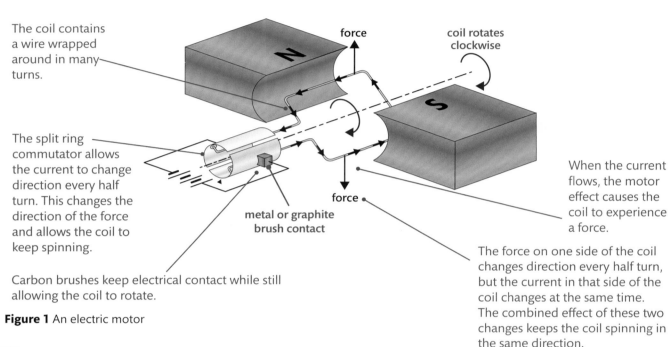

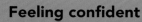

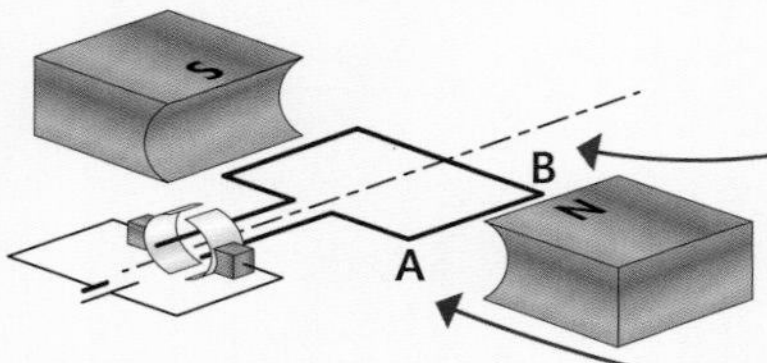


**Figure 2** An electric motor

Current flows from A to B.

Use Fleming's left-hand rule:
- The first finger (field) points left.
- The second finger points from A to B (into page).
- The thumb indicates that the side AB will move up.

Look at **Figure 2**.

**(a)** In which direction will the coil rotate? **[1 mark]**

Anticlockwise

**(b)** Give **three** ways in which the speed of the motor could be increased. **[3 marks]**

Anything that increases the motor effect force will make the motor spin faster. Revise these topics together as there is a lot of overlap.

Increasing the magnetic flux density or strength of the magnets; increasing the current; increasing the number of turns on the coil.

**(c)** How might you change the direction the motor is spinning? **[2 marks]**

Switch the poles or change current direction.

## Exam-style practice — Grade 7

1. Explain why the two sides of a coil experience a force in opposite directions. **[2 marks]**
2. Explain why the force on each side of the coil will be the same size. **[2 marks]**

# Transformers and the National Grid

You need to know how the National Grid transports electrical energy around the country.

## 10 The National Grid

The National Grid uses a system of cables and transformers to transfer electrical energy from power stations to consumers. When a current flows through a wire some energy is lost as heat. The National Grid transmits electricity at a low current to minimise heat loss. This requires a high voltage.

Power stations produce high potential difference electricity (page 189).

Step-up transformers are used to increase the potential difference from the power station to the transmission cables. This reduces the size of the current.

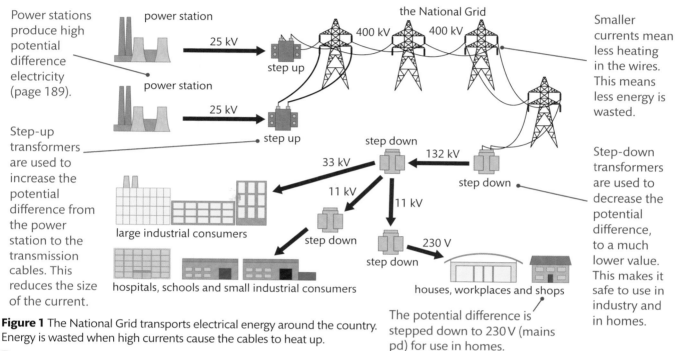

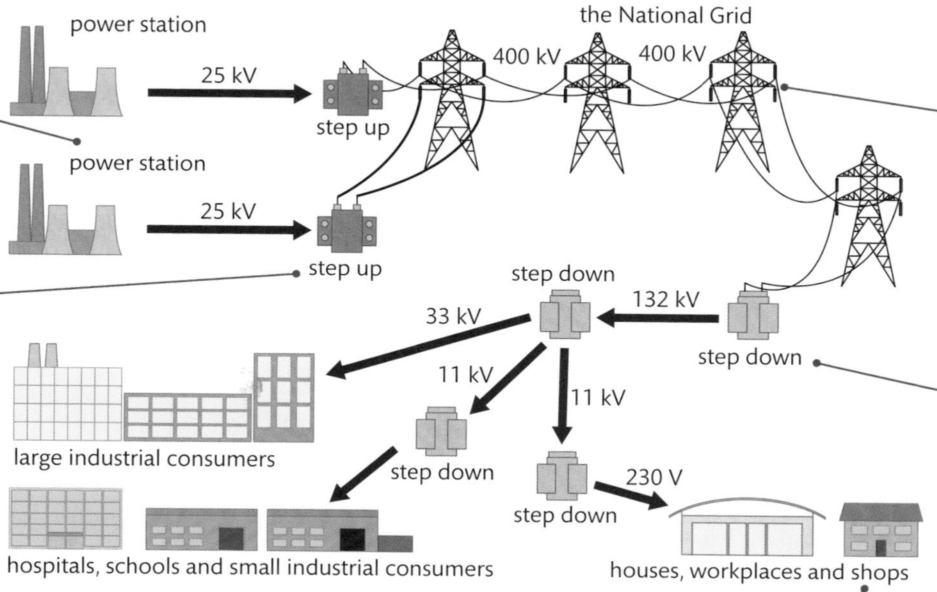


Smaller currents mean less heating in the wires. This means less energy is wasted.

Step-down transformers are used to decrease the potential difference, to a much lower value. This makes it safe to use in industry and in homes.

The potential difference is stepped down to 230 V (mains pd) for use in homes.

**Figure 1** The National Grid transports electrical energy around the country. Energy is wasted when high currents cause the cables to heat up.

## 2 Primary and secondary coils

A transformer can change the potential difference between the primary coil (input) and secondary coil (output). The power transfer must be constant.

Power out of the secondary coil = power into the primary coil

Primary potential difference  primary current = secondary potential difference  secondary current

$V_s I_s = V_p I_p$

## 2 Worked example — Grade 7

Explain the effects of not using transformers in the National Grid. **[4 marks]**

*The current would be very high, wasting lots of energy as heat in the wires. Electricity would become very expensive. More fuel would need to be burned in order to produce enough electricity to meet demand, releasing more greenhouse gases into the atmosphere and increasing global warming.*

## 10 Exam-style practice — Grade 7

1. Heating in wires is caused by the current and resistance in the wire. Other than reducing the current to very small values, suggest how the energy lost to heating might be reduced. **[2 marks]**
2. A transformer is used in a mobile phone charger to turn 230 V mains pd into 12 V to charge a battery. Give the name of this type of transformer. **[1 mark]**

# Energy transfers in a system

A system is an object or group of objects. Systems change when energy is transferred between different energy stores.

## 10 Principle of conservation of energy

Energy is either transferred usefully, stored or dissipated. Energy cannot be created or destroyed.

This means the total amount of energy in any closed system remains constant. Where energy appears to be 'lost', it is usually being wasted. Energy can be transferred by heating, forces and an electric current.

**Energy transfers in different devices**
(Wasted forms of energy are underlined.)

**Catching a ball**
kinetic ➔ thermal
A moving object hitting an obstacle transfers kinetic energy to thermal energy.

**Archer shooting an arrow into the air**
chemical (from muscles) ➔ strain potential (stored in the bow) ➔ kinetic (as arrow flies) ➔ gravitational potential energy (as arrow goes up) ➔ kinetic (as arrow falls back down) ➔ thermal
Some energy would be wasted as thermal energy due to work done against air resistance as the arrow moves.

**A boat constantly accelerating**
chemical ➔ kinetic and thermal
The boat gains kinetic energy as it accelerates, and thermal energy due to more work being done against the resistance of water on the boat.

**Vehicle braking**
kinetic ➔ thermal
The friction in the brakes transfers thermal energy.

**Electric kettle**
electrical ➔ thermal
Heat is used to boil the water.

## 5 Reducing energy losses

Energy is transferred to thermal energy when work is done against friction in moving parts. Friction can be reduced by lubricating moving parts, reducing the amount of energy wasted.

Thermal energy is often a wasted energy in electrical circuits. The wasted energy can be reduced by using low currents or decreasing the resistance of the circuit.

Thermal energy is wasted in many buildings as it can be conducted through the walls. The lower the thermal conductivity and the thicker the walls, the less energy wasted. Many types of building insulation are thick and contain trapped air. Air has poor thermal conductivity, which reduces the rate of wasted thermal energy being transferred from the house.

## 15 Exam-style practice — Grade 6

1. Name **one** device that uses or transfers each form of energy mentioned on this page. In each case, state if energy is being stored or transferred. **[6 marks]**
2. Describe the energy transfers for:
   **(a)** a horse galloping **[1 mark]**
   **(b)** a firework flying upwards **[1 mark]**
   **(c)** a car moving. **[1 mark]**
3. Identify how energy is wasted in a coal power station and suggest how it can be reduced. **[2 marks]**
4. Explain how thick woolly jumpers reduce the amount of thermal energy being transferred to the surroundings. **[3 marks]**

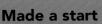

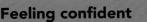

# Work done and energy transfer

Work done is energy used when a force moves an object through a distance. You need to be able to calculate work done, given the force and distance.

## Calculating $W$

work done (J) = force (N) × distance (m)

$W = Fs$

Distance is measured along the line of action of the force.

One joule of work is done when a force of one newton is applied over a distance of one metre.

When calculating work done, the force is measured along the same line of action as the displacement. You may need to resolve forces to calculate work done.

As work done = force × distance, you can give the unit for work done as newton metres (Nm) instead of joules.

## Energy transfer

If you do work pushing an object, it will gain kinetic energy. If you do work lifting an object, it gains **gravitational potential energy**.

Force × distance would have the unit newton metres, Nm, which is equal to work done measured in joules. So one newton metre is equal to one joule.

When a potential difference makes a current flow by 'pushing' charge around a circuit, it is doing work.

Work done against friction heats up the moving object.

## Worked example — Grade 7

**1** **Figure 1** shows a person carrying a box that weighs 20 N. How much work does the person do against gravity in carrying the box 10 m forwards? Explain your answer. **[2 marks]**

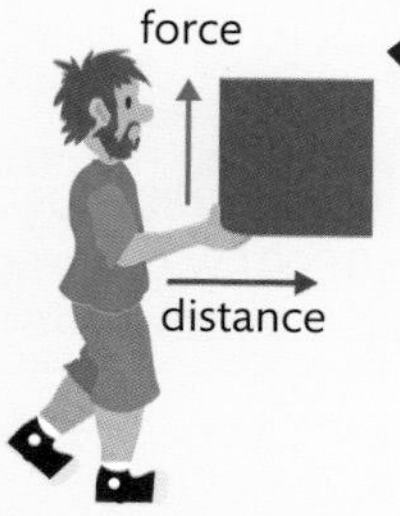


**Figure 1** A person carrying a box

None. The force applied to hold the box is up against its weight and the distance travelled is forwards, at 90° to the force.

The person will use energy and their arms will get tired from holding the box, but we do not call this energy *work*. Work would only be done when they lifted or put down the box as it is moving in the line of action of the force (up or down).

**2** **Figure 2** shows a person who weighs 650 N. How much work do they have to do against gravity to climb the stairs? **[2 marks]**

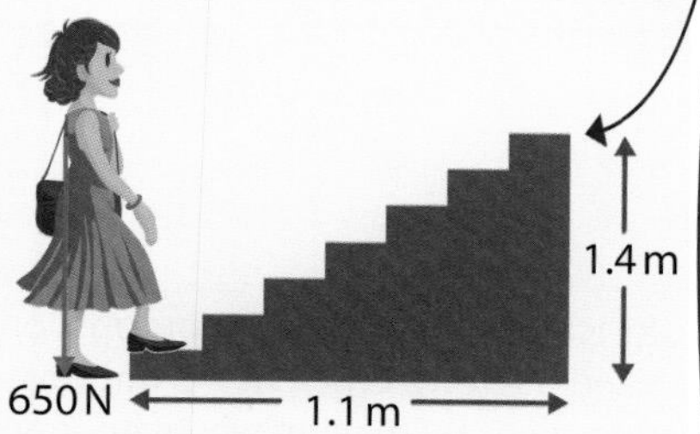


**Figure 2** A person climbing stairs

The person has weight 650 N, so the force they must use to climb the stairs must match their weight: 650 N.

As they are applying an upward force, you are only interested in the upwards motion; the 1.1 m is not used in the calculation.

$W = Fs = 650 \times 1.4 = 910\,\text{J}$

**3** A car has 20 000 J of kinetic energy when it starts to brake.

**(a)** How much work will the brakes need to do to stop the car? **[1 mark]**

20 000 J

**(b)** If the braking force of the car is 2 kN find its stopping distance. **[2 marks]**

$s = \frac{W}{F} = \frac{20\,000}{2000} = 10\,\text{m}$

## Exam-style practice — Grade 7

**1** Calculate how much work is done against gravity by:

**(a)** a person of weight 500 N walking 12 m **[1 mark]**

**(b)** a person of weight 500 N walking up a hill 35 m high **[1 mark]**

**(c)** a ball of weight 20 N falling 1.5 m **[1 mark]**

**(d)** a person pushing a shopping trolley along a flat floor 120 m with a force of 25 N. **[1 mark]**

**2** **(a)** An ice skater slides across ice and slowly comes to a stop. Explain if work has been done and what the energy change would be. **[3 marks]**

**(b)** The ice skater starts with 400 J of kinetic energy. The frictional force is 80 N. Calculate the distance they travel before coming to a stop. **[2 marks]**

**3** A cyclist, starting from rest, pedals up a hill. Describe the energy transfers taking place. **[3 marks]**

# Efficiency

Efficiency is a measure of how much of an energy transfer is used usefully. The more efficient something is, the less energy it wastes. You need to be able to calculate efficiency and comment on how efficient something is.

## 2 Calculating efficiency

You can calculate efficiency using the equation:

$$\text{efficiency} = \frac{\text{useful output energy transfer (J)}}{\text{total input energy transfer (J)}}$$

Efficiency can also be calculated in terms of power:

$$\text{efficiency} = \frac{\text{useful power output (W)}}{\text{total power input (W)}}$$

Energy is normally measured in joules and power in watts. As long as the units for both output and input are the same the calculation will work, for example, if both output and input energy are in MJ or output and input power are in kW.

## 2 Efficiency: key facts

- The equations will give you a result between 0 and 1.
- Efficiency does not have any units.
- You could multiply the efficiency value by 100 to get it as a percentage.
- The closer to 1 (or 100%), the more efficient the process and the less energy is wasted.
- If something is 65 per cent efficient, 65 per cent of the energy is used usefully and 35 per cent is wasted.

## 10 Worked example — Grade 7

A power station produces 150 000 kW of electrical power and uses chemical energy in coal at a rate of 380 000 000 W.

> Convert this to kW so the units match.
> 380 000 000 W ÷ 1000 = 380 000 kW

**(a)** Assuming all other energy is wasted as heat, what is the rate of thermal heat loss? **[2 marks]**

> All of the 380 000 kW that is taken in must be given out. 150 000 kW comes out as electrical energy so whatever is left must be the thermal energy.

380 000 kW − 150 000 kW = 230 000 kW

**(b)** Calculate the efficiency of the power station. **[2 marks]**

$$\text{efficiency} = \frac{150\,000}{380\,000} = 0.39$$

**(c)** In a load of coal, there is 250 kJ of energy. How much electrical energy will this produce? **[2 marks]**

> You need to use the efficiency from the previous answer and rearrange the equation for useful energy output.

useful energy output = efficiency × total energy input = 0.39 × 250 kJ = 97.5 kJ

**(d)** The power station recycles some of the lost heat to heat the buildings. Why does this improve its efficiency? **[1 mark]**

> Efficiency measures the proportion of energy that is used usefully. Efficiency is improved by reducing wasted energy or by making waste energy useful.

It increases the useful output of energy.

## 10 Exam-style practice — Grade 7

1. A TV uses 400 J of energy and wastes 150 J. Calculate its efficiency. **[1 mark]**
2. A house's central heating is 85 per cent efficient. Explain what **85 per cent efficient** means. **[1 mark]**
3. Appliance A has an input of 100 W. Appliance B has an input of 50 W. Explain which is more efficient if they both give out thermal energy at a rate of 35 W. **[2 marks]**
4. A heater gives out 2000 J of thermal energy. Find the input energy if it is 60% efficient. **[2 marks]**
5. Clockwork watches transfer elastic potential energy to kinetic energy. Some is lost as heat energy. Suggest how a watchmaker reduces the energy lost. **[1 mark]**

# Gravitational potential energy

You need to be able to calculate gravitational potential energy (g.p.e.), a type of stored energy that an object gains when it is lifted.

## 2 Calculating g.p.e.

The gravitational potential energy (g.p.e) of an object, measured in joules (J), depends on its mass, its height and the **gravitational field strength**.

It can be calculated using the equation:

g.p.e. (J) = mass (kg) × gravitational field strength (N/kg) × height (m)

$E_p = mgh$

The gravitational field strength of Earth is 9.8 N/kg.

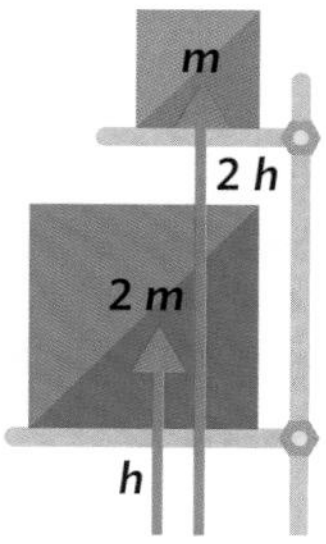


**Figure 1** Both of these boxes have the same gravitational potential energy. The bottom box has twice the mass of the top box, but has only half the height.

## 2 Kinetic energy

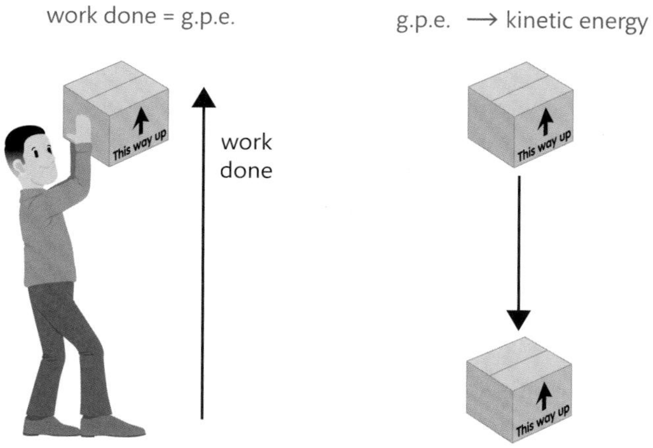


**Figure 2** Lifting and dropping a box

To lift the box, the g.p.e. is equal to the work done in lifting it. When dropped, the g.p.e. will turn into kinetic energy as it falls. The kinetic energy upon hitting the ground is equal to the g.p.e. it had at the top.

## 10 Worked example — Grade 7

A lift full of people has a mass of 550 kg.

**(a)** Calculate the g.p.e. gained by the lift if it moves upwards 20 m. ($g$ = 9.8 N/kg). **[2 marks]**

$E_p = mgh = 550 \times 9.8 \times 20 = 107\,800$ J

**(b)** How would the answer be different if the lift had carried fewer people? **[1 mark]**

G.p.e. would have been smaller.

The g.p.e. depends on mass. If there are fewer people there will be less mass so the change in g.p.e. will be smaller.

**(c)** How much g.p.e. would the lift have gained if it only went up 10 m? **[1 mark]**

$107\,800 \div 2 = 53\,900$ J

Notice that the height is half, therefore the g.p.e. will be half.

**(d)** Some passengers get off, and the lift moves up another 10 m. It gains 40 000 J of g.p.e. Calculate the new mass of the lift and its passengers. **[3 marks]**

$$m = \frac{E_p}{gh} = \frac{40\,000}{9.8 \times 10} = 408.2 \text{ kg}$$

**Maths skills**

When putting this into your calculator remember to use brackets on the (9.8 × 20) on the bottom of the fraction.

## 15 Exam-style practice — Grade 8

1. Calculate the energy in the gravitational potential energy store for a 70 kg rock climber 100 m up a cliff. ($g$ = 9.8 N/kg) **[2 marks]**
2. If the same rock climber only has 50 000 J of g.p.e., calculate their height. **[2 marks]**
3. Use the idea of energy transfer to explain:
   **(a)** why the speed of a ball increases as it falls. **[2 marks]**
   **(b)** why something dropped from a greater height will hit the ground faster. **[2 marks]**
4. **(a)** A crane lifts a crate 20 m and the crate gains 1000 J of g.p.e. Calculate how much more g.p.e. it will gain if it is lifted a further 40 m. **[2 marks]**
   **(b)** State how much work the crane has done in each case. **[2 marks]**

# Kinetic energy

All moving objects have kinetic energy. You should be able to work out how much kinetic energy moving bodies have.

## Calculating $E_k$

kinetic energy (J) = 0.5 × mass (kg) × (speed)² (m/s)

$$E_k = \frac{1}{2}mv^2$$

Doubling the mass will double the kinetic energy.

As the speed is squared, doubling the speed will make the kinetic energy four times larger.

## Key equations

**Finding mass**

$$m = \frac{E_k}{\frac{1}{2}v^2}$$

**Finding speed**

Rearrange for $v^2$ first: $v^2 = \frac{E_k}{\frac{1}{2}m}$

then square root both sides: $v = \sqrt{\frac{E_k}{\frac{1}{2}m}}$

**Maths skills**

40 m/s is two times the speed. The kinetic energy will be $2^2 = 4$ times larger.

60 m/s is three times the speed. The kinetic energy will be $3^2 = 9$ times larger.

When putting the numbers in your calculator, make sure you use brackets for the numbers on the bottom of the fraction and that only the speed is squared:

200 000 ÷ (0.5 × 20²)

Remember to square root the whole answer.

## Worked example — Grade 8

A vehicle has 200 000 J of kinetic energy at 20 m/s.

**(a)** Calculate the kinetic energy at 40 m/s and 60 m/s. **[3 marks]**

At 40 m/s: 200 000 × 4 = 800 000 J

At 60 m/s: 200 000 × 9 = 1 800 000 J

**(b)** Work out the mass of the vehicle. **[3 marks]**

$$m = \frac{E_k}{\frac{1}{2}v^2} = \frac{200\,000}{0.5 \times 20^2} = 1000\text{ kg}$$

**(c)** Work out how fast the vehicle is moving if it has 12 500 J of kinetic energy. **[3 marks]**

$$v = \sqrt{\frac{E_k}{\frac{1}{2}m}} = \sqrt{\frac{12\,500}{0.5 \times 1000}} = \sqrt{25} = 5\text{ m/s}$$

**(d)** When fully loaded with passengers, the vehicle requires more fuel to move around. Explain why. **[3 marks]**

It will have greater mass, so a higher kinetic energy (for the same speeds). At higher masses, the engine has to do more work to reach the same speed. Chemical energy from the fuel is transferred to kinetic energy, so the increase in energy means more fuel used.

## Energy transfers

If you do 500 J of work to move something you give it 500 J of kinetic energy. It will also take 500 J of work to stop it from moving. If it stops due to friction then it has done 500 J of work against friction.

**Figure 1** Moving a trolley

## Exam-style practice — Grade 8

1. **(a)** Calculate the kinetic energy of a 1200 kg car travelling at 20 m/s. **[2 marks]**
   **(b)** Determine how much work the brakes will have to do to stop the car. **[1 mark]**
2. A car and a van are driving on a straight road. The van has twice the mass of the car, but the car travels at twice the speed. Compare their kinetic energies. **[2 marks]**
3. **(a)** Calculate the mass of a horse with 12 000 J of kinetic energy travelling at 8 m/s. **[2 marks]**
   **(b)** Determine how fast the horse is travelling if it has 17 000 J of kinetic energy. **[2 marks]**

# Energy in a spring

When a spring is stretched or compressed, it stores energy, which is known as elastic potential energy (e.p.e.). You need to be able to calculate this, given the spring constant and extension. Anything that can be elastically deformed stores this kind of energy.

## 2 Stored energy

e.p.e. (J) = 0.5 × spring constant (N/m) × (extension)$^2$ (m)

$E_e = \frac{1}{2}ke^2$

This equation only works if the **limit of proportionality** has not been reached. If the spring becomes inelastically deformed, the energy is used to change its shape and not stored as elastic potential energy.

## 2 Key equations

**Finding the spring constant**

$$k = \frac{E_e}{\frac{1}{2}e^2}$$

**Finding extension**

rearrange for $e^2$ first:

$$e^2 = \frac{E_e}{\frac{1}{2}k}$$

then square root both sides:

$$e = \sqrt{\frac{E_e}{\frac{1}{2}k}}$$

## 10 Worked example — Grade 8

Eve pulls back an elastic band to catapult a piece of plastic. The elastic band acts like a spring.

**(a)** Describe the energy change as the elastic band is pulled back and then released. **[3 marks]**

Chemical energy in the muscles converts to elastic potential energy in the elastic band, then to kinetic energy as it is released.

**(b)** Eve pulls the elastic band back 49 cm, storing 72 J of elastic potential energy. Calculate the spring constant. **[3 marks]**

$$k = \frac{E_e}{\frac{1}{2}e^2} = \frac{72}{0.5 \times (0.49)^2} = 600 \text{ N/m}$$

**(c)** She then pulls the elastic band back twice as far. Work out how much energy is stored as elastic potential energy. **[1 mark]**

72 × 4 = 288 J

Elastic potential energy is always released as kinetic energy.

Check all units and make sure you convert them to m, J and N/m. 49 cm = 0.49 m

Make sure you are using brackets for the bottom of the fraction and only square the extension. Make sure you can get this answer on your calculator.

**Maths skills**

The elastic potential energy depends on extension$^2$. If the extension is twice as large, the energy stored will be $2^2 = 4$ times larger.

## 10 Exam-style practice — Grade 7

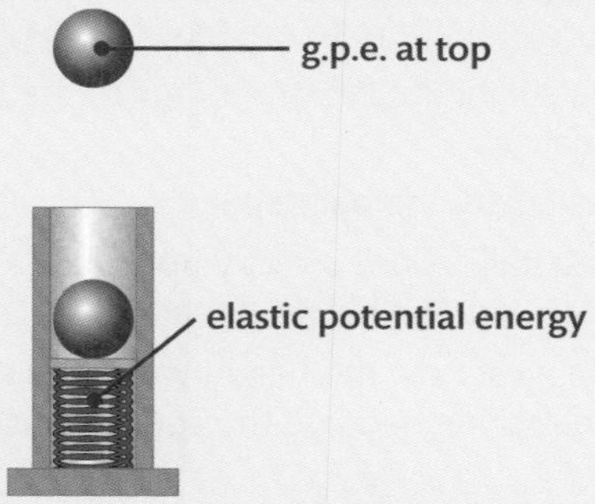


**Figure 1** The stored energy of the spring is released as kinetic energy of the ball and converts to gravitational potential energy of the ball.

**(a)** Calculate the energy stored by the spring in **Figure 1** if it has a spring constant of 60 N/m and is compressed by 20 cm. **[2 marks]**

**(b)** State how much gravitational energy the ball in **Figure 1** will have at its highest point. **[1 mark]**

**(c)** The ball needs to be fired to a much greater height. Describe how this could be done in as many ways as possible. **[3 marks]**

# Using energy equations

In your exam, you will need to be able to recall and apply energy equations.

## Worked example — Grade 8

**1** A slow-moving train has 31 000 J of kinetic energy and bumps into a buffer. The buffer contains a spring with spring constant of 1 300 000 N/m. Work out how much the spring compresses before the train is stopped. **[3 marks]**

> First look at what the energy change would be. In this case it would be kinetic to elastic potential in the buffer's spring.

> Think about the equations you know that might be related, for instance:
> $E_p = \frac{1}{2}ke^2$   $E_k = \frac{1}{2}mv^2$

$E_e = \frac{1}{2}ke^2$

The elastic potential energy is the same as the kinetic energy so:

$$e = \sqrt{\frac{E_e}{\frac{1}{2}k}} = \sqrt{\frac{31000}{\frac{1}{2} \times 1300\,000}} = 0.22\text{ m}$$

> You were given kinetic energy, but you know all this energy transfers to elastic potential energy, so you can use the elastic potential equation.

**2** A 0.3 kg ball is dropped 2.5 m.

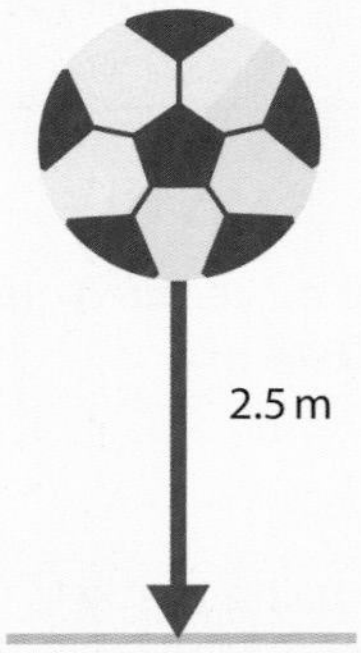


**(a)** Find its gravitational potential energy before it is dropped. ($g$ = 9.8 N/kg) **[2 marks]**

$E_e = mgh = 0.3 \times 9.8 \times 2.5 = 7.35\text{ J}$

**(b)** Calculate the speed at which it will hit the floor. **[3 marks]**

> You know that the gravitational energy will convert to kinetic energy as it falls and that the amount of kinetic energy it has when it hits the floor will be equal to the gravitational potential energy it had when it was dropped.

Rearrange $E_k = \frac{1}{2}mv^2$ for speed, $v$:

$$v = \sqrt{\frac{E_k}{\frac{1}{2}m}} = \sqrt{\frac{7.35}{0.5 \times 0.3}} = \sqrt{49} = 7.0\text{ m/s}$$

> Use your previous answer for the kinetic energy in this equation.

**3** A ball is thrown upwards and reaches 3 m. Using ideas about energy, explain what would happen if it was thrown up at twice the speed.

When it is thrown, it has kinetic energy which changes to gravitational potential energy.

$E_k = \frac{1}{2}mv^2$ so if the speed is doubled, the kinetic energy will be four times greater.

As $E_p = mgh$, if the energy is four times greater it will go four times as high.

## Exam focus

In the exam, you should use equations to show relationships between numbers, even if you are not working anything out.

## Exam-style practice — Grade 8

**1** A brick has 200 J of gravitational potential energy when dropped. ($g$ = 9.8 N/kg)

**(a)** State how much kinetic energy the brick has when it hits the floor. **[2 marks]**

**(b)** Suggest why the brick might have less kinetic energy than this in reality. **[1 mark]**

**2** A spring of spring constant 180 N/m is compressed 20 cm to fire a ball of mass 0.15 kg.

**(a)** Calculate the kinetic energy of the ball when released. **[2 marks]**

**(b)** Calculate the ball's speed. **[2 marks]**

**(c)** The ball is fired directly upwards. Calculate the height it reaches. **[2 marks]**

**(d)** Suggest how the height would be different if the spring had half the spring constant. **[2 marks]**

**(e)** Describe how the height would change if the original spring was compressed twice as much. **[2 marks]**

# Power

Power is a measure of the rate of energy transfer. It tells you how much energy is transferred per second. You need to how to calculate power using two different equations.

## 2 Calculating power

You can calculate power with the equation:

$$\text{power (W)} = \frac{\text{energy transfered (J)}}{\text{time (s)}} \quad P = \frac{E}{t}$$

or in terms of work done:

$$\text{power (W)} = \frac{\text{work done (J)}}{\text{time (s)}} \quad P = \frac{W}{t}$$

Power is the **rate** of energy transfer. It measures how quickly energy changes or transfers.

A power of 1 watt means 1 joule is being transferred every second. A 1000 W heater will transfer 1000 J of electrical energy into heat and waste energy every second.

## 5 Worked example — Grade 7

An electric heater has a power of 2 kW.

**(a)** It takes 20 minutes to heat a room from 5° C to 20 °C. How much energy is required to heat the room? **[2 marks]**

$E = P \times t$

$2000 \times 1200 = 2\,400\,000$ J

**(b)** Give your answer in standard form. **[1 mark]**

$2.4 \times 10^6$ J

**(c)** A back up heater has a power of 500 W. How many times longer would it take this heater to heat the same room from 5 °C to 20 °C, assuming no heat is lost? **[1 mark]**

4 times longer.

Watch the units. Electrical appliances will often have powers measured in kW. Remember 1 kW = 1000 W.
The time needs to be in seconds; 1 min = 60 s.

Energies can get very large so you must be prepared to use standard form. Make sure you know how to put standard form into your calculator and how read it.

**Exam focus**

Notice that the question did not ask for the *time*, it asked 'how many *times longer*'.

If it had asked for time, the answer would be 80 minutes. Make sure you read questions very carefully.

As the power is four times smaller, it will take four times longer to heat the room.

## 5 Units

$$\text{power (W)} = \frac{\text{energy transferred (J)}}{\text{time (s)}} = \frac{\text{work (J)}}{\text{time (s)}}$$

so the unit for power, watts, is the same as joules per second or $1\text{ W} = 1\frac{\text{J}}{\text{s}}$

Many appliances have large powers which are measured in kilowatts. 1 kW = 1000 W

Likewise for energy: 1 kJ = 1000 J

If you use kilojoules in the equation, the power will be in kilowatts. The time must still be in seconds.

## 10 Exam-style practice — Grade 8

1 **(a)** A motor transfers 4800 J of electrical energy in one minute. Calculate its power. **[2 marks]**

**(b)** The motor only transfers 2160 J of the electrical energy into kinetic energy. Calculate the rate of kinetic energy production. **[2 marks]**

2 **(a)** An athlete lifts herself 40 times in 90 s. If each lift takes 30 J of work, calculate her useful power output. **[2 marks]**

**(b)** Assuming she keeps a constant rate, calculate how much work the athlete would do if she did lifts for 10 minutes. **[2 marks]**

3 As a cup of coffee cools down, the rate of energy loss decreases. If the heat loss was measured as power, describe the relationship between power output and temperature. **[2 marks]**

Made a start — Feeling confident — Exam ready

# Renewable energy resources

Renewable energy resources provide alternative sources of energy that will not run out or are easy to replace. They are used for heating, transport, or to generate electricity. You need to know the advantages and disadvantages of renewable energy resources.

## 15 Advantages and disadvantages of renewable resources

| Renewable resource | Advantages | Disadvantages |
|---|---|---|
| **Sun** – can directly warm buildings or sunlight can be used to generate electricity using solar panels | free energy once installed<br>low maintenance costs (no moving parts)<br>works anywhere | only works when the sun shines<br>low power output |
| **Geothermal** – electricity is generated using heat from hot rocks underground | reliable<br>high power output<br>free energy | only works in certain places<br>free energy<br>expensive to drill |
| **Biofuels** – fuel for transport or electricity is made from vegetable oil, alcohol, wood, methane or waste | reliable<br>high power output | fuel crops can drive up the cost of food<br>environmental impact if forests cleared to make room for crops |
| **Wind** – wind turbines generate electricity | can be placed in isolated locations<br>free energy once installed, but some maintenance costs | danger to birds<br>noisy<br>spoil landscape<br>only work when it is windy<br>cannot be used in storms |
| **Hydro-electricity** – water movement rotates turbines to generate electricity | reliable<br>high power output<br>small waterwheels work in some isolated locations<br>free energy once installed, but some maintenance costs | building dams can flood valleys, which destroys habitats |
| **Tides** – the daily movement of the ocean is used to generate electricity | reliable<br>high power output<br>free energy once installed, but has maintenance costs | flooding river estuaries can destroy habitats |
| **Waves** – ocean waves turn turbines to generate electricity | free energy once installed | only works when there are waves<br>dangerous to maintain |

## 5 Worked example — Grade 7

An Arctic scientific base wants to power their camp using only solar cells. Give the advantages and disadvantages of this idea. **[5 marks]**

*It is a good idea because solar cells are portable so they are easily moved and can be set up anywhere. It might not work as they will only be able to provide electricity during the day and only when it is sunny; they would not produce electricity at any other time. The power outputs are quite low.*

## 10 Exam-style practice — Grade 6

1. Sugar cane is worth more as ethanol for fuel than as food. Explain why this could cause problems. **[2 marks]**
2. Discuss the reliability of each power source. **[3 marks]**
3. Give some examples of biofuels. Evaluate their environmental impact. **[4 marks]**

# Non-renewable energy resources

Non-renewable energy resources, such as fossil fuels and nuclear power (nuclear energy from atoms), are used to generate electricity used for heating and to power transport. You need to know the advantages and disadvantages of non-renewable energy resources.

## Non-renewable resources

People use fossil fuels directly by:

- burning coal, oil or natural gas to heat their homes or cook food
- using petrol or diesel in their cars.

People use fossil fuels or nuclear power indirectly when using electricity. The majority of electricity in the UK is generated by burning fossil fuels, mainly natural gas.

**Figure 1** Nuclear power is relatively clean but the nuclear waste has to be disposed of correctly.

## Three issues

1. If non-renewable energy resources run out, people will have to find other ways to produce energy.
2. Oil has many other uses, such as producing plastics. If oil runs out, people would have to find alternatives for these other uses.
3. Resources will become more expensive as they begin to run out.

## Worked example — Grade 7

Suggest whether or not using an electric car is more environmentally friendly than using a petrol or diesel car. **[2 marks]**

An electric car still needs to source its electricity from somewhere. If this is from a non-renewable source then it will still be responsible for producing greenhouse gases and smoke, but it will move it away from the source. This can reduce pollution in busy city centres.

## Comparing nuclear and fossil fuels

| | Nuclear power | Fossil fuels |
|---|---|---|
| **Advantages** | • Other than steam, no gases are emitted. There is no effect on global warming or health.<br>• Small amounts of fuel produce large amounts of energy. | • The fuels are relatively low cost.<br>• Fossil fuel power stations can be started up very quickly (especially gas). It is easy to adapt to changing power demands. |
| **Disadvantages** | • The nuclear waste stays radioactive for thousands of years and has to be safely stored.<br>• Transport of radioactive fuel and waste is dangerous and costly.<br>• Nuclear power plants are costly to decommission.<br>• Accidents can release radioactive substances into the environment.<br>• Nuclear power stations take a very long time to start up and shut down. | • Carbon dioxide, a greenhouse gas, is produced. Carbon dioxide contributes to global warming.<br>• Sulfur dioxide and smoke can cause breathing problems.<br>• A large amount of fuel needs to be transported with coal. |

## Exam-style practice — Grade 7

1. Compare the advantages and disadvantages of nuclear and coal-fired power stations. **[4 marks]**
2. The UK is moving to using more renewable rather than non-renewable resources. Suggest reasons for this trend. **[4 marks]**
3. Scientific studies have proven that using renewable resources is better for the environment. Explain why countries have not switched to using renewable resources for all their power needs. **[4 marks]**

Made a start / Feeling confident / Exam ready

# Density

You need to know how to calculate density, the amount of mass per unit volume.

## 2 Calculating density

Density is a property of a substance. You can work out the density of a substance using the equation:

$$\text{density (kg/m}^3\text{)} = \frac{\text{mass (kg)}}{\text{volume (m}^3\text{)}}$$

$$\rho = \frac{m}{V}$$

Having a higher density does not mean something will be heavier or have a larger mass. The mass also depends on the volume.

## 5 Worked example — Grade 7

**Figure 1** shows a copper cube with sides 25 cm. The mass of the cube is 140 kg.

**Figure 1** A copper cube

**(a)** Calculate the volume of the cube in m³. **[2 marks]**

25 cm = 0.25 m

$V = 0.25\text{ m} \times 0.25\text{ m} \times 0.25\text{ m} = 0.0156\text{ m}^3$

**(b)** Calculate the density of copper. **[2 marks]**

$\rho = \frac{m}{V} = \frac{140}{0.0156} = 8974\text{ kg/m}^3$

**(c)** Calculate the volume of a copper cube of mass 2.2 kg. **[2 marks]**

$V = \frac{m}{\rho} = \frac{2.2}{8794} = 2.5 \times 10^{-4}\text{ m}^3$ (= 0.00025 m³)

Convert the lengths to metres before working out the volume; it is more complicated to do so later.

The volume of a cube is the (length of a side)³.

**Maths skills**

You can calculate the volume of a cuboid using $V = abc$

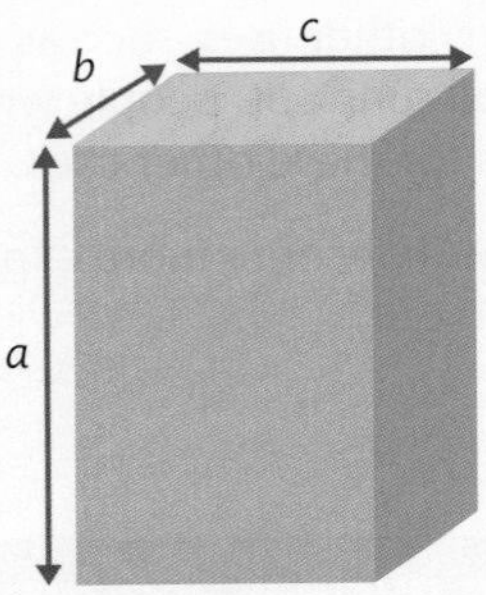


**Figure 2** Cuboid with sides a, b and c

As the density is a property of the material, any size piece of copper will have the same density.

Small volumes measured in m³ will be very small numbers and are best expressed in standard form. Make sure you can enter standard form into your calculator and read it off.

## 10 Exam-style practice — Grade 7

**1** A bucket contains twice as much water as a bottle. Compare the density, volume and mass of the water in the bucket with the water in the bottle. **[2 marks]**

**2** **(a)** The density of water is 1000 kg/m³. An object will float in water if its density is lower than water. State which of these objects will float in water. **[2 marks]**

| Object | apple | steel box | plastic | human |
|---|---|---|---|---|
| Mass (kg) | 0.074 | 1.3 | 0.5 | 70 |
| Volume (m³) | $1.04 \times 10^{-4}$ | $2 \times 10^{-3}$ | $4.1 \times 10^{-4}$ | 0.071 |

**(b)** Find the mass of an apple with volume $1.5 \times 10^{-4}\text{ m}^3$. **[2 marks]**

# Density of materials

You need to know how to accurately measure the mass and volume of an object so that you can calculate its density.

## Measuring density

$$\text{density (kg/m}^3) = \frac{\text{mass (kg)}}{\text{volume (m}^3)}$$

Go to page 220 to practise calculating density.

The mass of the object can be found using a digital balance. Using a mass balance with a higher level of precision will improve the precision of the answer.

Measuring the volume of an object depends on the size and shape of the object.

## Density of irregular shapes

You can find the volume by measuring the volume of water that the shape will displace.

1. Fill the displacement can to the spout.
2. Place the object in the can.
3. Collect the water that runs off in a measuring cylinder.

**Figure 1** Apparatus

## Measuring objects

To get an accurate volume, you need to measure the dimensions of a regular object to as high a precision as possible.

The size of a large object can be measured using a ruler or tape measure. Smaller objects can be measured using Vernier callipers. They will measure to 0.01 mm.

volume of a cuboid = length × width × depth

Remember to convert the lengths to metres to get the volume in $m^3$.

## Density of liquid

1. Measure the volume of liquid using a measuring cylinder.
2. Find the mass of the liquid by measuring the mass of the empty measuring cylinder on a digital balance. Make sure the measuring cylinder is completely dry.
3. Measure the mass of the measuring cylinder again with the liquid inside. The mass of the liquid will be the difference between the two measurements.

## Reducing errors

- Suspend the object from a piece of string so it can be lowered carefully into the water to avoid making a splash.
- Stand the measuring cylinder on a flat surface.
- Make sure your eyes are at the same level as the water.
- Read the level of the water, ignoring the meniscus created at the edge.

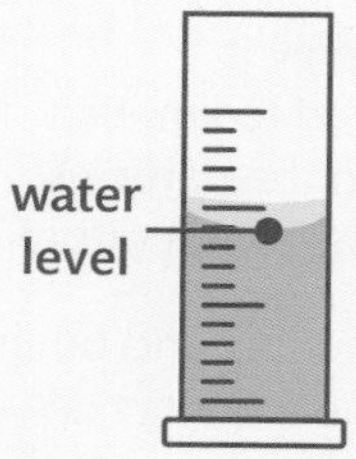


**Figure 2** Taking a reading from a measuring cylinder

## Worked example — Grade 8

A student finds the mass of a liquid. They measure the mass of the measuring cylinder full of liquid. They then empty the measuring cylinder and measure the mass again to find the difference. Suggest a problem with this method. **[2 marks]**

*There may be some liquid left over in the measuring cylinder when they weigh it 'empty'. It would be better to weigh the cylinder first while it is dry, or make sure it is thoroughly dry once emptied.*

## Exam-style practice — Grade 8

**(a)** Give the methods you would use to find the most accurate density of a rock, a metal cube and a sample of oil. **[3 marks]**

**(b)** For each method in (a), suggest **one** thing you could do to reduce the errors in the method. **[3 marks]**

# State changes

You need to know about the three states of matter: solid, liquid and gas.

## 5 States and state changes

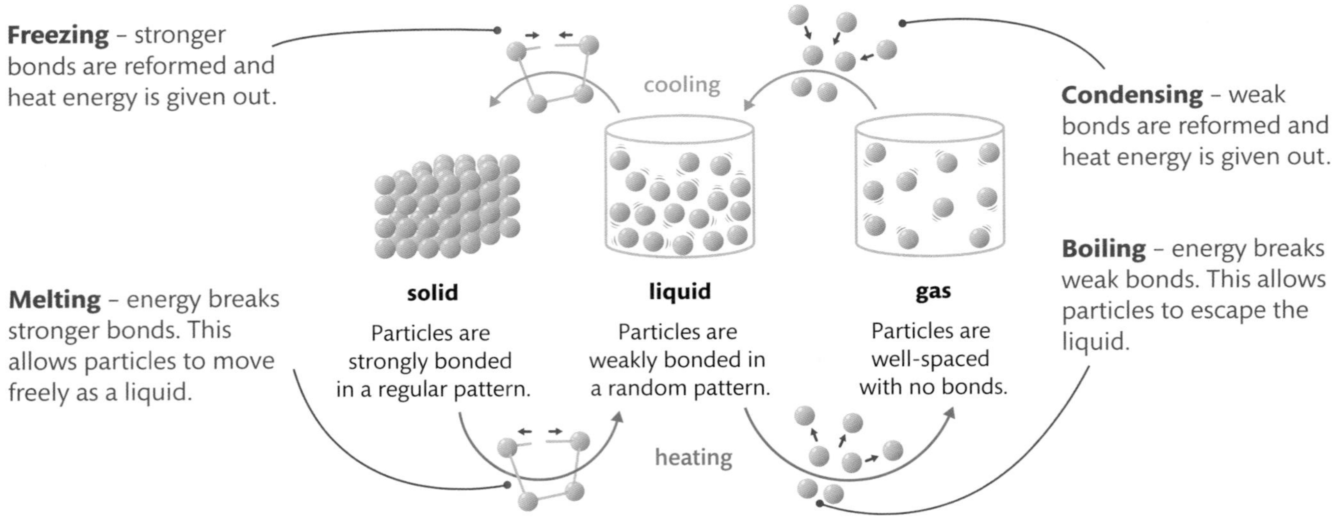


**Melting** – energy breaks stronger bonds. This allows particles to move freely as a liquid.

Particles are strongly bonded in a regular pattern.

Particles are weakly bonded in a random pattern.

Particles are well-spaced with no bonds.
**Boiling** – energy breaks weak bonds. This allows particles to escape the liquid.

**Figure 1** The particle model

## 2 State changes: key facts

- The temperature a substance both melts and freezes at is called the **melting point**.
- The temperature a substance both condenses and boils at is called the **boiling point**.
- Changes of state are physical and reversible.
- Particles in a solid are arranged more closely than in a liquid, so solids tend to have higher density.
- Particles in gases are very far apart, so gases have very low densities.
- The properties of a substance may change when it changes state. Its density and volume may alter, but the mass will stay the same. This is because the number of particles does not change.

## 5 Heating and cooling curves

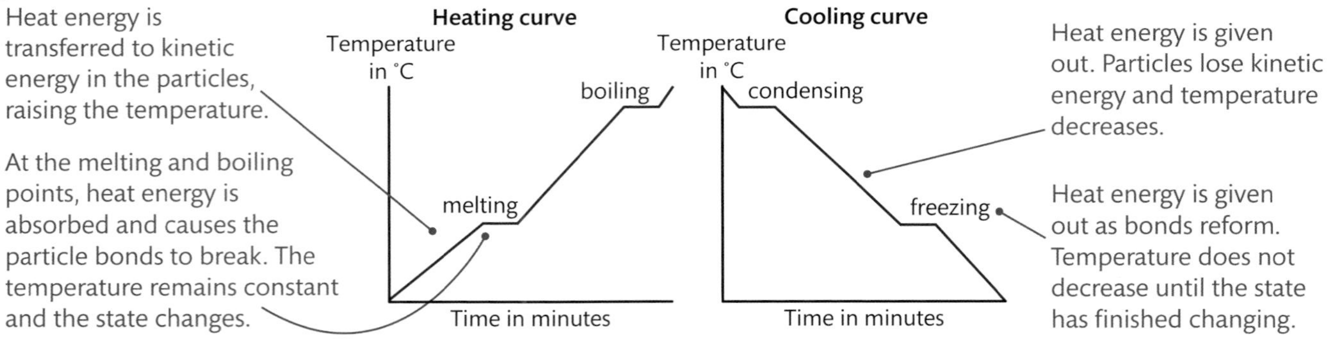

Heat energy is transferred to kinetic energy in the particles, raising the temperature.
At the melting and boiling points, heat energy is absorbed and causes the particle bonds to break. The temperature remains constant and the state changes.
Heating curve
Temperature in °C
boiling
melting
Time in minutes
Cooling curve
Temperature in °C
condensing
freezing
Time in minutes
Heat energy is given out. Particles lose kinetic energy and temperature decreases.
Heat energy is given out as bonds reform. Temperature does not decrease until the state has finished changing.

## 15 Exam-style practice — Grade 8

1. Water is heated to its boiling point of 100 °C. The water is heated further but the temperature stays constant. Explain what is happening to the energy. When will the temperature increase again? **[2 marks]**
2. Describe the motion of particles in a solid, a liquid and a gas. **[5 marks]**
3. An ice cube is placed in a glass of water. Describe the change in the arrangement of particles in both the ice and the water. **[4 marks]**

# Specific heat capacity

The specific heat capacity, *c*, is the energy needed to change the temperature of 1 kg of a substance by 1 °C. It is measured in joules per kilogram per degree Celsius.

## 5 Calculating specific heat capacity

change in thermal energy (J) = mass (kg) × specific heat capacity (J/kg°C) × temperature change (°C)

$\Delta E = mc\Delta\theta$

$\Delta$ (delta) means 'change in' and $\theta$ (theta) means temperature.

The higher or lower the specific heat capacity, the more energy it takes to warm up the same mass of substance.

Energy is stored in a system as internal energy, which is the total of all the kinetic and potential energy of the particles.

**Figure 1** Arrangement and movement of particles in a solid, liquid and a gas

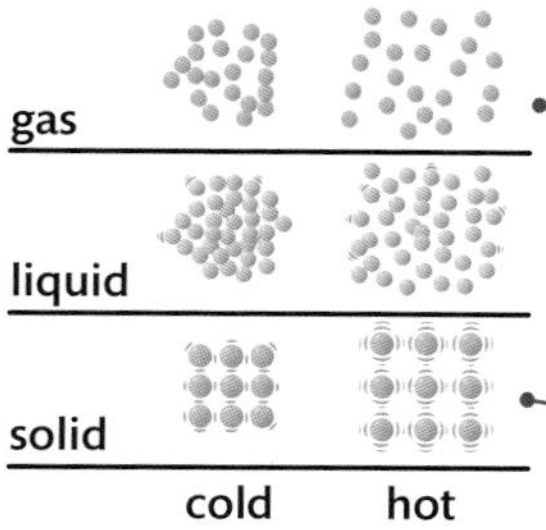


A higher temperature means the particles in a substance have greater kinetic energy. The particles in a solid will move around faster, or vibrate faster.

Heat energy added to a system is either used to break bonds and change the state or increase the energy of the particles and raise the temperature.

## 10 Worked example — Grade 7

| Liquid | Melting point (°C) | Boiling point (°C) | Specific heat capacity as a liquid (J/kg°C) |
|---|---|---|---|
| A | 15 | 80 | 200 |
| B | 0 | 100 | 4200 |
| C | −12 | 15 | 2150 |

Look carefully at the headings in a table of data so you are familiar with all the information it gives before you read the question.

**(a)** The three liquids in the table are heated by a 1 kW heater. Identify which liquid's temperature would rise most quickly. Explain why. **[3 marks]**

Liquid A, it has the lowest specific heat capacity so it takes the least energy to warm up.

Liquid A has the lowest specific heat capacity. This means it takes very little energy to increase the temperature, so it would warm up the fastest.

**(b)** 3 kg of liquid A is heated from 20 °C to boiling point. Work out how much energy it would take. **[2 marks]**

$\Delta E = mc\Delta\theta = 3 \times 200 \times 60 = 36000$ J

Work out the temperature change 20–80 °C first. Use the equation.

**(c)** Suggest which liquid would be best used in a central heating system? Give **two** reasons for your choice. **[2 marks]**

Liquid B. It has the highest specific heat capacity and is unlikely to reach its boiling point.

The one with the highest specific heat capacity would be best, as it will hold (and therefore give out) more heat energy. However, it also needs to still be a liquid at temperatures up to approximately 60 °C.

## 2 Finding units

Use this equation to help you remember the unit for specific heat capacity:

$$c = \frac{\Delta E}{m\Delta\theta} \rightarrow \frac{\text{J}}{\text{kg °C}} = \text{J/kg°C}$$

## 5 Exam-style practice — Grade 7

**1** 2 kg of liquid B was heated with 84 000 J of heat energy. Calculate the end temperature if it was heated from:
**(a)** 20 °C **(b)** 80 °C. **[3 marks]**

**2** Give **two** reasons why liquid A would be unsuitable as coolant liquid in a freezer. **[2 marks]**

Page 223 LINKS

# Specific heat capacity

You need to know how to investigate ways to determine the specific heat capacity of materials. This practical investigates two methods of finding a material's specific heat capacity: by electrical heating, or by placing in hot water.

## 5 Experiment 1: An electric heater

1. Measure the start temperature of 1 litre of water or 1 kilogram of metal.
2. Heat the water or metal for approximately 5 minutes (300 seconds).
3. Measure the highest temperature reached after the heater is switched off.

The energy input = power rating of heater × time

$$c\ (\text{J/kg °C}) = \frac{\text{energy (J)}}{\text{mass (kg)} \times \text{temperature change (°C)}}$$

This method works well for solid blocks or liquids. It does not work as well for insulating solids.

*c* stands for 'specific heat capacity'.

## 5 Worked example Grade 7

Describe the safety factors you must consider in each method described to measure specific heat capacity for a substance. **[4 marks]**

Finding specific heat capacity using an electric heater:

- Do not touch the heating element directly.
- Check equipment has cooled before moving it after the experiment.
- If heating water, take care when moving the container of hot water.
- Do not overfill the container, wait until cooled before moving it, or keep the temperature lower.
- Mop up any spills immediately and keep the water away from electrical equipment (apart from the heater).
- Do not lean the thermometer in a beaker of water in case it pulls it over.

Using warm water to find the specific heat capacity of an object:

- All the above apply.
- Place the object gently into the water to avoid splashing or breaking the beaker.
- Move the metal using tongs or attach a piece of string to avoid having to touch it and make it easier to remove it from the hot water.

## 5 Reducing errors

- Measure the temperature of water in the middle, as hot water rises to the top. Make sure not to touch the heater.
- Insulate the block or water. A lid on the water also reduces energy and mass loss by evaporation.
- Check the actual mass of the 1 kg block with a digital balance. Take the mass of water before and after and calculate an average.
- Limit heat loss to the environment by keeping heating time short.
- Reduce the initial temperature of the block to allow a greater increase in temperature. A temperature change of only a few degrees makes the result very inaccurate.
- The hotter the block gets the more energy it will lose to the environment.

These last two points work against each other, but it is acceptable to mention them both if asked in the exam.

## 5 Experiment 2: Warm water

An alternative method involves finding the specific heat capacity of a metal by adding it to warm water.

- Measure the starting temperature of 1 kg of room temperature metal and 1 L of warm water.
- Place the metal into the warm water. Heat energy flows from the water to the metal, cooling the water until both the metal and the water reach the same temperature.
- Measure the temperature of the metal and the water.

energy lost by water = $m_{water}\, c_{water}\, \Delta T_{water}$

$$c_{metal}\ (\text{J/kg °C}) = \frac{\text{energy lost by water (J)}}{\text{mass of metal (kg)} \times \text{temperature change (°C)}}$$

The temperature change of the metal is the difference between room temperature and final temperature of the water.

## 10 Exam-style practice Grade 7

1. Suggest why you do not take the end temperature of the first experiment at 5 minutes. **[2 marks]**
2. Explain why these experiments would be less effective if the material was a poor conductor of heat. **[3 marks]**
3. Identify actions that could be taken to minimise the errors in Experiment 2 above. **[3 marks]**

# Specific latent heat

Specific latent heat, *L*, is the energy required to change the state of 1 kg of a substance with no change in temperature.

## Calculating *L*

energy for a change of state = mass × specific latent heat
(J) (kg) (J/kg)

$E = mL$

The **specific latent heat of fusion** is the energy required to melt or freeze a substance.

The **specific latent heat of vaporisation** is the energy required to condense or evaporate a substance.

## Latent heat and particles

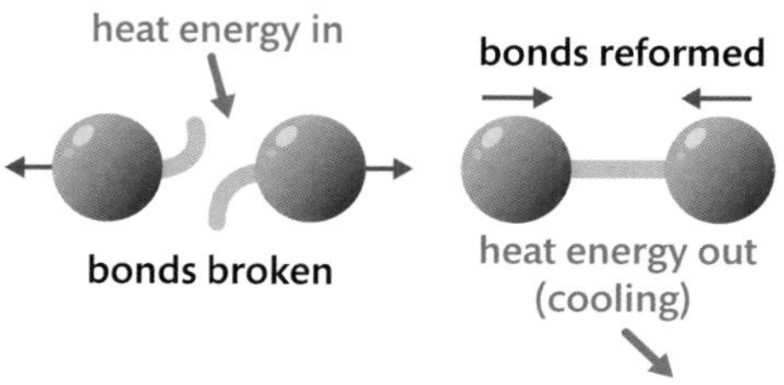


**Figure 1** When a substance changes state, energy is used to break bonds or is given out as the bonds reform.

As something cools down, heat energy is released from it. When it condenses or freezes, the temperature stays constant because the heat energy is transferred to form bonds between the particles.

## Worked example — Grade 7

120 kg of metal is heated to its melting point.

**(a)** The melting point of the metal is 1500 °C. Explain why the temperature will not increase until all of the metal has melted. **[3 marks]**

The heat energy is used to break bonds between metal atoms and change their state. The temperature will increase when the energy is used to increase the kinetic energy of the metal atoms. This will not happen until all the bonds have broken and all the metal is liquid.

> The temperature of any substance will stay constant while it changes state, whether it is being heated or cooled.

**(b)** If it takes 54 000 J of energy to melt the metal, find the specific latent heat. **[2 marks]**

$$L = \frac{E}{m} = \frac{54\,000}{120} = 450\text{ J/kg}$$

> **Exam focus**
> The units for specific latent heat are J/kg.
> You can use the equation to help you remember the unit:
> $L = \frac{E\text{ (J)}}{m\text{ (kg)}} \rightarrow \text{J/kg}$

**(c)** Explain why much more energy than this would actually be used while melting the metal. **[2 marks]**

At such a high temperature, a lot of heat energy would be transferred to the surroundings and not all would be used to break bonds in the metal.

**(d)** How much energy would be given out as 120 kg of molten metal turned solid? **[1 mark]**

54 000 J

> Latent heat works in both directions. You have to put 54 000 J in to melt 120 kg of metal. When you freeze 120 kg of metal you will get 54 000 J of energy back out.

## Exam-style practice — Grade 7

**1** Copper has a specific latent heat of 200 J/kg and gold has a specific latent heat of 64 J/kg.

**(a)** Compare the energies required to melt each metal. **[2 marks]**

**(b)** Work out the masses of gold and copper that could be melted with 2500 J of heat energy. **[3 marks]**

**2** Water has specific latent heat of fusion of 336 000 J/kg. Calculate how much heat energy will be removed from a drink in order to melt a 50 g ice cube. **[2 marks]**

# Particle motion in gases

Gas molecules are in constant random motion. You need to be able to explain the effect of temperature and type of container on particle motion in gases.

## 2 Heating gases

When a gas is heated, the particles gain kinetic energy. This means they move faster than in liquids and solids. As there are no forces between the particles, they spread out and expand as much as they are able to.

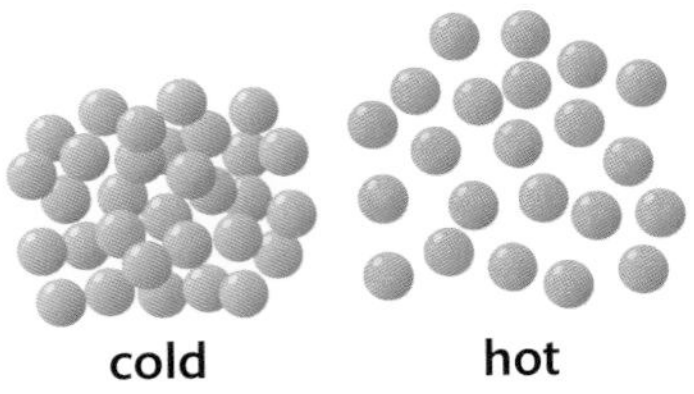


**Figure 1** Heating a gas

## 5 Gas in containers

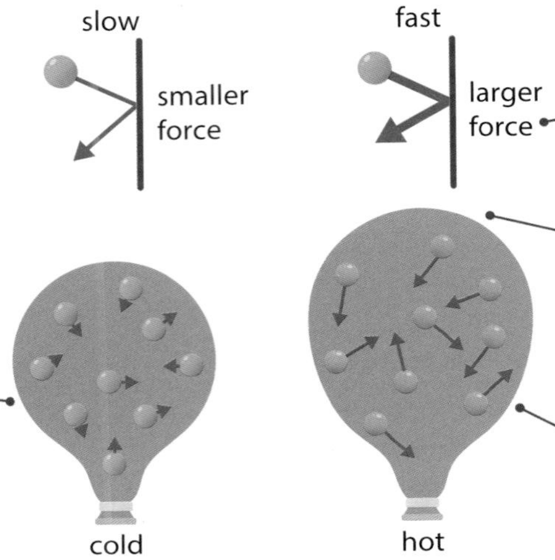

slow
smaller force
fast
larger force
Particles in heated gas have more kinetic energy so move faster.
More frequent and higher-force collisions increase the pressure exerted by the gas, so the balloon expands outwards.
Particles in cooler gases move more slowly and exert lower pressures.
Particles strike the side of balloon with more force.
cold
hot

**Figure 2** A container of gas

## 5 Worked example — Grade 7

Explain how heating the gas in a rigid container will have a different effect on the pressure to heating the gas in the balloon in **Figure 2**. **[3 marks]**

> In balloons, the volume can increase, so the pressure does not increase as much. In a rigid container, the volume stays constant so the pressure has to increase.

*In a rigid container, the pressure will increase because the volume is constant. In a balloon, the volume is allowed to increase so the pressure will stay the same as the gas is heated.*

> The pressure inside the balloon will equal the air pressure outside, so the volume will change while the pressure stays constant. However, there might be a slight increase in pressure as the rubber of the balloon stretches.

## 10 Exam-style practice — Grade 7

1. Explain what happens to the density of a gas that is heated in a balloon. Compare this to the density of a gas heated in a rigid container. **[2 marks]**
2. A container of air is heated and then sealed. When it has cooled it is difficult to remove the lid. Suggest why this might be. **[3 marks]**
3. A student heats up the air in a gas syringe. The volume increases. They say there must be more air in the syringe. Are they correct? If not, explain what has happened. **[3 marks]**

# The structure of an atom

All atoms are made of protons, neutrons and electrons. You need to know the structure of an atom, in terms of electrons, protons and neutrons.

## 10 Structure

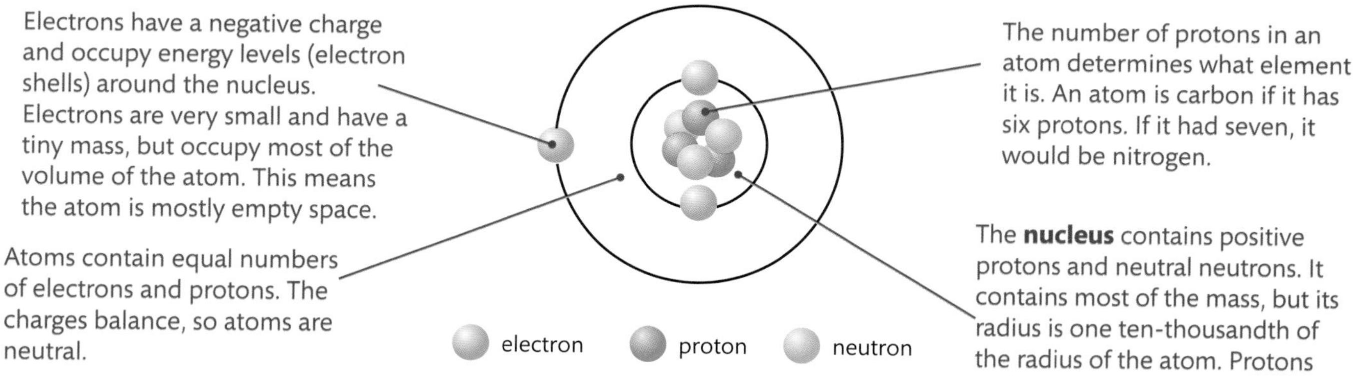

Electrons have a negative charge and occupy energy levels (electron shells) around the nucleus. Electrons are very small and have a tiny mass, but occupy most of the volume of the atom. This means the atom is mostly empty space.
Atoms contain equal numbers of electrons and protons. The charges balance, so atoms are neutral.
The number of protons in an atom determines what element it is. An atom is carbon if it has six protons. If it had seven, it would be nitrogen.
The **nucleus** contains positive protons and neutral neutrons. It contains most of the mass, but its radius is one ten-thousandth of the radius of the atom. Protons and neutrons have similar masses.
electron
proton
neutron

**Figure 1** Atoms are around $1 \times 10^{-10}$ m in radius

## 5 Absorption and emission of electromagnetic radiation

When electrons absorb electromagnetic radiation, they absorb the energy and move to a higher energy level further away from the nucleus.

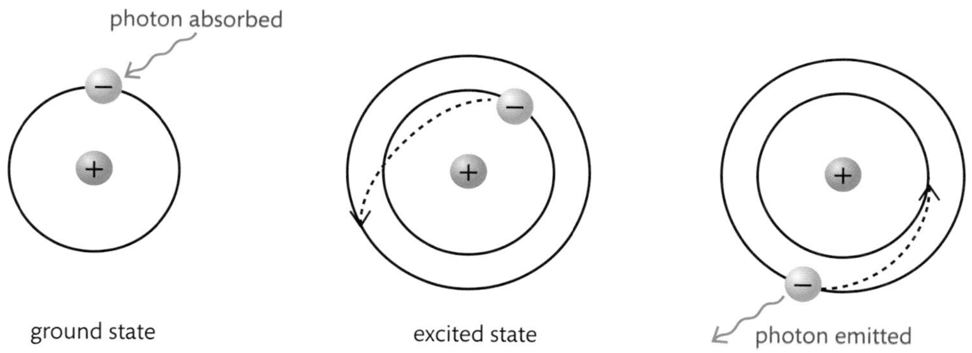


**Figure 2** As the electron drops back down to its ground state, its original energy level, it emits electromagnetic radiation.

## 2 Worked example — Grade 6

An atom is $1 \times 10^{-10}$ m in diameter. Calculate how many atoms would fit across a needle point that is 0.1 mm wide.

**[2 marks]**

$0.1 \div 1000 = 1 \times 10^{-4}$ m

Number of atoms $= 1 \times 10^{-4}$ m $\div 1 \times 10^{-10}$ m
$= 1000000$

## 10 Exam-style practice — Grade 6

1. A magnesium atom has 12 protons. How many electrons does it have? Explain your answer. **[2 marks]**
2. A student says that if you break a magnesium atom in half, you get two smaller magnesium atoms. Is this statement true? Explain your answer. **[3 marks]**
3. State **two** differences between electrons and protons. **[2 marks]**
4. State **two** similarities between protons and neutrons. **[2 marks]**

# Mass number, atomic number and isotopes

Every element has a mass number and an atomic number. You can use these numbers to work out how many protons and neutrons are in an element's nucleus.

## 10 Particles in an atom

number of neutrons = mass number − atomic number

$^{14}_{7}N$ has 7 protons and 7 neutrons (14 − 7). A nitrogen atom has 7 electrons.

$^{7}_{3}Li$ has 3 protons, 3 electrons and 4 neutrons (7 − 3).

$^{19}_{9}F$ has 9 protons, 9 electrons and 10 neutrons (19 − 9).

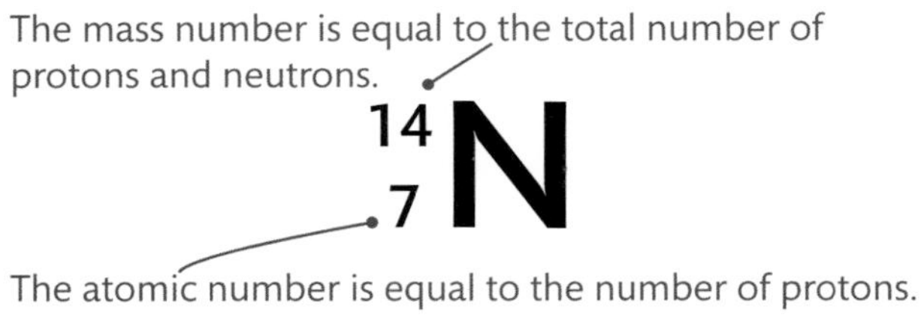

The mass number is equal to the total number of protons and neutrons.
14
7
N
The atomic number is equal to the number of protons.

**Figure 1** An atomic symbol

### Isotopes

**Isotopes** are atoms with the same atomic number (number of protons) but different mass numbers (protons + neutrons). As the number of protons is the same, this means there is a different number of neutrons.

Carbon $^{12}_{6}C$ has six protons and six neutrons. An atom is carbon only if it has six protons. Carbon $^{14}_{6}C$ is an isotope of carbon. It has six protons and eight neutrons. As $^{14}_{6}C$ has six protons, it is still carbon, but it is heavier because of the extra neutrons.

## 5 Ionisation

If an atom loses or gains electrons, it becomes charged. Charged atoms are called **ions**.

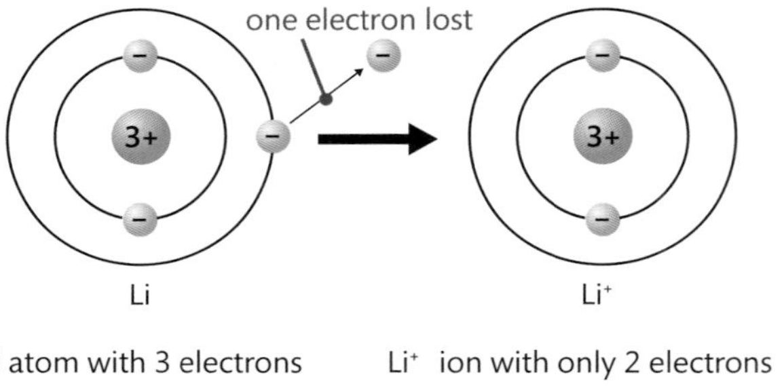


**Figure 2** If an atom loses one or more electrons, it becomes a positive ion.

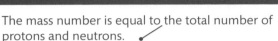

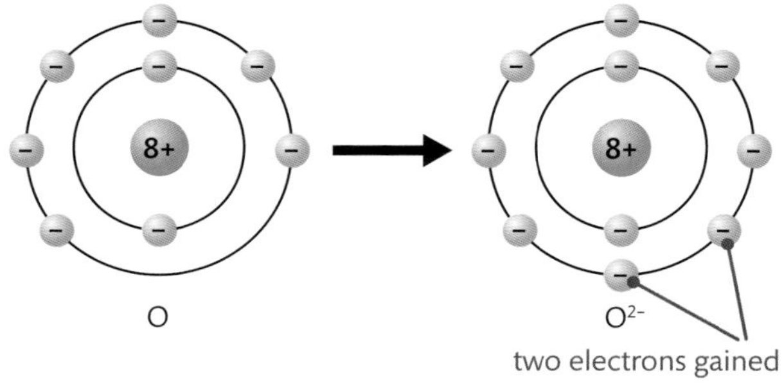


**Figure 3** When an atom gains electrons, it becomes a negative ion.

## 2 Worked example — Grade 6

An ion has 14 protons, 14 neutrons and 12 electrons. State the atomic and mass numbers and the charge on the ion.

**[2 marks]**

Atomic number 14, mass number 28. The neutral atom would have 14 electrons, so it has lost two, resulting in charge 2+.

## 15 Exam-style practice — Grade 6

1. State the number of particles in:
   **(a)** $^{9}_{4}Be$ **[1 mark]** **(b)** $^{7}_{3}Li$ **[1 mark]**
   **(c)** $^{56}_{26}Fe$ **[1 mark]**
2. State the number of electrons in:
   **(a)** $Be^{2+}$ **[1 mark]** **(b)** $Li^{+}$ **[1 mark]**
   **(c)** $Fe^{3+}$. **[1 mark]**
3. The most common form of carbon has six protons, six neutrons and six electrons. State an example of how these numbers can change but the atom can remain a carbon atom. **[2 marks]**

# Development of the atomic model

Scientists' theories about the atom changed as new experimental evidence was discovered. You need to know how the model of the atom has developed over time.

## 15 Developing the model of the atom

1. Before electrons were discovered, it was thought that atoms were tiny spheres that could not be divided into anything else.

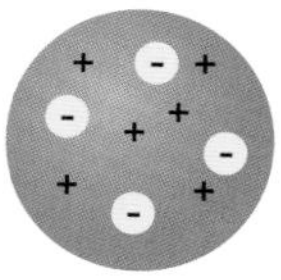

2. The **plum pudding model** was proposed by scientists who thought that the atom was like a positively charged 'pudding', with electrons like 'plums' embedded in it.

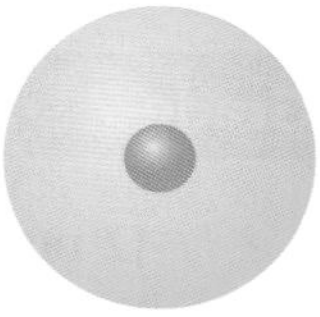

3. Ernest Rutherford tested the plum pudding model by aiming a beam of positively charged alpha particles at a very thin sheet of gold foil (scattering experiment). Some of the alpha particles were repelled by positively charged particles that were concentrated in the centre of the atom (the nucleus). Most alpha particles passed through unaffected, showing that the nucleus was only a very small part of the atom. This evidence gave rise to the **nuclear model**.

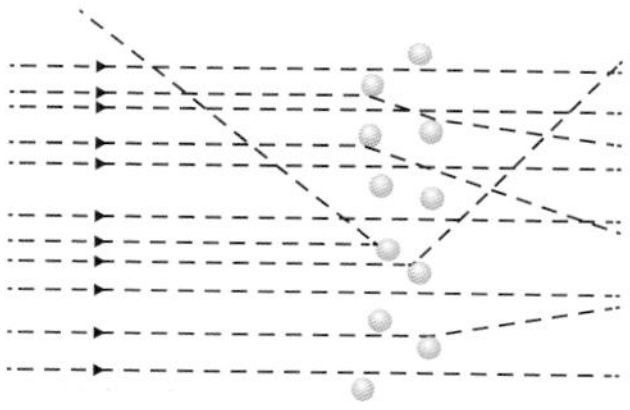

**Rutherford's scattering experiment**

4. Niels Bohr adapted the nuclear model. Using theoretical calculations alongside experimental observations, Bohr suggested that electrons travel in circular orbits around the nucleus. Further research showed that the nucleus was actually composed of smaller particles with equal amounts of positive charge. These became known as protons.

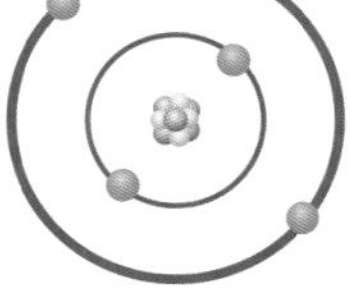

5. Approximately 20 years after the nuclear model became accepted, James Chadwick discovered that neutrons also existed in the nucleus.

## 5 Worked example — Grade 8

Explain how the alpha particle scattering experiment showed that the mass of an atom is concentrated at the centre and that atoms are mostly empty space.

**[2 marks]**

Most of the alpha particles passed straight through without hitting anything, showing that atoms are mostly empty space. Occasionally they were deflected or bounced back, showing they were repelled by the positive nucleus.

## 10 Exam-style practice — Grade 8

1. Describe the plum pudding model of the atom. **[3 marks]**
2. Give the differences between the plum pudding model and the nuclear model. **[2 marks]**
3. Describe how the results of the alpha scattering experiment would have been different if:
   **(a)** the plum pudding model was correct. **[2 marks]**
   **(b)** the nuclear model was correct, but the nucleus was negatively charged. **[2 marks]**
4. A student suggests that the plum pudding model of the atom was wrong and that the nuclear model is correct. Do you agree? Explain your answer. **[3 marks]**

# Radioactive decay and nuclear radiation

Radioactive decay can result in atoms emitting alpha or beta particles, neutrons, or gamma rays.

## 5 Radioactive decay

Radioisotopes are atoms with unstable nuclei. An unstable radioisotope will decay by emitting radiation. Decay is random; there is no way to tell which atom will decay next or when an atom will decay. All types of radiation are emitted from the nucleus of the atom.

### Activity and count rate

The activity is the rate at which atoms in a radioactive source decay. Activity is measured in bequerels (Bq). 10 Bq means 10 decays per second.

The count rate is the number of decays recorded per second by a detector such as a **Geiger-Muller** (G-M) tube.

## 5 Three uses of radiation

1. **Smoke detector**: Alpha radiation cannot penetrate smoke particles so can be used to detect smoke.
2. **Paper mill**: Beta radiation is used to monitor the thickness of paper in a paper mill. If the paper gets thicker, less beta radiation will be able to penetrate. Detectors can monitor the beta intensity to keep the paper a uniform thickness.
3. **Treatment of cancer**: Gamma radiation can pass easily into the body and be directed to kill cancerous cells.

## 2 Worked example — Grade 7

Suggest why the count rate measured by a G-M tube may be different to the activity of the source. **[2 marks]**

*The activity is the number of decays per second in a sample but the count rate is the number of decays detected. The radiation decays might not all go into the detector and they may not all be detected, so the count rate will be less than the activity.*

## 10 Properties of radiation

| Radiation | Particle | Charge | Ionisation power | Penetrative power |
|---|---|---|---|---|
| **Alpha** (α) | 2 protons; 2 neutrons (a helium nucleus) | +2 | high | low |
| **Beta** (β) | fast moving electron | −1 | medium | medium |
| **Gamma** (γ) | electromagnetic wave | 0 | low | high |

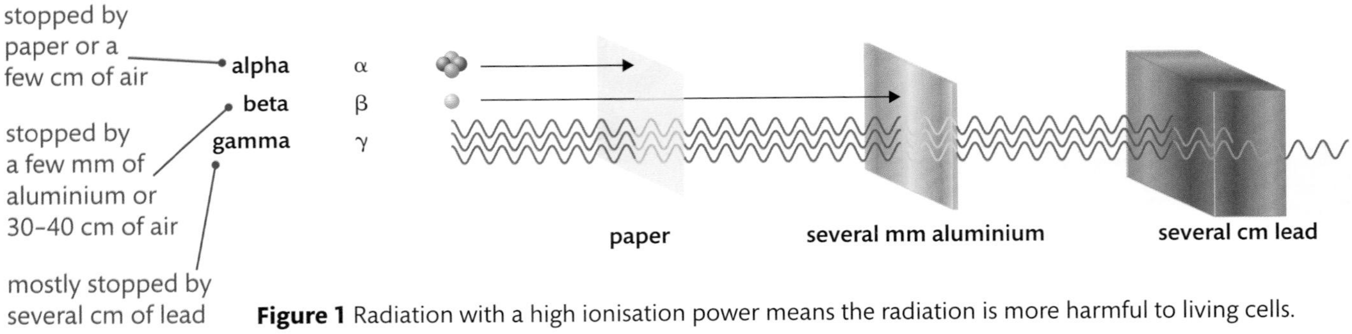


**Figure 1** Radiation with a high ionisation power means the radiation is more harmful to living cells.

## 10 Exam-style practice — Grade 7

1. Explain why alpha radiation has a higher ionisation power than beta or gamma. **[2 marks]**
2. Give a reason why alpha or gamma radiation could not be used to monitor the thickness of paper. **[2 marks]**
3. A tracer is a radioactive source injected into the blood. It can be detected outside the body and used in diagnosis. Suggest which type of radioactive source would be most suitable. **[2 marks]**

# Half-lives

Half-life is a measure of how radioactive a source is. It can be anything from a fraction of a second to many thousands of years. You need to be able to determine a substance's half-life from a graph or table of data.

## 5 Half-life

The half-life of a radioactive source is the time taken for either:

- the **count rate** (activity) to fall to half its initial value *or*
- half the radioactive nuclei in a sample to decay.

Half-life is an average time, resulting from the random nature of radioactive decay.

### Half-life from data

| Time (minutes) | Number of radioactive nuclei |
|---|---|
| 0 | 1000 |
| 2 | 842 |
| 4 | 681 |
| 6 | 540 |
| 8 | 428 |
| 10 | 353 |

The number of nuclei halves to 500 between 6 and 8 minutes. This means the half-life is between 6 and 8 minutes. You can use a graph to find a more accurate answer.

## 5 Worked example — Grade 7

The activity after a nuclear accident is 600 Bq. The area is considered safe when the activity drops under 75 Bq. If the radioactive source has a half-life of 20 years, work out how long this will take. **[4 marks]**

1 half-life → $\frac{1}{2}$ initial value = 300 Bq

2 half-lives → $\frac{1}{4}$ initial value = 150 Bq

3 half-lives → $\frac{1}{8}$ initial value = 75 Bq

3 half-lives is 3 × 20 = 60 years

## 5 Half-life graphs

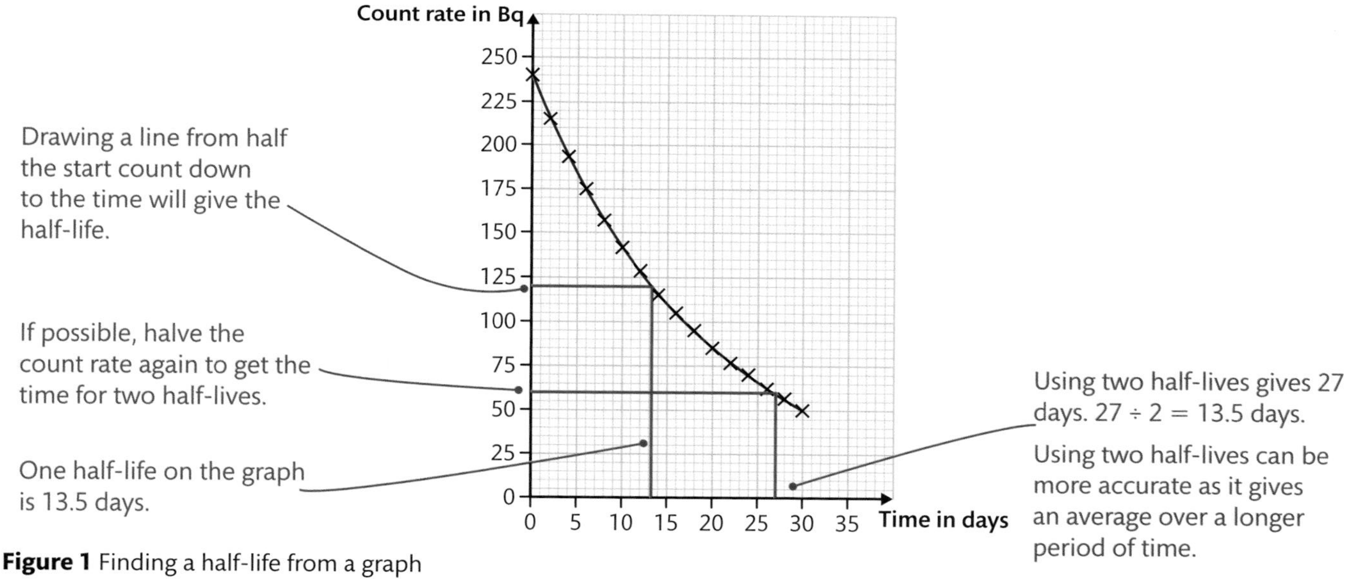

Count rate in Bq
250
225
200
175
150
125
100
75
50
25
0
0
5
10
15
20
25
30
35
Time in days
Drawing a line from half the start count down to the time will give the half-life.
If possible, halve the count rate again to get the time for two half-lives.
One half-life on the graph is 13.5 days.
Using two half-lives gives 27 days. 27 ÷ 2 = 13.5 days.
Using two half-lives can be more accurate as it gives an average over a longer period of time.

**Figure 1** Finding a half-life from a graph

## 10 Exam-style practice — Grade 8

1. Calculate the fraction of a radioactive isotope left in a sample after four half-lives. **[2 marks]**
2. A sample with a half-life of 10 mins has an activity of 45 Bq. If the sample started at 1440 Bq, calculate how old it is. **[2 marks]**
3. The activity of a sample drops from 640 Bq to 160 Bq in 12 years. Calculate its half-life. **[2 marks]**
4. If the half-life of a sample is 3 hours, calculate how long it will take for the activity to drop by a quarter. **[2 marks]**

# Nuclear equations

Nuclear equations for alpha and beta decays are similar to chemical equations, except the elements can change and particles are included. You need to be able to complete nuclear equations for alpha, beta and gamma decay.

## 2 Make-up of radiating particles

Nuclear equations are easier when you know the make-up of the radiating particles. An alpha particle (α) is made from two protons and two neutrons, the same as a helium nucleus. It has an atomic number of two and a mass number of four. You can write this as ${}^{4}_{2}He$ or ${}^{4}_{2}\alpha$. A beta particle (β) is a fast moving electron. It is very small, with a mass number of 0 and an atomic number of −1. You can write this as ${}^{0}_{-1}e$ or ${}^{0}_{-1}\beta$.

## 2 Worked example — Grade 7

${}^{230}_{92}U$ decays by emitting an alpha particle. Write an equation for this decay. **[2 marks]**

$${}^{230}_{92}U \rightarrow {}^{226}_{90}Th + {}^{4}_{2}He$$

The equation is balanced because the total mass number on each side is the same and the total atomic number is the same.

## 10 Types of decay

### Alpha decay

When a nucleus undergoes **alpha decay**, it loses two protons and two neutrons. The mass number of the nucleus decreases by four and the atomic number and the charge on the nucleus decrease by two. The nucleus becomes a new element.

For example, when a radium (Ra) nucleus alpha decays it becomes a radon (Rn) nucleus.

$${}^{226}_{88}Ra \longrightarrow {}^{222}_{86}Rn + {}^{4}_{2}\alpha$$

X mass number / atomic number → Y mass number −4 / atomic number −2 + ${}^{4}_{2}\alpha$

**Figure 1** Alpha decay

Remember that these decays happen randomly. The products, or **daughter nuclei**, created may be radioactive isotopes that decay again.

### Beta decay

During **beta decay**, a neutron changes into a proton and an electron. The electron is ejected from the nucleus. The mass doesn't change, but the charge increases.

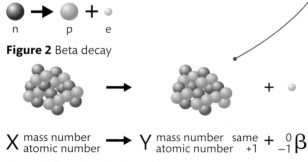

For example, when the isotope of carbon, ${}^{14}_{6}C$, decays it forms nitrogen.

$${}^{14}_{6}C \longrightarrow {}^{14}_{7}N + {}^{0}_{-1}\beta$$

There is still the same number of protons and neutrons in the nucleus overall, so the mass number and the charge do not change. As there is an extra proton, the atomic number increases by one. This makes a new element.

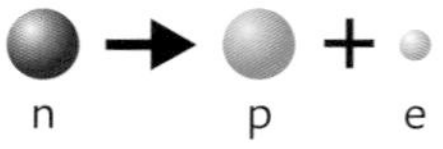


**Figure 2** Beta decay

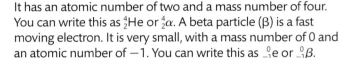

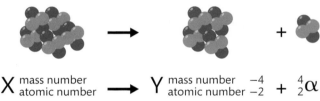

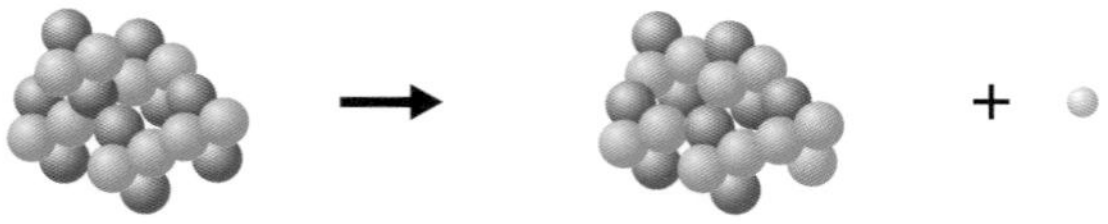

X mass number / atomic number → Y mass number same / atomic number +1 + ${}^{0}_{-1}\beta$

**Figure 3** Equation for beta decay

### Gamma decay

**Gamma decay** occurs when a nucleus has excess energy after a nuclear process. The energy is given off as a high energy electromagnetic wave. It does not contain any particles so the nucleus does not change.

## 15 Exam-style practice — Grade 7

1. Fill in the gaps.
   (a) ${}^{239}_{94}Pu \rightarrow$ __U + ${}^{4}_{2}$____ **[2 marks]**
   (b) __Na $\rightarrow {}^{25}_{12}Mg$ + ____e **[2 marks]**
2. Radon, ${}^{222}_{86}Rn$, decays to make polonium, ${}^{218}_{84}Po$. ${}^{218}_{84}Po$ then decays to lead ${}^{214}_{82}Pb$, which decays to bismuth ${}^{214}_{83}Bi$. Identify and write an equation for each type of decay. **[6 marks]**
3. Historically, alchemists tried to make gold from lead. Nuclear decays make it possible to change from one element to another. Use the periodic table to find out what element would be created if an isotope of lead:
   (a) alpha decayed **[1 mark]**
   (b) beta decayed. **[1 mark]**

# Radioactive contamination

Contamination and irradiation are both harmful to living organisms. You need to know about the measures taken to avoid radioactive contamination.

## 5 Irradiation

To be **irradiated** means to be exposed to a source of radiation, be it alpha, beta or gamma radiation. The irradiated object does not become radioactive. Irradiation can cause damage to cells, alter genes and cause mutations that can lead to cancer.

The amount of radiation an object is exposed to is called the **dose**. Doses are measured in sieverts or millisieverts. For small doses, such as radiation treatment in hospitals, the risks are much less than the benefit from the treatment.

A dose can be increased by:

- increased exposure time
- higher activity of the radioactive source
- being closer to the source.

A dose can be reduced by:

- wearing protective clothing and/or staying behind a screen
- keeping your distance from sources, for example, using long tweezers, tongs or robotic arms.

Ultraviolet rays and X-rays can have a similar hazardous effect on the body as gamma rays, although they are less powerful and less penetrating. UV can cause premature ageing of the skin and increase the risk of skin cancer.

## 5 Contamination

Touching a source can leave traces of radioactive material on you or an object. If this radioactive material is unwanted, it is called **contamination**. Contamination is dangerous, especially for living things, due to radioactive decay of the contaminating material. The level of hazard depends on the type of radiation. Contamination should be cleaned off immediately. Removing contaminated materials from skin can be difficult.

Avoid contamination by avoiding direct contact with sources. Precautions for reducing irradiation will reduce the risk of contamination. Liquid and powdery sources are particularly risky and need to be kept in sealed containers.

## 5 Worked example — Grade 8

When not in use, a radioactive source in a hospital is stored in a box. Suggest a material for the box and explain the role of scientific research in coming to your decision. **[3 marks]**

*It depends on the type of radiation being given off, but lead would stop all three types. Research informs this decision as it would tell us what type of radiation is being emitted, depending on the source, and also what material would stop this source. If it was beta, then a box made of a few mm thick pieces of aluminum could be used.*

## 5 Peer review and scientific research

Before a scientist publishes their research, their work is checked and evaluated by other scientists. This process is known as **peer review**. During this process, scientists check the findings, improve the methods and repeat the published experiments to check the results. This process makes scientists more confident about each other's findings.

It is important to understand the effects of radiation on human beings, in order to protect and treat anyone exposed to high levels of radiation. This means that people who work with radiation are better able to protect themselves and treat anyone who may have been contaminated or received a high dose of radiation.

## 10 Exam-style practice — Grade 8

1. A science teacher is using radioactive rocks. Explain why the teacher is at risk from both contamination and irradiation and what they can do to reduce the risk. **[4 marks]**
2. Explain the differences and similarities between irradiation and contamination. **[2 marks]**
3. Workers in a nuclear power station wear dosimeters to measure their exposure to ionising radiation. A total dose of less than 100 mSv per year is considered to have a low risk of cancer. After one year, two workers' doses are:
   person A: 28 mSv     person B: 56 mSv
   **(a)** Suggest why the dose for person B might be higher. **[2 marks]**
   **(b)** Is person A at risk of cancer? Give a reason for your answer. **[2 marks]**

Made a start | Feeling confident | Exam ready

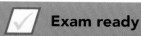

# Equations

You need to know which equations to use and how to rearrange them to answer questions in the exam. You will be given a formulae sheet with some equations on.

## 2 Three rules for rearranging

1. Decide what you want to work out. Get this on one side of the equation and everything else on the other.
2. Make sure the value you want to find is not on the bottom of a fraction.
3. When you move something across the equals sign, the operation needs to be reversed.

## 2 Exam focus

In the exam, you can save time by using symbols rather than words. For example, use:

$F = ma$ rather than force = mass × acceleration as it is quicker to write and rearrange.

Take your time when rearranging equations and allow time to check your calculations to ensure you have written the correct answer.

## 10 Maths skills

### Equations with three quantities

If you needed to calculate the mass, $m$:

$$F = ma \rightarrow \frac{F}{a} = m \rightarrow m = \frac{F}{a}$$

### Equations with four or more quantities

$$E_p = mgh \rightarrow \frac{E_p}{mg} = h \rightarrow h = \frac{E_p}{mg}$$

Divide both sides of the equation by $mg$.

### Equations with squares

$$E_k = \frac{1}{2}mv^2 \rightarrow v^2 = \frac{E_k}{\frac{1}{2}m} \rightarrow v = \sqrt{\frac{E_k}{\frac{1}{2}m}}$$

First rearrange for $v^2$, you can move the $\frac{1}{2}$ and $m$ as normal, then square root both sides.

$v^2 = u^2 + 2as$

To find $u$, first rearrange so that $u^2$ is on its own:

$u^2 = v^2 - 2as \rightarrow u = \sqrt{v^2 - 2as}$

To find $a$, first rearrange so that $2as$ is on its own:

$$v^2 - u^2 = 2as \rightarrow \frac{v^2 - u^2}{2s} = a \rightarrow a = \frac{v^2 - u^2}{2s}$$

1. Find out what you are being asked to find (current).
2. Identify which values you have been given in the question and what their units are: a potential difference (V), a resistance (Ω) and a power (W).
3. Think of the equation that includes the thing you want to find and the numbers that you have.
4. Rearrange the equation isolating the unknown value on one side and replace the symbols with the known values.
5. Check whether you need to convert the unit.

## 5 Worked example — Grade 7

A 12 V motor has resistance 4.8 Ω. Find its current if it has power 30 W. **[2 marks]**

power = potential difference × current

$P = IV \rightarrow I = \frac{P}{V} = \frac{30}{12} = 2.5\,\text{A}$

Alternatively, put the numbers in first then rearrange the equation.

$P = IV \rightarrow 30 = I \times 12 \rightarrow I = \frac{30}{12} = 2.5\,\text{A}$

## 10 Exam-style practice — Grade 5

1. Rearrange the following for each of the other quantities in the equation:

   **(a)** $\rho = \frac{m}{V}$ **[1 mark]**

   **(b)** $E_p = \frac{1}{2}ke^2$ **[1 mark]**

   **(c)** $\Delta E = mc\Delta\theta$ **[1 mark]**

   **(d)** $a = \frac{\Delta v}{t}$. **[1 mark]**

2. Give the name and units for each of the quantities in question 1. **[6 marks]**

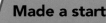

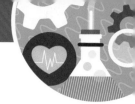

Pages 18, 25, 26 LINKS

# Converting units

You need to know how to convert quantities to the standard unit.

## Prefixes

| Prefix | nano | micro | milli | centi | kilo | mega | giga |
|---|---|---|---|---|---|---|---|
| Example unit | nm | μm | mm | cm | km | Mm | Gm |
| Standard form | $1\times10^{-9}$ | $1\times10^{-6}$ | $1\times10^{-3}$ | $1\times10^{-2}$ | $1\times10^{3}$ | $1\times10^{6}$ | $1\times10^{9}$ |
| Factor | 0.000000001 | 0.000001 | 0.001 | 0.01 | 1000 | 1 000 000 | 1 000 000 000 |
| Example | atom 0.1 nm | cells 1–100 μm | ball bearing few mm | pencil 15 cm | Mount Everest 9 km | Earth 13 Mm | Moon orbit 0.4 Gm |

Standard form is written in terms of powers of 10. Negative numbers mean you divide by 10 that many times and positive numbers mean you multiply by 10 that many times. This value is equal to: 1 × 9 = 1 000 000 000.

## Converting units

To convert 30 mm to m, first figure out what the conversion factor is between mm and m. There are 1000 ($10^3$) mm in a m.

Then decide if you need to multiply or divide.

30 mm is much smaller than a metre so should be a very small number:

30 mm ÷ 1000 = 0.03 m

### Complex units

To convert spring constant 4.5 N/cm to N/m, first figure out what the conversion factor is between cm and m (100).

4.5 N/cm × 100 = 450 N/m

Now, check logically: if it takes 4.5 N to stretch the spring 1 cm, you would expect a lot more force to stretch it 1 m, so 450 N makes sense.

### Time

Remember, that when dealing with time you need to multiply or divide by 60, not 100

1 hour = 60 minutes, 1 minute = 60 seconds

### Areas

When converting areas, take the normal conversion factor and square it.

Convert $cm^2$ to $m^2$

$250\ cm^2 \div 100^2 = 0.025\ m^2$

For volumes, cube the usual factor:

Convert $m^3$ to $mm^3$

$1.2\ m^3 \times 1000^3 = 1\ 200\ 000\ 000\ mm^3$

or $1.2\times10^9\ mm^3$

## Worked example — Grade 6

Convert:

**(a)** 0.56 kg to g **[1 mark]**

0.56 kg × 1000 = 560 g

**(b)** 12 mm to cm **[1 mark]**

12 mm ÷ 10 = 1.2 cm

**(c)** 25 MJ to J **[1 mark]**

25 MJ × $10^6$ = 25 000 000 J or $2.5\times10^7$ J

**(d)** 0.037 mm to μm **[1 mark]**

0.037 ÷ $10^3$ = 3.37 μm

## Matching units

$$\text{velocity} = \frac{\text{displacement}}{\text{time}}$$

Normally, the velocity is in m/s, so the displacement and time need to be converted into metres and seconds to match.

However, if the displacement is in kilometres and the time in hours, the velocity will be in km/h. Check which units you should use in your calculation and answer.

## Exam-style practice — Grade 6

1 Convert:

**(a)** 200 μg to g **[1 mark]**

**(b)** 10 N/kg to N/g **[1 mark]**

**(c)** 330 J/minute to J/s. **[1 mark]**

2 Calculate how many orders of magnitude larger 10 kg is than 1 g. **[1 mark]**

Pages 18, 25, 26 LINKS

# Making estimations

You need to know how to estimate the results of simple calculations.

## Estimating speeds and masses

### Speeds

You need to have an idea of how fast some objects move.

- Cars move at around 10 m/s up to 30 m/s at motorway speeds.
- People walk at around 1–2 m/s and sprint at up to around 10 m/s.
- Jet planes can fly up to around 250 m/s.

Try and picture an object moving and estimate how far you think it would get in 1 second. Use this to estimate its speed.

### Masses

You need to have an idea of the masses of certain objects.

The following are rough estimates and vary with size:

- a person – 50–70 kg
- a car – 1000 kg
- 1 litre of water – 1 kg
- a dog – 5–25 kg
- a mobile phone – 100–200 g.

You can estimate the mass of an object by comparing it with objects of a similar mass.

## Worked example — Grade 4

**1** Estimate the kinetic energy of a person sprinting in a race. **[3 marks]**

kinetic energy = ½ × mass × speed$^2$

mass ~ 60 kg and speed ~ 10 m/s

Kinetic energy = ½ × 60 kg × (10 m/s)$^2$ = 3000 J

**2** Calculate the increase in potential energy of a 1.45 kg mass lifted 9.5 m ($g$ = 9.8 N/kg). **[3 marks]**

$E_p = mgh = 1.45 \times 9.8 \times 9.5 = 135$ J

Check the answer is correct by rounding the numbers and working out an approximate answer.

1.5 × 10 × 10 = 150, so this answer is about right.

## Exam focus

If a question instructs you to 'calculate', you should work out the answer exactly using a calculator. It is good practice to then estimate the answer to check it is correct.

## Maths skills

If you are asked to estimate the area under a curve, you do not need to try and calculate the area. First, work out the value of each square, then count roughly how many squares there are on the graph and then multiply these two numbers together.

## Worked example — Grade 6

The time it takes an insulated beaker of hot water to cool by 5 °C is recorded.

| Thickness of insulation in mm | 2 | 4 | 6 | 8 |
|---|---|---|---|---|
| Time to cool in s | 250 | 569 | 603 | 798 |

**(a)** Using the table, estimate the time taken for 3 mm to cool. **[1 mark]**

400 seconds

**(b)** Using **Figure 1**, estimate the time taken for 7 mm to cool. **[1 mark]**

700 seconds

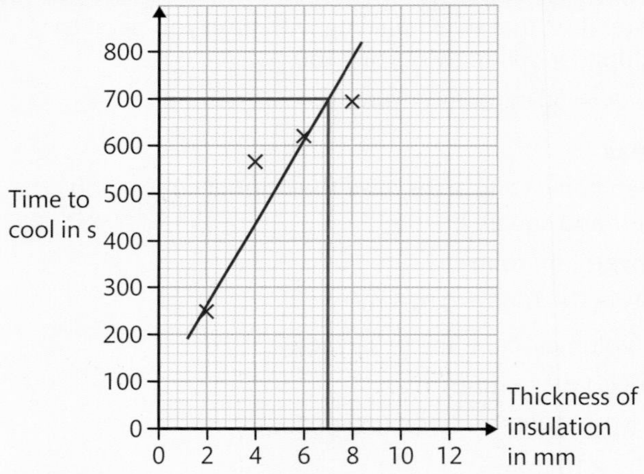


**Figure 1** Time taken for hot water to cool

## Exam-style practice — Grade 7

**1** Estimate the speed of a snail in mm/s. **[1 mark]**

**2** Estimate the mass of a person riding a bicycle. **[1 mark]**

**3** Use **Figure 1** to estimate the time it takes to cool a beaker with 5 mm of insulation. **[2 marks]**

LINKS Pages 18, 25, 26

# Interpreting data

In the exam, you will need to demonstrate that you can interpret data from a range of equipment, tables, charts and graphs.

## 2 Correlations

**Scatter graphs** show patterns, outliers and anomalies in numerical data. **Anomalies** do not fit the pattern at all, and **outliers** fit poorly. You may need to discount these results when finding an average for your data.

A **correlation** is a relationship between two variables that can easily be seen by drawing a line of best fit on a scatter graph. If the line is straight then the relationship is linear. If it also goes through the origin (0,0), you can say that the measurements are proportional. A lot of scatter can indicate random error affecting your experiment. Think about how you can reduce this.

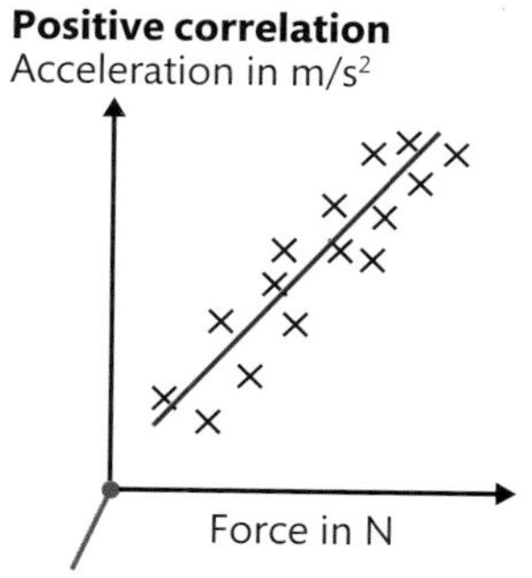


If the line of best fit should go through (0,0) and does not, this indicates a systematic error. All of your readings are likely to be too high or too low by the same amount.

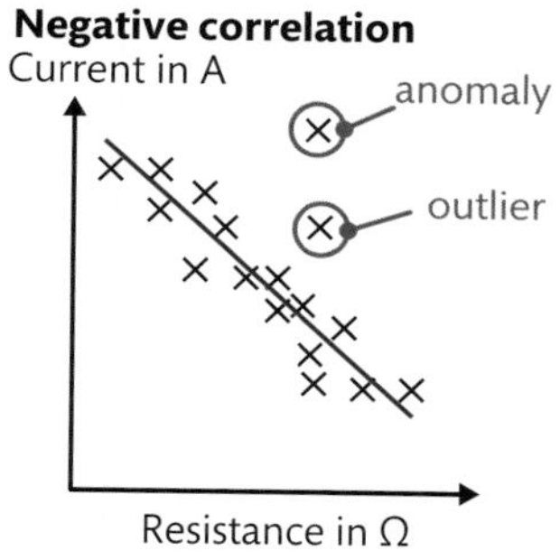


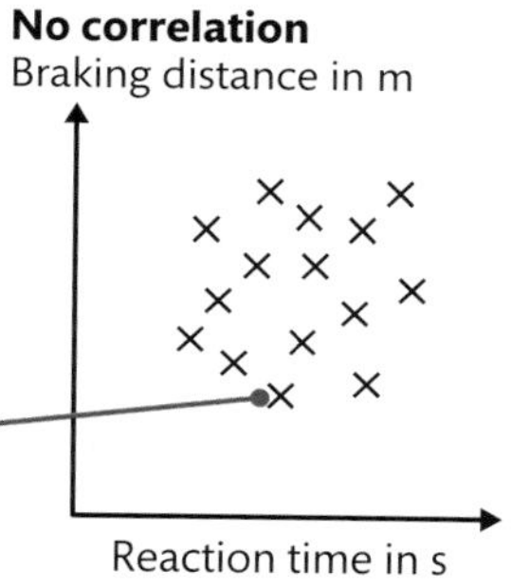


The closer together the results are, the more precise they are.

## 10 Worked example — Grade 7

A student is investigating the reaction between an acid and a metal. Give the volume of acid in the measuring cylinder.

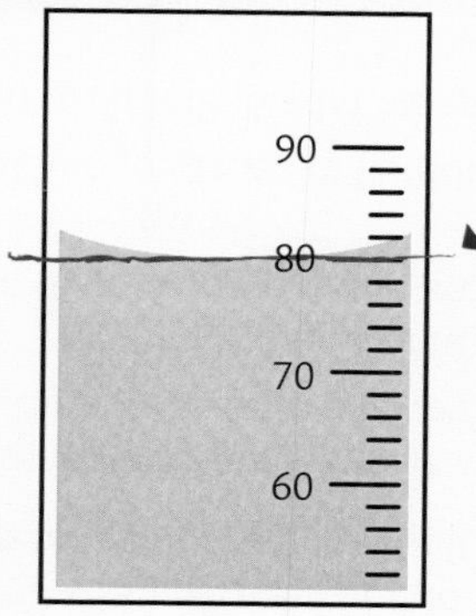


80 ml³

Make sure that you include the correct units. For area, this will be the unit squared. For volume, this will be the unit cubed.

## 5 Data in tables

If you are given data in a table, it is helpful to first of all look for a pattern to work out the relationship between the variables. In the table below, as speed increases, braking distance increases.

| **Speed in m/s** | 5 | 10 | 15 | 20 | 25 | 30 |
|---|---|---|---|---|---|---|
| **Braking distance in m** | 4 | 16 | 36 | 64 | 100 | 144 |

Now, look for further patterns. What happens when one of the quantities is doubled? As you double any speed the distance gets 4 times bigger.

You can make estimates for other speeds based on the values in the table. For example, the braking distance at a speed of 12 m/s would be between 16 m and 36 m.

As one measurement doubles, if the other:

- doubles, they are **directly proportional**
- halves, they **inversely proportional**.

## 2 Averages

$$\text{mean} = \frac{\text{sum of numbers}}{\text{amount of numbers}}$$

Use the **mean** for repeat readings. This is the most commonly used average in Science. However, it should not be used where the range includes extremely large or small numbers which would affect the mean.

The **mode** is the number or measurement that occurs most often. It could be used with measurements that are not numbers, like average eye colour.

The **median** is the middle number when values are placed in order of increasing size.

When measuring a volume of liquid, make sure you take your reading from the **bottom** of the meniscus (the curved line that the skin of the water makes). If this comes up in an exam, draw a line across the bottom of the meniscus to help you find the right value.

## 10 Exam-style practice — Grade 7

1. Puppies in a litter weigh 1.1 kg, 1.2 kg, 1.2 kg, 1.3 kg, 3.3 kg. Calculate the mean, mode and median. Comment on how suitably each number represents the average mass of puppies in the litter. **[4 marks]**
2. Calculate the stopping distance from a speed of 40 m/s. **[3 marks]**

Pages 18, 25, 26 LINKS

# Using charts and graphs

Graphs are commonly used in Science, particularly line and scatter graphs. You need to know how to interpret and draw a graph.

## 5 Types of graphs and charts

### Pie charts

Pie charts show the proportional measurements that make up a total. For example, percentage use of energy resource.

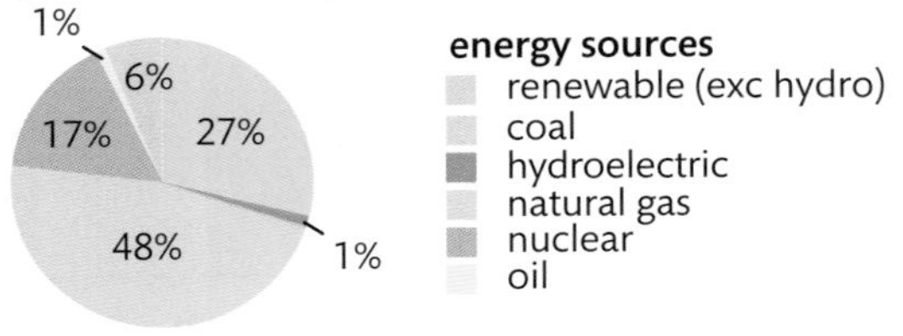


### Bar charts

Bar charts should only be used to show information about discrete data. For example, the strength of the gravitational field on different planets. They are not to be confused with histograms, which show continuous data.

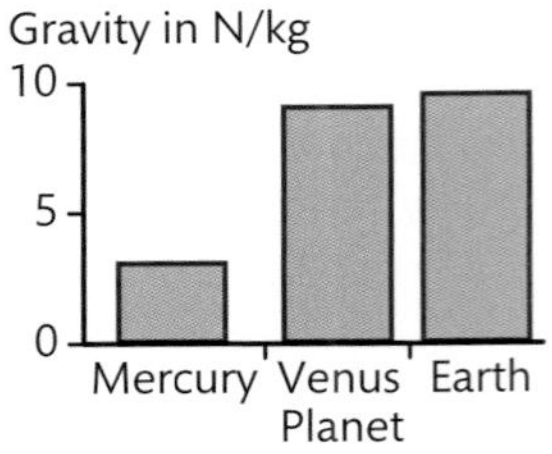


### Graphs

Graphs, such as scatter graphs, show the relationship between two variables. For example, length of wire and resistance, weight and mass.

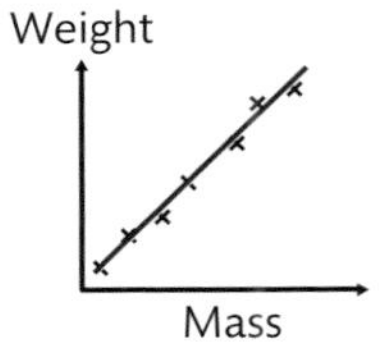


## 5 Worked example — Grade 7

The table shows a student's results for an investigation.

| Time in s | 0 | 10 | 20 | 30 | 40 | 50 | 60 |
|---|---|---|---|---|---|---|---|
| Temperature in °C | 5 | 6 | 11 | 17 | 35 | 72 | 180 |

**(a)** Use these results to draw a line graph. **[3 marks]**

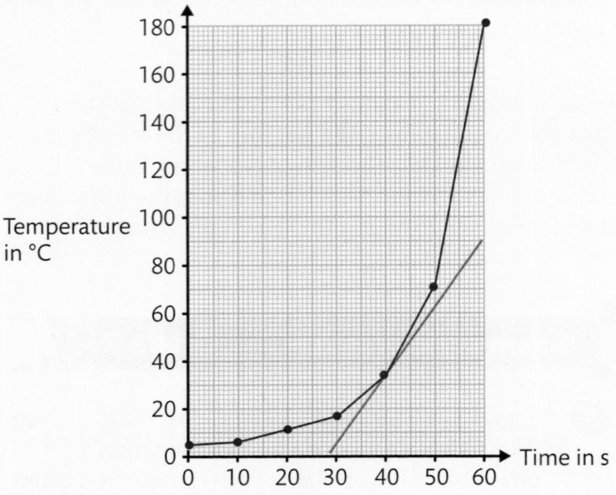


**(b)** Draw a tangent to work out the rate of reaction at 45 seconds. **[2 marks]**

$\frac{80-20}{54-36} = \frac{60}{18} = 3.33$

## 10 Interpreting graphs

### Straight line graphs

The general equation of a straight line is $y = mx + c$, where:

- $x$ and $y$ are values on the $x$ and $y$ axes
- $m$ is the gradient
- $c$ is where the line meets the $y$-axis.

A straight line represents a linear relationship. The equation for the line in the graph in **Figure 1** is $y = 0.5x + 2.5$. You can replace $x$ and $y$ with the quantities you have plotted.

The meaning of the gradient depends on the quantities being divided. For example, with speed on the $y$-axis and time on the $x$-axis the gradient is speed ÷ time = acceleration.

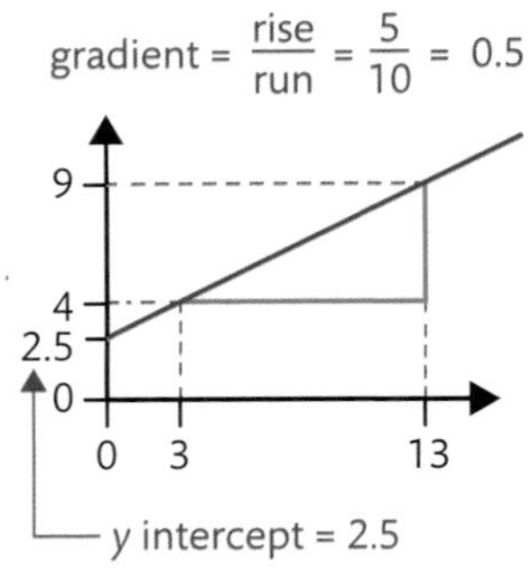


**Figure 1** Find the gradient

### Tangents

You can find the gradient of a curve at any point by drawing a tangent at that point. Find the gradient of the tangent but remember that the gradient is different at every point on the curve.

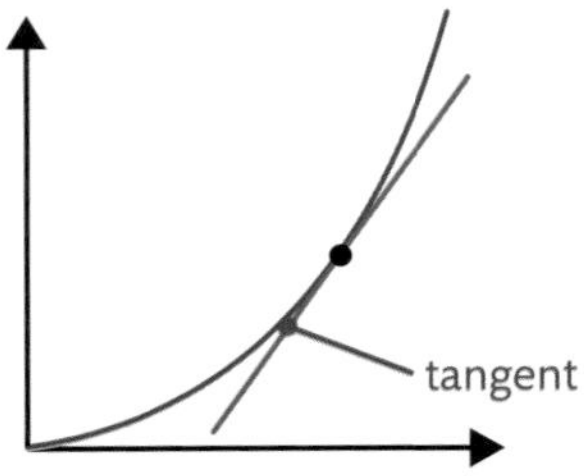


**Figure 2** Drawing a tangent

### Areas under the line

You can figure out what the area under the line represents by looking at the quantities that are being multiplied together. If the axes are speed and time, speed × time = distance. The area represents distance.

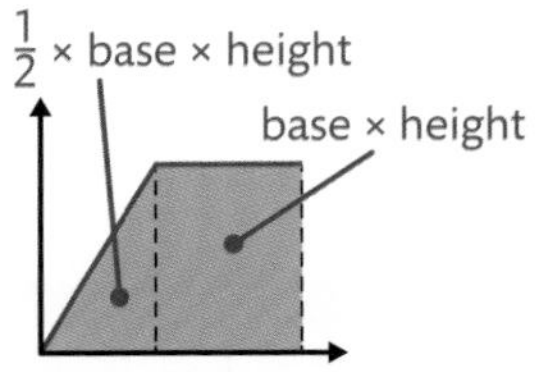


**Figure 3** Finding the area under a line

## 10 Exam-style practice — Grade 8

**1** State a suitable type of graph to show:

**(a)** the stopping distances of different cars **[1 mark]**

**(b)** the mass of salt that dissolves in water at different temperatures **[1 mark]**

**(c)** the percentage of energy lost from the windows, doors, walls and floors in a house. **[1 mark]**

**2** A straight line graph has force on the $y$-axis and extension on the $x$-axis. It has a gradient of 120 and goes through the origin. Give the equation of the line and the significance of the gradient. **[3 marks]**

Page 18, 83, 199 LINKS

# Using diagrams

You could be asked to draw or label a diagram in the exam. Diagrams can also help you to organise information to answer a question.

## Key questions

- Do you need to use a ruler?
- Do you need to label any parts?
- Should you add arrows to show direction?
- Should you draw anything to scale?
- Do you need to use symbols (like circuit symbols)?
- Do you need to use a particular shape or position?

## Worked example

Find the acceleration of a car of mass 1200 kg if the engine force is 1000 N and it experiences 350 N of air resistance and 200 N of friction. **[3 marks]**

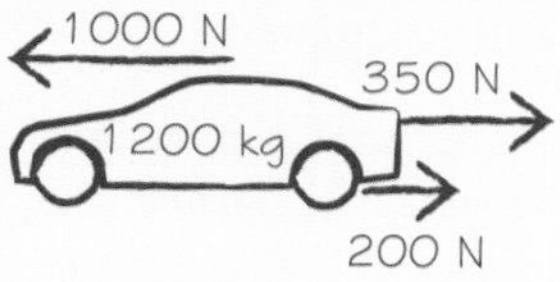


This sketch isn't part of the answer but it helps to organise all the numbers in the question.

Resultant force = 1000 − 350 − 200 = 450 N

$$\text{acceleration} = \frac{\text{force}}{\text{mass}} = \frac{450}{1200} = 0.375 \text{ m/s}^2$$

## Worked example — Grade 5

Draw a diagram of an animal cell and label the following features:

- nucleus
- ribosomes
- mitochondria
- cell membrane.

Include a scale bar.

**[4 marks]**

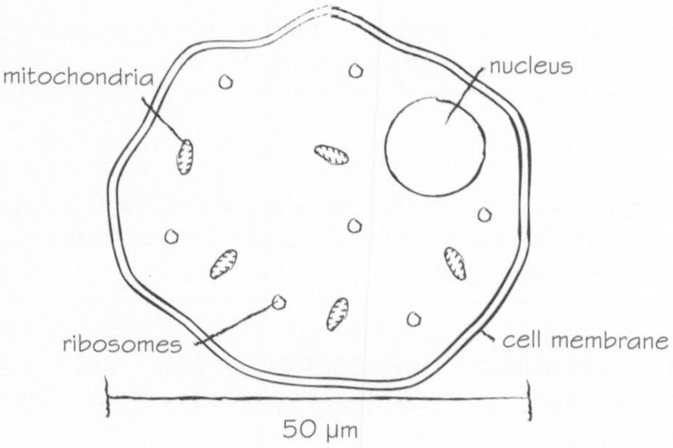


### Exam focus

When asked to add a label to a diagram, make sure you think carefully about the position and draw your labels in exactly the right place. Consider using arrows or lines to clearly show the position.

The crest is just one position, but amplitude and wavelength must indicate between two positions.

## Worked example — Grade 5

**Figure 1** A wave

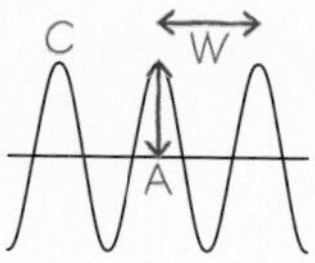


Look at the **Figure 1**.

**(a)** Label the crest of a wave with **C**. **[1 mark]**

**(b)** Indicate the amplitude and label it with an **A**. **[1 mark]**

**(c)** Indicate a wavelength and label it **W**. **[1 mark]**

The wavelength needs to be indicated exactly from the crest of one wave to the crest of the next and the amplitude from the centre line to the very highest point.

## Exam-style practice — Grade 5

1. Sketch a skydiver of weight 600 N experiencing 300 N air resistance upward and a 200 N side wind. **[3 marks]**
2. Draw a circuit diagram that could be used to find the resistance of a lightbulb. **[3 marks]**

Pages 18, 25, 26 LINKS

# Planning practicals

You need to know how to write a plan for a practical, including an equipment list, a method and details about control and safety measures.

## Worked example — Grade 8

A student makes the hypothesis that the average speed of a trolley rolling down a ramp increases with the height of the ramp.

**(a)** Identify the variables that would need to be measured and calculated. **[3 marks]**

*Change the height of the ramp and measure the distance the trolley moves and the time it takes to reach the bottom.*

$$\text{average speed} = \frac{\text{distance down ramp}}{\text{time}}$$

> The variables are speed and height. You either have to measure speed directly or measure distance and time for it to be calculated.

**(b)** Draw a diagram to show the equipment needed. List any other items not shown. **[3 marks]**

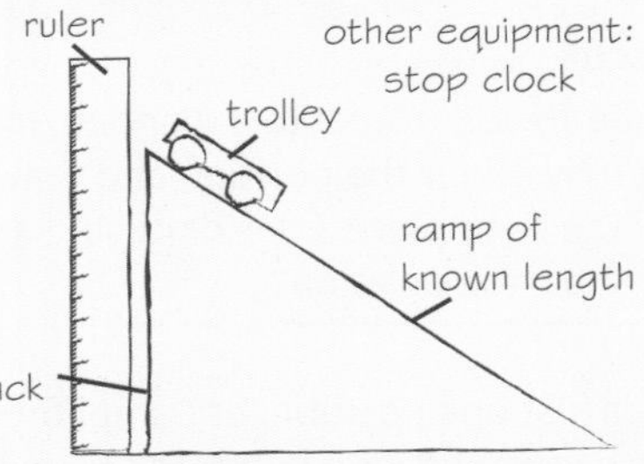


> Your equipment needs to reflect the variables you are going to measure.
> You could suggest using two light gates and a data logger set up for timing here instead. A sonic distance sensor and data logger could measure the speed of the trolley directly so no need to measure time and distance individually. This would also be a way to the remove reaction time uncertainty mentioned in (c).

> The diagram is meant to save you wasting space in a method describing the layout of equipment. Not every single piece needs to be shown, but every piece needs mentioning in an equipment list.
> It can be useful to label some of the variables on your diagram like height of ramp and distance.

**(c)** Why is there an uncertainty involved in using a stop clock in this experiment? **[1 mark]**

*The reaction time of the person who judges when the trolley reaches the bottom will affect the measurement of time.*

> There would also be an issue starting the stop clock at the same time as the trolley is released.

**(d)** Suggest how the uncertainty in **(c)** could be reduced. **[2 marks]**

*Use two light gates at a set distance and a data logger set to measure.*

> Using a longer ramp and small heights would increase the time. This would make the uncertainty in reaction time less significant.

**(e)** Give **one** hazard the student should consider when writing their method and what steps could be taken to reduce it. **[2 marks]**

*The trolley may roll onto the floor and become a trip hazard. Someone should catch it at the end of the ramp.*

> Even experiments without acid or fire have a small hazard. Keep your hazards and solutions simple, avoid getting too inventive.

## Exam-style practice — Grade 8

A student conducts two experiments:

**Experiment 1:** The first experiment is conducted to find out if a radioactive source emits alpha, beta or gamma radiation by seeing what materials it will pass through.

**Experiment 2:** The second experiment tests the hypothesis 'the higher the temperature of a length of wire, the higher its resistance'. For each experiment:

**(a)** Identify the variables that need measuring and controlling. **[2 marks]**

**(b)** List the equipment needed to take the measurements. **[2 marks]**

**(c)** Give **two** safety precautions the student should take. **[2 marks]**

Pages 18, 25, 26 LINKS



# Comparing data

You need to know how to compare data and be able to discuss the advantages and disadvantages of different ideas.

## Worked example — Grade 8

The table shows the estimated figures for the percentage of electricity produced from different resources in Spain and the UK.

| Resource | Electricity production | |
|---|---|---|
| | UK | Spain |
| wind turbine | 2.3% | 26.4% |
| solar | 0.2% | 2.6% |
| hydroelectric | 0.6% | 23.9% |
| biomass | 1.7% | 0.2% |
| fossil fuel | 87.4% | 17.9% |
| nuclear | 7.8% | 29.0% |

**(a)** Compare usage of renewable to non-renewable resources in each country. **[2 marks]**

4.8 per cent of electricity in UK comes from renewable resources compared to 53.1 per cent in Spain, which is over 10 times higher.

**(b)** Suggest a reason for the difference in solar electricity production by each country. **[2 marks]**

Spain may have more hours of sunshine, or less clouds, making solar power a more useful resource.

**(c)** Compare wind turbines with nuclear power as sources of electricity production. **[4 marks]**

Neither of the sources give out chemical pollution or carbon dioxide so they do not contribute to global warming. Nuclear power has a much higher and more reliable power output. You need a lot of wind turbines to match the output of a nuclear power plant, and turbines only produce electricity when it is windy. After the initial costs, wind turbines have free energy and low maintenance costs, while nuclear power plants are costly to run and to decommission at the end of their life cycle.

Compare the similarities, then say what is different about each one. It can be a good idea to work through some factors and compare each one in turn. For instance, power output, reliability, costs and effects on the environment. Make sure to mention some advantages and disadvantages of each one.

For every statement you make, you must compare it to the other resource, for instance wind turbines having low reliability must be compared to the higher consistency of nuclear power. If you only give facts about one then they are not being compared.

## Comparing data

- Look for patterns in the data.
- Identify and similarities or differences, and what they mean.
- Consider the advantages and disadvantages of different variables.

### Exam focus

When comparing data, look at the table's headings. Make sure you know exactly what the data is before answering the question.

When comparing, make sure you refer to both values and clearly state which is greater. Look for any patterns, e.g. if something is approximately 10 times larger.

First, look at what the difference is, then apply what you know about solar power to try and explain it.

## Exam-style practice — Grade 8

**1** A tyre manufacturer wants to compare the performance of two tyres. Using the same car and driver, they perform emergency stops at different speeds with each set of tyres, A and B.

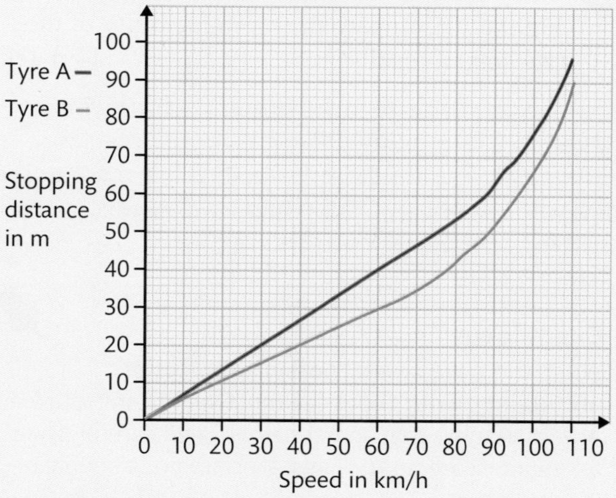


**(a)** Compare how the stopping distances of the two sets of tyres are affected by speed. **[3 marks]**

**(b)** Compare the stopping distances shown on the graph with what you might expect if the same test were performed on a wet road. **[2 marks]**

**2** Compare emitters of alpha, beta and gamma radiation for use in hospitals, where they are fired as a beam to destroy cancerous cells in the body. **[3 marks]**

Pages **18, 25, 26** LINKS

# Evaluating data

To evaluate an experiment, you need to look carefully at the data in tables and graphs and look critically at the method, and suggest improvements.

## 10 Evaluating data

Comment on how close the points are to the line of best fit. A lot of scatter can indicate random error affecting your experiment.

If your line should go through the origin (0,0) and does not, this indicates a systematic error. All your readings might be too high or too low by the same amount.

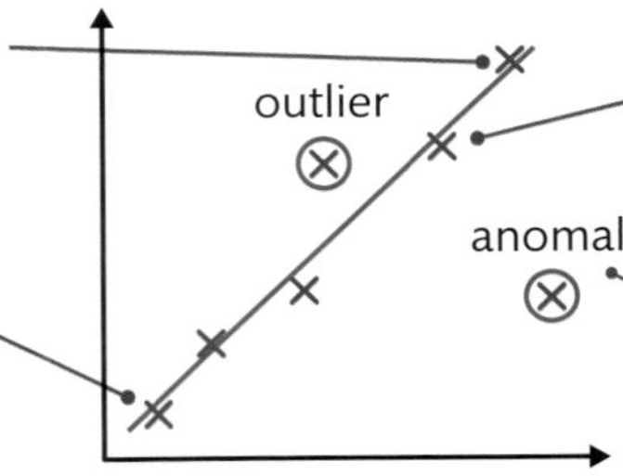


To be sure of the line of best fit you need at least four points to follow the pattern, or more for a curve.

The greater the number of anomalies, the less certain you can be about the position of your line of best fit.

## 5 Worked example — Grade 7

**Table 1**

| Potential difference in V | Current in A | | |
|---|---|---|---|
| | 1 | 2 | 3 |
| 2.0 | 0.12 | 0.13 | 0.12 |
| 4.0 | 0.24 | 0.22 | 0.23 |

range 0.01 A
range 0.02 A

**Table 2**

| Potential difference in V | Current in A | | |
|---|---|---|---|
| | 1 | 2 | 3 |
| 2.0 | 0.12 | 0.18 | 0.13 |
| 4.0 | 0.30 | 0.22 | 0.25 |

range 0.06 A
range 0.08 A

**1** Study the two sets of results in the extracts in **Figure 1**. Compare the reproducibility of the two sets of results. **[4 marks]**

*The repeat readings in Table 1 are similar, with a range of 0.01 A and 0.02 A making the results repeatable. The readings in Table 2 are more spread out, with ranges of 0.06 A and 0.08 A, which means that the results are not reproducible.*

**Exam focus**

When there are several possible sources of uncertainty, write about the most significant sources. Always assume that someone has been careful while taking measurements – mistakes are not a source of uncertainty.

**2** A student compares the insulating properties of two materials by wrapping them around two beakers. They boil a kettle and pour some hot water into the first beaker, recording the temperature of the water after 5 minutes. They then pour water into the second beaker and record the temperature after five minutes. The end temperatures are compared.

Identify **two** sources of uncertainty and suggest an improvement to the method. **[3 marks]**

*Different thicknesses of material used. Different start temperatures would affect the end temperature.*

**(b)** Suggest two ways that the student could improve the method. **[2 marks]**

*They could reheat the water and check the start temperature is the same each time.*

Measurements are **repeatable** if the same experiment by the same investigator gives a similar set of results (as in Table 1). They are **reproducible** if the same experiment by a different investigator, with different equipment, produces a similar set of results.

The more spread out the repeats, the less reproducible the results will be. To help you comment on the repeats, calculate the range of each set.

## 10 Exam-style practice — Grade 7

**1** Suggest other sources of uncertainty in question 2 of the worked example. How could you reduce these uncertainties? **[4 marks]**

**2** A graph shows the average speed of a ball rolling down a ramp at different heights. The graph contains a lot of scatter and none of the points are close to the line of best fit. Identify the type of error and suggest the cause. **[3 marks]**

Pages 18, 25, 26 LINKS



# Working scientifically

You need to demonstrate the ability to work scientifically through your experimental skills, analysis and evaluation of data.

## 10 Experimental skills

Experiments are designed to test hypotheses (an idea or explanation).

Scientists use experiments to find data, such as the specific heat capacity of a material. They are also used to test how one measured quantity affects another: one variable (the independent variable) is changed and another variable (the dependent variable) is measured.

### Planning

Being able to choose the correct equipment and method to carry out a practical is an important skill for scientists. A plan should include an equipment lists and a step-by-step method, as well as details about any control or safety measures.

### Evaluation and analysis

After making and recording their observations, scientists process and present data in a way that enables them to evaluate the validity of a hypothesis.

It is important to use scientific theories and explanations to explain data and reflect on whether patterns and observations support the original hypothesis. The evaluation should also include suggestions on how the practical could be improved.

### Development of scientific ideas

As new evidence comes to light, scientists change and develop their theories and knowledge. These changes may have ethical, social, environmental or economic implications.

Experimental results are published for peer review. This means other scientists can check the findings and carry out further experiments based on the original results.

## 15 Worked example — Grades 7–8

**1** A student makes a hypothesis that the higher the light intensity, the taller a plant will grow.

**(a)** Identify the dependent and independent variables. **[2 marks]**

*The independent variable is the level of light intensity, which needs changing. The height of the plant needs to be measured. This is the dependent variable.*

> The variables need to come from the hypothesis. In this case light intensity and height can be measured directly. However, for variables like speed, you might need to measure distance and time and then calculate the variable you are investigating.

**(b)** Give three factors that need to be controlled. **[3 marks]**

*Type of plant, time and growing conditions (water and carbon dioxide)*

> There are lots of other factors, but these three are the most important and you should always choose the most obvious first. Others could include: temperature or soil pH.

**(c)** How would the data collected best be presented? **[3 marks]**

*A scatter graph of light intensity on the x-axis and height of plant on the y-axis with a line of best fit.*

> A scatter or line graph is best for any experiment that tests the relationship between two numerical variables.

**2** Scientists are researching a cure for Parkinson's disease using embryonic stem cells. Compare the advantages and disadvantages of this method of stem cell treatment. **[4 marks]**

*The advantages are that it will replace the patients damaged cell with a healthy cell, which may help them to recover. It is also easier to extract cells from an embryo, which saves time and money. One disadvantage is that some people have ethical issues with the use of embryos in stem cell research, as embryos cannot consent to being used. Another disadvantage is that stem cell treatment can cause viral infections.*

> Consider the ethical, social, environmental and economic aspects. They may not all be relevant.

## 10 Exam-style practice — Grade 8

**1** A student wants to find out which metal is the best conductor of electricity. Identify the variables that can be changed and controlled, what equipment would be needed and how the data would best be presented. **[6 marks]**

**2** Describe the social implications of the development of alpha, beta and gamma radiation. **[6 marks]**

Pages 18, 25, 26 LINKS

# Formulae for Physics

In the exam, you could be asked about any of the equations on this page. Make sure you know how to rearrange each of the equations and learn the units that match each quantity.

## 10 Formulae to learn

| Word equation | Symbol equation |
|---|---|
| weight = mass × gravitational field strength | $W = m\,g$ |
| work done = force × distance (along the line of action of the force) | $W = F\,s$ |
| force applied to a spring = spring constant × extension | $F = k\,e$ |
| distance travelled = speed × time | $s = v\,t$ |
| acceleration = change in velocity ÷ time taken | $a = \frac{\Delta V}{t}$ |
| resultant force = mass × acceleration | $F = m\,a$ |
| momentum = mass × velocity | $p = m\,v$ |
| kinetic energy = 0.5 × mass × (speed)$^2$ | $E_k = \frac{1}{2} m\,v^2$ |
| gravitational potential energy = mass × gravitational field strength × height | $E_p = m\,g\,h$ |
| power = energy transferred ÷ time | $P = \frac{E}{t}$ |
| power = work done ÷ time | $P = \frac{W}{t}$ |
| efficiency = useful output energy transfer ÷ total input energy transfer | |
| efficiency = useful power output ÷ total power input | |
| wave speed = frequency × wavelength | $v = f\,\lambda$ |
| charge flow = current × time | $Q = I\,t$ |
| potential difference = current × resistance | $V = I\,R$ |
| power = potential difference × current | $P = V\,I$ |
| power = (current)$^2$ × resistance | $P = I^2\,R$ |
| energy transferred = power × time | $E = P\,t$ |
| energy transferred = charge flow × potential difference | $E = Q\,V$ |
| density = mass ÷ volume | $\rho = \frac{m}{V}$ |

## 5 Physics equation sheet

You will be given a list of some of the more complicated equations in the exam.

| Word equation | Symbol equation |
|---|---|
| (final velocity)$^2$ – (initial velocity)$^2$ = 2 × acceleration × distance | $v^2 - u^2 = 2\,a\,s$ |
| elastic potential energy = 0.5 × spring constant × (extension)$^2$ | $E_e = \frac{1}{2} k\,e^2$ |
| change in thermal energy = mass × specific heat capacity × temperature change | $\Delta E = m\,c\,\Delta\theta$ |
| period = $\frac{1}{\text{frequency}}$ | |
| force on a conductor (at right angles to a magnetic field) carrying a current = magnetic flux density × current × length | $F = B\,I\,l$ |
| thermal energy for a change of state = mass × specific latent heat | $E = m\,L$ |
| potential difference across primary coil × current in primary coil = potential difference across secondary coil × current in secondary coil | $V_p\,I_p = V_s\,I_s$ |



Made a start | Feeling confident | Exam ready

# Answers

## Page 1 Levels of organisation

1. A group of organs that collectively perform specific functions within a system, such as the respiratory system.
2. The respiratory system is an organ system made up of several organs, including the lungs, and heart, working together. The organs consist of different types of tissues, epithelial, muscle, nervous or connective tissues. The tissues are made up of cells, such as red blood cells.

## Page 2 Prokaryotic and eukaryotic cells

1. Differences:
   - Prokaryotic cells have a cell wall; eukaryotic cells do not.
   - Eukaryotic cells have their DNA inside a nucleus; prokaryotic cells do not.
   - Prokaryotic cells have a loops of DNA; eukaryotic cells do not.

   Similarities:
   - Both types of cells contain ribosomes, cytoplasm and a cell membrane.
2. Ribosomes, mitochondria, nucleus

## Page 3 Animal and plant cells

1. **(a)** The nucleus is the dark circle in the centre of the cell.
   **(b)** Approximately 5 times wider
2. Unlike animal cells, plant cells have a cell wall. Plant cells also contain chloroplasts and a permanent vacuole, whereas animal cells do not.

## Page 4 Microscopy

1. $\frac{200\,000}{100} = 2000$

   $2 \times 10^3$
2. $15 \times 50 = \times 750$

## Page 5 Using microscopes

1. To produce an image that the eye can see, light needs to be able to pass through the tissue.
2. Different tissues stain different colours with different dyes. This makes it easier to tell the tissues apart.

## Page 6 Specialised cells

Muscle cells contain many mitochondria, which provide energy for muscle contraction. Muscle cells are composed of protein fibres that slide over each other to cause the muscle to contract.

Sperm cells have a tail which enables them to move towards an egg cell. They also have an acrosome containing enzymes that digest the outer layers of the egg, enabling fertilisation to take place.

Phloem cells consist of sieve plates which allow solutions to move easily from cell to cell and companion cells which contain many mitochondria. These mitochondria provide the energy that is required for active transport.

## Page 7 Cell differentiation

1. Answers will vary, e.g.
   - hair growing
   - fingernails growing.
2. When a particular type of tissue is damaged, it can be replaced or repaired.

## Page 8 Diffusion

1. Oxygen diffuses from the lungs into the blood. A good blood supply carries the oxygen away very quickly, maintaining the maximum concentration gradient.
2. The larger the surface area, the more space there is for carbon dioxide to diffuse through the membrane from the blood into the lungs.

## Page 9 Osmosis

1. As the concentration of sugar increases, the concentration of water molecules decreases. This results in a greater difference in water concentration on either side of the membrane. This means water will pass through the membrane from the left to the right more quickly.
2. As the molecules get warmer they move across the membrane more quickly, increasing the rate of osmosis.

## Page 10 Investigating osmosis

1. Independent variable: concentration of solution

   Dependent variable: size of potato chips
2. The hypothesis was proven. This is supported by the results in the table.

## Page 11 Active transport

1. Diffusion is the movement of molecules from a high concentration to a low concentration, whereas active transport is the movement of molecules against the concentration gradient, from a low concentration to a high concentration. Active transport requires energy, whereas diffusion does not.
2. Answers will vary, e.g.
   - Plants absorbing mineral ions through their root hair cells.
   - Animals absorbing glucose through the cells of the intestine.

## Page 12 Aerobic and anaerobic respiration

Both aerobic and anaerobic respiration break down glucose and transfer energy. Both types of respiration are exothermic reactions. Aerobic respiration produces carbon dioxide and water, whereas anaerobic respiration produces lactic acid. Aerobic respiration transfers more energy and uses oxygen.

### Page 13 Response to exercise

1. The energy they need is released by anaerobic respiration, which does not require oxygen from breathing.
2. They run as fast as they can using aerobic respiration and try not to use anaerobic respiration until the end of the race.

### Page 14 Metabolism

1. Metabolism is the sum of all the chemical reactions that occur in plant and animal cells which are essential for life.
2. The energy for metabolism comes from respiration.

### Page 15 Photosynthesis

The equation for photosynthesis is:
$6CO_2 + 6H_2O \rightarrow C_6H_{12}O_6 + 6O_2$, which is the reverse of the equation for respiration:
$C_6H_{12}O_6 + 6O_2 \rightarrow 6CO_2 + 6H_2O$.

### Page 16 Rate of photosynthesis

**(a)** Light intensity
carbon dioxide concentration
temperature

**(b)** Light intensity - without enough light, a plant cannot photosynthesise very quickly, even if there is plenty of water and carbon dioxide.

**(c)** Temperature - if it gets too cold, the rate of photosynthesis will decrease. Plants cannot photosynthesise if it gets too hot.

**(d)** Intensity

### Page 17 Uses of photosynthesis

1. It is important that plants can store the glucose they make during the day to allow them to respire at night when there is no light for photosynthesis.
2. Any one of:
   - It is insoluble, so does not affect the water concentration in cells.
   - It can be converted to cellulose, proteins or back to glucose when it is needed.
3. Any three of:
   - seeds
   - roots
   - leaves
   - stems.

### Page 18 Investigating photosynthesis

Using a gas syringe

### Page 19 The leaf

A leaf has a thin, flat, large surface area. This makes it light, allows it to collect a lot of energy from sunlight and allows carbon dioxide and oxygen to easily diffuse in and out of it.

Guard cells open and close pores on the underside of the leaf called stomata. Guard cells control the rate of transpiration. Chloroplasts are near the upper surface of the leaf to trap as much sunlight energy as possible.

### Page 20 Plant tissues

1. root hair → root → xylem → leaf vein → stomata
2. A root hair cell has a thin cell membrane to allow diffusion to occur easily, and a large surface area to increase the rate of water and mineral absorption.

### Page 21 Digestion in humans

Enzymes in the small intestine need alkaline conditions, so the stomach acid must be neutralised.

### Page 22 Food tests

Add the food to ethanol, shake, then add a few drops of the ethanol to water. A milky white emulsion forms if lipids are present.

### Page 23 Investigating enzymes

1. Changes in temperature affect the activity of the enzyme, amylase. Higher temperatures will cause the amylase to break down the starch more quickly than lower temperatures. If the temperature is too high, the enzymes will become denatured and no more starch will be broken down.
2. Repeat the experiment several more times and take an average of the results.

### Page 24 The blood

1. Red blood cells have no nucleus, which increases the space available for haemoglobin. They are a biconcave shape, which increases the surface area for oxygen to diffuse in and out of the cell. They have a small surface area to volume ratio. They are small, which allows them to pass easily through capillaries.
2. Phagocytes are white blood cells which ingest and destroy pathogens.

### Page 25 The heart and lungs

1. left ventricle → aorta → body → vena cava → right atrium → right ventricle → pulmonary artery → lungs → pulmonary vein → left atrium
2. Alveoli have a large surface area to absorb oxygen and remove carbon dioxide. They also have thin, moist membranes to allow gases to diffuse easily. Capillaries have very thin walls, usually one cell thick, to allow substances, such as oxygen and urea, to diffuse to and from tissues.

### Page 26 The human nervous system

**(a)** For example, light receptors in the retina or touch receptors in the skin

**(b)** For example, a muscle or a gland.

### Page 27 Reaction times

**(a)** mean = 110

**(b)** median = 111.5

**(c)** mean reaction time = 0.0474 s or 474 ms

### Page 28 Homeostasis

1. The body needs to maintain a constant temperature of about 37 °C to create the optimum conditions for enzymes to work.
2. The kidneys regulate the water levels within the body. If you drink too much water, the kidneys produce a large amount of dilute urine. If you don't drink enough water or lose water by sweating, the kidneys produce small amounts of concentrated urine.

### Page 29 Human endocrine system

1. C
2. A hormone is a substance that helps regulate processes in the body.

### Page 30 Control of blood glucose

Type 1 diabetes is where the pancreas does not produce sufficient insulin. Whereas, Type 2 is where the cells in the body no longer respond to insulin.

Type 1 diabetes is controlled by injections of insulin. Whereas, Type 2 is controlled by diet.

Obesity is a risk factor for Type 2 diabetes but not for Type 1.

### Page 31 Hormones in reproduction

1. During the 28 day menstrual cycle, the level of luteinising hormone increases and stimulates the release of an egg. The hormone level then falls, and the cycle is repeated.
2. Follicle stimulating hormone (FSH) stimulates oestrogen production. Oestrogen inhibits FSH production.
3. Progesterone

### Page 32 Hormones to treat infertility

1. Both are used to enable pregnancy to take place.

   In infertility treatment, hormones are used to bring about ovulation, whereas in IVF a woman's egg is fertilised in a Petri dish and then returned to her ovary.
2. Drugs that include follicle stimulating hormone (FSH) and luteinising hormone (LH) are sometimes used to stimulate ovulation. The woman can then become pregnant through intercourse.

### Page 33 Contraception

1. Scientific evidence and data can provide reliable information about the different types of contraception, which helps people to make an informed decision.
2. Is it morally right to use contraception?

   How much will it cost?

### Page 34 Negative feedback

1. Thyroxine increases the basal metabolic rate, helping with the manufacture of proteins and the growth of the long bones in the arms and legs.
2. Negative feedback happens where an output of a process, such as a hormone, feeds back into the system to reverse any changes and bring them back to a set level.
3. In the adrenal glands

### Page 35 Health issues

1. **(a)** Communicable diseases can be passed on by or caught from another person. Non-communicable diseases cannot.

   **(b)**
   - Quarantine can prevent diseases being passed on to another person.
   - Vaccinations make people immune to the disease.
2. **(a)** Pathogens are microorganisms that cause disease.

   **(b)** They can be spread by water, air and direct contact.

### Page 36 Coronary heart disease

1. All surgeries carry some risk. It may be very small, but it means that any surgery is not 100 per cent safe.
2. A stent or drugs such as statins

### Page 37 Effects of lifestyle

1. Obesity causes cells to become less sensitive to insulin.
2. Answers will vary, e.g:
   - Reduce levels of obesity by running a healthy eating campaign.
   - Run a campaign encouraging people to take more exercise.
3. Poor diet affects both physical health, by causing obesity or nutritional deficiencies, and mental health.

### Page 38 Cancer

**(a)** People aged 29 or less

**(b)** People who have never smoked can still get lung cancer. The older you are when you stop smoking, the more likely you are to get lung cancer.

**(c)** **(i)** Approximately 0.5 per cent

**(ii)** Approximately 5.5 per cent

### Page 39 Infections

1. A disease that can be passed from one person to another.
2. Infectious microorganisms can be breathed in without coming into contact with the infected person.

### Page 40 Viral diseases

Viruses are much smaller than bacteria. They consist of small packets of DNA that take over the host cell when they invade it. The DNA in a virus instructs the cell to make more copies of the virus.

### Page 41 Bacterial diseases

1. Some bacteria produce toxins, which attack and kill cells. The destruction of cells and tissue causes symptoms of the disease to appear.
2. The spread of gonorrhoea can be prevented by abstaining from sex, using a condom and regular screening followed by treatment if necessary.

### Page 42 Fungal diseases

1. Fungi reproduce through spores, which means they are not an animal. Fungal cells have a cell wall, like plants, but do

not contain any chlorophyll. This means that, unlike plants, they cannot make their own food.

2. The leaves should be burned so that the spores cannot infect healthy rose leaves.

### Page 43 Protist diseases

1. Mosquitoes
2. Because it is the protist, the parasite, which is carried by the mosquito, that causes the disease.

### Page 44 Human defence systems

1. White blood cells engulf bacteria and produce antibodies that kill them.
2. The person's immune system responds by producing white blood cells, which kill the pathogen. The white blood cells produce antibodies that stay in the blood to kill the pathogen if it returns. Memory cells that remember how to produce the antibodies stay in the bloodstream.

### Page 45 Vaccination

1. They vaccinate their children so that they will not pass the disease onto others.
2. When a sufficient number of the population is immune to the disease, the pathogen is less likely to be passed on so it dies out.
3. They may be worried about reactions or allergies, or be sceptical about the effectiveness of vaccinations.
4. Memory cells recognise reinvading antigens and produce specific antibodies to destroy them.

### Page 46 Antibiotics and painkillers

1. Viruses are packets of DNA, not living things, so cannot be killed by antibiotics.
2. Answers will vary, for example:
   - Penicillin is an antibiotic that kills the bacteria causing an infection.
   - Aspirin treats the symptoms of the infection, such as high body temperature, but does not kill the bacteria causing it.
3. Rainforests contain many different species of plant, some of which may contain useful drugs.

### Page 47 Resistant bacteria

1. Bacteria develop resistance to antibiotics by evolution and natural selection. Some bacteria have mutations which make them resistant to a particular antibiotic. These resistant bacteria will survive and reproduce rapidly. The bacteria that are susceptible to the antibiotic will be destroyed. Eventually, only bacteria that are resistant to the antibiotic will exist.
2. Mutations cause some bacteria to become resistant to an antibiotic. Mutations occur randomly when DNA replicates during reproduction and bacteria reproduce very rapidly.

### Page 48 Development of drugs

1. The work of one scientist is checked by others to make sure that it is verified.
2. 9 to 14 years

### Page 49 Asexual and sexual reproduction

1. Sexual reproduction involves the fusion of male and female gametes. Asexual reproduction does not.
2. A gamete is a sex cell which contains genetic information.

### Page 50 Chromosomes, mitosis and the cell cycle

1. The cell needs to grow and increase its sub-cellular structures, such as ribosomes and mitochondria.
2. Firstly, the DNA is replicated, then the pairs of chromosomes are separated. Finally, the cells divide to produce two identical copies.
3. 46 (23 pairs)

### Page 51 Meiosis

1. The sex cells fuse during fertilisation; the offspring therefore receive chromosomes from both parents. As there are two alleles, inherited variation may occur.
2. **(a)** Half the number of chromosomes (haploid)

   **(b)** 23 chromosomes (unpaired)

### Page 52 DNA and the genome

1. A sample of DNA can be taken from the foetus and compared with the genome of a cystic fibrosis sufferer to identify if the gene for cystic fibrosis is present.
2. By identifying the mutated gene and knowing what the healthy gene should be, scientists can develop methods of treating genetic mutations.
3. It can be used to identify genetic diseases, trace human migration and identify disease-causing genes.

### Page 53 Genetic inheritance

**(a)**

| | | Mother | |
|---|---|---|---|
| | | D | D |
| Father | d | Dd | Dd |
| | d | Dd | Dd |

**(b)** 100 per cent

### Page 54 Inherited disorders

1. **(a)** FF

   **(b)** They will be homozygous (ff) because the condition is recessive (represented by a lowercase f). This means that to have the condition, the person must inherit both alleles for it.

   **(c)**

| | | Mother | |
|---|---|---|---|
| | | F | f |
| Father | F | FF | Ff |
| | f | Ff | ff |

Therefore the probability of being affected (ff) is 25 per cent.

2. Any one advantage from the following:
   - prevents having a child with the disorder who could suffer
   - reduces the chance of the disease being passed on
   - embryo cells could be used in stem cell treatment
   - saves long term cost of treating a child with a disorder.

   Any one disadvantage from the following:
   - may lead to damage or destruction of the embryo (leading to miscarriage)
   - the embryo is unable to give consent
   - can lead to prejudice.

### Page 55 Variation and mutation

1. Answers will vary, e.g.:
   - genetic – tongue rolling, Down's syndrome, blood group, eye colour, hair colour
   - environmental – weight, language spoken, religion.
2. A mutation is a change in the genetic material. Mutations can occur when DNA replicates, or it can be caused by environmental factors such as smoking cigarettes or exposure to high levels of radiation.
3. Mutation could improve chances of survival or crops could mutate to become resistant to the disease.

### Page 56 Sex determination

1. **(a)** XX
   **(b)** One chromosome (always an X)
   **(c)** 0.5 / ½ / 50% / 1:1 / 50:50 / 1 in 2
   Half of the sperm contains a Y chromosome, so half will be male.

### Page 57 Communities

1. **(a)** When the population of algae increases, the population of snails increases shortly after. This is because there is more food for the snails, which makes them more likely to reproduce. As the population of snails increases, the amount of food available per individual decreases, causing the them to compete for it. Some die, decreasing the population. The cycle then begins again.
   **(b)** The snail population would decrease. With less snails to feed on it, the algae population would then increase.

### Page 58 Abiotic factors

1. Temperature, rainfall, moisture levels
2. A change in temperature could cause the ice to melt, which would damage or destroy animal and plant habitats. It could also lead to a lack of food, causing starvation of certain species and possible extinction.

### Page 59 Biotic factors

1. Predators (e.g. polar bears), plants (e.g. lichen), food (e.g. fish for seals and polar bears)
2. Abiotic factors: temperature, carbon dioxide levels, wind intensity.
   Biotic factors: new pathogens, food availability, predators.
3. Grey squirrels competed with red squirrels for food and territory, causing a great decrease in the population of red squirrels.

### Page 60 Adaptations

1. Migration
2. Hibernation lowers metabolism to conserve energy.
3. For camouflage – the fox is brown in the summer to help it hide in earth and white in the winter to help it hide in the snow.

### Page 61 Organisation of an ecosystem

1. Consumers cannot produce their own energy, so must obtain it by eating other organisms.
2. Green plant or alga.
3. Because for this measurement to be taken, all water must be removed from organisms, which can be a difficult process.
4. The third consumer (producer → primary consumer → secondary consumer → tertiary consumer)

### Page 62 Investigating population size

**(a)** $3 + 5 + 3 + 1 + 3 + 5 + 2 + 2 = 24$
$24 \div 8 = 3$
**(b)** $2000 \div 1 = 2000$
$2000 \times 3 = 6000$

### Page 63 Biodiversity

1. For example:
   - limiting how many fish can be caught in a given period of time
   - returning the young fish to the sea so that they can reproduce.
2. Species maintain stable ecosystems by providing food and shelter for one another. If one species becomes extinct, others could also be affected too, reducing biodiversity.

### Page 64 Maintaining biodiversity

1. Burn less fossil fuels and use alternative fuel sources instead.
   Use methods such as carbon capture and storage (sequestration).
2. Advantage: it increases the biodiversity and so strengthens the ecosystem.
   Disadvantage: it takes up valuable farm land that could be used to grow crops.

### Page 65 Cycling materials

1. The dead animal is decayed and broken down by microorganisms/detritus feeders/decomposers. When these respire, they release the carbon as carbon dioxide.

2. The Earth has a fixed amount of water, and the water cycle allows fresh water to move around the planet, providing a supply to sustain plants and animals. Without it, we would run out of fresh water.

## Page 66 Classification

1. It is a very easy system to use.
   It is very quick to identify an unknown organism.
2. Any two from:
   - improvements to microscopes
   - DNA analysis and sequencing
   - improved understanding of biological processes.

## Page 67 Evolution

1. Variation occurs between organisms within a species. Those most suited to their environment ('the fittest') survive, and their genes (alleles) are passed on to their offspring.
2. Birds and other predators will assume the kingsnake is harmful and not attempt to eat it. This means that the snake is left to reproduce.
3. All species have evolved from simpler organisms over billions of years.

## Page 68 Fossils

1. There are no fossils that old, so there is little evidence.
2. It was too cold for microorganisms to function on the glaciers, so organisms that died there didn't decay.
3. The shapes of bones and skeletons can be seen in rocks.

## Page 69 Selective breeding

1. Answers will vary, e.g.:
   - to keep them disease free
   - for an improved appearance
   - so that they are docile.
2. Selective breeding involves humans choosing and enhancing desired characteristics in an organism. Natural selection is where a feature is passed down through generations because it gives an organism a better chance of survival, making it more likely to reproduce.
3. Random genetic mutations can occur, leading to genetic disease.
   There is a reduction in the gene pool, making the species more susceptible to disease.
4. It can make them more disease resistant and improve yield.

## Page 70 Genetic engineering

1. It may lead to cloning of animals. Some people consider it unethical. It may create new genetic disorders.
2. Farmers may use more herbicide. The herbicides may harm people who eat the crops. It may also cause a herbicide-resistant weed to develop.

## Page 71 Stem cells

1. Any one advantage from:
   - Farmers can grow a whole field of disease-resistant crops.
   - Farmers can grow crops with a large yield.
2. Ethical considerations include:
   - the embryo's right to life
   - the sufferer's right to a better quality of life.

## Page 72 Extinction

1. Answers will vary, e.g.:
   - record of numbers
   - breeding programs
   - protection orders to prevent hunting
   - protected habitats.
2. It means that there are no more individuals of that species alive and the loss of the species is permanent.
3. It destroys habitats, wiping out food sources. Some species are unable to survive the change in temperature or are not adapted to cold temperatures.

## Page 73 Waste management

1. Increased pollution is causing acid rain and global warming. Increased use of landfills is damaging and destroying habitats.
2. The human population is increasing, so humans are emitting more carbon dioxide. Industrialisation means we are burning more fossil fuels to generate energy.

## Page 74 Land use

1. Decaying and burning peat increases the release of carbon dioxide into the atmosphere.
2. They will have less habitat and less food, so populations will decrease.
3. Increased building of houses will produce more pollution and waste and destroy natural habitats.
4. Advantage: it is nutrient rich, which encourages crop growth.
   Disadvantage: increases carbon dioxide levels in the atmosphere.

## Page 75 Deforestation

1. There are less trees so less photosynthesis. Burning wood releases carbon dioxide into the atmosphere. As the trees die they are decayed by microorganisms, which release carbondioxide when they respire.
2. Answers will vary, e.g.:
   - Flooding – fewer trees will absorb less rain water, leading to flooding.
   - Climate change – fewer trees mean more carbon dioxide in the atmosphere because less is absorbed for photosynthesis. Trees also affect the levels of water vapour in the atmosphere, which contributes to global warming.
   - Loss of species – the more trees that are destroyed, the less habitat there is available for species to live in.

- Soil erosion – tree roots anchor soil. Without them, the soil can be eroded quickly making it difficult to grow crops.
- Water pollution – soil erosion can lead to silt entering water sources, which decreases the quality of the water.

## Page 76 Global warming

**Three** biological effects, e.g.:

- Changes in biodiversity – some species could become extinct leading to gaps in the food chain.
- Changes in migration patterns – migration timings are altering which could have an impact on food availability.
- Changes in habitats – animals may move to new habitats that are more suitable to their needs.
- Changes in the timings of plant and animal reproduction.
- Increased adaptation – species will have to adapt to cope with the changes in the environment.
- Increase in pests and disease – pests and disease can survive in warmer conditions.

## Page 77 States of matter

1. LiCl – solid
   $BeCl_2$ – solid
   $CCl_4$ – liquid
   $NCl_3$ – liquid
   $OCl_2$ – gas
2. Liquid
3. Liquid

## Page 78 Atoms, elements and compounds

1. Atom
2. Al
3. **(a)** Sodium
   **(b) (i)** Hydrogen, H
   **(ii)** hydrogen + chlorine → hydrogen chloride

## Page 79 Pure substances

1. Compare the boiling point, melting point and density of the sample with the given data.
2. All the atoms or molecules are the same within the substance.
3. The sample is impure.

## Page 80 Mixtures

1. Ink and water – simple distillation
   Sand and water – filtration
   Crude oil – fractional distillation
   Sugar and water – evaporation
2. W – conical flask; X – filter paper; Y – filter funnel

## Page 81 Formulations

1. **(a)** Formulation
   **(b)** It is used to give the paint its colour.
2. The correct quantities are required to give the product the desired properties.
3. Any one of the following: paints, cosmetics, food and drink

## Page 82 Chromatography

1. The brown food colourant contains yellow, red and purple pigment (or yellow and purple).
2. $R_f$ values tell you the ratio of the distance moved by the dye and the distance moved by the solvent.
3. $R_f$ values are not given units because they are a ratio.

## Page 83 Paper chromatography

1. If the base line is below the level of solvent the spots of dye will dissolve into the solvent.
2. Pencil will not dissolve in the solvent, but pen will.
3. 0.31

## Page 84 The model of the atom

In Rutherford's scattering experiment, some of the alpha particles were repelled by positively charged particles in the nucleus, although most of the alpha particles passed through the atom without being repelled, which showed that the nucleus was only a small part of the atom.

## Page 85 Subatomic particles

1. 0.00001 nm
2. Positive
3. Protons and neutrons
4. **(a)** 2
   **(b)** There are the same number of positive protons as there are negative electrons.
   **(c)** A helium atom contains two protons and two neutrons in the nucleus, and two electrons in the first electron shell.

## Page 86 Size and mass of atoms

**(a)** The atomic number is the number of protons.

The mass number is the number of protons plus the number of neutrons.

**(b)**

| Subatomic particle | Relative mass | Relative charge |
|---|---|---|
| electron | $\frac{1}{1840}$ | −1 |
| neutron | 1 | 0 |
| proton | 1 | +1 |

**(c)** 10

## Page 87 Isotopes and relative atomic mass

**(a)** R and S, because the isotopes have the same number of protons (same atomic number) but a different number of neutrons (different atomic mass).

**(b)** Lithium

### Page 88 Electronic structure

**(a)** C **(b)** B **(c)** D **(d)** C

### Page 89 The periodic table

1. **(a)** Group 5
   **(b)** Period 3
   **(c)** Nitrogen
2. **(a)** Group 2
   **(b)** Period 3
3. The elements are arranged in the periodic table in ascending order of atomic number.

### Page 90 Developing the periodic table

**(a)** Boron and aluminium
**(b)** A - atomic mass
**(c)** They all have one electron in their outer shell.

### Page 91 Metals and non-metals

Any one of:

- resistant to corrosion so won't react with food
- low density so practical as a lightweight wrapping.

### Page 92 Group 0

1. **(a)** 0
   **(b)** Unreactive
2. **(a)** The atomic mass increases because there are more protons in the atom.
   **(b)** Because their outer shells are full, noble gas atoms are unreactive.
3. 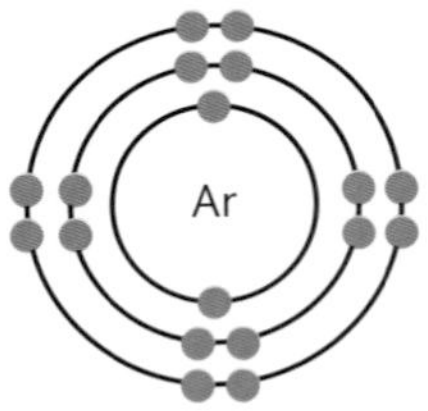


### Page 93 Group 1

1. As you move down the group the elements gain an electron shell, so the outer electron is further away from the positively charged nucleus. This means that the outer electrons are held less strongly and are lost more easily, making the elements more reactive.
2. Lithium and water produce hydrogen gas (and lithium hydroxide). The bubbles are the gas being produced.
3. Less than 65 °C (it is approximately 39 °C)

### Page 94 Group 7

1. bromine + potassium iodide → potassium bromide + iodine
2. Chlorine is more reactive than iodine.
3. Chlorine or fluorine
4. Fluorine is more reactive. This is because its outer electron shell is closer to the nucleus, so there is a stronger force of attraction for electrons, and these are more easily gained in reactions (than they are in iodine).

### Page 95 Conservation of mass

1. 50 g
2. **(a)** magnesium carbonate → magnesium oxide + carbon dioxide
   **(b)** 84 g = 40 + ?
   84 - 40 = 44 g of carbon dioxide

### Page 96 Relative formula mass

1. $9 \times 12 = 108$
   $4 \times 16 = 64$
   $8 \times 1 = 8$
   $108 + 64 + 8 = 180$
2. $2 \times 27 = 54$
   $3 \times 32 = 96$
   $12 \times 16 = 192$
   $54 + 96 + 192 = 342$

### Page 97 Balancing equations

1. $\mathbf{4}Fe + \mathbf{3}O_2 \rightarrow \mathbf{2}Fe_2O_3$
2. Balanced equations give the formulas of substances. They show how many molecules of each substance are involved in the reaction.
3. Chemical equations always balance because mass cannot be created or destroyed in a chemical reaction.

### Page 98 Mass changes

1. **(a)** zinc carbonate → zinc oxide + carbon dioxide
   **(b)** Carbon dioxide gas produced in the reaction escaped.
   **(c)** The zinc carbonate could be heated with oxygen in a test tube and the gases collected, which would allow the products to be measured more accurately.
2. **(a)** $C_2H_5OH\ (l) + \mathbf{3}O_2\ (g) \rightarrow \mathbf{2}CO_2\ (g) + \mathbf{3}H_2O\ (l)$
   **(b)** The reaction has taken in oxygen from the atmosphere.

### Page 99 Chemical measurements

Mean = 162.98 seconds
Range = 16.90 seconds
Value of uncertainty = 8.45 seconds

### Page 100 Moles

1. 1 mol $O_2$ = 2 × mass of O = 2 × 16 = 32 g
2. Mg = 1
   HCl = 2
3. $M_r$ = Ca + C + (3 × O)
   40 + 12 + (3 × 16) = 100
   1 mole $CaCO_3$ is 100 g, so in 10 000 g there are 10 000 ÷ 100 = 100 mol of $CaCO_3$.

## Page 101 Amount of substances

1. **(a)** **2**Mg(s) + $O_2$(g) → **2**MgO(s)

   **(b)** 1 : 1

   24    40

   55 × 24    55 × 24 × 40

   2.29    91.67 g to 2 s.f

2. Ca(s) + 2HCl(aq) → $CaCl_2$(aq) + $H_2$(g)

   1 : 1

   40    111

   0.5 × 111 x 40    0.5 × 111

   0.18 g    0.0045 g

## Page 102 Concentrations of solutions

1. 40 g/dm$^3$
2. 50 g
3. The concentration will increase as the mass of solute used increases.

## Page 103 Using mass to balance equations

1. 15.9    0.4    12.7    3.6

   79.5    2    63.5    18

   0.2    0.2    0.2    0.2

   **CuO** + **$H_2$** → **Cu** + **$H_2O$**

2. **(a)** 13    14.6    27.2    0.4

   65    36.5    136    2

   0.2    0.4    0.2    0.2

   1 : 2 : 1 : 1

   **Zn** + 2**HCl** → **$ZnCl_2$** + **$H_2$**

   **(b)** The numbers represent how many molecules of that substance are involved in the reaction.

## Page 104 Chemical bonds

**(a)** They are electrons that are free to move.

**(b)** Metallic bonding

## Page 105 Ionic bonding

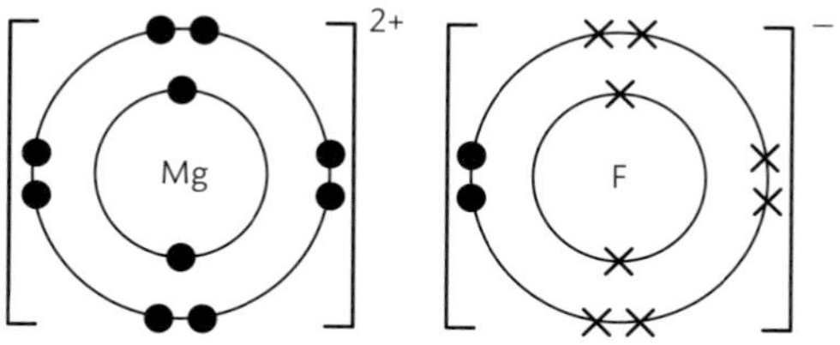


magnesium ion, $Mg^{2+}$    fluoride ion, $F^-$

## Page 106 Ionic compounds

1. Sodium chloride forms a giant **ionic** lattice, with strong **electrostatic** forces of attraction.
2. **(a)** Ionic

   **(b)** NaCl

   **(c)** Limitation: The diagram incorrectly suggests there are gaps between the atoms.
   Advantage: The diagram shows bonds between the atoms.

## Page 107 Properties of ionic compounds

1. **(a)** 2Na + $Cl_2$ → 2NaCl

   **(b)**

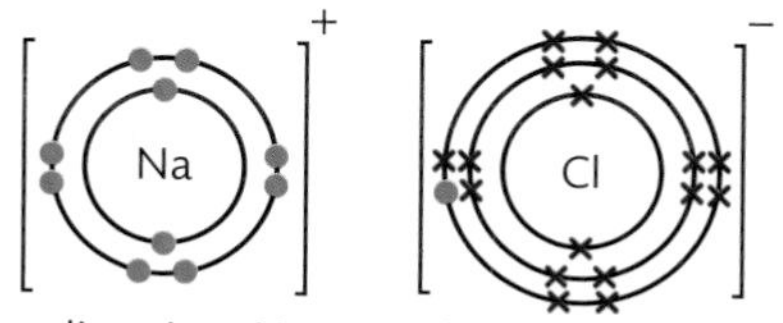


sodium ion, **$Na^+$**    chloride ion, **$Cl^-$**

2. **(a)** Magnesium oxide is an ionic compound formed by the transfer of two electrons from a magnesium atom to a oxygen atom, forming $Mg^{2+}$ and $O^{2-}$.

   **(b)** When molten, the ions are free to move, which allows electrical charge to flow.

   **(c)** Ionic bonds are very strong. There are many bonds in an ionic lattice and they must all be broken to melt magnesium oxide.

## Page 108 Reversible reactions

1. The products of the reaction can react to form the original reactants.
2. **(a)** By reversing the reaction (adding water) the original substance (hydrated copper sulfate) is formed.

   **(b)** hydrated copper sulfate ⇌ anhydrous copper sulfate + water

## Page 109 Energy changes in reversible reactions

1. The reaction requires energy, which it draws from the surroundings.
2. It is an endothermic reaction, because it requires heat energy.
3. 256 kJ/mol

## Page 110 Equilibrium and changing conditions

**(a)** Temperature and pressure

**(b)** A reaction that releases energy

**(c)** Reducing the particles drives the reaction to the right-hand side, producing more sulfur trioxide.

## Page 111 Concentration and equilibrium

**(a)** The yield of hydrogen would increase because the system would try to oppose the change and reduce the amount of methane present.

**(b)** An equilibrium is reached in a reversible reaction when the forward reaction occurs at exactly the same rate as the reverse reaction.

## Page 112 Temperature and equilibrium

**(a)** Heat energy is needed to drive the forward reaction to maximise the production of hydrogen gas.

**(b)** Endothermic

## Page 113 Pressure and equilibrium

**(a)** A and C

**(b)** A, because it has more product molecules, so the system will move equilibrium to reduce the number of molecules.

**(c)** The yield of methanol will decrease, because the system will move equilibrium to increase the number of molecules.

## Page 114 Covalent bonding

1. A bond between non-metal atoms sharing a pair of electrons
2. 3
3. 

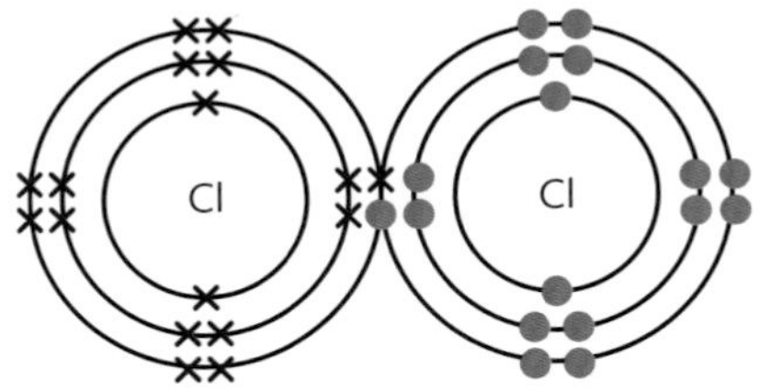


## Page 115 Properties of small molecules

1. B and C
2. The substance must be heated to provide enough energy for intermolecular forces between molecules to be overcome.

## Page 116 Giant covalent structures

1. Three
2. Four
3. Covalent
4. Giant covalent lattice

   There are many strong covalent bonds between the atoms, which must be broken to melt the silicon dioxide.

## Page 117 Diamond

1. **(a)** The bonds between the carbon atoms are very strong, so it takes a lot of energy to break them.

   **(b)** It does not have any charged particles that are free to move. It has a giant structure (lattice).
2. Its atoms are bonded with strong covalent bonds. Each carbon atom is bonded to four other carbon atoms. A lot of energy is needed to break the bonds. This makes diamond a very hard substance, which means it is able to cut through other materials.

## Page 118 Graphite

**(a)** It conducts electricity and it has a high melting point.

**(b)** Three covalent

**(c)** A

**(d)** Pencil lead and lubricant

## Page 119 Graphene and fullerenes

1. Carbon
2. Similarities:
   - In both, each carbon atom is bonded to three others.
   - They both conduct electricity.

   Difference:
   - Graphite is soft because it consists of layers, whereas nanotubes are strong.

## Page 120 Calculating rate of reaction

**(a)** $cm^3/s$

**(b)** $120 \div 120 = 1\ cm^3/s$

**(c)** It has increased the rate of reaction. However, the same amount of product is formed.

## Page 121 Factors affecting rate of reaction

**(a)** No more bubbles/gas were produced.

**(b)**

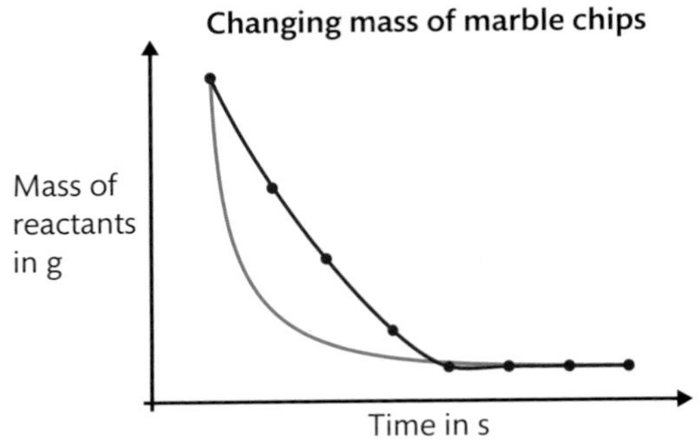


**(c)** Increase the concentration of hydrochloric acid.

Increase the surface area of the marble chips.

## Page 122 Rate of reaction

**(a)** The more concentrated the acid is, the faster the reaction will be and the quicker the cross will disappear. This is because a greater number of acid particles in the reaction mixture increases the chance of successful collisions.

**(b)** Independent variable – the concentration of the acid
Dependent variable – the time taken for the cross to disappear

Control variables – the volume of acid, the volume and concentration of thiosulfate and the temperature of the reaction

## Page 123 Testing for gases

Chlorine – bleaches litmus paper

Hydrogen – squeaky pop

Oxygen – relights a glowing splint

Carbon dioxide – limewater turns cloudy

## Page 124 The reactivity series

1. A – magnesium

   B – iron

   C – copper

   D – calcium
2. The more easily a metal forms a positive ion, the more reactive it will be.
3. $Ca(s) + \mathbf{2}H_2O(l) \rightarrow Ca(OH)_2 + H_2(g)$

## Page 125 Limiting reactants

1. **(a)** Gas syringe

   **(b)** When the student adds more hydrochloric acid to the reaction mixture, more gas is produced so the reaction restarts.

2. $CaCO_3 \rightarrow CaO + CO_2$

   100 56

   $100 \div 56 = 1.79$ $x \times 56 = 1.79$

   $x = 1.79 \times 56 = 100\,g$

## Page 126 Oxidation and reduction

**(a)** $Mg + CuO \rightarrow MgO + Cu$

**(b)** $Mg \rightarrow Mg^{2+} + 2e^-$

## Page 127 Reactions of acids with metals

1. $Mg(s) + 2HCl(aq) \rightarrow MgCl_2(aq) + H_2(g)$
2. Reduction is the addition of electrons and loss of oxygen.

## Page 128 Electrolysis

1. Electrolyte – liquid used for electrolysis

   Electrode – solid, electrical conductor

   Anode – electrode with a positive charge

   Cathode – electrode with a negative charge
2. The cathode/negative electrode

## Page 129 Electrolysis of molten ionic compounds

1. **(a)**

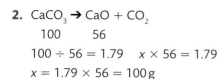

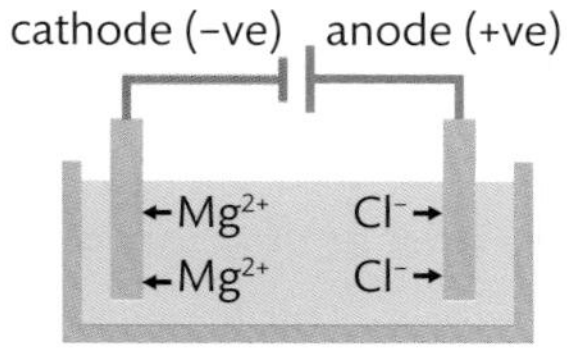


   **(b)** $Mg^{2+} + \mathbf{2e^-} \rightarrow Mg$

   $2Cl^- \rightarrow Cl_2 + \mathbf{2e^-}$

   **(c)** Magnesium ions are reduced
2. **(a)** Cathode: lead Anode: bromine

   **(b)** Cathode: zinc Anode: iodine

   **(c)** Cathode: magnesium Anode: oxygen

   **(d)** Cathode: lithium Anode: chlorine

## Page 130 Electrolysis of aqueous solutions

**(a)** The solution conducts electricity.

Bubbling is seen at the electrodes (as hydrogen and chlorine gas are produced).

The ions move to oppositely charged electrodes.

The negative ions lose electrons and the positive ions gain electrons.

**(b)** $2Cl^- - 2e^- \rightarrow Cl_2$

## Page 131 Electrolysis of copper(II) chloride

**(a)** Chlorine, hydrogen and sodium hydroxide

**(b)** Chloride ions are negative, so are attracted to the anode. Hydrogen ions are positive, so are attracted to the cathode.

## Page 132 Half equations

1. Anode: $2Cl^- \rightarrow Cl_2 + 2e^-$

   Cathode: $Cu^{2+} + 2e^- \rightarrow Cu$
2. So that the electrodes don't react with the electrolyte

## Page 133 Meta

1. C – nuclei
2. The metal particles hav
   from the delocalised elect
   metal particle is positively cha
3. The metal's outer electrons are delo ive charge
   attracted to the positive nuclei of the r of the

## Page 134 Metal oxides

**(a)** iron + oxygen → iron oxide

**(b)** redox

**(c)** oxygen

## Page 135 Extraction of metals and reduction

1. **(a)** lead oxide + carbon → lead + carbon dioxide

   **(b)** Oxidation

   **(c)** The lead in lead oxide has an oxidation state of +2.

   After reduction to lead the oxidation state is zero, so the lead has gained electrons.
2. Calcium is above carbon in the reactivity series. Metals can only be extracted by elements that are more reactive than them.

## Page 136 Electrolysis to extract metals

1. Large amounts of energy are needed to melt the magnesium chloride.
2. It is dissolved in cryolite.
3. Reduction requires a lot of energy to be provided in the form of high temperatures, which is expensive. It usually involves burning fossil fuels, which are a limited resource. Burning fossil fuels and reduction also produce carbon dioxide, which enhances the greenhouse effect. Additionally, reduction can only be used for metals lower on the reactivity series than carbon and metal products are impure and may need further processing.

   Electrolysis is very expensive as it requires a lot of energy to melt the metal and to provide electricity for the electrolysis process. It also involves burning fossil fuels, which are limited and cause global warming. Electrodes often need replacing.

   However, it can be used to extract any metal and metal products are pure.

## Page 137 Alternative methods of extracting metals

1. Any two of:
   - Copper ores are running out.
   - Only small amounts of high-grade copper ores are left.
   - Copper is in high demand.
   - Copper is expensive.
   - It is now economical to extract copper from low-grade ores.
2. Plants that naturally absorb copper ions are grown. The plants are then burned and copper compounds are removed from the ash.

…ich has a negative impact …cies. It also creates dust and

3. Bioleaching …ing requires a lot of energy, making …also involves burning fossil fuels which

4. Minin… …esource. Carbon dioxide is produced during …ocess, which leads to global warming. In addition, …aste rock needs to be disposed of – usually as landfill.

Phytomining improves habitats and the landscape as plants grow. Plants are carbon neutral so don't contribute to global warming. Phytomining saves valuable ores of copper and uses low percentage sources of copper.

### Page 138 Properties of metals and alloys

**(a)** The strong metallic bonds between positive metal nuclei and negative delocalised electrons take a large amount of heat energy to break.

**(b)** Gold is too soft, but gold alloy is harder.

### Page 139 Metals as conductors

1. A conductor
2. Metals have delocalised electrons that carry thermal energy.
3. When a metal is heated, its delocalised electrons gain energy and vibrate more vigorously. These particles bump into nearby particles causing them to vibrate more and transferring thermal energy through the metal by conduction.

### Page 140 The pH scale and neutralisation

1. hydrochloric acid + sodium hydroxide → sodium chloride + water
2. **(a)** alkali/base

   **(b)** $OH^-$
3. By using a pH probe

### Page 141 Strong and weak acids

1. A strong acid is one that completely dissociates (splits up) into ions in aqueous solution.
2. Any two of:
   - sulfuric acid
   - nitric acid
   - hydrochloric acid.
3. **(a)** $H^+ + OH^- \rightarrow H_2O$

   **(b)** $H^+$

   **(c)** The hydrogen ion concentration increases by a factor of ten for every pH unit decrease.

### Page 142 Salt production

1. Potassium nitrate
2. Neutralisation
3. Hydrochloric acid
4. $Zn^{2+} + SO_4^{2-} \rightarrow ZnSO_4$
5. **(a)** $Li_2SO_4$

   **(b)** $MgCl_2$

   **(c)** $Ca(NO_3)_2$

### Page 143 Soluble salts

1. Filtration
2. C
3. copper nitrate
4. The substance will dissolve in water.

### Page 144 Making salts

1. C Warm dilute sulfuric acid and add excess zinc hydroxide.

   E Filter the solution.

   B Heat the solution until it has evaporated and crystals start to form.

   A Leave to cool so more crystals will form.

   D Dry the crystals obtained.
2. Zinc sulfate

### Page 145 Exothermic and endothermic reactions

1. Exothermic
2. It will decrease.

### Page 146 Temperature changes

–6.3 °C

The reaction was endothermic because the temperature decreased.

### Page 147 Collision theory and activation energy

1. The rate of reaction will increase. This is because the particles have more energy and therefore will move quicker, increasing the chance of collisions.
2. The gas particles become more crowded, so there is more chance of successful collisions and a higher rate of reaction.

### Page 148 Reaction profiles

1.

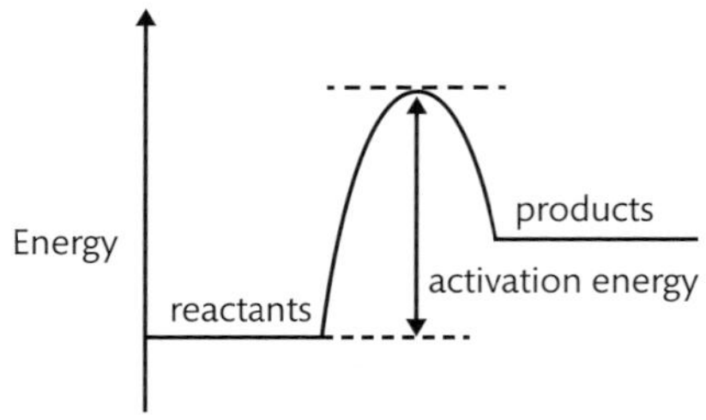


2. **(a)** Exothermic, because the products have less energy than the reactants (as heat is lost to the surroundings).

   **(b)**

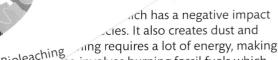

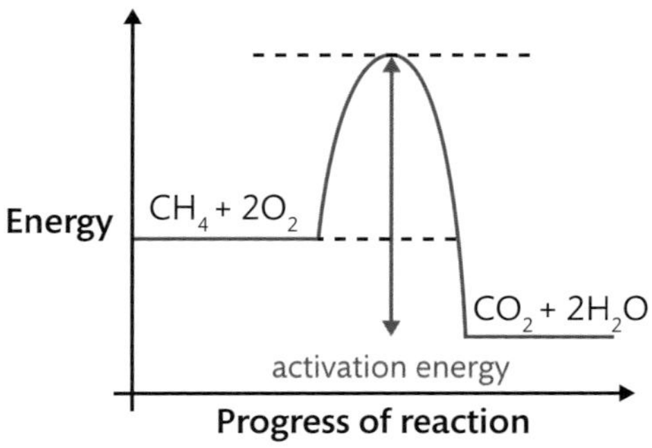

## Page 149 Energy changes in reactions

**(a)** −549 kJ/mol

**(b)** Exothermic

## 150 Catalysts

**1.**

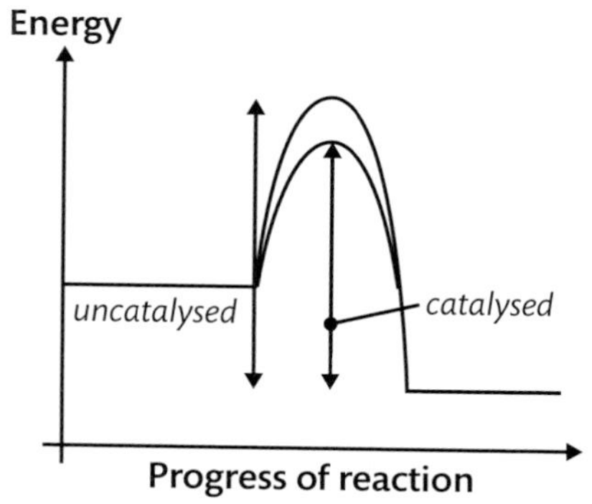

**2.** Enzymes

## Page 151 Crude oil, hydrocarbons and alkanes

**1.** A limited supply that will eventually run out.

**2.** They only contain single bonds between carbon atoms. There are no double bonds.

**3.** If C = 6

$H = (6 \times 2) + 2 = 12 + 2 = 14$

## Page 152 Fractional distillation

**1.** The crude oil is heated to evaporate the hydrocarbons. The column is cooler at the top and hotter at the bottom. The gaseous fractions travel up the column until they reach their boiling point, where they condense and can be collected.

**2.** X – evaporation

Z – condensation

## Page 153 Properties of hydrocarbons

**1.** Water and carbon dioxide

**2.** $2C_2H_6 + 7O_2 \rightarrow 4CO_2 + 6H_2O$

**3.** As molecular size increases, viscosity increases too.

**4.** Because in the combustion of a hydrocarbon both the carbon and the hydrogen atoms gain oxygen.

## Page 154 Cracking and alkenes

**1.** It is used in the oil industry because the shorter hydrocarbon molecules produced can be used to make fuels, such as petrol.

**2** $C_8H_{18}$

## Page 155 Atmospheric pollutants

**1.** Carbon dioxide – global warming

Sulfur dioxide – acid rain

Solid particulates – global dimming

Carbon monoxide – toxic gas

**2.** Sulfur dioxide causes acid rain

**3. (a)** Carbon monoxide and soot are produced when a fuel burns in a limited supply of oxygen.

**(b)** Sulfur dioxide is produced when a fuel containing sulfur is burned, such as coal.

**(c)** Oxides of nitrogen are produced when the heat from car engines causes nitrogen and oxygen in the air to react together.

## Page 156 Polymers

**1.**

$$\left( \begin{array}{c} H \quad H \quad H \\ | \quad\; | \quad\; | \\ C - C - C \\ | \quad\; | \quad\; | \\ H \quad H \quad H \end{array} \right)_n$$

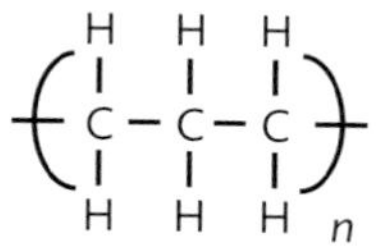

**2.** Polymers are very large molecules made from many smaller molecules joined together by strong covalent bonds in long chains.

**3.** Covalent bonds

## Page 157 Gases in the atmosphere

**1.** 78–80 per cent

**2.** The fraction of oxygen is about 20%, which is $\dfrac{20}{100}$.

Divide both by a common factor to get the lowest values:

$20 \div 20 = 1$

$100 \div 20 = 5$

So oxygen is $\dfrac{1}{5}$.

## Page 158 Earth's early atmosphere

**(a)** 3.5%

**(b)** There are no plants to carry out photosynthesis and produce oxygen.

**(c)** Argon is inert/unreactive.

## Page 159 Oxygen and carbon dioxide levels

**1.** Approximately 20%

**2.** Calcium carbonate includes carbon, so it is a carbon store, which reduces the amount of carbon dioxide in the atmosphere.

**3.** Carbon from carbon dioxide is used by plants to make glucose. When plants and animals die, the carbon inside them became trapped. Under specific conditions of temperature and pressure their remains become fossil fuels.

## Page 160 Greenhouse gases

**1.** Methane, carbon dioxide and water vapour

**2.** Greenhouse gases do not absorb the short-wave radiation from the sun. Instead, the radiation passes through the atmosphere and warms the Earth. Energy reflected back from the Earth has a longer wavelength that can be absorbed by the greenhouse gases. The reflected energy becomes trapped, maintaining the temperature of the planet.

**3.** By volcanoes

## Page 161 Human contribution to greenhouse gases

1. Any two of:
   - increased combustion of fossil fuels
   - increased population
   - increased waste
   - deforestation.
2. It ensures that the evidence used to support a theory is reliable.
3. They think it may lead to global climate change.
4. It is that important scientists' results are widely available so that other scientists can use their results to inform their own work, and so that results which have an impact on the wider population can be communicated to as many people as possible.

## Page 162 Global climate change

1. Any two of:
   - rising sea levels
   - heat waves
   - change in precipitation patterns
   - increasing storm intensity.
2. More rainfall could cause flooding, which would damage crops and homes.

   Less rainfall could lead to drought, which would cause crops to fail, leading to starvation.
3. An increase in greenhouse gases in the atmosphere contributing to increasing global temperatures

## Page 163 The carbon footprint

1. Any two of:
   - use energy efficient appliances
   - switch off appliances when not in use
   - walk or use public transport
   - buy local produce
   - recycle and reuse.
2. Any two of:
   - use local resources
   - use renewable energy
   - use energy efficient appliances
   - encourage employees to reduce their carbon footprint.

## Page 164 Earth's resources

1. Sustainable development is where the use of resources is balanced to meet current demand without compromising future need.
2. Advantage – they have a high energy value.

   Disadvantage – they are a finite resource.
3. A renewable resource is a resource which will always naturally be available, such as solar or wind power, or can be replaced within a short enough period of time that the resource will not run out, for example wood and cotton.

   A finite resource has a limited supply that will eventually run out.

## Page 165 Potable water

1. Distillation and reverse osmosis
2. One of:
   - chlorine
   - ozone
3. It contains large amounts of dissolved solids/salt.
4. Rainwater
5. Any three from:
   - rainwater
   - groundwater
   - rivers
   - lakes
   - oceans.

## Page 166 Purifying water

1. Distillation
2. Leave a small sample of water out to evaporate; any dissolved solids will appear at the bottom.
3. 100 °C

## Page 167 Waste water treatment

1. Any two of:
   - dishwasher
   - toilet
   - shower
   - bath
   - washing machine
   - tumble dryer.
2. If it enters the waterways, pesticides and fertilisers could harm aquatic life.

   If it is absorbed by aquatic life, substances that are harmful to animals and humans could enter the human food chain.
3. Anaerobic digestion is the breakdown of material in the absence of oxygen.

## Page 168 Life cycle assessment

1.

| | Paper bag | Plastic bag |
|---|---|---|
| **Raw material** | wood | crude oil |
| **Manufacture** | Wood is pulped and bleached. Lots of waste produced. | Less waste, but lots of energy used in fractional distillation, cracking and polymerisation. |
| **Use** | one use | reusable |
| **Disposal** | biodegradable | landfill or recycle |

2. Raw materials – burning fuel to power the crude oil extraction process releases carbon dioxide into the atmosphere.

   Manufacture – burning fuel to power fractional distillation and convert the fraction to a polymer releases greenhouse gases.

   Use – no pollution

   Disposal – plastic bags can be reused, reducing pollution, but their disposal is damanging to the environment. If burned they produce greenhouse gases, and if sent to landfill they pollute and use up valuable land.

### Page 169 Reducing the use of resources

1. It will produce less waste, less pollution and less carbon dioxide by reducing the amount of iron ore that has to be extracted.
2. Recycling needs energy to melt the product down. Burning fossil fuels to power this process releases carbon dioxide into the atmosphere, leading to global warming.

   Transporting the products to and from the recycling plant requires the burning of fuel to power the vehicle used to transport the products. This produces greenhouse gases and may also produce nitrogen oxides and sulphur dioxide, leading to global warming and acid rain.

### Page 170 Scalars and vector quantities

1. **(a)** 77 m/s due north

   **(b)** 53 m/s due south
2. 15 m/s at 37° East of North (or bearing 037°)

### Page 171 Distance and displacement

**(a)** Distance = 600 km
Displacement = 200 km east

**(b)** Distance = 230 m
Displacement = 187 m at 16° to the vertical (or 74° to the floor)

**(c)** Distance = 700 m
Displacement = 0 m

**(d)** Distance = 2 × π × 5 = 31.42 m
Displacement = 0 m

### Page 172 Speed and velocity

1. 22000 ÷ 3 = 7333 s

   7333 ÷ 60 = 122 mins
2. A: 600 ÷ 24 = 25 m/s
   B: 200000 ÷ (1.5 × 60 × 60) = 37 m/s,
   C: 20 ÷ 0.5 = 40 m/s,
   D: 3000000 ÷ (24 × 60 × 60)s = 35 m/s.
   C is fastest on average.

### Page 173 Distance-time relationships

1. The gradient is increasing, which means the speed is increasing. Therefore, it is accelerating.
2. 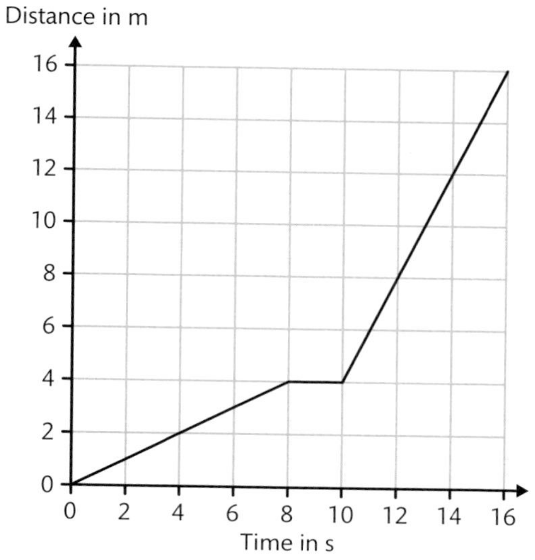


### Page 174 Uniform acceleration

1. 1.5 × 9.8 = 14.7 m/s
2. **(a)** 65 m/s ÷ 5 m/s² = 13 s

   **(b)** $-(65)^2 \div (-2 \times 5) = 422.5$ m
3. Any change in velocity is called acceleration. If an object is moving in a circle, its direction is changing. This means that its velocity is changing, even if the size of that velocity constant.
4. **(a)** The object is getting faster.

   **(b)** The object is getting slower (decelerating).

### Page 175 Velocity-time graphs

**(a)** The velocity is increasing, but the acceleration is decreasing because the gradient is becoming less steep.

**(b)** At 10 s the gradient is 0.3–0.4 $m/s^2$.
At 35 s the gradient is 0.1–0.2 $m/s^2$.

### Page 176 Gravity

1. In the middle of the hole
2. Using a calibrated spring or force meter (like a newton meter)
3. Downwards, towards the center of the planet
4. It is true that an astronaut might have difficulty walking on the Moon. However, this is not because of a lack of atmosphere. The Moon has less gravity than Earth because it has less mass. The astronaut would experience less downwards force on the Moon, which would make them feel lighter and more bouncy. This could make it more difficult to move.

### Page 177 Newton's laws of motion

1. For a car to move at a constant speed, all forces need to be balanced. The car will experience backwards force from friction and air resistance, so an equal forwards force from the engine is needed. This balances the friction and air resistance, making the resultant force zero. Without the forwards force from the engine, the imbalance would cause the car to slow down.

2. **(a)** 30 N

   **(b)** The student applies a 30 N force to the desk. If the desk is in equilibrium, there is no resultant force. Something must be balancing the force out, for example friction acting in the opposite direction to the 30 N force applied by the student.

## Page 178 Newton's second law

**(a)** $m = F \div a = (300 - 50) \div 1.67 = 150$ kg

**(b)** It would be half as much:
$1.67 \div 2 = 0.835$ m/s$^2$

## Page 179 Forces

1.

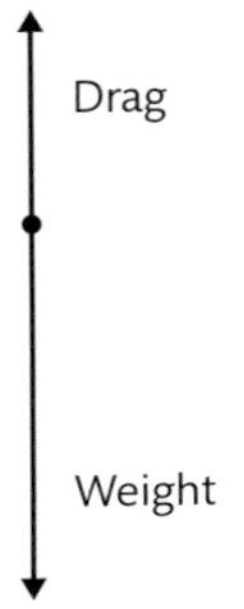


The weight arrow must be longer than the drag arrow.

2. Electrostatic force
3. Air resistance is caused by air particles hitting a moving object. The particles have to touch the object to apply the force, so it is a contact force.

## Page 180 Resultant forces

1. The resultant force is zero. Resultant forces make an object accelerate, so to travel at a constant speed, all the forces must be balanced.
2. $F = ma = 1200 \times 1.4 = 1680$ N

   The force from the engine must be $1680 + 800 = 2480$ N in order to cancel out the drag and provide enough force to accelerate the car.

## Page 181 Investigation acceleration

1. The force accelerating the trolley is found by calculating the weight of the masses using the equation:

   weight = mass × gravitational field strength
2. In theory, the trolley's acceleration should be constant. As long as the light gate is placed where the trolley is still accelerating, its position should not matter. However, there could be a change in friction as the trolley increases in speed, which would affect the resultant force on the trolley and therefore change its acceleration. The light gate might give a different reading for acceleration if it is moved to a faster or slower part of the movement.
3. Mass is inversely proportional to acceleration. If the mass of the trolley doubled, the acceleration would halve (for the same force). Force and acceleration are proportional. If the force doubles, the acceleration would double too.

## Page 182 Forces and elasticity

**(a)** 18 N

**(b)** The graph is not a straight line past the limit of proportionality.

**(c)** The limit of proportionality is where $e = 0.4$ m

Energy stored $= 0.5 \times 44.7 \times 0.4^2$
$= 3.576$ J

**(d)** Extension at 10 N = 22.5 cm
$22.5 + 9$ cm $= 31.5$ cm

## Page 183 Force and extension

**(a)** gradient = 19.4 N/m

**(b)** Measure the extension for forces above 7 N and plot them on the graph to see whether they follow a straight line of best fit or continue to curve.

**(c)** The scatter is caused by random error, such as variations in the masses. This could be reduced by measuring them using a mass balance. Another source of random error could be the masses bouncing on the spring after each one is added. Reduce this error by ensuring the masses are still before measuring the extension.

## Page 184 Stopping distance

1. distance = speed ÷ time = 31 m/s × 0.6 = 18.6 m
2. Only method 1 actually measures reaction time, method 2 does not use a time, but a distance. Both methods can be used to compare reaction times. Method 1 is more useful because if the time doubled we can say reaction time has doubled, however as the ruler is accelerating downwards, if the distance doubled this does not mean the reaction time has doubled. The repeat readings in method 1 were more similar, suggesting this is a more reliable (repeatable) method. Method 2 repeat readings were more varied suggesting this is a less reliable method.

## Page 185 Braking distance

1. $F = \dfrac{mv^2}{2d}$

   $1200 \times 25^2 \div 2 \times 40 = 9375$ N
2. Kinetic energy $= \frac{1}{2} \times$ mass $\times$ velocity$^2$. Doubling the speed increases the kinetic energy by four times. The brakes have to do four times the work to stop the car, so the car has to travel four times further when braking. Therefore, the braking distance is four times larger. Doubling the speed doubles the distance the car travels while the driver reacts, so the thinking distance is doubled.

## Page 186 Momentum

1. **(a)** $m = p \div v = 5400 \div 12 = 450$ kg

   **(b)** –5400 kg m/s
2. 1.5 cm/s = 0.015 m/s, 22 g = 0.022 kg

   $p = mv = 0.022 \times 0.015 = 0.00033$
   $3.3 \times 10^{-4}$ kg m/s

3. Start momentum = 0.85 × 20 = 17 kg m/s
   New mass = 850 – 300 = 550g or 0.55 kg
   End momentum = 0.55 × 35 = 19.25 kg m/s
   Change in momentum = 19.25 – 17 = 2.25 kg m/s.

## Page 187 Conservation of momentum

1. The cannonball is fired forwards with a large velocity and the cannon moves backwards with a smaller velocity. Before the cannon fires the momentum is zero. For the total momentum to still be zero, the cannon and ball must have equal momentums, but one will be negative (so they would add up to zero).

   Momentum = mass × velocity. The cannonball has a much smaller mass and therefore will have a higher velocity to give it the same momentum.
2. Momentum must be conserved so the two players after the tackle must have the same momentum as both the players running before the tackle. As the mass of the object moving has increased after the tackle (being two people it has roughly doubled) the velocity must decrease in order to have the same momentum (in fact it will roughly halve to 4 m/s).

## Page 188 Circuit diagrams

1. Bulb A would not light. There is no complete circuit from the positive to negative of the cell through the lamp.

   Bulbs B and C and the LED would not light. The LED would allow current to flow anticlockwise around the loop, but the current from the cell would flow clockwise.
2. **(a)**

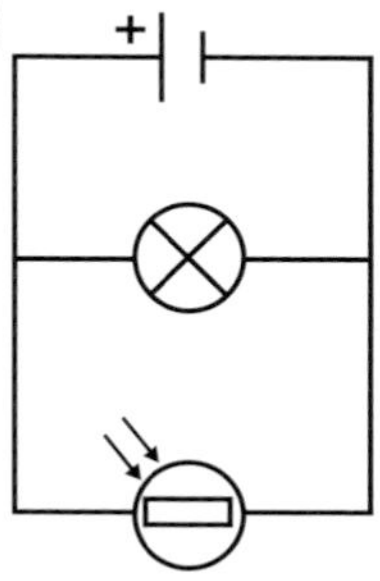


**(b)**

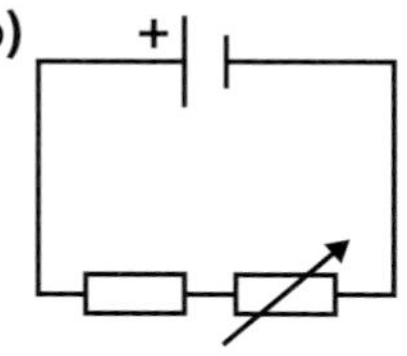


3. All three have resistances that can change. An LDR's resistance increases in low light intensity. A thermistor's resistance increases in low temperature. A variable resistor's resistance is changed manually.

   LDRs are used in circuits that are controlled by light levels, for example street lights that switch on when it gets dark. Thermistors are mostly used in thermostats, for example to control the temperature of ovens, central heating or refrigerators. Variable resistors are used in circuits where the current is altered by a dial. For example, volume controls, speed controls on electric motors and dimmer switches.

## Page 189 Current, resistance and potential difference

1. $R = \frac{V}{I} = \frac{6}{0.1} = 60\,\Omega$
2. It would have no effect on the potential difference of the battery. The potential difference would be shared between the two bulbs, so they would get 3 V each.
3. **(a)** $I = \frac{V}{R} = \frac{6}{80} = 0.075$ A

   **(b)** Doubling the potential difference of the battery to 12 V would double the current (0.075 × 2 = 0.15 A).

## Page 190 Electrical charge

1. 2 A means 2 C are transferred every second.
2. $t = \frac{Q}{I} = \frac{30}{60} = 5$ s
3. **(a)** 0.6 A

   **(b)** $Q = It = 0.6 \times 15 = 9$ C

## Page 191 Resistance

For the LDR:

Replace the test wire in the circuit with an LDR.

Shine a light source on the LDR from different distances, measuring the distance, voltage and current.

Calculate the resistance using voltage ÷ current.

Plot a graph with distance to light source on the *x*-axis and resistance of LDR on the *y*-axis. The resistance of the LDR should decrease as the light source gets closer.

For the thermistor:

Replace the test wire in the circuit with a thermistor.

Place the thermistor in hot water, being careful not to get water near the electrical equipment.

At regular time intervals, measure the temperature of the water using a thermometer and record the potential difference and current.

Calculate the resistance at difference temperatures using voltage ÷ current.

Plot a graph with temperature on the *x*-axis and resistance on the *y*-axis. The resistance should decrease as the temperature increases.

## Page 192 Resistors

1.

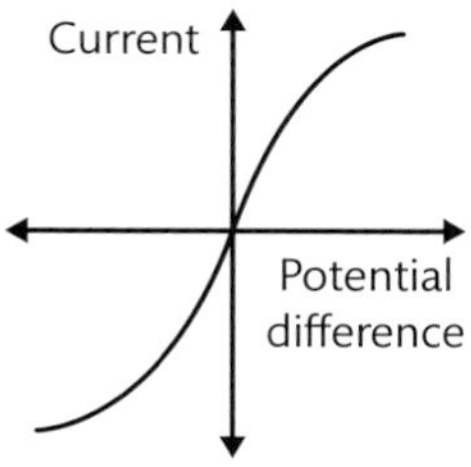


2. The lines on the *I*-*V* graph for a resistor are straight and pass through the origin. This shows that if you double *V* you double *I*, and therefore *I* is proportional to *V*.
   For a filament bulb the line is not straight so *V* is not proportional to *I* and the resistance is changing.

## Page 193 Series and parallel circuits

1. $12 + 4 = 16\Omega$
2. As more bulbs are added in series, they become less bright. As each bulb is added, the overall resistance increases and the current through each bulb decreases. The potential difference is shared out between more bulbs, so each receives less volts.

   If more bulbs are added in parallel, they all have same potential difference, so are equally bright. This means that each bulb receives the same current, so the total current increases as bulbs are added.
3. If one of the heating elements breaks there are less routes for current to take. This means the current would decrease, because the resistance has increased.

## Page 194 *I–V* characteristics

1. The graph's decreasing gradient shows that the resistance is increasing at higher potential differences, or currents. This is probably caused by the wire heating up when larger currents pass through it.

   To improve the experiment, the student could:
   - use smaller potential differences to keep the current low
   - make sure the circuit is switched off and allowed to cool between each measurement
   - use longer lengths of wire to keep the resistance high and stop the current getting too large
   - place a resistor in the series with the wire to reduce the potential difference across the wire.
2. They could reduce random error by taking repeat readings, letting the component cool down between tests.

## Page 195 Mains electricity

1. If the appliance has a case made of plastic (or another insulating material), it cannot conduct electric current. If there is a fault inside, the casing cannot become live and shock a person who touches it, so there is no need for an earth wire.
2. - ac constantly changes direction, whereas dc flows only one way.
   - ac comes from power stations, whereas dc comes from batteries (though it is possible to convert ac into dc, for example in your phone charger).
   - ac changes between a positive and negative voltage, whereas dc maintains a constant voltage.
3. The potential difference goes up and down. However, it is always positive, so always flows the same direction and is therefore dc.

## Page 196 Energy transfers in appliances

1. *Wasted energy is underlined.*

   **(a)** electrical ➔ sound + <u>thermal</u>

   **(b)** electrical ➔ kinetic + <u>thermal</u> + <u>sound</u>

   **(c)** chemical ➔ electrical ➔ kinetic + <u>sound</u> + <u>thermal</u>

   **(d)** chemical ➔ thermal (light and <u>heat</u>) + sound
2. Not all of the heat it produces will go into warming up the room. Some is used to warm up parts of the heater first and some of the heat might escape from the room.
3. 200J must have been transferred and wasted as heat energy.

## Page 197 Electrical power

1. power rating $= 230 \times 5 = 1150\,\text{W}$
2. $I = \sqrt{\frac{P}{R}} = \sqrt{\frac{2200}{140}} = 3.96\,\text{A}$
3. **(a)** $0.4 \times 1.5 = 0.6\,\text{W}$

   **(b)** $t = \frac{E}{P} = \frac{13\,000}{0.6} = 21\,667\,\text{s}$

   $(\div 60 \div 60 = 6 \text{ hours})$

## Page 198 Types of wave

1. Using speed = distance/time the student can use distance = 400 m (distance to the wall and back) and time = the time recorded divided by 10 (as they timed for 10 claps). Inputting these into the equation will give the speed of sound.
2. Ocean waves are transverse as they transfer mass perpendicular to the direction of the wave. It also demonstrates that the water itself is not travelling as the wave travels.
3. Any wind will change the time taken for the sound to be heard. The student could do the test inside to adjust for this.
4. There are no particles for sound to transfer through.

## Page 199 Properties of waves

1. **(a)** Frequency: $f = 1 \div T$

   Green: $1 \div 2 = 0.5\,\text{Hz}$

   Blue: $1 \div 7 = 0.14\,\text{Hz}$

   **(b)** Wavelength: $\lambda = \frac{v}{f}$

   Green: $\lambda = \frac{1.5}{0.5} = 3\,\text{m}$

   Blue: $\lambda = \frac{1.5}{0.14} = 10.7\,\text{m}$
2. speed $= \frac{\text{distance}}{\text{time}}$

   $\frac{500}{1.51} = 331\,\text{m/s}$
3. time $= \frac{\text{distance}}{\text{speed}}$

   $\frac{2000}{1500} = 1.33\,\text{s}$
4. 20 waves $\div$ 5 = 4 waves per second or 4 Hz

   period $= 1 \div f = \frac{1}{4} = 0.25\,\text{s}$

   wavelength: 20 waves are 15 cm long, so one wave is 15 cm $\div$ 20 waves = 0.75 cm (0.0075 m)

   wave speed = frequency $\times$ wavelength
   $4\,\text{Hz} \times 0.0075\,\text{m} = 0.03\,\text{m/s}$ (or 3 cm/s)

## Page 200 Investigating waves

Student B will obtain the most accurate value, because the stopwatch used by Student A depends on the student to press the button. This can be affected by a range of human errors, such as the student's reaction time or how good their hearing is.

## Page 201 Types of electromagnetic waves

1. Patients are exposed to very small doses of radiation, so the risk of cell damage only increases slightly. This is considered less of a risk than being unable to diagnose and treat conditions.
2. Any two of the following:
   - premature ageing of the skin
   - skin cancer (caused by UV light)
   - sunburn.
3. As the frequency of a wave increases, it becomes more dangerous.
4. **(a)** $50 \div 0.1 = 500$ X-rays per year

   **(b)** This number is not considered safe, because greater exposure to X-rays means greater risk. X-rays are kept to a minimum to keep the risk as low as possible.

## Page 202 Properties of electromagnetic waves

1. Thermal energy
2. **(a)** Only the green light is transmitted, because the other colours are absorbed.

   **(b)** All the colours are absorbed.

   **(c)** All the colours are reflected, so the car appears white.
3. The prism shows refraction. The light slows down when it enters glass, causing it to change direction. When it exits the prism it speeds up and changes direction again. The spectrum caused by a prism shows that the different colours in white light slow down by different rates when they enter the glass. Red light bends the least, so must slow down the least, and therefore travels fastest inside glass.
4. They are not correct. Light still slows down as it enters glass, but it only bends when the light hits the surface at an angle, because only then is one part of the wavefront affected before the rest.

## Page 203 Infrared radiation

1. It would help them to decide what colours to paint the walls to trap heat inside the house. Making the inside light or shiny would reflect radiated heat back into the rooms. Painting the outside black would absorb heat from the environment, or painting it silver would reduce the heat emitted.
2. A light, shiny colour would be best, because it would emit less infra-red when hot, causing the drink to lose energy more slowly.
3. Tin foil would conduct heat relatively easily, but paper would insulate, making the test unfair.
4. Firstly, the data would be would be recorded in a table. Then, this could be represented as a bar chart with colour along the *x*-axis and temperature change along the *y*-axis.

## Page 204 Applications of EM waves

1. Radio: TV, radio, two-way radio

   Microwaves: mobile phones, satellites, satellite TV

   Infrared: remote controls, wireless links between computers

   Visible light: car indicators, warning lights, flashing torches, optical fibres
2. Any two of:
   - to make documents such as passports, driving licenses and bank cards harder to counterfeit
   - to make it easier for the police to identify the owner of stolen items
   - to write secret messages
   - to stamp the hands of event attendees without leaving an unsightly mark.
3. Radio waves are produced by vibrating electrons in electrical circuits. The flow of current in an electrical device can produce radio waves that might be picked up by the radio aerial receiver, causing interference.

## Page 205 Magnetic fields

1. Place a compass near one of the poles. If the north arrow on the compass points towards the pole, it is the south. If it points away, it is the north.

   Or:

   Place the north pole of another bar magnet near one pole. It will be attracted to the south pole and repelled by the north.
2. A compass's arrow follows magnetic field lines, which point from north to south. This means that for a compass to point towards the top of the Earth, its North Pole must be magnetic south.
3. Use a magnet to repel or attract another without touching it.

   Or:

   Show how a magnet moves a compass arrow without touching it.
4. A permanent magnet always has a magnetic field. An induced magnet only has one when placed near another magnet.

   A bar magnet is a permanent magnet. An induced magnet is an object made of cobalt, iron, nickel or steel that is being attracted to a magnet, for example, a fridge door with a magnet stuck to it.

### Page 206 Electromagnetism

1. It can be switched off to put objects down, and its strength can be increased to pick up heavier objects.
2. 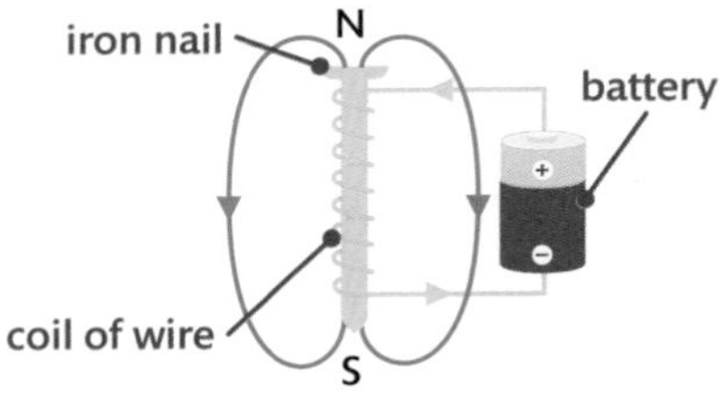


   North is at the top.
3. Change the direction of the electric current.

### Page 207 The motor effect

1. To the left
2. The force would change direction when the current changed, but then change direction again when the poles were swapped, so it would still be acting downwards.
3. $F = BIl$

   $0.1 \times 3 \times 0.05 = 0.015\,N$
4. Any three from:
   - Increase the strength of the magnets / increase the flux density.
   - Increase the current in the wire.
   - Use longer or wider magnets so there can be a longer length of wire in the field.
   - Wrap the wire into a coil so there can be a longer length of wire in the field.

### Page 208 Electric motors

1. As the current goes around the coil it moves in a different direction on either side. Fleming's left-hand rule tells us that if the current changes direction, the force changes direction, provided the magnetic field stays the same.
2. The force depends on the strength of the magnets (the flux density), the size of the current, the length of the wire and the number of turns on the coil. These will be same on each side, so the force will be the same on each side.

### Page 209 Transformers and the National Grid

1. Reduce the resistance by using wires with a wider diameter, or multiple wires in parallel. The wires could also be made from metals that are better conductors.
2. The potential difference is being decreased, so it is a step down transformer.

### Page 210 Energy transfers in a system

1. - Thermal energy (e.g. a heater) can be transferred if it is moving or can be stored if it is just making an object warmer.
   - Nuclear energy (e.g. an atomic bomb) is energy stored in the nucleus of an atom.
   - Kinetic energy (e.g. in a moving object) is being stored by that object as it moves.
   - Electrical energy (e.g any appliance that requires batteries or mains supply) is energy being transferred by electrical current.
   - Chemical energy (e.g. batteries, food or fuel) is stored energy.
   - Strain potential (e.g. a compressed spring) is stored energy.
   - Gravitational potential (anything that has been lifted) is stored energy.
   - Sound (e.g. music) is energy being transferred by vibrations in the air.
2. **(a)** chemical ➔ thermal + kinetic + sound

   **(b)** chemical ➔ kinetic (dissipated as light + thermal + sound) ➔ gravitational potential energy

   **(c)** chemical ➔ kinetic + thermal + sound
3. Thermal energy is wasted when water is heated to make steam, in the wires and through friction between the moving parts of the turbines. This could be reduced by insulating the pipes or reusing the wasted energy for heating, lubricating the moving parts in the turbines, and using thicker wires to reduce resistance.
4. The jumper is thick and the wool traps air. Air has poor thermal conductivity, so reduces the jumper's rate of heat loss. In contrast, a t-shirt is thin and traps little air, so has higher thermal conductivity and loses heat more quickly.

### Page 211 Work done and energy transfer

1. **(a)** 0J, the force and distance are in different directions so no work is done.

   **(b)** $500 \times 35 = 17\,500$J

   **(c)** $20 \times 1.5 = 30$J

   **(d)** $25 \times 120 = 3000$J
2. **(a)** Work has been done as friction will have caused them to stop which would have acted in the opposite direction to the way they were moving. Kinetic energy has been transferred to thermal energy.

   **(b)** 400J of work would be needed to stop them.

   $s = W \div F$

   $400 \div 80 = 5$ m.
3. They are doing work as the bicycle is moving in the direction of the force. It is partially transferred to kinetic energy as the bike speeds up and then to gravitational potential energy as the bike moves up the hill. (In actual fact the cyclist pushes down on the pedal which moves down, so they start by doing work with their legs.)

### Page 212 Efficiency

1. Useful energy = 400 – 150 = 250J
   Efficiency = 250 ÷ 400 = 0.625
2. 85 per cent of the energy produced is used to heat the house, and 15 per cent is lost or wasted.
3. Appliance A: 35 ÷ 100 = 0.35

   Appliance B: 35 ÷ 50 = 0.70

   Appliance B has the higher efficiency because it uses a greater proportion of the input power usefully.

4. Efficiency of 60 per cent
   $60 \div 100 = 0.6$ as a decimal
   input energy = useful output energy ÷ efficiency
   $2000 \div 0.6 = 3333$ J.
5. Thermal energy is produced by friction in moving parts. Friction can be reduced by making sure any surfaces that touch are smooth, making sure that moving parts can move freely and fit together perfectly, or by adding lubrication.

## Page 213 Gravitational potential energy

1. $70 \times 9.8 \times 100 = 68\,600$ J
2. $h = E_p \div (m \times g) = 50\,000 \div (70 \times 9.8) = 72.9$ m
3. **(a)** As the ball falls its height decreases, which means its g.p.e. decreases. The g.p.e. is being transferred to kinetic energy, which increases. Therefore, its speed increases.
   **(b)** An object's g.p.e. transfers to kinetic energy as it falls. An object dropped from a greater height begins with more g.p.e. to transfer, so will have more kinetic energy when it reaches the ground. Therefore, it will hit the ground faster.
4. **(a)** Twice the change in height, so twice the increase in g.p.e.: $1000 \times 2 = 2000$ J
   **(b)** The work done by the crane is equal to the g.p.e. gained, so 1000 J and 2000 J respectively.

## Page 214 Kinetic energy

1. **(a)** $0.5 \times 1200 \times 20^2 = 240\,000$ J
   **(b)** 240 000 J
2. The van has twice the mass of the car, so has twice the kinetic energy if they are travelling at the same speed. However, the car has twice the speed of the van, so has four times the kinetic energy. Overall, the car has twice as much kinetic energy.
3. **(a)** $m = 12\,000 \div (0.5 \times 8^2) = 375$ kg
   **(b)** $v = \sqrt{\dfrac{17\,000}{0.5 \times 375}} = 9.5$ m/s

## Page 215 Energy in a spring

**(a)** $E_p = 0.5 \times 60 \times 0.2^2 = 1.2$ J
**(b)** 1.2 J
**(c)** Compress the spring further or swap with one with a higher spring constant. Alternatively, use a ball with a lower mass.

## Page 216 Using energy equations

1. **(a)** The g.p.e. will change to kinetic energy so it will have 200 J.
   **(b)** It might have less than this because some of the kinetic energy will be lost as thermal energy to air resistance as it falls.
2. **(a)** The kinetic energy on release
   = elastic potential stored by the spring
   $= \dfrac{1}{2}ke^2 = 0.5 \times 180\,\text{N/m} \times (0.2\,\text{m})^2 = 3.6$ J.
   **(b)** $v = \sqrt{\dfrac{E_k}{\frac{1}{2}m}} = \sqrt{\dfrac{3.6}{0.5 \times 0.15}} = \sqrt{48} = 6.9$ m/s
   **(c)** At the highest point, it would have 3.6 J of gravitational potential energy.
   $h = E_p \div (mg) = 3.6 \div (0.15 \times 10) = 2.4$ m
   **(d)** As $E_p = \dfrac{1}{2}ke^2$, for the same amount of compression, with half the spring constant the spring would store half the elastic potential. There would be half the amount of gravitational potential energy and as $E_p = mgh$ the ball would only go half as high, $2.4 \div 2 = 1.2$ m.
   **(e)** As $E_p = \dfrac{1}{2}ke^2$, doubling the compression would store $2^2 = 4$ times the energy. As $E_p = mgh$, giving the ball four times the energy would make it travel four times higher.

## Page 217 Power

1. **(a)** $P = E \div t = 4800 \div 60 = 80$ W
   **(b)** $P = E \div t = 2160 \div 60 = 36$ W
2. **(a)** Total work done $= 40 \times 30 = 1200$ J
   $P = W \div t = 1200 \div 90 = 13.3$ W
   **(b)** (10 mins × 60 = 600 s) $W = P \times t = 13.3 \times 600 = 7980$ J (or 8000 J)
3. If the rate of energy loss decreases as it cools, the power of the heat loss is decreasing as temperature decreases.

## Page 218 Renewable energy resources

1. If a farmer can make more money selling sugar cane as a fuel they would stop selling it as a source of food. This would increase the price of food and could cause a food shortage.
2. The most reliable energy resources are, in no particular order, geothermal, biofuel and hydroelectric. Then, tidal is predictable, but there are only two tides a day. Finally, sun, wind and wave power are the least reliable.
3. Wood from trees, vegetable oil from crops, methane from decaying organic matter and rubbish are examples of biofuels. These are carbon neutral because when burned they put the carbon back into the atmosphere that was removed in order to make the fuel. Plastic is made from oil, so if this is burned as waste it is not carbon neutral.

## Page 219 Non-renewable energy resources

1. Nuclear and coal fired power stations are equally as reliable and both have a high power output. Nuclear power stations are clean and do not produce any smoke or greenhouse gasses. However, they do produce nuclear waste that must be stored safely; if there is an accident, there is a risk of radiation getting into the environment. Coal power stations do produce smoke, greenhouse gasses and sulfur dioxide. This can cause respiratory diseases, increase global warming and cause acid rain. They also need a large amount of coal to be transported.

2. Any four of:
   - Non-renewables are running out so renewables need to be used to replace the demand for energy.
   - Other than biofuel, renewables produce little chemical pollution.
   - No renewable resource adds to carbon emissions (biofuels do produce $CO_2$ when burned, but are carbon neutral overall) and so do not contribute to global warming, whereas fossil fuels do.
   - Nuclear accidents can affect a large area for a long period of time, but renewable resources tend to be safer.
   - While the cost of building some renewable power sources is still high, the running costs or fuel costs are cheaper and in some cases virtually free, compared to the rising cost of non-renewable resources, especially as they become rarer.
   - People are more interested in saving the environment so it has become popular for individuals to use renewable resources to generate electricity in their own home or use biofuels in cars.
   - Governments are under pressure to reduce the carbon emissions produced by their countries which has caused a shift towards more renewable resources like wind farms and solar cells.
   - Farms are using spare land to generate electricity by creating wind or solar farms to generate additional income.
3. Any four of:
   - The cost of replacing all the current power stations would be high, it makes more sense to replace them gradually over time.
   - Public opinion may be against renewable resources, for example protesting about building wind turbines because they spoil a landscape. They can also be a danger to wildlife and cannot be built where there are endangered birds.
   - In countries like the UK, poor weather makes solar resources less reliable so relying only on renewables might not produce enough electricity at peak times. Some biofuels use food crops or land which would otherwise be used for food. This can drive up the cost of food.
   - People have not shifted to using renewable resources (like biofuels or fuel cells) for cars because the technology is new and still more expensive than diesel or petrol powered cars.
   - Some people dislike change and are wary of relying too quickly on alternative methods of energy production.

## Page 220 Density

1. The density stays the same as it is a property of water. The volume of the water in the bucket is greater as there is a higher capacity than in the bottle. The mass of water in the bucket will also be greater.
2. **(a)** Densities:
   - apple: $0.074 \div 1.04 \times 10^{-4} = 712\,kg/m^3$ - floats
   - steel box: $1.3 \div 2 \times 10^{-3} = 650\,kg/m^3$ - floats
   - plastic: $0.5 \div 4.1 \times 10^{-4} = 1220\,kg/m^3$ - sinks
   - human: $70 \div 0.071 = 986\,kg/m^3$ - floats

   **(b)** $m = \rho \times V = 712 \times 1.5 \times 10^{-4} = 0.107\,kg$

## Page 221 Density of materials

**(a)** The density can be calculated from mass divided by volume. The masses of the rock and metal cubes could be found using an electronic balance. The mass of the oil could be found by measuring the mass of a container then pouring in the oil and measuring the mass again; the difference would be the mass of the oil. The volume of the metal cube can be found using vernier calipers to get the length, depth and width. Volume = width × depth × length. The volume of the rock can be found by placing it in a displacement can filled with water and measure the amount of water it displaces in a measuring cylinder. The volume of the oil can be measured in a measuring cylinder.

**(b)** Some of the things you could mention are:
- stand the measuring cylinder on a flat surface when measuring liquid volumes
- ignore the meniscus when measuring water volume in a measuring cylinder
- use a vernier caliper to measure the metal cube to a high precision
- make sure all the water droplets have fallen out of the spout when using the displacement can.

## Page 222 State changes

1. At its boiling point, the water will start to evaporate. The energy is used to break the weak bonds in water to make steam, rather than going into kinetic energy of the particles that would increase the temperature. The temperature will only increase again when the water has completely changed state to a gas/steam. The energy will then be used to increase the kinetic energy of the particles and raise the temperature.
2. Solid - stuck in place, so they will vibrate.

   Liquid - loosely bonded together and allowed to move around randomly. They will collide with each other.

   Gas - very well spaced out and fast moving, free to move around with no bonds between particles. They will collide with each other.
3. The energy will flow from the water (higher temperature) to the ice (lower temperature). The particles in the water will collide with the particles in the ice and lose kinetic energy. The water particles will slow down as the temperature decreases. The particles in the ice will gain kinetic energy and vibrate more quickly. When the ice reaches melting point (0 °C), the energy lost from the kinetic energy in the water particles is passed to the ice by collision. This will be used to break bonds between particles in the ice and cause it to melt and therefore change state.

### Page 223 Specific heat capacity

1. **(a)** Temperature change = $\frac{\text{energy}}{(\text{mass} \times \text{specific heat capacity})} = \frac{84\,000}{(2 \times 4200)} = 10°$.

   Temperature = 20 + 10 = 30°

   **(b)** Temperature = 80 + 10 = 90°
2. Liquid A has a melting point of 15°C, which means it would be solid at freezer temperatures (0°C and below). It also has a very low specific heat capacity, which means it would heat up very quickly without removing much energy (or would not be able to carry much energy out of the freezer).

### Page 224 Specific heat capacity

1. There is still energy in the heater that needs to conduct into the metal or water and be detected by the thermometer. It may take some time for the thermal energy to conduct to the thermometer.
2. When heating the materials, the energy would not conduct evenly through it so some parts would be hotter. This would make any measurement of temperature less reliable. The energy would also conduct a lot more slowly into and out of the materials, meaning the experiment would take longer to complete and would lose more heat to the surroundings, making the results less accurate.
3. Measure the temperature of water in the middle, as hot water rises to the top.

### Page 225 Specific latent heat

1. **(a)** It takes 200 J to melt 1 kg of copper, it takes a lot less energy to melt 1 kg of gold (64 J).

   **(b)** Mass of copper = $E \div l = 2500 \div 200 = 12.5$ kg

   Mass of gold = $E \div l = 2500 \div 64 = 39$ kg
2. $E = ml = 0.05 \times 336000 = 16800$ J

### Page 226 Particle motion in gases

1. The density will decrease because the gas will expand as it is heated. This gives it a greater volume, but it still has the same mass so the density will be lower.

   In a rigid container, it cannot expand so the volume will stay constant and the density will not change. (Note, the pressure will increase, but this has no effect on density).
2. When it is heated but not sealed, the gas will expand, increasing the pressure more than the pressure outside. The gas will then escape, reducing the mass of gas in the container. After it is sealed and cooled, the pressure of the gas will drop again, but air from outside cannot get into the container to even up the pressure. As the pressure pushing down on the lid from outside is greater than the pressure pushing out, the lid will take more force to remove.
3. No. When heated, the particles gain kinetic energy and collide with the side of syringe with more force, more frequently. This means they exert more pressure, which forces the syringe out. The gas takes up more volume, but it is the same mass of gas inside.

### Page 227 The structure of an atom

1. It will have 12 electrons. As an atom it has neutral charge and so must have equal numbers of electrons and protons.
2. If a magnesium atom was broken in half there would be 6 protons on each side. The atom needs to have 12 protons to be magnesium. The atom with 6 protons is carbon.
3. Differences: electrons are negative and have a very small mass; protons are positive and have a larger mass. They are also found in different places in the atom.
4. Similarities: protons and neutrons have similar masses and are both found in the nucleus.

### Page 228 Mass number, atomic number and isotopes

1. **(a)** 4 protons, 4 electrons, 5 neutrons

   **(b)** 39 protons, 39 electrons, 50 neutrons

   **(c)** 26 protons, 26 electrons, 30 neutrons
2. **(a)** 2 electrons

   **(b)** 40 electrons

   **(c)** 23 electrons
3. The number of neutrons can be different if it is an isotope of carbon. The number of electrons can change if it is an ion.

### Page 229 Development of the atomic model

1. The atom is a positively charged sphere with tiny negatively charged electrons embedded in it.
2. Unlike the plum pudding model, the nuclear model puts the majority of the mass and the positive charge at the centre, the outside carries the negative charge and the rest is empty space.
3. **(a)** The alpha particles would all have bounced back. None, or very few, would have passed straight through.

   **(b)** Alpha particles would still have mostly passed through, some would be diverted when they passed close to the nucleus. The ones that hit would be attracted rather than repelled and so would not have bounced back, showing the nucleus is negative.
4. No model is considered correct, just the best idea based on the evidence. As more evidence is found the models will change, including the nuclear model.

### Page 230 Radioactive decay and nuclear radiation

1. The alpha has a higher mass and charge so it can ionize (cause atoms to lose or gain electrons) more easily.
2. Alpha would not get through the paper regardless of how thick or thin it was. Gamma would get through the paper and would not be reduced if the paper thickness increased.
3. Gamma would be the most suitable because it can be easily detected as it can pass out of the body easily and is also the least harmful to living cells. Alpha would not penetrate the skin and could not be detected outside

the body. It is also most ionizing and therefore would be damaging to the cells in the body. Similarly for beta, it would not be detected if it was too deep inside the body and would also be quite harmful.

## Page 231 Half-lives

1. 1 half-life → 1/2, 2 half-lives → 1/4, 3 half-lives → 1/8, 4 half-lives → 1/16
2. $1440 \div 2 = 720$ Bq
   $720 \div 2 = 360$ Bq
   $360 \div 2 = 180$ Bq
   $180 \div 2 = 90$ Bq
   $90 \div 2 = 45$ Bq
   5 half-lives
   $5 \times 10 = 50$ mins
3. $640 \div 2 = 320$ Bq
   $320 \div 2 = 160$ Bq
   2 half-lives
   $12 \div 2 = 6$ years
4. 2 half-lives. $2 \times 3 = 6$ hours

## Page 232 Nuclear equations

1. **(a)** $^{239}_{94}Pu \rightarrow ^{235}_{92}U + ^{4}_{2}He$
   **(b)** $^{25}_{11}Na \rightarrow ^{25}_{12}Mg + ^{0}_{-1}e$
2. Alpha decay: $^{222}_{86}Rn \rightarrow ^{218}_{84}Po + ^{4}_{2}He$
   Alpha decay: $^{214}_{84}Po \rightarrow ^{214}_{82}Pb + ^{4}_{2}He$
   Beta decay: $^{214}_{82}Pb \rightarrow ^{214}_{83}Bi + ^{0}_{-1}e$
3. **(a)** Mercury
   **(b)** Bismuth

## Page 233 Radioactive contamination

1. They are at risk of irradiation because they are quite close to the rocks. They are at risk of contamination because the rocks may produce dust particles that would stick to their skin if they came into contact. They should not touch the rocks and should keep them in a sealed container to avoid contamination. To reduce their dose they should keep their distance from the sources, use them at arm's length by using long tongs or tweezers and only be near them when actually using them.
2. Irradiation is when radiation from a source is absorbed by something. Contamination is when something gets the radioactive material on it. They can both damage cells, change genes and possibly cause cancer. If you are being irradiated, you can stop or reduce this by moving away from the source or moving behind a screen. If you are contaminated, the source is already on you so you cannot move away from it, and are being irradiated constantly until it is cleaned off.
3. **(a)** The person may be exposed to radiation for longer periods of time, may work closer to sources of radiation or be exposed to radiation that has a higher activity. It is possible that Person A has a higher level of protective equipment, making their dose lower.
   **(b)** Person A has a lower risk of cancer than Person B, and it is much less than the 100 mSv which is considered low risk. It is never true to say that any amount of radiation exposure is completely safe.

## Page 234 Equations

1. **(a)** $m = \rho V, V = \frac{m}{\rho}$
   **(b)** $k = E_p \div \left(\frac{1}{2}e^2\right), e = \sqrt{\frac{V}{\left(\frac{1}{2}k\right)}}$
   **(c)** $m = \frac{E}{c\,\Delta\,\theta}, c = \frac{E}{m\,\Delta\,\theta}, \Delta\,\theta = \frac{E}{mc}.$
   **(d)** $\Delta v = at, t = \frac{\Delta v}{a}.$
2. $m$ - mass kg, $\rho$ - density kg/m$^3$, $V$ - volume m$^3$, $E$ - Energy J, $k$ - spring constant N/m, $e$ - extension m, $\Delta\theta$ - change of temperature °C, $a$ - acceleration m/s$^2$, $t$– time s, $\Delta\theta$ - change in velocity m/s.

## Page 235 Converting units

1. **(a)** 200 µg $\div 10^6 = 2\times10^{-4}$ g
   **(b)** $10 \div 1000 = 0.01$ N/g
   **(c)** $330 \div 60 = 5.5$ J/s
2. 1 kg is 1000 so $10^3$ or three orders of magnitude larger. So 10 kg is 4 orders of magnitude larger than 1 g.

## Page 236 Making estimations

*All these numbers are approximate and any similar number would be acceptable.*

1. 1–6 mm/s
2. 80–100 kg
3. From **Figure 1** around 500 s.

## Page 237 Interpreting data

1. Mean:
   (1.1 kg + 1.2 kg + 1.2 kg + 1.3 kg + 2.3 kg) $\div$ 5 = 1.62 kg.
   As there is one larger puppy, the mean is much larger than most of the puppies.
   The mode and median are both 1.2 kg, which is in the middle of and close to most of the puppies' weights, so it represents the majority of puppies well.
2. The distance at a speed of 40 m/s will be double the distance at a speed of 20 m/s. $4\times64$ m = 256 m

## Page 238 Using charts and graphs

1. **(a)** Bar chart - different cars are a discrete variable.
   **(b)** Line graph (or scatter graph with line of best fit) - they best show the relationship between two quantities.
   **(c)** Pie chart - they are best for showing the proportions of something that can be compared.

2. $y = mx + c$ becomes force = 120 × extension. As it goes through the origin, the y intercept, $c = 0$. This is like the equation force = spring constant × extension so the gradient tells us that the spring constant is 120 (N/m).

## Page 239 Using diagrams

1.

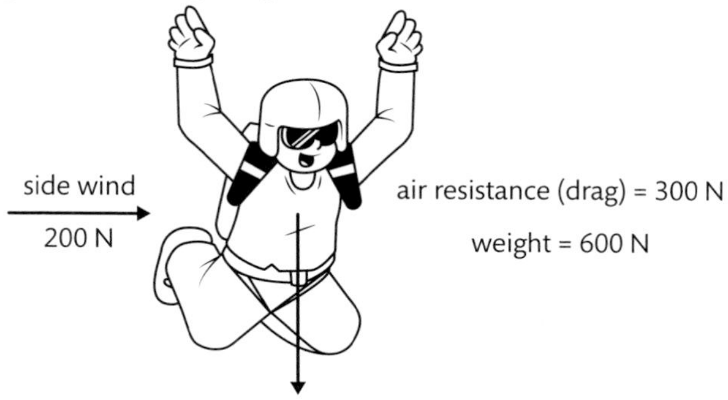


2.

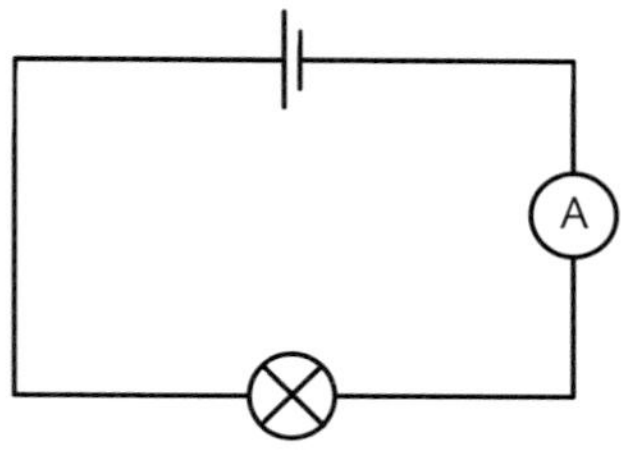


## Page 240 Planning practicals

1. **(a)** Change the material, either thin paper, a few mm of aluminium or several cm of lead. You would measure the activity of the source (through the material). You should keep the amount of air between the source and detector the same and leave the detector counting the activity rate for the same time in each test.
   **(b)** A ruler will be needed to maintain the air distance and measure the thickness of materials (or a vernier caliper or micrometer). A Geiger-Muller (GM) tube and counter will detect the radiation.
   **(c)** Not handle the source directly and use tongs or tweezers. Handle them at arms length and limit their exposure to as short a time as possible by putting the source in a radioactive container when not in use.
2. **(a)** The temperature of the metal (placing it in warm water perhaps) and the resistance which is found by measuring the current and potential difference. $R = V \div I$. You should use the same piece of wire, keeping the length and diameter constant for each test. The current should be kept the same each time. The current should also be kept low as possible to avoid internal heating.
   **(b)** Potential difference by a voltmeter, current by an ammeter, a thermometer to monitor the temperature of the water, or if the wire is heated in some other way an infrared thermometer would measure its temperature directly.
   **(c)** If using water to heat the wire, the water should be kept in a tray to avoid spilling water near the power supply and reduce the chance of electrocution. The wire and water will be hot and should not be touched, or insulated gloves need to be used if the beaker needs to be moved.

## Page 241 Comparing data

1. **(a)** For both sets of tyres, as speed increases, stopping distance increases. At lower speeds, stopping distance is proportional to speed. At higher speeds the gradients of both lines increases, meaning that the stopping distance increases more for the same increase in speed. This happens at around 70 km/h for tyre B and 80 km/h for tyre A. At all speeds, the stopping distance of tyre A is greater than tyre B. The difference in stopping distance increases and is greatest around 70 km/h, but they become more similar as the speed increases above this.
   **(b)** We would expect that the wet road would make the stopping distances much longer. Water on the road means there is less friction and therefore a lower braking force, meaning the car has to travel further to stop.
2. They are all ionizing forms of radiation and so are all able to destroy cancerous cells. Alpha is the most ionizing and would be destroy cells most easily, though this makes it more likely to destroy healthy cells as well. Beta is less ionizing, and gamma is the least ionizing, so they would do less damage to both cancerous and healthy cells. Alpha cannot penetrate paper and so will be unable to penetrate the skin. Beta is stopped by a few mm of aluminum and so would not be able to penetrate deeply into the skin, whereas gamma can pass through the body so could be used to target cells anywhere in the body. Overall, gamma would be the best suited. Although it is least ionizing, it will still destroy cancerous cells, be able to reach them anywhere in the body and do the least damage to healthy cells.

## Page 242 Evaluating data

1. If the materials have different thicknesses, this would affect their thermal conductivity; this could be improved by applying the same thickness of insulation to each beaker. Another thing to consider would be ensuring the thermometer is held in the middle of the water while reading the temperature and that the starting temperature of each beaker was the same. It is also important to avoid reusing the beaker, as it will have been cold when the hot water was added the first time and warm the second.
2. A lot of scatter is random error. This is caused by something that affects the experiment differently with each measurement. If a stop clock was used, then human reaction time could cause this. Not ensuring a start speed of zero, or an exact starting point might affect the calculation of speed. If using a data logger and light gate, allowing the position of the sensor to move between experiments would affect where the speed was measured. If the ramp is not perfectly smooth or straight, the ball might be affected by friction differently on each run.

## Page 243 Working scientifically

1. The independent variable (the one you change) would be the type of metal. To measure the resistance, you would need to measure the potential difference and current through the sample of metal and calculate resistance = potential difference ÷ current. This requires wires and crocodile clips to connect the metal, a power source like a cell, an ammeter and a voltmeter. The variables that could affect the resistance and need to be controlled are: temperature of the metal (an infra-red thermometer could be used to monitor this); the length of the sample of wire (metre rule); and the diameter or cross sectional area of a sample (vernier calipers or micrometer). The current/potential difference should be the same and kept quite low to avoid heating. The resistance of each metal could be presented in a table or as a bar chart.

2. Understanding how alpha, beta and gamma radiation can be stopped and what damage they do to living cells makes working with radiation safer and also tells us which uses are unsafe. Knowledge of the properties have led to uses in industry, such as beta being used to produce paper of uniform thickness, which has developed the paper industry and therefore created jobs. Alpha can be used in smoke detectors, which can save lives by detecting and warning people of smoke and fires that could otherwise be fatal. Gamma radiation is used to diagnose and treat cancer and so also saves lives. It is also used to sterilise medical equipment, reducing deaths through infection in surgery, and to sterilise food. This means fresh food lasts longer and increases the opportunity for the food industry to export fresh food over longer distances, expanding the food industry and creating jobs.

   There is no right or wrong answer here, if you can justify the link to the effect then it is worth marks.

Published by BBC Active, an imprint of Educational Publishers LLP, part of the Pearson Education Group, 80 Strand, London, WC2R 0RL.

www.pearsonschools.co.uk/BBCBitesize



Typeset by Jouve India Private Limited

Produced and illustrated by Elektra Media Ltd

Cover design by Andrew Magee & Pearson Education Limited 2018

Cover illustration by Darren Lingard / Oxford Designers & Illustrators



First published 2018

21 20 19 18

10 9 8 7 6 5 4 3 2 1

**British Library Cataloguing in Publication Data**

A catalogue record for this book is available from the British Library

ISBN 978 1 406 68617 3



Printed and bound in Slovakia by Neografia.

The Publisher's policy is to use paper manufactured from sustainable forests.

**Note from the publisher**

Pearson has robust editorial processes, including answer and fact checks, to ensure the accuracy of the content in this publication, and every effort is made to ensure this publication is free of errors. We are, however, only human, and occasionally errors do occur. Pearson is not liable for any misunderstandings that arise as a result of errors in this publication, but it is our priority to ensure that the content is accurate. If you spot an error, please do contact us at resourcescorrections@pearson.com so we can make sure it is corrected.

**Acknowledgements**

The authors and publisher would like to thank the following individuals and organisations for their kind permission to reproduce copyright material.

**Text**

Page 163: 'Sources of carbon emissions in the UK', https://www.ovoenergy.com/binaries/content/gallery/ovowebsitessuite/images/guides/ukcabonsources.gif, Ovo Energy © Crown copyright, Source: Office for National Statistics licensed under the Open Government License v.3.0.

**Photographs**

(Key: b-bottom; c-centre; l-left; r-right; t-top)

**Alamy Stock Photo:** Peter Hermes Furian 3, F1online digitale Bildagentur GmbH/Norbert Michalke 4, **Shutterstock: Pistolseven** 7r, **Science Photo Library:** Andre Labbe, ISM 7l, **Alextype 13, 123RF:** Chirawan Somsanuk 24, **Shutterstock: Cliparea l Custom media** 36t, **ChaNaWiT 36b, NatUlrich** 40t, **Plant Pathology 40b,** Nigel Cattlin 42, **Alamy Stock Photo:** PR Bouree/BSIP SA 43, Chronicle 46, Wayne Lynch/All Canada Photos 58, **Shutterstock: SvenButstraen 63, Alamy Stock Photo:** Xinhua 64, Avico Ltd 68, **Science Photo Library:** James King-Holmes 71, **Alamy Stock Photo:** Premaphotos 72, Studio/PhotoCuisine RM 133, **Shutterstock: Vladimir Nenezic 137, TFoxFoto 164l, Jerry Horbert 164r, Alamy Stock Photo:** Andrew Findlay 186, **Shutterstock: Peteri 219.**

All other images © Pearson Education

**Websites**

Pearson Education Limited is not responsible for the content of third-party websites.